Perfume and
Flavor Materials of
Natural Origin

Perfume and Flavor Materials of Natural Origin

By

STEFFEN ARCTANDER

1960

ELIZABETH, N.J. (U.S.A.)

AN ORCHARD INNOVATIONS REPRINT EDITION
Printed in the United States of America

Perfume and Flavor Materials of Natural Origin was originally published by the author in 1960.

ISBN: 978-1-951682-05-7

To

RUTGERS - THE STATE UNIVERSITY

For pioneering the first college programs in
perfumery and essential oils through its School
of Chemistry and Newark Extension Center.

Perfume and Flavor Materials of Natural Origin

A perfumer's and flavorist's practical description of available materials, their origin, production and processing, appearance, odor and flavor type, evaluation, application and availability with brief notes on their main constituents, replacements and most common adulterants.

Preface

The present work is the result of many years of private study to which has been added three years of evening and off-duty work, mainly at the University Extension Division of *Rutgers* – The State University of New Jersey.

Notes were collected and compiled from many lengthy travels to faraway producing areas. Samples were submitted to the author from other areas, and first-hand information was received from research stations, universities, distilleries, growers and exporters all over the world.

By august 1958, the author found himself in possession of an almost complete collection of perfume and flavor materials of natural origin. These materials were all available or could be made available upon request at due notice. Dozens of varieties and different qualities of each individual raw material were closely studied for appearance, odor, flavor and possible adulterations. Suggestions have been made in this book for the use of these materials in perfumes and flavors, based partly upon the author's previous work, partly upon entirely new experiments which were carried out at the University Extension Division of *Rutgers*, The State University of New Jersey.

During three years of lecturing at the University Extension Division, the author became aware of the fact that the perfumery and flavor literature does not include any work that describes the odor *and flavor* of the raw materials from nature in everyday words. There is no recent or up-to-date handbook of raw materials suggesting the use of the materials, the replacement of one material for another, the proportional strength of flavor materials, etc. Furthermore, there was no up-to-date work which gave any practical indication of availability and present world production of these materials. Export figures are obviously not always indicative of the true production.

In order to present the compiled material in the handiest and most up-to-date form, the author decided to publish a one-volume dictionary form of practical handbook. The two-column set-up is a suggestion for which the author gives his printers all the credit and praise. The photographs are, with a few exceptions, taken by the author. Two-thirds of the photographs were taken during may-july 1960, and not a single photograph is more than five years old when this book appears. It was the author's express wish that this work should include full-color reproductions of some of the flower photographs.

A work of this type is strongly subjective by its very nature. All odor and flavor experiments were carried out by the author personally, and were repeated as recently as possible in order to make the information most true to the facts. When literature sources are not given, it is because information was never taken for granted if it was at all possible for the author to check and re-check the information personally. This principle has been carried out throughout the book, and the author is convinced that this policy should be of definite advantage to the reader who seeks actual and practical information. No information or statement has been entered in the book without being checked during the five-year period 1956–1960, and the greater part of all information has been re-checked during 1959–1960.

The perfume and flavor trade has been veiled and concealed for decades, if not for centuries. It is true that perfumery and flavor creation is an art and a science, and we all realize that the art cannot be taught or developed by research through generations. But it is the author's firm belief that science is a necessary part of perfumery and flavor creation. Consequently, we should not conceal what is already known or what can be concluded from the facts. In science, we all stand on the shoulders of our predecessors; our present knowledge is greater because they gave us a flying start. The same applies to that part of perfumery and flavor creation which is dependent upon science. It is the author's hope that the present work may contribute to the wider and further expanded knowledge of perfume and flavor materials from nature.

Elizabeth, New Jersey (U.S.A.)
August, 1960.

STEFFEN ARCTANDER

Acknowledgements

Although this work is an entirely personal undertaking, the author wishes to express his gratitude to a large number of individuals: friends in the industry, growers and distillers, scientists and artists, laymen and specialists in the perfume and flavor fields. Without the correct and highly up-to-date information graciously supplied by these people and institutions, this work would not have been possible.

The University Extension Division, *Rutgers*, The State University of New Jersey (U.S.A.) has been most helpful to the author in his making contact with authoritative sources of information on certain subjects.

The perfume and flavor industry has lent great support to the author in the areas of verifying information, procuring samples of certain rare materials, welcoming his personal visits to various installations, etc.

Planters and distillers all over the world have been most cooperative with respect to furnishing samples and information of production, future aspects, local use, etc. of many of the materials in the book.

Fellow perfumers and students at the University Extension Division have contributed greatly to the completion of this work by their direct and indirect encouragement to the author.

Through their correspondence with the author since long before the book was conceived, agricultural institutes, research stations, laboratories, etc. all over the world have been most helpful and co-operative in exchanging information, samples, etc. with the author.

Certain periodicals, technical monthly reviews, etc. have encouraged the author to a great measure, and have connected him with important sources of information, etc.

The printers in Copenhagen, Denmark, cannot be praised highly enough. Without their immediate readiness, this work would have lost years in achieving actuality. The entire outlining of the shape, set-up, binding and two-column printing, etc. was the prompt routine work of the printers. Proofreading was reduced through their outstanding accuracy. The reproduction of the author's photographs in black/white and in color has the unreserved admiration of the author.

The author's thanks also go to Natalie Fine for her efforts in correcting linguistic and grammatical errors committed by the author in his rough manuscript, and for her expert advice with respect to phraseology, etc. The author wishes to add that he takes full responsibility for omissions in this important part of the work of writing; changes and additions inevitably had to be made right up to the eleventh hour of the book's production.

The author wishes finally to state his affectionate appreciation of the patience and co-operation offered by his wife. The long hours of collecting and collating information, taking care of lengthy and prolific correspondence, and the never-ending checking and re-checking of flavor and odor experiments were only made possible through her loyal and patient encouragement.

Elizabeth, New Jersey (U.S.A.)
August, 1960.

STEFFEN ARCTANDER

Table of Contents

The materials are listed alphabetically, using the most common commercial names in English. Reference is made to synonyms and foreign names on the widest possible scale. In many cases, however, it has been necessary to use the botanical Latin name where no commercial name exists, or where the English name does not describe the material unambiguously. Condensed French, German and Spanish indices are included at the end of the book.

Bold type is used in the text to indicate reference from the index and to emphasize the location of the topic name, etc., thus saving time for the reader who wants a brief information on a certain specific subject.

The *strict alphabetical order* suffers from certain drawbacks:
Lemongrass Oil is placed between **Lemon Aroma** and **Lemon Oil. Gingergrass Oil** is between **Ginger Absolute** and **Ginger Oil. Ho Leaf Oil** and **Ho Wood Oil** are separated by the entries of **Hop** and **Horseradish**, etc.

Abbreviations

°C. = degrees centigrade.

cms. = centimeters.

mg% = milligrams per 100 grams = thousandth of one percent. One mg% equals ten parts per million (10 ppm.).

ml. = millilitres.

mm. Hg. = millimeters of mercury pressure, an indication of low pressure in connection with vacuum distillation.

sp. = species (of plants).

tons = metric tons (one ton = 1000 kilos or 2200 lbs.).

var. = variety of (Latin: varietas) a botanical species.

PART ONE

Definitions and Methods of Processing

A

Absolute.

An **Absolute** is a prepared perfume material. Absolutes are highly concentrated, entirely alcohol-soluble and usually liquid perfume materials. They are obtained by alcohol-extraction of concrètes (see this monograph) or other hydrocarbon-types of extracts or from fat-extracts of plant material (see below). Waxes, terpenes, sesquiterpenes and most of the odorless matters are eliminated from the concrètes during the preparation of absolutes. The concrète is usually extracted at room temperature or under gentle heat. Several extractions may be required in order to completely exhaust the odorous matter from the concrète. The mixed alcoholic extracts are then chilled under stirring for a considerable length of time (up to several weeks). Waxes, sesquiterpenes etc. are precipitated in the cold and by subsequent cold filtration of the alcoholic extract, or by centrifuging, the alcoholic solution of the absolute is obtained. The alcohol is recovered by evaporation, which requires a gentle vacuum towards the end of the distillation. Most absolutes will contain traces of ethylalcohol (i.e. 2% or less). If the ethylalcohol has been denatured with a nonvolatile or high-boiling material, this denaturant will be present in the absolute in significant amounts, since the extraction of an absolute requires many times the quantity of alcohol.

Absolutes can in exceptional cases be solid or semi-solid (e.g. sage clary absolute, beeswax absolute, bruyère absolute, etc.). Under **Hyacinth Absolute** (see this monograph in Part Two of this book) is described briefly an adsorption method for the production of absolutes.

Occasionally the alcohol-soluble fraction of a **Resinoid** is called an **Absolute**. The resulting product is not identical to the so-called alcohol-resinoid, also commercially known as **Resin Absolute**. The latter is prepared by direct alcohol extraction of the natural raw material (gum resin, oleoresin, etc.). See monograph on **Resin Absolute** in Part One of this book.

If a natural raw material is first extracted with petroleum ether to produce a **Resinoid** (see this) and the resinoid in turn is extracted with alcohol, this process will yield a highly refined and pale colored "**Absolute**". Under **Labdanum Absolute from Resinoid** in Part Two of this book is described one such material. Petroleum ether extraction of natural gum resins, oleoresins etc. often yield very light colored resinoids, very suitable for further processing to **Absolutes** of attractive appearance and odor.

Butaflor is a registered name (P. Robertet & Cie.) given to a series of highly concentrated perfume materials produced by extraction with butane at subnormal temperature. The solvent is recovered by evaporation at room temperature (boiling point of butane is −0°.50C.). The low extraction temperature and the selective solvent result in a pale-colored, almost waxfree and terpeneless product. The method is particularly useful and advantageous when applied to very delicate or heat-sensitive botanical materials, e.g. lilac flowers, lily of the valley (muguet), orange flowers, jasmin, rose, etc. Certain staple materials are also treated by this method, e.g. ginger rhizomes. It should be kept in mind, that not all **Butaflors** are completely alcohol-soluble.

Absolute from Châssis.

See also **Pommade**. When the flowers are removed in the daily batches from the greased trays ("châssis"), some fat will adhere to these exhaust flowers. The fat contains perfume oil. Extraction of the flowers with a hydrocarbon type of solvent will isolate the perfumed fat as a "concrète de châssis" from which an **Absolute from Châssis** is in turn produced by alcohol extraction, chilling, filtration and evaporation.

Absolute from distillation water.

During the steam- or water distillation of geranium oil, lavandin, lavender, neroli, petitgrain, rose etc. the distillation waters contain significant amounts of dissolved or dispersed odorous matter which will not readily separate. Such distillation waters are often extracted with petroleum ether or benzene. After solvent recovery the residual "distillation water concrète" is extracted with alcohol, or it may be used as it comes from the first extraction. **Lavender Water-Absolute, Rose Water-Absolute**, etc. are prepared this way. These absolutes are practically terpeneless and consist mainly of water-soluble components of the essential oil in the plant material. In certain cases, they are "the missing links" between absolutes and essential oils from same plant material. Water absolutes present highly interesting perfume notes which are often missing or wanted in essential oils or perfume bases. Various **Water-Absolutes** are described under the monographs of the respective plant materials in Part Two of this book.

Absolute from Pommade.

These materials are by some authors considered as essential oils in the sense, that they are "volatile oils". This reasoning is also justified by the definitions given in the present book. Pommade-absolutes are prepared in the same way as described under **Absolute (from Concrète)**, but the starting material in this case is a **Pommade** (see this monograph). Under certain circumstances, the pommade-absolutes are prepared from a **Concrète from Pommade** (see this). **Absolute from Pommade** is also known as: **Pommade Concentrate**.

Absolute Oil.

This term usually refers to the steam distillable part of an **Absolute**. Very few, if any, absolute oils are commercially available. They are, however, frequently prepared in analytical laboratories in order to establish datas of the constituents of an absolute as compared to the corresponding essential oil. **Absolute Oils** constitute only a fraction of the quantity of the parent absolute, but they often display the most refined notes of its fragrance.

Anhydrols are a form of diluted **Absolute Oils**, (see **Anhydrol**).

Adulteration.

The reader may find that this term occurs rather frequently in this book. The author has endeavoured to reduce the frequency of the occurrence of this word, in order not to discourage the readers beyond the inevitable and justified measure. Terms like **"Sophistication"**, **"Cutting"**, "diluting", **"Bouquetting"** (from the French: bouquettage), "rounding-off" etc. etc. are all more or less poor attempts to disguise the cruel truth: plain adulteration. Certain suppliers with highly developed imagination will even use the term "enobling" for the disfiguration of an essential oil.

The author has nothing in principle against the addition of foreign or "unnatural" materials to essential oils etc. as long as the intention *and the result* is an indisputable improvement in respect to perfumery performance and effect. To the author's opinion it is up to every perfumer to improve perfume materials, and this may be achieved with no ban whatsoever on the means or materials used. The author is well aware that such statements are bound to release a landslide of disagreements, but it is his firm belief that most perfumers at the bottom of their hearts will agree that this matter is a development which we have to face. It is a natural result of the appearance of a rapidly growing number of interesting synthetic perfume materials.

The synthetic perfume materials are supposed to enhance and support the use of natural raw materials, not to replace them, nor in any way to beat them off the market. The synthetic chemicals present a certain challenge to nature, and the perfumer can assist nature in her fight by utilizing the synthetic materials to the advantage of the natural raw materials.

However, the above philosophy should not indicate that the author approves of **Adulteration** of natural perfume materials. On the contrary. But the meaning of the term **Adulteration** should be taken literally: with the intention of acquiring the business (order) through a devaluation of the oil in relation to the labelling of its container. The consumers of perfume oils are buying odor, not certain physico-chemical data. If the odor and the perfumery (or flavor-) effect is in agreement with the customer's standards, there is no reason to talk about adulteration: the oil is then worth the full price of a true, natural oil and the "adulteration", if any, has not been a means of direct economical gains. One could speak only of a more or less ethical handling of the natural materials and their labelling. The author assumes in the above case, that the customer's standards are representative of average commercial lots of the materials in question.

In certain cases there is a special reason for "bouquettage" or "doctoring" of an essential oil. Cumin oil, e.g. and other umbellifer-fruit oils, oil of black pepper, etc. will, immediately after distillation often present a most obnoxious or putrid top-note. Other examples are the common "still-notes", where a distinctly burnt-acrylic or sweet-furfuralic or protein-like note is present in freshly distilled oils, or in drums of crude oils, for a long time kept closed. Essential oils from primitive stills, from direct-fire stills and in general oils from stills in warm countries contain a substantial amount of water. When these oils are shipped to colder countries, the water separates (often $\frac{1}{2}$ to 1% or more) in the drum. Through decay or other micro-organism activity, this water can produce quite unpleasant off-notes. Well-known examples are: bois de rose oil, citronella oil, geranium oil, petitgrain Paraguay oil, etc. The aforementioned still-notes can be subdued or eliminated by a special bouquettage, e.g. an addition of one or more perfume materials which may conceal the putrid note. The latter "water-and-decay" note may often be eliminated by simple aeration (airing) of the oil, by washing and drying, by filtration etc. generally known as "conditioning". A redistillation will also eliminate the water content in these natural oils.

Much emphasis has been attached to the mention of possible or known adulterations of materials listed in this book. The author wants to repeat, that this primarily aims at the numerous cases of "unethical" handling of the oil, where the customer is actually deprived of the full yield of natural odor or flavor effect when he buys such "cut" oils.

Anhydrol.

Anhydrols are processed perfume- or flavor materials. **Anhydrol** is the brand name of a series of distilled extracts, produced by L. Givaudan & Cie. in Geneva or by Givaudan-Delawanna Inc. in the United States. As indicated through the name, these materials are produced from natural raw materials without the presence of water (or steam). **Anhydrols** are usually viscous liquids of pale color.

They are the results of a combination of extraction of the natural raw material and subsequent molecular distillation of the extract. The solvent may be ethyleneglycol, other glycols, isopropylmyristate or other high-boiling, odorless solvents, mostly of the oil-soluble type.

The resulting extract may then be distilled in a molecular still at approximately 10^{-3} torr. A molecular distillation is a physical process, during which a liquid or a low-melting solid of high boiling point is converted into vapor phase, removed from the liquid phase and condensed back to liquid phase, separated from the liquid in the still. The new liquid phase, the condensate, is the molecular distillate. There is no fractionation, no reflux, no column on the still. It is basically a simple distillation at very reduced pressure and under such circumstances, that the material to be distilled is exposed to the heat as briefly as possible. There are many types of stills and various designs of rotating heaters, where the liquid is spread as a film to speed the evaporation and reduce the heating time.

Obviously, the **Anhydrols** will contain significant amounts of the solvent with which they have been extracted. But this co-distillation is just one of the advantages of the process. The solvent may form so-called azeotropes with one or more of the odorous ingredients in the extract and thus reduce the distillation temperature. Plant colors and other odorless matter will be retained in the still. According to some theories, anything that has a measurable vapor pressure, also has an odor. According to that theory the **Anhydrols** should be ideal: no odorless material at all. Many aromatic components of the extracts, which are not distillable with steam, will distil in the molecular co-distillation process. Consequently, this method is mainly applied to such perfume or flavor materials which yield little essential oil on steam or water distillation or which are too high-boiling to yield an oil unchanged.

Among available **Anhydrols** are myrrh, olibanum, oakmoss, opopanax, patchouli, Peru balsam, Virginia tobacco leaf, tea leaf, tolu balsam, vetiver, etc.

Anhydrols are soluble in alcohol and essential oils as well as in most synthetic perfume materials.

Resinoines are purified, partially decolorized, concentrated products. Some are low-pressure-distillates of extracts, others are mixtures of distillates and extracts. **Resinoine** is a brand name of the Grasse house, P. Robertet et Cie. Well-known **Resinoines** are, e.g. labdanum, patchouli, tabac, thé, tolu, etc.

Aroma.

The term **Aroma** is often used for the rather intangible conception "odor + flavor". In the following, however, **Aroma** refers to a processed raw material used by the flavorist. Thus we meet again wild confusion, if we try to establish a standard, not to speak of a definition.

The conventional **Aroma** is a highly concentrated solution of a partially terpeneless oil or plant extract in a solvent which also contains a certain amount of water.

Alcohol-aromas: The essential oil is stirred vigorously with one, two or more parts of pure ethylalcohol. If the oil is clearly soluble in the alcohol, it serves no purpose to stir the solution. If the oil is not clearly soluble, stirring is continued for some time, whereafter water is added to the mixture. The amount of water is calculated according to the character of the oil and to the ratio of the solvent to the oil. Separation takes place, but stirring is continued for an hour or two. The mixture is then left in a cool place to complete the separation. Terpenes, sesquiterpenes, waxes and other components which are poorly soluble in diluted alcohol will usually rise to the surface. The diluted alcohol contains most of the "aromatic" principles in solution. This solution is drained off and filtered. The filtrate constitute the **Aroma**. As an example is given below: **Bitter Orange Aroma:**

> 1000 grams Guinea (or Spanish) bitter orange oil dissolve in
> 1000 grams pure ethylalcohol,
>   add under continuous stirring
> 1000 grams distilled water.

Stir, leave, and chill. Separate and filtrate the alcoholic layer. Yield approximately 2000 grams. The terpene-layer amounts to 900 to 920 grams and may appear on the market under the name of "washed citrus oil" or "citrus terpenes", see monograph on **Lemon Aroma** in Part Two of this book. The alcoholic filtrate is occasionally distilled at atmospheric pressure until the distillate shows an alcohol percentage of 65 or 60, according to the needs of the consumer. The product is called **Aroma-Distillate** from essential oil. See also **Aroma-Distillate** in Part One of this book.

Glycol-Aromas: These are prepared in a similar way as described under **Alcohol-Aromas.** However, the glycol is usually not diluted quite as much as was the case with alcohol. Generally, the water addition amounts to 20% up to almost 50% in rare cases, calculated upon the amount of glycol. Propylene glycol is considered one of the best and most suitable solvents for flavors. It is far less toxic than ethylene glycol. It has similar solvent effects and is also miscible with water. It is a commercial solvent, available in almost unlimited quantities and at a price only slightly higher than taxfree, pure ethyl alcohol. **Glycol-Aromas** are not redistilled and the filtrate is used as is.

Diolane (brand name for hexylene glycol, presumably 2-methylpentane-2,4-diol) is a solvent with the rare ability of being miscible with water and at the same time to a certain degree being miscible with hydrocarbons, e.g. terpenes. **Diolane** is not suitable for the production of the above **Aromas.** This solvent is distinctly bitter of taste even at the dilution of 2 mg%, contrary to the frequently published statement, that **Diolane** is "virtually odorless and tasteless".

Aromas are slowly being replaced in the flavorist's formulas by solutions of terpeneless oils, although these are not really comparable materials to the above aromas. It is still customary to prepare **Aromas** of such natural raw materials, where the botanical drug material is not locally at hand or not a commercial article, e.g. bitter orange, bergamot, lime, vetiver etc. while it is usually preferred to prepare **Aroma-Distillates** from the botanical plant material wherever possible, e.g. orange, lemon, angelica-root, spices etc.

Aroma-Distillate.

Aroma-Distillates or **Distillates** are prepared materials for use in flavor compounding.

If there is little by way of standardization and specifications in the processing of perfumery intermediates, e.g. resinoids, tinctures, etc., there is practically none with respect to flavor ingredients. In the processing of **Aroma-Distillates**, however, the principles are as follows, in broad outline:

The natural raw material is coarsely chopped, sliced, or cut. Peels from citrus fruits often come out of the peeling machine as long, thin strings, 100 to 200 cm. long; these can be used as is. Apples can be peeled in a machine to advantage, since the meat of the apples yields very little flavor. Berries are usually cold-pressed since the juice by itself is a valuable flavor material. The press-cake from berries offers an excellent starting material for the production of aroma-distillates.

The natural raw material is percolated at room temperature or at less than 50°C. The heat may be supplied by a steam jacket. The menstruum (usually pure ethyl alcohol) is circulated through the botanical material by action of a pump which returns the solvent to the top of the extractor. By means of gravity, the solvent penetrates the botanical material which is spread out on wire-trays or perforated plates stacked inside the extractor. The alcohol strength is adjusted to the nature of the raw material. Citrus peels are usually extracted with 99% or 90% alcohol, berries with weaker alcohol. The temperature and the time of extraction varies according to the construction of the automatic percolator and the nature of the raw material.

The alcoholic extract is now drained from the percolator. The adherent alcohol on the plant material is distilled off under gentle heat from the steam jacket. The distillate is collected in a reservoir beneath a cooling system. Steam is then blown directly through the botanical material in the percolator, partly to recover all alcohol with dissolved aromas, partly in order to recover steam distillable aromatic principles in the raw material. The aqueous distillate in the condenser is mixed with the alcoholic percolates, and left for 24 hours to cool and separate terpenes and other poorly soluble matter.

The hydro-alcoholic mixture is now distilled slowly—often in an all-glass still and over a short packed column. The distillation is continued until the entire distillate in the glass receptacle shows the desired alcohol percentage (60, 50, 45, or whatever percentage is wanted in the individual case). Citrus peel distillates are usually adjusted to 60% vol./vol., while berries, apples, hops, lupulin, and other distillates are adjusted to about 45% vol./vol. alcohol.

It will be necessary, in certain cases, to redistil the aroma-distillate after a few days of maturing. Terpenes may continue to separate from citrus-distillates; other materials may cause haziness. Freshly prepared distillates often display a so-called unpleasant "still-note". This note fades away after proper ageing at 12 to 15°C. in the course of one to several months. In many cases,

the still-note can be eliminated by "aerating" the distillate in open containers, or by decanting the distillate repeatedly during a couple of days. "Still-notes" are well known among essential oils, and a perfumer or a flavorist must decide whether to accept or reject a material which displays a "still-note" on the basis of experience. Certain aromatic botanicals do not yield **Aroma-Distillates**: Angostura bark, capsicum fruit, cayenne or paprika, fenugreek seed, tonka bean, vanilla fruit, etc. will yield either a distillate of poor and uncharacteristic odor compared to the parent natural material, or they will yield no aroma at all in an experimental distillate.

It is preferable to prepare **Water Extracts, Alcohol-Water Extracts, Oleoresins** or **Tinctures** from such botanical materials in order to obtain concentrated liquid aromas.

See also monograph on **Aromas**.

B

Balsam.

A **Balsam** is a natural raw material exuded from a tree or a plant; the balsam may be either a physiological or a pathological product of the plant. **Balsams** are resinous masses, semi-solid materials or viscous liquids, insoluble in water, completely or almost completely soluble in ethyl-alcohol, but only partly soluble in hydrocarbons. A **Balsam** is characterized by its high content of benzoic acid, benzoates, cinnamic acid or cinnamates.

Peru Balsam is a typical **Balsam**.

Benzoin is not entirely soluble in alcohol, and it could be characterized as a **Balsamic Resin**. It can be considered a **Balsam** which has been rendered less soluble through age and subsequent resinification. Accordingly, most true balsams are those which can be obtained immediately by incisions in trees. Older exudations are usually resinous and less aromatic.

C

Classification of materials.

Certain types of odor occur in botanical materials from species of the same botanical family. It is very tempting to draw conclusions and make comparisons when such similarities appear. The author has preferred to go strictly by alphabetical order, using the most common commercial names as entries for the individual monographs. In certain cases where there is great similarity in names or in cases of possible confusion, the internationally acknowledged Latin name is used as entry. In order to clarify further reasons for using alphabetical order, some examples are given below:

In a classification according to botanical relationship, we would find the following materials grouped together:

> ginger, galanga, curcuma (rhizomes)
> broom, cassie, mimosa (flowers)
> anise and fennel (fruits)
> lavender, rosemary, sage, savory (herbs)
> angelica and lovage (roots)
> chamomile, erigeron, everlasting (flowers).

Such a grouping would be perfectly justified and reasonable, but the system would also include a grouping such as this:

> boronia and neroli (flowers)
> elemi and opopanax (oleo-resin and oleo-gum-resin)
> pimenta leaf and leptospermum citratum (leaves)
> carrot and coriander (fruits)
> origanum, patchouli, and hyssop (herbs),

which would be quite misleading or plainly erratic as an odor type of grouping.

In the above examples, the subjects have been identical parts of various plants from the same family. If we disregard this point in our comparisons, the differences may become still wider:

> citronella and vetiver (herb and rootlets, but same bot. family)
> garlic and hyacinth (bulb and flowers)
> ginger and longoza (rhizome and flower)
> champaca and star anise (flower and fruit)
> cinnamon bark and sassafras (bark and wood)
> amyris and boronia (wood and flower),

which makes no sense at all to a perfumer or a flavorist.

Using the botanical system for grouping, the perfumer would also lose such interesting comparisons as these:

> anise and star anise (fruits, from different botanical families)
> boronia and henna (flowers)

> huon pine wood oil and meleleuca bracteata leaf oil
> clove leaf oil and cinnamon leaf oil
> schinus molle and black pepper oils (from fruits)

etc. This grouping is undoubtedly the one which is the most pertinent to the everyday work of the perfumer; he is concerned with odors, and not with technical, botanical or other scientific data. The author has aimed at this type of grouping in the broadest possible way by giving cross-references at the end of each individual monograph.

Furthermore, a botanical grouping may tend to compare such essential oils which have the main constituent in common (by analysis). In many cases, this chemical similarity is not at all apparent in the odor of the essential oils from closely related plants, e.g.:

> clove bud oil and clove leaf oil,
> sage clary and mentha citrata,
> grapefruit and sweet orange oils.

For all these reasons, the alphabetical system is maintained throughout this work.

Concrète.

A **Concrète** is a prepared perfumery material. The **Concrètes** are extracted from non-resinous or low resinous natural raw materials in a method of preparation quite similar to that of the **Resinoids** (see this monograph in Part One of this book). The natural raw materials from which **Concrètes** are prepared are almost exclusively of vegetable origin, e.g. bark, flower, herb, leaf, root, etc. **Concrètes** are extracted from previously live tissue, while **Resinoids** are extracted from plant exudations (not tissue).

Concrètes are thus representative of the natural raw material in the sense that they contain all the hydrocarbon-soluble matter, while water and water-extractive matter have been left out. Plant tissue, fibres, cellulose, etc. have also been eliminated. The resulting concrète is soluble only to a certain degree in perfume oils and other liquid perfume materials.

Concrètes are usually solid, waxy, non-crystalline masses which, on standing, may deposit crystals of almost pure constituents from the extract. The concrètes contain higher fatty acids, frequently lauric and myristic acid. Furthermore, they contain large amounts of alcohol-soluble matter known as **Absolute** (see this monograph).

The amount of **Absolute** in a **Concrète** ranges from less than 20% (which is rare) up to 80% (which is also rare). In the latter case, the concrète is often liquid, e.g. concrète of **Ylang-Ylang**. A content of about 50% of **Absolute** is most common in flower **Concrètes**. **Jasmin Concrète** is a typical and well-known **Concrète**. **Atractylis** and **Orris Concrètes** are essential oils which just happen to be solid because their major constituents are solid. They are not true concrètes (extracts).

Concrète from Châssis.

Concrète from châssis is the extraction product from the exhaust flowers on the "châssis", see monograph on **Pommade**. The "defleuraged" flowers are extracted with a hydrocarbon solvent to yield the **Concrète from Châssis** after recovery of the solvent.

The so-called **"Jasmin Châssis"** is a well-known example.

Concrète from Pommade.

This is a little known product, and hardly a commercial article any more.

It is produced from the **Pommade** (see this monograph in Part One of the present book) by extraction with warm alcohol. When alcohol is recovered from this total extract, the yield is **Concrète from Pommade**. But the process has always been carried further by freezing of the alcoholic extract, cold filtration and subsequent recovery of alcohol. This process yields **Absolute from Pommade**, see that monograph.

E

Essential Oil.

An **Essential Oil** is a volatile material, derived by a physical process from odorous plant material of a single botanical form and species with which it agrees in name and odor.

Essential Oils generally constitute the odorous principles of the plants in which they exist. In exceptional cases, the essential oil may be formed during processing when the plant tissue is brought into contact with water. A few essential oils represent volatile products, formed during destructive distillation of the natural raw material.

Certain botanical species are scarcely odorous at all, yet they produce essential oils when distilled subsequent to maceration. The maceration may start off a fermentation or an enzymatic process, neither of which are physical processes. As examples, see the monographs on **Almond Oil, Bitter,** and **Wintergreen Oil** in Part Two of this book.

Essential Oils are either distilled or expressed. **Distillation** can be **Water Distillation,**
    Steam Distillation,
    Water-and-Steam Distillation,
    or
    Dry Distillation.

In a water distillation, the plant material is in direct contact with the boiling water. If heat is supplied from a steam jacket, there is no great risk of burning the plant material. In the case of a "direct-fire" still, the plant material may come in contact with the heated metal plate. Essential oils from such types of stills usually present a distinct "still-note" or "burnt" note which fades away only after proper aerating of the oil. Most "direct-fire" stills are provided with a grid above the surface of the boiling water. It is a primitive form of steam distillation, and not much different from the water-and-steam distillation during which steam is blown into the mixture of water and comminuted plant material. The grid prevents the plant material from contacting the heated surface of the alembic.

Steam Distillation is usually of the so-called **Indirect Steam** type. The steam is produced in a boiler separate from the still. Through a pipe in the bottom of the still, the steam is blown through the plant material which rests on a grid or on a stack of trays for quick removal after exhaustion. The steam inlet usually ends in a circular perforated pipe to allow for better dispersion of the steam.

The direct fire still obviously produces a distillation at 100°C. (atmospheric pressure). It is worth noticing that water boils at temperatures between 88°C. and 93°C. at many of the locations where essential oils are distilled (altitude 1500 to 2500 metres). The decrease in boiling point has a significant influence upon the hydrolytic effect of the steam on the essential oil. (See monographs on **Lavender Oil** and **Linaloe Seed Oil** in Part Two of this book). A more recent technique in the distillation of essential oils involves steam distillation under partial vacuum, e.g. 100 to 200 mm. Hg.-pressure. This method gives a very quick distillation with a minimum of hydrolytic decomposition of the oil. This type of still requires a very effective cooling system in order to condense the fast-travelling vapors quantitatively.

High-pressure steam is applied whenever the plant material and its essential oil are sufficiently heat-resistant and non-hydrolyzable. The method is the fastest way by far of distilling essential oils, particularly those with important high-boiling constituents such as vetiver, sandalwood, clove stem, etc. In some of these cases, the still may be filled (under the grid) with salt water which boils above 100°. Sea water is used in certain installations in remote islands. The slightly increased temperature reduces the time of the lengthy distillation. Most of the European and American field stills are of the high-pressure steam type, e.g. lavandin, peppermint, spearmint, etc. Distillation time for these oils is usually less than one hour. In the case of many wood-oils, root oils and other oils with significant amounts of high-boiling constituents, the distillation time is much longer, often in excess of 24 hours, amyris oil for example.

There is a significant difference between essential oils from the same botanical material when they are "locally distilled" and when they are produced in a modern American or European still, e.g. patchouli oil. Modern stills are in operation in the growing areas now, and these stills often present the major solution to the problem of economic production of the oil, e.g. clove stem oil, sandalwood oil. During the years since World War II, many of the plant-growing areas have endeavored to improve their stills, e.g. the Belgian Congo where a great number of stainless steel stills have been erected since 1958, particularly for the production of geranium oil.

A few essential oils are produced by **Direct** and **Dry Distillation** from the natural material, e.g. **Copaiba Oil**. Still more crude is the **Destructive Distillation** during which odorous materials are formed which were not present in the botanical raw material, e.g. amber oil, cade oil, etc., all of which exist in a rectified form also.

Rectification literally means a correcting or a cleaning process. A steam distillation, a vacuum distillation or any other type of "second" distillation of an essential oil may be considered a

Rectification. The term **Redistillation** basically means a second distillation of the material without specifications with respect to fractionation or distillation conditions. The two terms are often used indiscriminately. However, a few examples may clarify the correct usage of these terms: **Birch Tar** is rectified to yield a clear, almost colorless oil which is known as **Birch Tar** (oil) **Rectified.** **Peppermint Oil** is produced in the growing area as a **Natural Peppermint Oil.** This oil is later redistilled and sold as **Redistilled Peppermint Oil.** For special purposes (candy, toothpaste, chewing gum, etc.), the natural peppermint oil may be **Rectified.** The latter term refers to a fractionated distillation, either under vacuum or with steam at atmospheric pressure. Only certain fractions are bulked into a "rectified" oil according to the specific needs of the consumer. Thus, a **Redistillation** usually aims at the removal of color, water, resinous matter and perhaps certain unpleasant topnotes. **Rectification** often involves a significant loss of material if a high-grade "heart-fraction" ("cœur de distillation") is wanted.

Expression is performed exclusively in the cases of peels of citrus fruits. This method leads to oils which are not entirely volatile, but are nevertheless acknowledged as **Essential Oils.** Expression can be made by hand or by machine. The production of essential oils from citrus fruits has been comprehensively described in recent works on the subject of essential oils. So-called cold-pressed citrus oils are among our most basic natural perfume materials. They can be used in perfumes and flavors exactly as they occur in Nature. Very few perfume materials come into this category (e.g. **Copaiba Balsam**).

According to the present definition, **Absolutes from Concrètes** are not essential oils. They are not entirely volatile, and they should be considered as fractionated extracts. Enfleurage absolutes (see **Pommade** and **Absolute from Pommade**, Part One of this book) are essential oils according to our definitions. Steam distilled oils from absolutes, the so-called **Absolute Oils**, could also be considered as essential oils. They have no importance in practical perfumery.

The amount of essential oil which we can derive from a natural raw material is only a small fraction of all the essential oil originally produced in the plant. But up to now, no one has yet devised a method of continuously milking the living flower of its perfume. The nearest approach to this ideal is in the process known as **Enfleurage**, see monograph on **Pommade**.

Essential oils are, with a few exceptions, liquid.

Extract.

Extracts are prepared materials. The term **Extract** is used for perfume materials, flavor materials, pharmaceutical products and many other commercial products.

The word **Extract** should not be confused with a direct translation of the French word, "extrait". (See monograph on **Extrait**). Generally speaking, the term **Extract** refers to concentrated products, obtained by treating a natural raw material with a solvent. The solution of active ingredients from the natural raw material is subsequently concentrated by evaporation of the solvent, either partially or totally. True extracts do not contain significant amounts of solvent.

The following types of extracts are individually described in Part One of this book:

Absolutes, Concrètes, Extraits (dissolved extracts), **Oleoresins** (prepared), **Resinoids, Tinctures** (dissolved extracts). According to our definitions **Pommades** are not extracts. They should be considered as solutions of volatile oils, obtained by adsorption on the non-volatile solvent.

In flavor terms, the word **Extract** is used even more indiscriminately. It is often applied to dilutions or emulsions of flavor materials in vegetable oils, tasteless solvents or water. True flavor extracts are concentrated materials, liquid, semi-liquid or solid. They are obtained from natural raw materials by treatment with solvents, and with particular attention to their application in food or beverages. They are generally prepared in the same way as perfumery extracts or pharmaceutical extracts.

A solvent-free alcoholic extract of a resinous raw material is often called a **Resin Absolute** (see this). It is a further development of the tincture or the infusion which is concentrated.

Extrait.

Extraits are prepared perfumery materials. The French name, "extrait", is used in perfumery all over the world, but it should not be confused with "extract" (see this monograph).

An **Extrait** is an alcoholic solution of the odorous part of a **Pommade** (see this). Extraits can be considered as **Tinctures** from **Pommades**.

Extraits are thus intermediate products in the preparation of **Absolutes** (from pommades). They present the advantage of being cold-processed and fairly concentrated materials, while the **Absolute** is obtained through a process that usually requires heat. As a rule (with exceptions), the flower oil concentrates enter perfume formulas in small percentages. Accordingly, it may not be any disadvantage at all that these concentrates (the **Absolutes**) are used in the original solution as **Extraits**.

Furthermore, the **Extraits** present the advantage of being aged, mellowed, matured or well "rounded-off" solutions of the fragrant principles in the flowers. **Extraits** are usually prepared in fairly large amounts in order to ensure that a well-aged **Extrait** is always on hand.

Briefly, the principles in the production of **Extraits** are as follows:

The **Pommade** is "washed" with alcohol which dissolves the fat (the "corps gras") only to a minor degree. The filtered washings form the **Extrait**. The first washing will be the best, but, as a rule, one kilo of **Extrait** is prepared from one kilo of **Pommade**. Freezing removes most of the dissolved fat, and the cold filtrate is subsequently evaporated, i.e. the alcohol is recovered in vacuum. This leaves the **Absolute from Pommade** (see this) as the yield. Only few **Extraits** are now commercially available. Well-known examples are **Extraits** of **Jasmin, Orange Flower**, and **Rose**.

F

Fixatives.

In perfumery, a **Fixative** literally means a material which slows down the rate of evaporation of the more volatile materials in a perfume composition. There are several types of fixative (also called "fixers"):

1) The true fixatives:

These are materials which retard the evaporation of the other components of the perfume by distinct physical effect. Their effect is that of an adsorption due to the high-molecular structure of the fixative. A typical example of a natural fixative in this group is benzoin.

2) The "arbitrary" fixatives:

These are odorous substances which lend a particular note to the perfume throughout all stages of evaporation. But they do not significantly influence the evaporation of other perfume materials in the composition. A typical example of a natural "arbitrary" fixative is oakmoss.

3) The exalting fixatives:

These materials act as "odor carriers" and often act also as synergists by improving, fortifying or transporting the vapors of the other perfume materials in the composition. The exalting fixatives may also lend a highly appreciated "wearability" to a perfume, a combination of diffusive effect and retention of the full fragrance of the perfume, slowly exhaled from the human skin to which it has been applied. Although the effect of these fixatives may be considered a physical one, it is inconceivable that the effect is due to an increase in the boiling point of the total perfume composition. The effect of these fixatives is often obtained through the addition of mere traces with respect to quantity. Typical exalting fixatives are musk and civet.

4) The so-called fixatives:

These are odorless or almost odorless crystalline materials or viscous liquids. They are high-boiling materials, and their effect is a physical one, caused by simple increase of the boiling point of the perfume composition. Their odor, if they have any, plays a minor role. Their action is merely a stabilizing one which paralyzes the odor of the low-boiling materials. In a way they "steal" effect from the perfume, but they also conceal minor errors, misbalance or "rough corners" in the perfume. A surprisingly large number of "fixatives" from perfumery literature belong to this group. From a perfumer's standpoint, such additions represent a direct loss of fragrance which, in turn, is an economical loss. A typical natural fixative in group #4 is amyris oil.

One perfume material can belong to one or several of the above groups of fixatives. A true physical fixation in terms of a decreased vapor pressure can never be obtained through the addition of fractions of one percent of a certain material, even if the material conforms to the specifications of group #1 of the above list.

Flavors.

Minimum Perceptible and Threshold Concentration: In this book, the term **Minimum Perceptible** is used where flavor materials are discussed. **Minimum Perceptible** expresses the lowest concentration of flavor material in a diluent at which the characteristic notes of the flavor are sufficiently perceptible to permit distinct identification of the flavor. In many cases, a further dilution is possible without totally eliminating all traces of flavor notes, but this ultimate limit has little or no interest to the flavorist.

The term **Threshold Concentration** is generally applied to describe the absolute minimum of material which produces a flavor (or taste stimulus) as compared to a tasteless diluent. In certain cases, the flavor material may lose its characteristic notes step by step during the dilution, e.g. peppermint oil:

At a concentration of about 2.0 to 4.0 mg%, the cooling effect disappears, but the flavor remains distinctly that of peppermint until a dilution of about 0.2 mg%. Below that concentration, there is only an uncharacteristic difference in flavor as compared to the pure diluent.

The **Minimum Perceptible** is given in mg%, which is an abbreviation of milligram percent. It indicates how many milligrams of material there are in 100 grams of diluent. 1.0 mg%, then, corresponds to 10.0 ppm (parts-per-million) which is a common English-American unit for low concentrations. Since the **Minimum Perceptible** is very often around 1.0 mg%, the author has preferred to use this unit.

In the experiments upon which the flavor concentrations in this book are based, the diluent is a 9% solution of cane sugar in tap water at 10°C. It is important that the temperature be kept at a constant level during all the experiments. It may take two or three times as much flavor material to produce the same flavor stimulus at 5°C. as it does at room temperature.

Tests were carried out on a series of many different flavor materials in order to avoid or reduce the influence of flavor fatigue, and in order to establish a certain relation among the results.

The indication of a **Minimum Perceptible** is obviously a strictly subjective matter, although the author has repeated the experiments under widely different conditions and circumstances. The figures given in this book for **Minimum Perceptible** can be accepted for their individual ratio, which will be pretty much the same if tests are performed by other "tasters" under similar conditions in various parts of the world.

Acidity and fruit flavors:

Fruit flavors do not approach any degree of naturalness unless accompanied by a certain amount of acid. But since fresh fruits are omitted in this work (see following monograph on **Fruits**), the author has maintained the above neutral sugar water as a standard medium in all tests.

See also **Spices** in Part One of the present work.

Fruits.

The author feels that **Fruits** which are applicable in flavor work only in the shape of juices, dehydrated concentrates, pastes, preserves, etc. should not be included in the monographs of this book.

This applies to:

Apple (The peel yields a useful flavor distillate, see **Aroma-Distillate**).

Orange and all other citrus fruits (considered as juice-fruits).

Aroma-Distillates are made from the peels, see **Lemon Aroma.**

Pear and quince.

Plum, apricot, peach, clementine, etc.

Avocado, mango, guava, banana, pineapple, etc.

Strawberry, raspberry, currant, gooseberry, etc. (Distillates are produced from the press-cake, see **Aroma-Distillate**).

Grape (see also **Cognac Oil**, Part Two of this book).

Elderberry, cherry, blueberry, cranberry, etc. (Distillates from the press-cake).

Coconut, hazelnut, Brazil nut, cashew, walnut, almond, pistachio, etc. However, a perfume oil is extracted from the meat of coconuts, see **Coconut Absolute**, and an essential oil is produced from the press-cake of bitter almonds, see **Almond Oil, Bitter** (both Part Two of this book).

Cocoa, coffee, etc.

Vegetables which are used as a nourishing or dietetic part of human food, are not included in the monographs of this book.

G

Gum.

A **Gum** is either a natural or a synthetic material. Strictly speaking, the term **Gum** should be used only for water-soluble materials. Natural gums are anionic materials, often of glycoside-like structure and with abnormally high molecular weights.

In perfumery, the term **Gum** is often applied to **Resins**, particularly since various turpentines are referred to as **Gums,** and since many Australian eucalyptus trees are locally called **Gum** trees.

In order to distinguish between **Gums** and **Resins**, it should therefore be emphasized that **Gums** form neutral or slightly acid solutions or sols with water. Gums are often good emulsifiers (surface-active ingredients) or stabilizers (they increase the viscosity of their solutions). While **Resins** are insoluble in water and are usually of pronounced acid character, they do not affect the surface tension of an aqueous solution. In the presence of alkali, the **Resins** become water-soluble and form soaps which affect the surface tension of aqueous solutions.

Gums, as defined in the above paragraphs, are virtually odorless, and are not used in perfumery as active fragrance ingredients. A typical **Gum** is gum arabic (also known as acacia gum), not listed in this book.

Myrrh (see Part Two of this book) contains from 50% to 70% of a water-soluble **Gum** which is left as a residue when the **Myrrh** is extracted with alcohol or a hydrocarbon solvent.

See **Gum-Resin** and **Oleo-Gum-Resin** in Part One of this book.

Gum Resin.

Gum Resins are natural exudations from plants or trees. They consist of gums and resins, often accompanied by smaller amounts of essential oil. In that case, the correct term to use is **Oleo-Gum-Resin** (see this monograph). **Gum Resins** with no content of essential oil are obviously of limited interest to the perfumer, but these materials occur frequently as adulterations in the fragrant **Oleo-Gum-Resins.**

Gum Resins and **Oleo-Gum-Resins** are only partly soluble in alcohol, hydrocarbons, acetone, or chlorinated solvents. According to the content of **Gum,** the gum-resins and oleo-gum-resins are also partly soluble in water. They form emulsions when triturated with water. The essential oil and the resinous part are usually soluble in alcohol or in the above mentioned solvents.

A typical **Gum Resin** is Gamboge (known as gummi-gutta). It is not used in perfumery or flavor work. It consists of gum and resin, and does not contain any appreciable amount of essential oil.

Benzoin "Sumatra" is a balsamic type of gum-resin with extensive application in perfumery.

Myrrh is a typical **Oleo-Gum-Resin.**

See also monograph on **Oleo-Gum-Resin.**

I

Infusion.

Infusions are prepared perfumery materials. They can be defined as tinctures, in the preparation of which heat has been applied. However, the modus operandi for the preparation of infusions has quite wide limits. The application of heat may vary from five minutes' time up to many hours. Usually reflux is called for if heating is applied over a long time.

Infusions are made from the following types of materials:

1) Crude botanical drugs (botanicals), including exudations from plants and trees.
2) Fat-extracts from flower material, e.g. **Pommades.**
3) Animal raw materials.

Infusions, now more or less abandoned in modern perfumery, are distinguished from tinctures of the same raw materials by the difference in mellowness. This is particularly noticeable in cases where the raw material is a natural **Oleo-Gum-Resin.** The hot treatment with alcohol in the presence of acids (from the resin) will lead to the formation of significant amounts of various ethyl esters, etc. Acetaldehyde is formed by oxidation of the ethyl alcohol under the influence of terpenes or terpene oxides in the botanical raw material. The presence of these ethyl alcohol derivatives will change the odor characteristics of the infusion significantly.

This may be one of the reasons why infusions have lost importance in perfumery: it is too

difficult to conduct or control the unwanted esterification, etc. of the solvent in use (ethyl alcohol). For the same reason, the production of **Resinoids** is rarely carried out by direct and hot ethyl alcohol extraction even if a so-called **Absolute** is wanted. See however the monograph on **Resin Absolute,** Part One of this book. A two-step extraction, or even better: 1) hydrocarbon extraction, 2) neutralization by alkali washing and 3) alcohol extraction, will lead to an acid-free, alcohol soluble extract of the natural oleo-gum-resin without the presence of "unnatural" ethyl esters, acetaldehyde, etc. This type of **Absolute** is reproduceable, and depends only upon the quality of the crude botanical.

A deliberate utilization of esterification during hot extraction with ethyl alcohol is displayed in the product known as **Oakmoss Resin** (see Part Two of this book). **Anhydrol Ethyl Labdanate** is a similar example (see **Labdanum Resin Absolute** in Part Two of this book).

Isolate.

Isolates are prepared materials for perfumes and flavors. They are beyond the borderline of materials which will be covered by the text of this book. Isolates are produced from natural raw materials by various processes:

1) Physical isolation:

Fractionated distillation or freezing. Chromatographic separation is a type of physical isolation not yet performed on a large, commercial scale.

Well-known distilled isolates are: Phellandrene, safrole, santalol, vetiverol. Safrole is also isolated by freezing. None of these materials are produced synthetically on a commercial scale. Distilled isolates like citral, geraniol, and linalool are now produced by chemical synthesis on a large scale. However, a significant number of the so-called "synthetic" perfume and flavor materials are strongly dependent upon natural starting materials, e.g. menthol, geraniol, citronellol, carvone, anethole, etc. Camphor, menthol, thymol, and eucalyptol are illustrations of isolates obtained by freezing. The three former are now produced synthetically on a large scale, but they remain dependent on natural raw materials (see above). Eucalyptol (cineole) is produced exclusively by isolation from essential oils with a high content of this material.

2) Chemical isolation:
   Extraction or separation through simple chemical reagents.

Well-known chemical isolates are citronellal, eugenol and other aldehydes and phenols. Eugenol is produced exclusively as an isolate while citronellal is also produced synthetically. A large number of **Terpenes** are produced as isolates, mainly by fractionated distillation. They also appear as by-products in the preparation of **Terpeneless Oils**, see that monograph in Part One of this book.

In the United States, terpineol is produced mainly as an isolate from pine oil, while terpineol in Europe must be considered as a synthetic material, derived from turpentine oil from which the isolate alpha-pinene is first produced.

From the above, it can be seen that **Isolates** are strictly dependent on the availability of the parent essential oil or other natural raw material. Consequently, more and more of the previously isolated perfume and flavor materials are now produced by chemical synthesis. Only a small number of the so-called new synthetic materials are completely independent of natural raw materials (essential oils, etc.).

L

Literature references—and Sources of information.

There is a wealth of technical information on the physico-chemical properties of essential oils, etc. available in several languages. This kind of information has been completely omitted from the present book. In every case where the author has made use of earlier publications from other authors, the given information has been checked and often re-checked. Whenever necessary, this information has been substantially revised, corrected and brought up to date. Only in cases where the author has been unable to check the published information is a source of literature (information) given.

This applies to appearance, odor and flavor of the material, origin of the botanical raw material, method of processing, estimate of annual production, price levels, etc. Adulterations, suggested application, replacements and special properties have also been treated in this way.

Odor and flavor descriptions are highly subjective. As a matter of fact, the major part of the contents of this book is subjective by nature. In a few rare cases the author has based his odor or flavor descriptions upon the study of only one sample of the material in question. Thus, it is conceiveable that the reader may disagree with the given odor description if he is in possession of a different sample with the same labelling. It is a well-known fact that no two perfumers give identical odor descriptions of the same perfume material, particularly when we speak about the complex odors of natural materials. During decades of apprenticeship and experience, perfumers learn to appreciate different notes in the same perfume material depending on factors such as which company they work for, and according to their mood, habits, origin, collegues, etc., etc.

See also the chapter on **Odor Description** in Part One of this book.

It serves little or no purpose to list 10, 20 or more pages of literature references if these are merely unchecked quotations from even older literature sources. This is, unfortunately, very often the case in perfume literature.

Furthermore, it is a well-known fact that a number of perfume materials have actually changed appearance, odor, and origin during the past few decades or even more recently, e.g. **Lavandin Oil** and **Galbanum**. The latter is one striking example of a raw material which has not yet been described as it is to-day. Up-to-date information is needed in the perfume and flavor trade and production. This industry is growing and moving rapidly.

O

Odor Description.

The description of the odor of a perfume material (or of the flavor of a flavor material) has been, and still is, the source of endless discussions among perfumers, pseudo-perfumers and laymen. The more exactly one attempts to describe a material, the fewer people are able to agree with the author on his description. Some brief and basic very general terms from everyday talk and work seem to offer the best midway solution to this problem. Obviously no odor can be described verbally—in any language—in such a way that every reader will immediately visualize the material and be enabled immediately to identify it if he is faced with an unlabelled sample of the material.

Various systems of grouping perfume materials have been suggested. Probably one of the most logical, from a perfumer's point of view, is that of Poucher who has based his grouping (or classification) upon the "length of the life" of the material on a perfume blotter. See Poucher's publication in "Journal of the Society of Cosmetic Chemists", Vol. VI, page 80 (1955).

It is the author's practice, in the description of odors in this book, not to describe one odor in terms of another unknown odor. He has also deliberately avoided describing the odor of a non-complex material through the use of the name of a complex material. However, since this book deals exclusively with natural raw materials, practically all the odors are of a complex nature. Natural materials can in many cases be described to a certain degree through mention of their main constituents, whereas the opposite way of description would be a very unjust one (e.g. clove stem oil does smell of eugenol—and of other materials —while eugenol cannot be adequately described as having a "clove odor" or "clove stem oil odor".)

The general principle may be illustrated by this example: to describe anethole as having a rich, sweet, mild-spicy, non-floral odor. Anise oil can well be described as having an anethole-like odor as a background of its fresh-spicy sweetness. Positively misleading is the term "licorice-like" in a description of anise or anethole. This type of odor description is typical of modern associations, in this case, an association with licorice candy which owes its flavor to anethol (or anise oil) more than to licorice extract. The latter only imparts a sweet taste and a faint rootlike odor-flavor. A much more common error of this type is found in the description of vanillin. The layman will often identify the odor of vanillin as "chocolate". Common chocolate or chocolate candy is strongly flavored with vanillin (or its homologues). The consumers, who are not familiar with these chemicals or their odors, will inevitably associate the odor of vanillin with that of chocolate. Very few chocolate eaters know the odor or flavor of natural cocoa beans or roasted cocoa beans before these are artificially flavored.

To describe the odor of hydroxycitronellal as "the closest approach of all perfume materials to the odor of muguet" is, in the author's opinion, an insult to nature. The odor of this chemical is delicately sweet, intensely floral, tenacious, etc. —the latter term is even a physical fact. The odor is not only widely different from that of the "lily of the valley", but the odor of hydroxycitronellal is so much less complex that a comparison would be directly misleading. Besides, not many of the readers of perfume books know a muguet flower "in natura".

It is part of a perfumer's training and apprenticeship to form in his own mind the "unspoken" terms in which he thinks when he smells and recognizes a perfume material. But, when communicating with fellow perfumers, he must seek more general expressions in order to be well understood. The drawbacks of a "basic terms" system for odor descriptions are equally obvious:

No descriptions are unambiguous or even very striking. But if we could describe every single of our perfume materials in such a way that no two descriptions were alike, and so that every one fitted like a key to only one material, we could lean back on a wreath of laurels. We would have conceived the "impossible": we would have invented the perfect and foolproof odor classification system.

Part of the "romance" or "thrill" in perfumery work lies in the fact that, not only are all the materials different in odor but hardly ever will two perfumers give identical descriptions of the same material or the same perfume. This coincidence will not occur even if the two perfumers have been working or have perhaps been educated in the same perfume laboratory for years. An odor is not "woody" just because someone else says so; it will always have a particular print in your mind. Unfortunately, you are more or less unable to translate this print verbally to fellow perfumers, let alone to laymen.

This work does not pretend to be a "codex" for the perfume industry. The rules and statements in this book can hardly apply to the conventional terms used in price lists, etc. For technical reasons, for lack of space perhaps, the odor descriptions of perfume materials in price lists are often abrupt and yet exaggerated. But it certainly is the author's hope that the present work may serve as an appeal to the raw material suppliers in the perfume industry to standardize their labelling and descriptions of perfume and flavor materials. This would minimize the confusion which has grown tremendously among small and medium-size consumers, and has even affected the very largest consumers as well.

The odor descriptions in this work are based upon studies of the materials during repeated **Blotter**-tests. A perfume **Blotter**, also called a "smelling-strip", is a piece of pure, odorless, white, higly absorbent filter paper, about 6 mm. wide and 12 to 14 cms. long. This strip is marked clearly with the name or number of the sample of the perfume material, and is then dipped in the perfume sample to about 5 mm. or up to 2 cms. on the opposite end.

The odor from the blotter is studied immediately, then again after a few minutes, a half hour, several hours, next morning, etc. until there is no characteristic odor left. Notes are taken during all stages of evaporation. Certain materials are studied in dilution, e. g. oakmoss absolutes, flower absolutes, civet, etc. The blotter is thoroughly studied when the perfume oil has "dried" into the paper. Particularly in oils of high terpene content, there is a perceptible effect of chromatographic separation of the individual components of the oil. The "lighter" notes run quickly up the blotter, while the larger molecules remain at the end, where it was dipped.

The **Topnote** ("la note de départ") is studied repeatedly since it may be of very short duration. It is the very first perceptible note, the first impression of odor. The topnote can be very characteristic of an essential oil and it is also very often a difficult one to reproduce in the work on "artificial" essential oils, adulterations, cuttings, etc. The true **Topnote** of an essential oil can be masked by so-called "still-odors" which are unwanted notes. Still-notes are usually removed by aeration or ageing of the oil (see also **Aroma-Distillates**).

The main and characteristic overall odor of the oil in the perfume blotter is called the **Body-Note**. It has a much longer life on the blotter than has the topnote, but it is less characteristic of the odor of the oil, and it is easier to reproduce in the work on artificial essential oils, etc.

The **Dry-Out** note is equally as important as the topnote for evaluation of the oil. The dry-out will appear after one hour, several hours, or perhaps not until the next day. It often reveals adulteration of an essential oil, and it should be studied repeatedly and carefully.

The **Dry-Out** notes show the fixative effect of the components in the oil; it may reveal weakness, diluents or other foreign additives. Certain oils do not show a typical dry-out note within the same day as they are "blottered", e.g. patchouli oil, vetiver, civet, everlasting, longoza, etc. These oils can not be justly evaluated within minutes or hours. It requires at least 24 hours of study and careful notes. The dry-out note will show the bodynote, but not the topnote. In exceptional cases, the topnote is carried along far into the bodynote and may be perceptible in the dry-out, e. g. angelica root oil.

The dry-out note tells us about the **Tenacity** of the perfume material. The **Tenacity**, also called the lasting effect, is a highly appreciated effect in perfume materials, particularly if the bodynote and the dry-out note are pleasant fragrances. Lemon oil has a fresh and pleasant **Topnote** of very short duration. It has only a faint and rather uncharacteristic **Bodynote**, which may last one or two hours on a perfume blotter. The **Dry-Out** is very faint, uninteresting, yet characteristic, but of little use to the perfumer. There is no **Tenacity** in the odor of lemon oil.

Sage clary oil displays a fresh and delicate **Topnote**, which slides gently into a very rich, sweet-herbaceous **Bodynote** of long duration. Its **Dry-Out** is balsamic-ambra-like, reminiscent of tobacco and sweet hay, tea-leaves, and with an unusual **Tenacity**.

In order to study the behavior of essential oils on perfume blotters correctly, it is of great importance that a constant room temperature and relative humidity be maintained. The author has personal preference for temperatures lower than 20°C. in a perfume laboratory, although in certain countries, a much higher temperature is quite common (22 to 27°C.). Several ultra-modern laboratories in Europe are provided with thermostats and humidity regulators to maintain about 17°C. and 45 to 50% relative humidity. The author has experienced an almost odor-free atmosphere in Mid-Sahara, where the temperature was 64°C. on the sand surface, and the relative humidity was about 0.3%. The author was unable to smell the peel of an orange which was squeezed between the fingers under these circumstances.

Excessively high humidity is equally unfavorable to smelling if the temperature is well above 20°C. It should be noted, however, that during the study of a dry-out note, the perfumer will often attempt to produce a "steam-distillation" by exhaling breath from his nostrils upon the dry blotter in order to enhance the evaporation of a weak-smelling material.

The technique of smelling and evaluating perfume materials has been thoroughly described in several works on perfumery practice during the past decade.

Oleo-Gum-Resin.

An **Oleo-Gum-Resin** is a natural exudation from plants or trees. It consists mainly of essential oil, gum, and resin. Various names are used commercially for this type of material, e.g. **Gum, Gum-Resin,** etc. Sometimes merely the botanical name is used, e.g. **Myrrh,** which is a typical **Oleo-Gum-Resin** according to the above definition. Oleo-gum-resins are only partly soluble in alcohol and hydrocarbon solvents, both of which leave the gum as an insoluble residue. See also **Gum-Resin** (Part One of this book) and the individual monographs on **Myrrh, Olibanum, Opopanax,** etc. in Part Two of this book.

Oleo-Resin.

An **Oleo-Resin** is either a natural or a prepared material. Natural oleo-resins are exudations from tree-trunks, barks, etc. Prepared oleo-resins are liquid preparations, extracted from botanical drugs with solvents which can extract oil and resinous matter from the botanical, yielding the **Oleo-Resin** as evaporation residue. Prepared oleo-resins may also contain non-volatile oils (so-called "fixed" oils). Prepared oleo-resins present the most concentrated liquid form of the botanical material in question. The type of solvent used in the extraction of prepared oleo-resins should be chosen with due consideration of the fact that solvents are difficult to remove totally even under vacuum, and that prepared oleo-resins are often used in food preparations.

As the name indicates, the two types of **Oleo-Resins** are characterized by the fact that they consist entirely—or mainly—of essential oil and resin.

Copaiba Balsam is a typical natural **Oleo-Resin.**

See also **Balsam** in Part One of this book for a definition of this term. Oleo-resin **Ginger** is a well-known prepared **Oleo-Resin.**

Natural oleo-resins are usually characterized as clear, viscous and light-colored liquids, while the prepared oleo-resins in general are heterogeneous masses of dark color.

Turpentines can be considered as a sub-group of the natural oleo-resins. **Turpentines** are exudations of either physiological or pathological nature from tree trunks, barks, etc. They consist almost entirely of essential oil and resin. The resin consists mainly of acids and acid anhydrides, formed by oxidation of terpenes.

Turpentines are derived from coniferes, particularly from species of **Abies** and **Pinus.** Various turpentines are described in Part Two of this work.

Canada Balsam is a true **Turpentine.**

Elemi is a natural oleo-resin, with a composition similar to a turpentine.

P

Pommade.

Pommades are prepared perfume materials. They are obtained by the so-called **Enfleurage** process which is carried out almost exclusively in the South of France. Certain tropical flowers, e.g. **Pandanus** ("kewda"), are treated in a similar way locally (in India) to yield **Pommades.**

The **Enfleurage** process is mainly applied to flowers that do not yield any appreciable amount of essential oil by steam or water distillation, or it may be applied to flowers that are too delicate to withstand exposure to heat and steam. Furthermore, certain flower petals continue to develop and give off perfume oil even long after they have been harvested. During the **Enfleurage** process, a fatty or greasy base on a plate will adsorb all the perfume oil which is present in and exhaled from the flower. The trays or stacks of greased plates, with the flowers adhering to the fat, are left for 24 hours. The flowers are then picked off by hand, and a new batch of flowers is sprinkled on the same layer of fat. The spent flowers are extracted with a hydrocarbon solvent to produce **"Concrète de Châssis"**, which in turn is processed into **Absolute from Châssis,** see this monograph.

After many batches, each consisting of 24

1: Modern installation for vacuum **Distillation** and **Rectification** of essential oils and isolates.

(Courtesy of **Dragoco,** *Holzminden, Germany)*

2: Vacuum **Distillation** of essential oils in all-glass stills, 50 and 200 litres capacity.

(*Courtesy of Q.V.F., Ltd., Staffordshire, England*)

hours of flower treatment on the trays (and up to
36 batches on the same layer of fat), the fragrance-
saturated fat (known as "corps gras") is removed
from the plates or trays (the "châssis"). The
saturated fat is known as **Pommade**. The fat used
in this process must be neutral and odorless;
it must not become rancid, and must have a high
adsorbent ability and a certain viscosity; it should
be almost insoluble in cold alcohol.

As such the **Pommade** is hardly used any more.
It is further processed into **Extrait** and to **Abso-
lute from Pommade**, see these monographs in
Part One of this book.

R

Resin.

A **Resin** is either a natural or a prepared product.

Natural **Resins** are exudations from trees or
plants and they are formed in Nature by the
oxidation of terpenes. Many **Resins** are acids or
acid anhydrides.

Prepared **Resins** are **Oleo-Resins** (see this) from
which the essential oil has been removed.

Resins are solid or semi-solid, usually non-
crystalline (amorphous) and, if they are waterfree
they are translucent masses.

Resins are almost odorless, insoluble in water,
but often soluble in alkali solutions.

Dammar and **Mastic** are typical natural **Resins.**
Rosin is a typical prepared **Resin.**

"**Resin Labdanum**" (a misnomer) is a fraction
of a labdanum extract.

"**Resin Oakmoss**" (a misnomer) is a hot-
processed alcoholic extract of oakmoss often
"touched up" with synthetic perfume materials.

Copal: A copal is a natural resin of particularly
high melting point and of hard texture. **Copals**
often derive from trees, long since extinct. The
copals from such trees are found in the soil or on
the ground. Living trees mainly in tropical Africa,
South America, Australia and Asia also yield
Copals. Some of these "recent-fossil" copals
become sufficiently hard and brittle to be used as
the real "prehistoric" fossil **Copals**.

Copals are not used in perfumes or flavors but
they are highly appreciated in the finer varnish
and lacquer industry.

Amber is the hardest of the fossil resins from
various species of pinus, long since extinct. **Amber**
is odorless, but it yields an "essential" oil on
destructive distillation, see **Amber Oil**, Part Two
of this book.

Resin Absolute.

"**Resin Absolute**" is a term frequently applied to
extracts from botanical raw materials, plant
material or exudations (so-called gums) directly
with hot alcohol. The resulting extract from which
all alcohol has been recovered by distillation
under vacuum is the so-called **Resin Absolute**. The
product can be considered as a concentrated
Infusion (see this monograph in Part One of the
book). During the distillation, the evaporated
alcohol may be partially substituted for by a
high-boiling, odorless solvent in order to make the
extract handy and pourable. The addition of
such a "plasticizer" is, however, not without a
depressing effect upon the odor of the extract.
The "plasticized" extract is not truly a "**Resin
Absolute**". Common plasticizers are diethylphthalate, diethylsebacate, benzyl benzoate, isopropylmyristate, isopropyl palmitate, various ethylene
glycol ether-esters, diethylene glycol monolaurate,
etc., etc.

Some manufacturers will evaporate the extract
to a content of 50% extractive matter (calculated
in advance from the results of a test-run). The
resulting extract then contains 50% alcohol in
which small amounts of water from the raw
material is now included. This extract should be
labelled: "**Resin Absolute of xxx, 50% solution in
alcohol**".

Well-known exceptions are: **Oakmoss**: The
direct extraction product with hot alcohol is
called **Oakmoss Resin** (see Part Two of this book);
Labdanum: The direct extraction product from
"gum" labdanum is usually called "**Labdanum
Resin Absolute**", but the plant material (the herb
Cistus Ladaniferus) is not extracted this way;
Orris: The direct extraction product of the pow-
dered rhizome with hot alcohol is usually called
Orris Resin (see Part Two of this book).

Resinoid.

A **Resinoid** is a perfumery material prepared from
natural, resinous substances by extraction with a
hydrocarbon type of solvent. True resinoids

contain all the hydrocarbon-soluble matter from the natural starting material, including the resins, but they contain no solvent (see below).

The most frequently used solvents are: petroleum ether, benzene, gasoline, butane (see **Butaflor** under **Absolutes**), or, in certain cases, acetone, methylene dichloride, trichloro ethylene and other solvents which are not exactly hydrocarbons. Non-volatile solvents are occasionally used: diethylphthalate, benzyl benzoate, diethyl sebacate, isopropyl myristate, etc. (See **Resin Absolute** (Part One) and **Galbanum** (Part Two)).

In contradistinction to **Concrètes**, the **Resinoids** are generally produced from "dead" (i.e. non-cellular) organic material, while the **Concrètes** are derived from previously "live" (= cellular) tissue, etc. Resinous materials are, e.g. balsams, gum-resins, natural resins, oleo-gum-resins, etc.

Resinoids can be viscous liquids, semi-solid or solid, but usually homogeneous masses of non-crystalline (amorphous) character. Their main constituents are rosin acids, rosin acid anhydrides, sesquiterpenes, essential oils, plant colors, waxes, and other hydrocarbon-soluble matter.

No essential oil or other odorous matter should be removed or added during the preparation of a resinoid. However, it may be necessary to add a plasticizing diluent during the solvent recovery in order to spare the resinoid from excessive heat exposure, and to make the finished product easier to pour and handle. Plasticizing diluents are mentioned above and also under **Resin Absolute** (previous monograph).

Olibanum Resinoid is a typical resinoid. The natural oleo-gum-resin (olibanum) has been made applicable and soluble in perfume materials by the removal of the water-soluble gum.

See also **Concrète, Oleo-Resin, Resin, Resin Absolute** (Part One of this book).

Clairs, etc.: Clair is the registered French name of a series of purified, light-colored, soluble extracts of natural raw materials. Some of these products are distilled extracts; others are decolorized by means of activated carbon and other adsorbents. **Clairs** present the advantage of a much paler color than the corresponding resinoid or absolute, better solubility and, in most cases, higher odor concentration also. Certain **Clairs** are, however, entirely different in odor type from the equivalent resinoid or concrète (e.g. clove, nutmeg, etc.).

Resinoines are similar highly concentrated extracts of pale color and good solubility. (See **Anhydrol** in Part One of this book). Other **Resinoid**-specialities are based upon neutralization of the resin acids in order to avoid esterification with ethyl alcohol used in the second extraction. Resin acids also react with alkali in soaps. The main difficulty in the use of such specialties is that they are very difficult to replace or substitute with resinoids from other suppliers. Once these specialties are included in an established formula, they present "current business" for the manufacturer of this specialty.

S

Sesquiterpeneless Oils.

These oils are also called: **Terpene-** and **Sesquiterpeneless Oils**. The abbreviation "TRSQF" is occasionally met in Europe (Germany) where the terpeneless oils are called TRF oils.

For details of the processing, see **Terpeneless Oils** in Part One of this book. Method "A" for removal of the terpenes is not specific in the sense that only terpenes are removed. Since the sesquiterpenes have higher boiling point than most of our perfume and flavor materials (of natural origin), method "A" will never lead to a **Sesquiterpeneless Oil**.

Methods "B" or "C", or a combination of methods "A"+"B" will be recommended for the production of sesquiterpeneless oils. Certain essential oils contain little or no monoterpenes, but significant amounts of sesquiterpenes, e.g. clove oils, vetiver oil etc. These oils are deterpenized by the above methods. The so-called terpeneless clove oil is actually **Sesquiterpeneless** clove oil. Chemically, monoterpenes and sesquiterpenes are part of a group known as "terpenoid compounds". In Nature, these materials are found almost entirely in the plant kingdom. They are usually defined as derivatives from the basic material isoprene with the empirical formula C_5H_8. Monoterpenes are built up from two such structures (formula $C_{10}H_{16}$), and sesquiterpenes are $C_{15}H_{24}$. The syllabus "sesqui" refers to "six quarts" or "one-and-one-half times".

Sesquiterpenes are removed from essential oils

for several reasons, although not quite the same reasons as those given for the removal of mono-terpenes:

1) To improve the solubility of the oil in diluted alcohol or in flavor solvents;
2) To improve the perfume and flavor of the essential oil;
3) To lift the overall fragrance or flavor of the oil since the sesquiterpenes tend to depress the odor or flavor through the fixative effect of these high-boiling components.

Point 1) is mutual for mono- and sesqui-terpenes.

Points 2) and 3) pertain particularly to sesqui-terpenes. There is hardly any rancidity or instab-ility problem connected with the sesquiterpenes. In this respect, they are less troublesome than the monoterpenes. Generally speaking, the sesqui-terpenes are more of a nuisance in flavors than they are in perfumes. Sesquiterpenes have, as a rule, a rather poor flavor, and most of them are distinctly bitter. Only a very few sesquiterpenes are available in a pure state, and none have yet been produced synthetically on a commercial scale. Well-known sesquiterpenes are: Caryophyl-lene, bisabolene, cadinene, cedrene, etc.

Spices.

The definition of the term **Spice** is usually a very flexible one. Generally, spices are considered as being singular materials of plant origin (botanical substance), characterized by pungency or biting *mouthfeel*, strong odor and sweet or bitter taste. It so happens that spices most often originate in tropical areas, but this is not exactly a prerequisite for a spice.

A combination of several spices and/or strong herbs is usually called a **Condiment.**

The addition of basic flavor effects (stimuli) by the use of sugar, salt, vinegar, etc. is considered a **Seasoning.**

However, vinegar as used in salad dressing is often called a **Condiment**; this, in the author's opinion, is misleading.

For those interested in legal definitions, it is suggested that the paragraphs in the various pharmacopoeias, etc. should be consulted, as well as the definitions given by the Food and Drug Administration (of the U.S.A.) and other state authorities.

Physiologically, a **Seasoning** is a **Taste Stimulus.**

There are four basic taste stimuli: bitter, salt, sour, sweet. Under the monograph **Soybean** (Part Two of this book), a "fifth" stimulus is mentioned, popularly known under the name of the "third spice" (*monosodiumglutamate*). Truly, this chemical acts as a synergist for other stimuli. Other chemicals are known to act more or less as specific stimulus-paralyzers, e.g. *gymnemic acid*. This chemical is extracted from the leaves of a plant of the N.O. Asclepiadaceae, a family from which few, if any, essential oils of interest are derived.

A **Condiment** is then a *mouthfeel* stimulus, while the **Culinary Herbs** are Odor-Flavor Stimuli. The **Spices** also belong to this physiological group. Some authorities discriminate between **Spices** and **Aromatic Seeds.** Coriander, anise, dillfruit, etc. are then considered **Aromatic Seeds.** They have a feature in common with spices in that their flavor is primarily derived from an essential oil (a volatile substance). **Culinary Herbs,** on the other hand, owe their flavor to essential oils plus a bitter principle (sage, basil, origanum, thyme, etc.).

Another classification is formed by the **Pungent** materials. **Capsicum** has no essential oil, but the extract of capsicum is very pungent. **Ginger** and **Black Pepper** are pungent *and* aromatic.

Finally, there is a small group of botanical materials that contain practically no essential oil and have no pungency, but they do produce useful flavor extracts, e.g. vanilla, tonka, fenugreek, St. John's bread, etc.

Certain seeds are used partly to produce a mechanical *mouthfeel*, partly as a mild flavor additive. **Poppy Seed** is one of these materials. It is interesting to note that the U.S.A. imports thousands of tons of these tiny seeds every year, mainly from Denmark and Holland.

T

Terpeneless Oils.

Terpeneless essential oils are processed perfume or flavor materials. Literally speaking, they are essential oils from which all monoterpenes ($C_{10}H_{16}$) have been removed. The term "**Terpene-less**", however, is one of the most unscrupulously used terms in the flavor and perfume industry.

Most often, these oils are "partially deterpenized" and this again can be achieved in many ways. Terpenes are removed for several reasons:

1) To improve the solubility of the oil in low-proof alcohol, in food solvents, etc., and to make the oil clearly soluble in water at normal usage level (e. g. in carbonated drinks);

2) To concentrate the active perfume and flavor ingredients according to the theory that terpenes play a minor role in the overall flavor or perfume gamut. However, this is not always so. Terpenes are comparatively weak aromatics, but they do present certain effects which are indispensable in the reproduction of "true-to-nature" perfumes or flavors;

3) To increase the stability of the essential oil, and to prevent the appearance of rancid notes, the formation of resins, etc.

The terpenes are removed from essential oils by various methods:

A) By fractionated distillation. One cannot expect to remove all the monoterpenes by this method, not even with highly effective distillation columns, fine vacuum, or slow distillation (regulated reflux ratio), etc.

B) By selective solvent extraction. Various methods have been patented (e.g. "Naardenized oils"). The hydrocarbon pentane will dissolve terpenes, while diluted methanol will dissolve the so-called oxygenated compounds (perfume and flavor materials). Pentane is almost insoluble in diluted methanol. Through countercurrent liquid-liquid extraction, two solutions are obtained: one is the pentane with terpenes; the other is the diluted methanol with the aromatic principles of the oil. The methanol solution is separated (lower layer) and evaporated in vacuum until all methanol and water is removed. A special technique is required during this operation in order to avoid water-distillation and consequent loss of the aromatic components. The non-distilled residue from this distillation is the terpeneless oil. This method differs from method A) in the sense that it also removes the sesquiterpenes ($C_{15}H_{24}$). In method A), the sesquiterpenes are left in the distillation pot, together with the monoterpeneless oil.

C) A third method is actually a combination of A) and B): the bulk of the monoterpenes are removed by careful distillation under vacuum. Distillation temperature must not exceed 30°, and the temperature of the oil should not exceed 50°C. A very simple, but extremely suitable apparatus is available in Quickfit glass in sizes up to 200 litres. Heating is provided by an outside heat-exchanger which is connected to the bottom of the distillation flask (feed of cold oil) and with an outlet into the flask above the oil surface (exit of oil vapors after heating). This apparatus presents an excellent solution to the problem of overheating sensitive oils (citrus oils, etc.). When the distillation is running smoothly, only the oil in the heat exchanger is somewhat warmer than the vapors of oil at the still head. The temperature of the main portion of the oil (in the distillation flask) is significantly lower than the temperature in the heat exchanger, and it is only a little above the still head temperature, dependent upon the size and construction of the column. A glass column of 15 cms. diameter and 150 to 200 cms. height, packed with raschig rings, is suitable for citrus oils.

When about two-thirds of the monoterpenes have been removed by this method, the distillation is stopped. The residue in the flask is extracted with diluted alcohol. The strength of the alcohol is adjusted to the type of oil in question, usually about 50% to 60% of alcohol by weight. This diluted alcohol will hardly dissolve any monoterpenes, sesquiterpenes, or waxes. Several extractions are necessary in order to exhaust completely all the oxygenated materials from the still residue. The alcoholic extracts are combined and evaporated under vacuum. Care must be taken that the water from the diluted alcohol does not carry over significant amounts of aromatic substances. The residue from this second distillation consists of waxes (in case of orange oil), sesquiterpenes (in case of lemon oil), etc. The residue from orange oil is solid at room temperature. Most of the other residues are viscous liquids.

The evaporated alcoholic extract (now free from solvent) is sometimes rectified at very low pressure (less than 0.1 mm. Hg.). This leads to an almost water-white terpeneless oil. The finished oil is now bulked from the absolutely terpeneless distillate with addition of certain selected terpene fractions, head fractions and perhaps parts of the freezing trap fraction from the first distillation. These small additions (cut-backs) are most important for the reproduction of true-to-nature notes in the terpeneless oils.

In flavor work, it is of paramount importance to keep the flavor of the "terpeneless" oil within the limits of reasonable similarity to the natural starting material. A partially monoterpeneless oil, from which all sesquiterpenes and waxes have been eliminated, will present a good solubility and improved stability, yet it will still display the freshness and topnotes of the parent oil. These "dewaxed" and partially deterpenized citrus oils are particularly useful in flavor work. A calculated concentration of 6 to 6¼ times (by weight) from the natural oil seems to offer the best solution. This oil still contains a significant amount of monoterpenes. In case of lemon oil, for example, there will be over 50% monoterpenes in a 6¼ times concentrated oil, but the terpenes will have been selected for flavor performance. It should be remembered at this point that the flavor "body" obtained from one kilo of a 6¼ times concentrated oil is much weaker or "thinner" than the flavor body obtained from 6¼ kilos of natural oil. The true concentration in flavor effect is considerably less than the calculated figure.

Lemon oil, long since evaluated by many customers by its citral content only, cannot be judged from the content of this chemical alone. Citral is a comparatively low-boiling flavor chemical, and a certain quantity of citral is lost during the vacuum distillation of lemon oil. By counter-current extraction (see method B), there is no loss due to low boiling points of oxygenated components.

Method A) will often remove low-boiling constituents other than the terpenes. The method may thus substantially change the character of the oil. Many essential oils contain useful materials which boil and distil below or near the boiling point of most monoterpenes. The A) and the B) methods, therefore, will yield quite different "terpeneless" oils.

There are still other methods of removing the terpenes from essential oils;

D) By chromatographic separation of the constituents. In this process, the terpeneless oil is dissolved in petroleum ether or other anionic solvent. The solution is forced through a column of silicic acid or other adsorbent matter. Separation takes place due to difference in molecular size, and the section of the column containing the oxygenated components of the oil can be isolated and subsequently flushed with a polar solvent.

Various patents cover various methods, some of which claim to be so highly perfected that the terpenefraction contains 0.0% oxygenated components, and the terpeneless oil comes out in a theoretical yield.

E) A further development of the B) method. Water-diluted acids, alcohols, ketones, etc. have been used to extract the oxygenated components of the oils and leave the terpenes undissolved.

Terpeneless Oils form a separate series of perfume and flavor materials. The terpeneless oils are an addition to the selection of raw materials at the disposal of the perfumer and the flavorist. These oils cannot be considered as replacements for natural oils. They can not be used directly as a substitute for a natural oil when solubility, etc. prevents the use of the terpenic oil. The difference is particularly obvious in the case of citrus oils which contain over 90% terpenes. In other cases, the terpenes constitute only a minor part of the natural oil, but they may impart an unpleasant odor or flavor, e.g. peppermint oil, lavender oil, bay leaf oil, petitgrain oil, etc. A number of terpeneless oils are described in Part Two of this book. They are listed next to their respective natural oils.

Tincture.

A Tincture is a prepared perfumery material, flavor material or pharmaceutical product. Tinctures can be considered alcoholic extracts of natural raw materials; the solvent is left in the extract as a diluent. Consequently, tinctures are not exposed to heat during preparation. (See Infusion, Part One of this book). There is no general rule governing the strength of perfumery or flavor tinctures. Pharmaceutical tinctures are generally prepared from one part of natural raw material plus five parts of an 86% weight/weight ethyl alcohol or, in some cases, a 61% w/w ethyl alcohol. Certain tinctures are made in the ratio 1 : 10, and in most of such cases the alcohol is 86% w/w.

As a result of the method of preparation, tinctures do not always represent the total amount of natural raw material from which they are prepared. The natural raw material may not be completely exhausted, and the alcohol is not quantitatively flushed out of the tissues of botanical matter, etc. before the spent raw material is discarded.

Most perfumery tinctures are made by **Maceration** (e.g. from gum-resins, natural oleo-resins, etc.). A **Maceration** is a soaking of the comminuted material in the menstruum (alcohol or diluted alcohol) until the cellular structure of the raw material is thoroughly penetrated, and the soluble portions softened and dissolved. The maceration is usually extended over a period of many days, sometimes up to two weeks, during which time the raw material is frequently agitated in the alcohol. If the raw material is suspended in a gauze bag in the upper part of the alcohol, the method is called **Circulatory Maceration**. It offers certain advantages such as more rapid extraction of the drug.

Other tinctures are prepared by **Percolation**, e.g. from ambrette seed, vanilla fruits, etc. **Percolation** is a process during which the comminuted raw material is put in a suitable container and is then deprived of its soluble constituents by the descent of a solvent through it. It is one of the most basic, yet important methods of preparing pharmaceutical extracts. In a few cases, **Tinctures** are made by simple solution. These tinctures are dilutions rather than real tinctures, but the term "tinctures" is still applied to this type of preparation. Alcoholic solutions of **Resinoids, Resin-Absolutes**, etc. are among the more recent additions to the perfumer's shelf. These tinctures are easier to standardize and simple to prepare. **Resinoids** (see this monograph in Part One of this book) are not necessarily alcohol-soluble. Furthermore, it is necessary to know the exact strength of the parent resinoid when tinctures are prepared from these materials.

A number of "classical" perfume tinctures are prepared in special manners, although many perfume houses now prefer to make 5%, 10% or 20% tinctures as a standard on all raw materials:

Tincture of Ambra (ambergris): 3% ambra in a 90% ethyl alcohol. Alkali is usually added to neutralize acids and to facilitate solution (a "solubilizer"). Age for not less than 6 months.

Tincture of Ambrette Seed: 12½% in pure ethyl alcohol. The tincture can be prepared by maceration or by percolation. The former method requires up to two months extraction time.

Tincture of Castoreum: 6% in pure ethyl alcohol. To be macerated and subsequently aged for 6 to 8 weeks before filtration.

Tincture of Civet: 3½% in pure ethyl alcohol. Gentle heat is applied since the fatty raw material is almost insoluble in cold alcohol and tends to "protect" the active ingredients from being extracted. A 10% tincture is also produced.

Tincture of Musk: 3% musk in a 90% ethyl alcohol. *Alkali* and other additives are often used during the maceration. To be aged for not less than 6 months before filtration.

Tincture of Orris: 25% orris root in 95% ethyl alcohol. To be macerated for one month. This product is growing quite rare. It is substituted for by solutions of **Orris "Resin"** (see Part Two of this book).

Tincture of Vanilla: For perfumes: 15% vanilla fruits in a 95% denatured ethyl alcohol. Macerate for two weeks, age for 2 to 6 months. For flavors: 10% vanilla fruits in a 38% alcohol. Prepared by percolation with alcohol of decreasing strength. The term, "vanilla tincture", is among the most abused labellings, and the product is one of the most frequently adulterated of all flavor products.

Tinctures of **Benzoin, Labdanum, Olibanum, Opopanax, Peru, Tolu** balsam, etc. are generally prepared from 20% of the natural raw material with pure ethyl alcohol. After proper maceration, the tincture is filtered and aged.

Various **Tinctures** are described in the monographs of the parent raw material in Part Two of this book.

U

Ultrasonic Extracts.

Ultrasonic Extracts are prepared flavor materials, or, in a few cases, perfume materials. Several methods of extracting natural raw materials with the aid of supersonic sound vibrations have been described in scientific literature, and many extractors have been patented. A few European flavor and perfume material suppliers specialize in such extracts, e.g. Camilli, Albert et Laloue in Grasse, France.

It is claimed that this method:

1) gives higher yields,
2) reduces the amount of solvent needed,
3) greatly improves the flavor or odor in the sense that they become more true-to-nature,
4) reduces the extraction time considerably,
5) makes possible an extraction with water or low-proof alcohol where this is otherwise not too effective.

Capacity of the extractors has hitherto been the major problem which has kept this method from becoming popular. But extractors of sufficient size can now be constructed so as to give a reasonable capacity. The finely ground raw material is suspended in the menstruum (solvent) in the extractor. High-frequency vibration is applied, and, in an amazingly short time, the drug is exhausted. Due to the better yield given by this method in comparison to ordinary extraction, the ultrasonic extracts are often cheaper in use than the old types of extracts.

The method is particularly useful for extraction of flavors from sensitive (heat-sensitive) raw materials, e.g. coffee, spices, etc., but flowers and herbs are also treated by this method now, e.g. mimosa, thyme, etc. A number of **Ultrasonic Extracts** are described under the monographs of their parent raw material in Part Two of this book.

PART TWO

Monographs on Crude and Processed Raw Materials of Natural Origin

A

Abies Alba.

Synonyms: **Abies Excelsa, Abies Pectinata, Abies Picea**, "silver spruce", "white spruce". Under the present monograph only the essential oil from the needles will be described. From the cones of **Abies Alba** is distilled another essential oil, see **Templin Oil**. **Abies Alba** is a relatively small tree which grows in Austria (Tirol), Eastern France, Germany, Poland, and Yougoslavia. The tree is planted in many European countries for lumber, wood-pulp production and also for Christmas trees.

The essential oil is distilled from the needles alone or from the twigs with needles. Experiments have shown, that there is but little difference in the essential oils from the two parts of the tree. The steam distillation produces a colorless or pale yellow mobile liquid of rich balsamic-sweet and pleasant oily-pinaceous fragrance. Oils from Austria are known for their outstanding quality and fine fragrance.

Abies Alba oil finds application in perfumes for bath preparations, air-fresheners, disinfectants, fougère-colognes, soap perfumes, detergents, etc. The oil is most popular in Europe, where the demand is rarely in excess of the availability of this oil. Although the oil belongs to the group of "low-ester" and "high-terpene" containing "fir" and spruce needle oils, it has great power, good stability and performance in compositions for the above purposes. It blends excellently with coumarin, galbanum, ionones, labdanum, lavandin, linalool, methylionones, nitromusks, oakmoss, rosemary oil, etc.

Under the name of **"Fir Needle Oil"** comes also an oil, distilled from needles and branchlets of **Picea Excelsa** in Yougoslavia and Roumania. The odor of this oil is somewhat similar to that of **Abies Alba** needles oil. **Picea Excelsa** is described under its Latin name in this book.

Because of frequent and extensive "cutting" and adulteration of this oil with pinene, isobornyl-acetate, camphene, limonene, dodecanal, decanal, palatone, etc., it is difficult to obtain reliable figures of the annual production. It is estimated, that between 5 and 20 tons of true oil are produced annually in Europe.

Abies sp.

Spruces ("firs") grow all over the world and are planted for various purposes in numerous countries. Essential oils are often produced from such local species for domestic use and hardly ever exported.

In Japan—particularly on Hokkaido Island—between 100 and 200 tons of "fir" needle oils were produced annually in postwar years. These oils found use in the perfuming of soaps, low-cost household cleaners, detergents, etc. The production of these oils has decreased in the past few years.

Abies Mayriana and **Abies Sachalinensis** are two of the most important Japanese firs, from which essential oils are distilled. The production in 1958 of the two oils was about 10 tons. These oils are of comparatively high ester content: 22–26% bornylacetate. In this respect the oils are only slightly inferior to the oil of **Balsam Fir**, see this monograph.

Acaroid.

The so-called **Acaroid Resin** is a natural oleo-gum-resin, exuded from various species of **Xanthorrhoea** trees in Australia, Tasmania, and New Zealand. There are two **Acaroids** of interest for perfumery:

1) Yellow **Acaroid** from **Xanthorrhoea Hastilis** and

2) Red **Acaroid** from **Xanthorrhoea Australis.**

The crude material is dark orange to dark brown in lumps of 2 to 5 cms. of diameter, mostly round but on one side flat with visible marks from the bark of the tree, showing bark surface and leaf base scars etc. The odor of the "resin" is faintly balsamic-cinnamic and sweet.

Other species are important to the lacquer industry.

From the above two natural materials are prepared tinctures or resinoids. Acaroid contains more than 70% alcohol-soluble matter. The prepared resinoid suffers from the disadvantage of being very dark of color.

Acaroid resinoid and Acaroid tincture are excellent fixatives for low-cost soap perfumes or industrial perfumes, particularly those of sweet-balsamic type. The odor type of Acaroid is quite similar to that of peru, styrax, and tolu balsams, however, much weaker in odor strength. Apart from the color drawback, Acaroid could well replace the Sumatra benzoin, and it blends well with cinnamic aldehyde, e.g. in an artificial cassia oil. In this case, the dark color of the Acaroid is no disadvantage at all.

Acaroid is readily available in ton-lots, and it is one of the most inexpensive of the natural oleo-gum-resins.

Agar Oil.

This oil is water-distilled from fungus-infected wood of the tree Aquilaria Agallocha, growing in northeastern India. The tree is also found in certain parts of China. Healthy trees have an odorless wood which produces no essential oil. Only older trees are attacked by the fungi; thereafter an oleoresin is produced inside the wood. After proper maceration of the wood, this oleoresin will yield an essential oil upon distillation. Wood from infected trees is cut and coarsely chopped, then soaked in water prior to distillation. It is common practice to add salt (sodium chloride) to the water (compare vetiver distillation in Reunion Island).

Being a distillation at atmospheric pressure (100°C.), the process of total exhaustion of the wood is a lengthy one. The oil is high-boiling, and the distillation waters must be cohobated (i.e. returned to the still and redistilled) in order to produce a reasonable yield and a complete oil.

A related tree, Aquilaria Crassna which grows in various parts of Indochina, is also attacked by fungi, resulting in the formation of an odorous secretion which can be extracted. This wood is locally known as Eagle Wood. Neither wood nor oils or resinous matter from this tree seem to be available outside of the country of origin.

The name "Aloe-Wood" is used quite indiscriminately in India for a number of fragrant woods. The true Agar Wood has been known for several thousand years, and its use is possibly as old as that of sandalwood.

Agar Oil is pale yellow to brownish yellow or dark amber in color; it is a very viscous liquid of rich and sweet-woody, almost balsamic odor not unlike that of vetiverol or purified styrene-free styrax, and with a sweetness similar to that of sandalwood oil. Agar Oil is not produced on a commercial scale unless demanded on firm orders. Locally, the so-called "attars" are used extensively in perfumery. These products are dilutions of the perfume oil in sandalwood oil or even in vegetable oils, e.g. sesame oil. For more details on "attars", see monograph on Pandanus.

Agar Oil could find use in perfumery for oriental bases, woody-aldehydic bases, chypres, fougères, etc. when blended with vetiver oil, sandalwood, geranium, methylionones, linalool, etc. The oil produces interesting notes with isoeugenol in carnation bases.

The taste of Agar Oil is extremely bitter, and it is not likely that the oil can find use in flavors beyond the local use for betel, tobacco, etc.

Agleia Odorata.
Synonym: Agleia Odoratissima.

An essential oil is distilled from the seeds of this tree which grows in India, Indonesia and China. Other parts of the tree are regularly used locally as a medicine.

In Java, the fragrant flowers of this tree are added to tea sold mainly on the local market. This addition can not be considered as an adulteration of the tea. It is more like an improvement which, however, is not generally appreciated by tea-drinkers in other areas of the world.

The essential oil of Agleia Odorata is not regularly produced on a commercial scale, but the botanical material is abundantly available for production in case of increased interest.

Ajowan.
Ajowan Oil is steam distilled from the fruits (= seeds) or, occasionally, from the whole overground plant of Ptychotis Ajowan, also known as

Carum Ajowan or Carum Copticum. This herb is cultivated in India, in the Seychelle Islands and in the West Indies (Montserrat).

It is customary in India to extract the fruits or the entire herb with diluted alcohol in order to prepare a tincture. This tincture is a powerful germicide and it has attained rather wide-spread use in local medicine in areas where the plant grows.

Ajowan Oil is a yellow-orange to pale brownish or red-brown liquid of a pungent, herbaceous-spicy and medicinal odor, reminiscent of red Thyme. However, unlike the rich odor of red thyme, Ajowan Oil presents a sharper, more cymene-like topnote and very little herbaceous-mellow body. The fresh, almost green-cuminic topnote is characteristic of Ajowan Oil. Its flavor is somewhat sweeter than that of thyme, sharp and biting at high concentration, sweet and pleasant near the Minimum Perceptible which is about 0.10 to 0.20 mg%. Suggested use level is 2.0 to 3.0 mg%, but may go higher in products such as meat sauces, pickles, etc.

Ajowan Oil is hardly used outside its countries of production. It does not present any distinct advantage over Thyme Oil. Years ago, ajowan oil was used for the isolation of Thymol, but this chemical is now produced synthetically. The thymol content in ajowan oil is about equal to that of an average grade Spanish red thyme oil, but, as mentioned above, the latter yields a richer body-note in perfumes than does the ajowan oil. The oil could find use in soap perfumes, detergents, air-fresheners, etc. and in flavors for canned foods, but it is not likely that Ajowan oil will ever attain a permanent place among the materials on the perfumer's or flavorist's shelf.

Almond Oil, bitter.

An essential oil which is commercially known as Bitter Almond Oil can be distilled from one of the following materials:

1) The partially de-oleated press-cake of Bitter Almond kernels from the tree Prunus Amygdalus, var. amara., or

2) The partially-de-oleated press-cakes from the kernels of:

Apricots (from Prunus Armeniaca, the peach tree),

Cherries (from Cerasus species, various cherry trees),

Plums (from Prunus Domestica, tree of blue preserve-plums),

Peach (Amygdalus Persica, the peach tree),

the latter being of little importance in respect to production of Bitter Almond Oil.

The Bitter Almond Tree is cultivated particularly in the U.S.A., Israel, Syria, Turkey Morocco, Spain and France. Apricot kernels are plentiful in California, U.S.A. and in Israel. Distillation of essential oil from one or more of the above raw materials is carried out in the U.S.A., France, Israel, England, Holland, etc. Prior to distillation, the press-cake is macerated in luke-warm water for 12 to 24 hours. This allows the formation of the essential oil which is not present as such either in the kernels or in the dry, partially de-oleated press-cake. The above botanical materials contain a glycoside, Amygdalin, in the kernels. Enzymatic processes initiate the decomposition of this glycoside, whereby Benzaldehyde and Hydrocyanic Acid are formed. The crude essential oil thus contains significant amounts of the highly toxic hydrocyanic acid which must be removed before the oil can be used in flavors or perfumes. As little as 0.02 grams of this poison is lethal to the average human being. This amount of hydrocyanic acid can be present in about 8 to 10 drops of crude, unrectified Bitter Almond Oil. It is interesting to note that hydrocyanic acid has an odor which is somewhat similar to that of Benzaldehyde, the main constituent of bitter almond oil. The two chemicals have nothing in common with respect to chemical structure. Hydrocyanic acid is eliminated from the crude bitter almond oil by alkali washing and rectification.

Bitter Almond Oil is a colorless liquid of strong, but sweet and clean odor, reminiscent of crushed, wet bitter almonds or of a very high grade of benzaldehyde (which it might well be!). The odor is also familiar to those who prepare or enjoy the European candy known as "Marcipan" (panis marci is Latin for "marcus' loaf of bread") or "Almond Paste". This is probably an old Italian specialty, now a popular candy- and pastry-filling in many European countries. It is (or should be) made from mashed sweet almond kernels to which a few bitter almond kernels are added for flavor (less than 1% is sufficient). Old recipes also include rose water or orange flower water. The paste is worked up with icing sugar to a solid, slow-drying mass.

Bitter Almond Oil, which is almost pure

Benzaldehyde, is not a very stable oil. An addition of 10% (but not less) of ethyl alcohol is recommended as a stabilizer, and the oil should be stored in well filled glass containers, protected from daylight, moisture and air; the containers should be adjusted in size according to the rate of comsumption of the contents. Crystals of benzoic acid will quickly appear around the cork as well as at the surface and the bottom of the container as soon as it has been opened just once.

Bitter Almond Oil finds very little use in perfumery where it is replaced by a high grade of benzaldehyde (see below). Both materials are highly volatile and have no fixative effect at all. They blend well with anisic-balsamic types of odor, e.g. in lilac and other sweet florals.

In flavors, it may be possible to tell the difference between a natural **Bitter Almond Oil** and a synthetic, high-grade **Benzaldehyde.** Bitter almond oil is a sweetener in apple, apricot, cherry, peach, pistachio, plum, raspberry, almond and countless other flavors. It is also used extensively in baked goods, candy, sugar fondants, etc., often without any other flavor material. However, a great deal of flavor is lost when the oil is used as such in baked goods. Fixatives, e.g. vanillin, anisic alcohol, benzaldehyde-phenylglycidates, etc. may greatly improve the tenacity and stability of the oil. The average use level in flavors is about 5 to 8 mg%, while the **Minimum Perceptible** is about 1.0 to 1.5 mg%. It is worth noticing that the flavor is sweet, not bitter. The bitter taste produced from chewing bitter almond kernels is due to a non-volatile bitter principle which decomposes in aqueous media.

Bitter Almond Oil is very rarely produced from bitter almonds. If the oil is a natural distillate at all, it is most often produced from other kernels (see above). A large part of all the so-called bitter almond oil in the market is actually a refined synthetic benzaldehyde, supposedly free from chlorine. The labelling FFPA stands for "free from prussic acid" (old name for hydrocyanic acid). The abbreviation FFC means "free from chlorine", and is obviously applied to synthetic products.

If the analyst finds chlorine in a sample of bitter almond oil, this may very well be solid proof that the oil is synthetic benzaldehyde, either wholly or partially. If he finds hydrocyanic acid, this finding could be an indication of natural origin of the oil. But, unfortunately, this may not always be so. The perfumers in the supply houses are clever too. The hydrocyanic acid traces may have been added deliberately to a chlorine-free synthetic benzaldehyde in order to make the imitation well-nigh perfect. In such cases, it is hardly possible to tell the difference, and it really makes no difference either. Benzaldehyde is, of course, considerably cheaper than true bitter almond oil. Other well-known "monocomponent" oils are: **Birch Bark Oil, Wintergreen Oil, Ho Leaf Oil, Ocotea Pretiosa Oil,** etc.

In view of the fact that there are thousands of tons of kernels from apricots and other "canning" fruits available as a low-cost raw material after the hydraulic expression of the fixed oil, it is conceivable that the production of "true" bitter almond oil (from such de-oleated kernels) may continue in the future.

Amber Oil.

Amber Oil, crude: This essential oil is produced by destructive (dry) distillation of **Amber** at atmospheric pressure. **Amber** is one of the oldest and hardest fossil resins, exuded millions of years ago, presumably from **Pinus Succinifera,** a fir.

The fossil resin, which is odorless, is found on the shores of the Baltic Sea, particularly in Poland, eastern Germany, and also along the North Sea coasts in Denmark, Holland, and England. A further quantity of **Amber** is obtained by mining.

Amber pieces which are unfit for jewelry as well as dust and residues from the gem industry, etc. are submitted to dry distillation in order to yield the so-called **Succinol** or **Crude Amber Oil. Crude** (or pyroligneous) **Amber Oil** is a dark amber-colored or brownish, but clear oily liquid. Its odor is smoky, tarlike, resinous, with a distinct resemblance to the odor of tanned leather. The crude oil finds some application in perfumery where it blends excellently with labdanum, castoreum, ionones, amylsalicylate, etc. and it is sweetened with cananga oil, benzylsalicylate, zingerone, etc. for typical "leather" bases, e.g. in men's colognes and after-shaves.

Amber Oil, rectified: This oil is produced by steam distillation of the crude, pyroligneous amber oil. The steam distilled oil is a pale yellow and clear liquid with a peculiar burnt-woody, somewhat camphoraceous odor, reminiscent of the "still-note" in certain fresh-distilled fir and spruce needle oils. The odor also resembles that of crude pine oil with a kerosene-styrene topnote. Rectified **Amber Oil** finds very little use in perfumery.

Under the name of **Retinol**, an oil is distilled from various resins, particularly from **Pine Rosin** (= colophony). These oils are used as solvents, e.g. for phosphorus. They find some use in pharmaceutical preparations.

Ambra.

Ambra, also called **Ambregris** or **Ambergris**, is a substance of animal tissue, formed in the stomach or intestine of **Physeter Catodon**, the cachalot whale. It is conceivable that **Ambra** is the result of a pathological condition caused by irritation of the whale's stomach walls due to certain indigestible particles in the whale's food. Consequently, **Ambra** is one of the few natural perfumery raw materials which cannot be "cultivated", not even in the same way that pearls, for example, are cultivated.

Pieces of **Ambra** are either washed ashore on various temperate ocean coasts and islands, or they are found inside the whales when these great mammals are captured for their oil (sperm-aceti oil). There is no particular area where **Ambra** can be found or searched for with regular success. The "big" finds in the history of **Ambra** are those of New Zealand, East India, West Africa (near Dakar), Southwest Africa, Madagascar, Indonesia, Brazil, Norway, etc. Actually, all the seashores of the seven seas can boast **Ambra** finds, and all the seas have brought **Ambra** to the whaling ships at one time or another. There is ample literature in scientific and popular periodicals and even in newspapers about individual finds from time to time. One of the truest things ever said about **Ambra,** to quote from Ed Sagarin's "The Science and Art of Perfumery", is: "- - - of all the animal perfume products, none is better known to the public, none less used by the perfumer" (about **Ambra**).

Ambra is a pale grayish or creamy-yellow to brown or dark brown waxy solid mass which melts in boiling water. Its odor is rather subtle, reminiscent of seaweed, wood, moss, with a peculiar sweet, yet very dry undertone of unequalled tenacity. There is rarely any animal note at all in a good grade of **Ambra**. On ageing, the material lightens in color, particularly when exposed to daylight and salt water. Consequently, it can be expected that floating pieces of **Ambra** from the sea (surface) are of superior quality in many cases. This is not a rule, but ageing is generally considered a necessity in order to obtain full maturity of odor.

Ambra is never used as such in perfumes. From the powdered **Ambra** (e.g. powdered with an inert grinding material), **Tinctures** and **Extracts** are produced. A conventional **Tincture** of Amber-gris is described under **Tinctures** in Part One of this book. The greater part of a good grade of **Ambra** is soluble in alcohol. By concentration of the tincture, the so-called **Resinoid** of Ambergris is obtained. In terms of the definitions in this book, the so-called resinoid is an alcoholic extract, resembling the so-called **Resin Absolutes** (see this monograph in Part One of this book). When concentrated 20 times, the ambergris tincture turns into a light brown, semi-solid mass, which could be called "20-fold tincture of amber-gris".

True absolutes are not commercially available or regularly produced by the supply houses. It is generally believed that ambra tinctures must mature 6 months or longer prior to their use in perfumes. Thus, it serves no purpose to concentrate much further than the above mentioned 20-fold. This concentrate will usually contain about 50% solvent. If the tincture has been prepared with heat applied, the result is actually an **Infusion**. This extract will contain significant amounts of fats (waxes), soluble in hot alcohol, but not in cold alcohol. This waxy matter is responsible for the semi-solid consistency of dilutions of the 20-fold tincture.

Hydrocarbon solvent extracts of **Ambra** have been prepared, but they do not seem to offer advantages over the alcoholic extracts beyond the fact that the hydrocarbon extracts make it possible to eliminate some of the insoluble and odorless substance in **Ambra**.

Ambra and tinctures and extracts thereof are used mainly in perfumery although the use is rare as above mentioned. It should not be thought, however, that **Ambra** has a limited application. On the contrary: it is possible to introduce this material in countless perfume types, and with good results. But the irregular availability, the lack of experience in selecting good from poor raw material—or tincture (if so purchased),—and the comparatively high cost of good **Ambra** has made it a rare item on the perfumer's shelf. Until the very recent identification of some of the most important constituents in the odor principle of **Ambra** (by Firmenich & Cie.), the perfumer had to use various "ambre" bases when true **Ambra** products were unavailable or too expensive. These "ambre" bases are made up from certain fractions of labdanum extracts, from sage clary oil, terpeneless cypress oil, delta-methylionone (beta-isomethylionone), cedarwood derivatives, chamomile oil moroccan, nerol, isobutyl cinnamate, undecenal, oakmoss fractions, seaweed extracts, beta-caryophyllenes, agar wood oil, etc., etc. Countless "ambre" specialties are available; some of them are excellent.

Ambra Tincture ("ambergris" tincture) is often used in combination with at least one other *"animal"* material. **Ambra** has comparatively little diffusive power, but it has a tremendous tenacity. **Musk** or **Civet** are required to improve the "wearability" of a perfume. Consequently, **Ambra Tincture** is particularly recommended in the more delicate florals, e.g. muguet, sweet pea, lilac, freesia, cyclamen, white rose, etc. In the modern aldehydic "fantasy" perfume bases, the use of **Ambra** or a similar "bouquetting" agent is a necessity in order to "round off" the stubborn chemical notes of aliphatic aldehydes.

Tincture of Ambra is also used in flavors, mainly as a bouquetting additive to round off and mellow the blend of synthetic flavor materials. Fruit flavors, tobacco flavors and liqueur flavors are frequently improved with this exquisite material.

Ambra is obviously subject to adulteration. It is characteristic of many of these rare perfume materials that one finds their best evaluators among the suppliers, not among the perfumers. In London and in New York, certain houses that have specialized in dealing with comparatively few natural raw materials for perfumes and flavors can be proud of having on their staffs some of the world's finest experts on **Ambra.** However, samples or deliveries of **Ambra** or preparations thereof should, in all cases, be subjected to thorough olfactory examination prior to purchase or use of these delicate materials.

Mainly in order to avoid confusion with the fossil resin **Amber,** the author has preferred to use the more international word **Ambra** for the material which is better known in English-speaking countries under the name of **Ambergris.**

Ambrette Seed.

Ambrette Seeds are produced in the fruits of a cultivated plant, **Hibiscus Abelmoschus,** in Angola (West Africa), Ecuador, Hai-nan (China), Indonesia, Madagascar (Nossi-Bé), Martinique (West Indies), Seychelles (Indian Ocean), etc.

The essential oil has been produced locally in Nossi-Bé, but distillation is now carried out mostly in Europe and in the United States of America. Four different perfume and flavor materials can be produced from the seeds:

1) **Ambrette Seed Oil,** liquid or solid.
2) **Ambrette Seed Concrète,** and from the concrète:
3) **Ambrette Seed Absolute.** Finally, an
4) **Ambrette Seed Tincture** is produced.

Product No. 2) is of little or no importance. It is an intermediate, and is rarely produced at all. Product No. 3) is prepared by "purification" of product No. 1). For details, see below. A true **Concrète** of Ambrette Seed and a **Tincture** are occasionally used in certain flavor compositions where they lend excellent "body" to synthetic mixtures of flavor materials.

Ambrette Seed Absolute.

A "true-to-the-name" **Ambrette Seed Absolute** can be produced from the true **Concrète** (see below) by alcohol washing of the lukewarm concrète, followed by chilling and filtering of the alcoholic extracts. After evaporation of the alcohol, a colorless to pale yellow liquid oil is left: this is **Ambrette Seed Absolute.**

Commercial **Ambrette Seed Absolute** is not produced by this method. It is produced from the essential (distilled) oil either by neutralization and subsequent elimination of the fatty acids, or it is steam distilled from the extracted (true) concrète. In other words, the absolute is the essential oil minus the fatty acids which are solid and insoluble in cold alcohol. They also tend to produce a rancid odor in ambrette seed oil upon ageing. **Ambrette Seed Absolute** is thus not a true absolute according to the definitions in this book. It is somewhat similar to an **Absolute Oil.** Various suppliers will supply quite different products. Application and odor description fall generally within the notes given in the monograph on **Ambrette Seed Oil,** see below.

3: **Water-distillation** of roses in southern Morocco. Aromag-Chiris factory in the Dadès valley.

(Fot. S. Arctander, 1960)

4: Rondon rotary **Extractors** for production of rose concrète at the Aromag-Chiris factory. Dadès valley, southern Morocco.

(Fot. S. Arctander, 1960)

5: A fluid-circulating heat-exchanger in a Q.V.F. all-glass 100-litre still for **Deterpenization** of essential oils at very low pressure and temperature. *(Fot. S. Arctander, 1957)*

6: Modern field **Distillery** for peppermint in Indiana, U.S.A. The still-tanks are interchangeable for quick removal of exhaust material and replacement with fresh batches. *(Fot. S. Arctander, 1958)*

Ambrette Seed Oil.

When **Ambrette Seeds** are distilled whole (un-crushed), a liquid essential oil is produced. This oil contains only small amounts of the odorless palmitic acid. Crushed seeds yield a solid essential oil (so-called "concrète"; compare this to "**Orris Concrète**"). The solid oil contains a very high amount of palmitic acid, and the oil is quite similar to the concrète extraction product (true **Ambrette Seed Concrète**).

A true **Concrète** is produced by hydrocarbon extraction of the crushed seeds. It consists mainly of palmitic and myristic acids, unstable and odorless materials. This type of concrète has very little importance in perfumery or flavor work. From the above summary, it can be seen that some confusion exists with respect to the nomenclature of ambrette seed products.

Liquid **Ambrette Seed Oil** should be allowed to age for several months before being used in perfumes or flavors. By then, the initial fatty notes are subdued, and a rich, sweet, floral-musky, distinctly wine-like or brandy-like odor is developed with a bouquet and roundness rarely found in any other perfume material. The odor has some notes in common with cypress oil, Bulgarian rose oil, sage clary and cognac oil. There are certain tobacco-like and "overripe fruit"-like notes with great similarity to higher esters of decyl alcohol. The water-white or pale yellow oil displays a tenacity of odor which is almost incredible. As a flavor material, it also displays features which are quite unique. A suggested use level would be 0.10 to 0.30 mg%, while the **Minimum Perceptible** is about 0.01 to 0.04 mg%. One part of **Ambrette Seed Oil** in ten million parts of neutral sweetened fluid is distinctly recognizable to the taste. The odor of these dilutions remains very characteristic of ambrette seed oil.

The oil should be stored in a 50% or 10% alcoholic solution at reduced temperature in order to prevent the appearance of rancid notes due to a possible decomposition of traces of fatty oils and acids in the essential oil (or in the absolute).

Ambrette Seed Oil and **Ambrette Seed Absolute** find application in perfumes of the more sophisticated type. These materials blend excellently with rose, neroli, methylionones, sandalwood oil, cyclamal, hydroxycitronellal and aliphatic aldehydes, etc.

Ambrette Seed (oil or absolute) are known for the "exalting" effect which they impart to perfumes, and for the unique bouquet they lend to perfumes and flavors. They are very expensive materials, and the annual production can be measured in two-figured kilo-amounts. Adulteration with synthetic **Ambrettolide** (a natural constituent of ambrette seed) or with similar macrocyclic lactones, and with farnesol, etc. is not infrequent.

Ambrette Seed Tincture.

This tincture is produced by maceration of the crushed ambrette seeds in ethyl alcohol of 80% to 90% strength. The conventional proportion is 25 parts of seeds to 100 parts of diluted alcohol. The tincture finds occasional use in lotion perfumes and in tobacco flavoring, liqueurs and some fruit flavors.

Ammoniac Gum.

Ammoniac Gum (also called **Ammoniacum**) is a natural oleo-gum-resin which is exuded after incisions in the stem of the tall plant, **Dorema Ammoniacum** (in Iran), or from various **Ferula** species (in Libya and Morocco). The substance is a physiological formation inside of the stems of the plant (compare **Asafoetida**). When incisions are made, the milky juice oozes out and quickly resinifies into tear-shaped bodies. The ammoniac gum is known commercially in this form.

The natural material contains about 75% alcohol-soluble substances, including about 3% essential oil.

Tinctures and resinoids are produced from this material, and are used in perfume and flavor work to a limited extent. Tincture of ammoniac gum has some fixative value and imparts a certain "animal" note to perfumes. It blends well with rose, jasmin, sweet wood oils, heavy oriental perfumes, etc. and all materials of the "balsamic-sweet" type.

The essential oil of **Ammoniac Gum** is produced by steam distillation of the crude botanical. The oil is not produced on a commercial scale and it is not regularly available. It is a pale yellow to pale orange colored, mobile liquid of penetrating sulphuraceous-mercaptanelike odor, reminiscent of onions. The alcoholsoluble portion of the essential-oil-free ammoniac gum is a pleasant-smelling, balsamic type of fixative material. The essential oil could find some use in flavor work for meat sauces, seasonings, etc.

Amyris Oil.

Amyris Oil is steam distilled from the wood of Amyris Balsamifera, the so-called West Indian Rosewood. The tree grows in northern parts of South America, in Central America and in the West Indies. It has been introduced in many tropical zones all over the world. Distillation takes place mainly in Haiti, and to a lesser extent, in the neighboring Dominican Republic, in Jamaica and Venezuela. Occasionally the wood is exported in billets and distilled elsewhere (Europe, U.S.A.). The wood is an excellent furniture wood. Amyris Oil was earlier known as West Indian Sandalwood Oil. To avoid further confusion, this misnomer will be omitted from the monographs in the present work.

Amyris Oil is a viscous liquid of pale yellow, yellow or brownish-yellow color. Its odor is faintly woody, not dry. It has a slightly oily-sweet, balsamic note, and occasionally displays a faintly peppery topnote, reminiscent of guaiacwood or cubeb. The body-odor is very tenacious, but it rapidly loses the rich, complex odor, fading out in a very weak, woody-balsamic note. The odor varies considerably, depending on the age of the oil and the age of the wood prior to distillation.

Amyris Oil has recently become subject to extensive adulteration, particularly in the sense that certain fractions are sold separately, while other fractions are cut with cedarwood oil (type "Virginia") or with copaiba balsam. The natural unfractionated amyris oil has some perfumery value beyond its well-known fixative power. But its woody effect is far inferior to that of sandalwood oil, for example.

Amyris Oil and its fractions are also acetylated to yield so-called "Amyris Acetate", a product of very ill-defined character. If the acetylated oil is isolated from the accompanying monoterpenes and sesquiterpenes, a fairly interesting "amyris acetate" can be produced. The odor of this material is lighter, fresher, greener than that of amyris oil, and it is also less fatty-sweet.

Amyris oil finds extensive application as a mild blender in numerous types of perfume, particularly in soap perfumes. It blends well with ionones, methylionones, lavandin oil, coumarin, oakmoss products, terpineol, citronella oils, sassafras or ocotea oils, amylsalicylate, etc.

The oil is readily available in large quantities. During the past 10 years, the annual production has fluctuated between 15 and 75 tons. Its very low cost has made it a popular fixative for soap perfumes and other low-cost fragrances. In recent years, Amyris Oil has been used for the "official and conventional" cutting of Haiti Vetiver Oil. The "rule" is that 5% amyris oil is added to all locally produced vetiver oils before these are exported from Haiti.

Anethum Sowa.

Little known, and hardly used outside of India and Japan, the oil of Anethum Sowa is steam distilled in India from the fruits (so-called seeds) of the locally grown dill, Anethum Sowa. A similar species is grown and distilled in Japan.

The essential oil of Anethum Sowa is a pale yellow mobile liquid of sweet-herbaceous, somewhat woody-spicy odor. When freshly distilled, the oil displays a rather unpleasant topnote. The dryout is very faint, woody and not very pleasant. The overall odor type is distinctly different from that of the European or American Dill Fruit Oil (particularly the English dill fruit oil), the latter being closely related to the caraway oil, while the Anethum Sowa is more like the parsley fruit oil in type. The author has very little experience with the application of Anethum Sowa oil in perfumes or flavors, and it is not conceivable that this oil will ever attain any importance in European or American perfumery or flavor work.

See also Dill "Seed" Oil and Dill Weed Oil.

Angelica Root Absolute.

Angelica Root Absolute is produced by a two-step extraction of angelica roots. For details of botanical origin etc., see Angelica Root Oil. The comminuted roots are first extracted with petroleum ether or benzene, and the solvent is completely recovered in vacuum. The residue (= the concrète extract) is subsequently extracted with ethyl alcohol. The alcoholic extract is chilled, filtered and evaporated under vacuum. After recovery of the alcohol, the Angelica Root Absolute is left as a viscous, yellow-brownish liquid. According to the method of extraction and depending particularly upon the strength of alcohol used, the absolute contains little or no **Phellandrene.** This fact is distinctly reflected in the odor-flavor characteristics of **Angelica Root Absolute.**

Its odor is intensely musky-woody, heavy, sweet, somewhat spicy, with a resemblance to **Pimpinella** root. The richness in odor body has some similarity to that of ambrette seed absolute, but the earthy, root-like notes of the angelica root absolute recall the odor of a drugstore. There is hardly any distinct topnote or pepperiness at all. (Note the difference from the odor of angelica root oil).

Angelica Root Absolute is particularly well qualified for flavors where the poorly soluble and unstable monoterpene **Phellandrene,** would be a drawback. The **Minimum Perceptible** of the absolute is about 0.005 to 0.010 mg%, placing this material among the most powerful flavor materials of natural origin. Angelica root absolute can be used in perfumery for its unusual tenacity and peculiar animal note, combined with a rich body. The absolute does not impart the typical topnote effects which can be obtained with the essential oil from the root.

Angelica Root Absolute is produced almost exclusively in France, and only on a very limited scale; locally grown or imported root material is extracted in the Grasse region. The absolute is considerably more expensive than the essential oil, although the comparatively good yield by extraction should make possible a lower cost of the absolute in case of increased demand.

Angelica Root Oil.

This oil is steam distilled from the dried roots of **Angelica Archangelica,** a tall plant which is cultivated in Belgium (near Lessines), Holland, France, Germany, Hungary, and northern India. Distillation takes place in most of the countries where the plant is grown. The dried roots are subject to insect attacks and do not keep well. This is an interesting fact since the essential oil from this plant is now in the limelight as an insect attractant, with special regard to the so-called "Mediterranean fruit fly", a dreaded hazard to the citrus fruit growers in many countries, including Florida, U.S.A. Belgian roots are highly esteemed, and are exported for distillation abroad. The angelica plant is an overwintering,

mansize umbellifer plant. The fruits (= seeds) from this plant are also distilled (see **Angelica Seed Oil**). The stalks are used in confectionery, either preserved in heavy syrup or in a candied form.

Angelica Root Oil is one of the more expensive essential oils, for several reasons:
1) The yield by steam distillation is very low.
2) The distillation demands a significant amount of steam, and it takes 12 to 24 hours to exhaust the root material.
3) It is preferable that the roots should be not more than 2 years old. It takes three years for the plant to produce seed (fruits), which are also used for distillation of an essential oil (see **Angelica Seed Oil**). When seeds are harvested from three year old plants for distillation, the roots from these plants yield much less oil. The oil from old roots is different from that of young roots, but not inferior in respect to fixative value. The monoterpenes have resinified, and the old oil has little or no peppery topnote.
4) It is troublesome and hard work to harvest and clean the roots.

Angelica Root Oil is a water-white or pale yellow to orange-brown colored liquid. Its color and viscosity varies according to the root material used for distillation and according to the age of the oil. The main constituent is **Phellandrene,** a monoterpene of comparatively minor value in perfumes and flavors. It is responsible for the light, somewhat peppery topnote of oils from young roots. Beneath the peppery topnote grows a rich, somewhat herbaceous-earthy, woody bodynote of unique tenacity and great diffusive power. The note is also slightly musky-animal-like with a spicy undertone. Various lactones, occurring in trace amounts in the oil, are held responsible for these special effects of the oil and for the synergistic effect it imparts to other perfume materials in compositions. One of these lactones is **Cyclopentadecanolide** which is available as a synthetic material under a wealth of brand names. The discoveries of this lactone in angelica root oil and of **Ambrettolide** in ambrette seed oil belong to the milestones of the twentieth century in the development of synthetic perfumery materials. The scientists Ruzicka, Stoll and Kerschbaum made history with these and related materials in the late 1920's.

Angelica Root Oil is very highly esteemed in

perfumery and flavor work. Its power is easily underestimated, and it is an art in itself to use this oil correctly, and to adjust the application and concentration according to the inevitable type-variations in the various shipments of oil even from the same producer. The oil blends well with patchouli, opopanax, costus, sage clary, vetiver, oakmoss, coumarin, etc., in heavy chypres, oriental bases, etc. or in special citrus colognes and fougères.

In flavors, the oil finds wide application in liqueurs, particularly those of the "Cointreau" type. The taste is similar to the odor and extremely powerful. Suggested use level is 0.30 to 0.60 mg%, but the **Minimum Perceptible** is as low as 0.01 to 0.02 mg%. Wide variations in these figures can be expected in various qualities of this oil.

Angelica Root Oil is produced on a very limited scale only. A Belgian and a Dutch producer turn out the bulk of the annual world production which is less than one ton.

Angelica Seed Oil.

This oil is distilled by steam from the seeds (fruits) of the same plant which yields angelica roots (see **Angelica Root Oil**). The seeds are produced in the third year of growth. Cultivation and production areas are the same as those mentioned under the root oil.

Angelica Seed Oil is a water-white or very pale yellow, mobile oil of strong, fresh, light and peppery odor. The topnote is distinctly terpene-like, at times almost harsh in its roughness, but also quite fresh. A sweet, almost anisic undertone is quite characteristic, and there is less woodiness, less earthiness in the seed oil than in the root oil. The seed oil has less tenacity, and presents a very weak dryout note of the same type as found in the root oil. Here again, there are wide variations according to the age and quality of the oil. The flavor is somewhat pungent, terpene-like, but quite powerful. Suggested use level is 0.50 to 1.0 mg%, and the **Minimum Perceptible** is about 0.02 to 0.04 mg%.

Angelica Seed Oil was initially used in chypres, fougères and similar complex fragrances. It has also been used in Continental types of toothpaste flavors. The root oil is preferred in perfumery for its superior tenacity, while the seed oil presents a unique fresh-peppery topnote, although a very expensive one. A less ethical use of the seed oil

is that of cutting the root oil. This adulteration can be very hard to detect.

The main constituent is a monoterpene **Phellandrene** which is prone to polymerise or resinify when the oil is improperly stored. Cool, dark and dry storage in well-filled small containers of glass is recommended.

The annual world production of **Angelica Seed Oil** (mainly from a Dutch and a Belgian producer) is estimated at less than one ton. The seed oil, too, is subject to intensive research in connection with studies on insect attractants (see monograph on **Root** oil).

Angostura.

Angostura Bark is obtained from a wild growing tree, **Galipea Cusparia**, in the mountains along the Orinoco river in Venezuela. The bark is used locally as a febrifuge, and some therapeutic effect is attributed to glycosides in the bark. It is claimed that an essential oil can be produced by steam distillation of the bark, and the yield is given at somewhere between 0.16% and 1.90% with little or no reference to actual or recent experiments. The author has never conducted such experiments, nor is he aware of having ever seen a true essential oil of **Angustura Bark**. However, the bark is often extracted with alcohol to yield a tincture which contains the bitter elements, glycosides, aromatic substances, coloring matter, etc. Tinctures or extracts are more truly representative of the total flavor of the bark than an essential oil would be, even if such an oil were available. **Angostura Tinctures** are used in the flavoring of alcoholic beverages where a bitter or "astringent" effect is called for. Many famous bitters owe their flavor partly to this ingredient, but the most famous of all "Angostura Bitters" is actually made without any angostura bark at all. This bitter-tincture is prepared from gentian root, bitter orange peel, cinnamon bark and probably other spicy botanicals, culinary herbs, etc. A few drops of this so-called "Angostura Bitter" in a glass of plain carbonated water ("Club Soda") produces a delicious thirst-quencher for hot and humid summer-days, and this simple drink has more flavor than a "Quinine Tonic". But it does not contain any **Angostura** bark at all. The author has used a 20% tincture of **Angostura Bark** (2 weeks maceration) for experiments, and these experiments confirm the fact that the true tincture has less flavor than the above so-called "Angostura Bitters". The author finds it inconceivable that **Angostura** products will ever find much application in perfumes or flavors.

Anise.

See also **Star Anise Oil.**

True **Anise Oil** is steam distilled from the dried and crushed fruits ("seeds") of the annual herb, **Pimpinella Anisum.** The herb originated in the Near East, and is now cultivated in many countries: Argentina, Bulgaria, Chili, China, France, Germany, Greece, Hungary, India, Italy, Mexico, Morocco, Poland, Spain, Syria, Tunisia, Turkey, USSR, Yugoslavia, etc. Most of the Turkish production goes into "raki", a popular alcoholic beverage.

Only a few of the above countries produce **Anise Oil.** The fruit is also distilled outside of the growing areas. Poland and the USSR are among the largest producers of **Anise Oil** from locally grown fruits.

Anise Oil, also called **Anise Seed Oil** or **Aniseed Oil,** is a water-white or very pale yellow liquid of intensely sweet and clean odor, truly reminiscent of the crushed fruit. A very common description is that of "licorice odor". Obviously, this is another example of circle-minded association (like the "chocolate odor of vanilla or vanillin). **Anise Oil** and its derivatives are used as flavoring ingredients in licorice candy, but the licorice extract itself (i.e. the extract of the rhizome) does not have any odor resemblance to anise.

The flavor of **Anise Oil** is also sweet, soft and mild, although, at the same time, it is quite rich and powerful in effect. Characteristic of a good **Anise Oil** (and also of pure anethole) is the wide limits of concentration in the application of these oils. In other words, it is not easy to overdose when anise flavor is called for. Suggested use level is about 5.0 to 10.0 mg% (lower when anise oil is used as a sweetener only). The **Minimum Perceptible** is 0.30 to 0.60 mg%. It is not a *very* powerful flavor material.

Anise Oil is used mainly in flavors. It is an important ingredient in the flavoring of licorice candy, cough-drops, baked goods, pharmaceutical preparations, etc. It is also used in certain types of tobacco flavor, e.g. pipe tobaccos. In perfumes, the oil finds some use as a masking agent for obnoxious odors such as hydrogen sulfide, e.g. in cold-wave preparations and depilatories. It is also useful for masking the odor of cod liver oil and other rancid odors, particularly in combination with sweet orange oil and coumarin. However, for industrial perfuming and technical preparations, it is not economically feasible to use the essential oil. Synthetic **Anethole** is cheaper, and does not have to meet the same strict specifications for toxicity as those demanded of anise oil for flavors. The toxic cis-**Anethole** (isomer of anethole) does not occur in anise fruit oil (see monograph on **Star Anise Oil** and toxicity of cis-anethole).

Anise (fruit) **Oil** was once used quite extensively in flavors for candy, liqueurs, brandies ("raki" in Turkey, "anisette" in France and overseas French territories), tobacco, baked goods, spice blends, canned foods, pickles, etc. However, the oil has been largely replaced by synthetic anethole (e.g. from estragole, isolated in the fractionated distillation of American pine oil). (See monograph on **Star Anise Oil** and cis-anethole).

For a period of several decades, the Chinese and Indochinese **Star Anise Oil** entered the market, replacing the anise fruit oil so effectively that even the Pharmacopoeias ackowledged the use of the two oils indiscriminately. When star anise oil became unavailable during and after World War II, a synthetic anethole was produced whose purity of flavor was perfected to such a degree that the synthetic anethole now completely dominates as an anise flavor ingredient. Substantial quantities of true anise fruit oil are still produced in Poland and the USSR, and good lots of these oils are shipped all over the world. In respect to cost, it cannot compete with the synthetic anethole, but its flavor is still preferred by many connaisseurs for its fine and delicate sweetness, its rich body and bouquet.

True **Anise** (fruit) **Oil** may not disappear completely from the flavor market, but the oil has become scarce, and it is unlikely that its production will be increased in the future.

An oil, distilled from the plant **Osmorrhiza Longistylis** is occasionally sold as **Anise Oil** or **Sweet Cicely Oil** (in the U.S.A.). See also **Clausena Anisata** and **Star Anise Oil.**

Anona Squamosa.

The essential oil of **Anona Squamosa** is steam distilled from the leaves of a small tree belonging to the N.O. Anonaceae. The tree is extensively cultivated in India where it is known as "sitaphal".

Anona Squamosa oil is yellow, olive-green or greenish. It has a pleasant, somewhat spicy-woody odor reminiscent of cedar, cubeb, cardamom, etc. The taste is distinctly bitter, and it is not conceivable that this oil could find use in flavors. The oil is occasionally used in local perfumery when woody-spicy, fresh and somewhat dry-tenacious notes are wanted.

Anona Squamosa oil is fairly inexpensive, but it is not available in sizeable quantities outside of its country of origin.

The oil consists mainly of terpenes and sesquiterpenes of which beta-caryophyllene forms the major part.

The tree Anona Squamosa is widely cultivated in tropical zones for its highly aromatic fruits, known as Sugar Apples, Custard Apples, Pommes-Cannelle, Sweet Sop, etc. Thus, there is ample supply of leaf material for distillation in the event that the essential oil should prove of greater interest in the future. These fruits are of the size of a small orange and resemble giant raspberries or pine cones in appearance (compare "pine"-apple). When fully ripe, the fruits are so tender—almost creamy—that they cannot be shipped over long distances. Their aroma is so rich, strong and peculiar that many people have never become accustomed to enjoying this tropical delicacy fully.

Anthocephalus Cadamba.

From the flowers of the Kadamba (or cadamba) tree in northern India is produced an essential oil by water distillation and a concrète by benzene extraction. The tree grows wild in most parts of India, and it is cultivated in the western and northwestern parts of that country (U.P.). The cadamba tree is related to gardenia and karo-karoundé and, although it is not a very large tree, it carries flowers of quite impressive size (average 10 grams per flower). At night, the flowers exhale a strong, heavy-sweet fragrance reminiscent of orange flowers, jasmin, and gardenia. These creamy-colored or orange-yellow flowers form globe-like clusters at the terminal branches, the globes being about 1–2 inches in diameter (2½ to 5 cms.).

The yield of essential oil is extremely small, and it is necessary to collect the distillate in benzene

in order to avoid a total loss of oil in the distillation waters. The yield of concrète from benzene extraction of the flowers is about 0.2%, and the content of absolute in this concrète is very small.

Anthocephalus Cadamba oil is a pale yellow or yellow oily liquid of a woody-floral and sweet odor with a short-lived, but strong minty-borneolic topnote. The dryout is delightfully sweet-floral, reminiscent of champaca and neroli. The tenacity of this fragrance is almost incredible. In perfumery, the oil could undoubtedly find quite extensive use. It blends excellently with ylang-ylang, neroli, jasmin, cassie, mimosa, alpha-iso-methylionone, heliotropine, cassione, aliphatic aldehydes, etc. The full yield of this interesting perfume oil is obtained only when the oil is skillfully and cautiously supported by mild, sweet florals, fixers and modifiers. Neroli oil would supply a suitable topnote.

Partly because of the very poor yield by water distillation, partly because of the highly developed local technique of co-distilling botanical material with a certain amount of a more readily available essential oil (in the still pot or the receiver), Cadamba oil is frequently offered as an "attar", distilled into a receiver with sandalwood oil.

Concrète and "attar" of Cadamba are available on a limited scale, and the items are produced regularly in the provinces where the tree is cultivated. In the author's personal opinion, this is one of the many rare perfume materials which really deserves a permanent and prominent place on the perfumer's shelf.

Apopin Oil.

Apopin Oil is the name given to the essential oil which is water-and-steam distilled from the wood of a species of Cinnamomum Camphora, native to China and Formosa. The tree is one of the so-called camphor trees, and it is furthermore the most common of all the camphor trees. However, the essential oil of this particular species, locally known as Yu-Sho or Shu-Yu, is not the oil from which camphor is isolated. (See monograph on Camphor Oils).

Apopin Oil contains camphor, eucalyptol (= cineole) and terpineol in almost equal amounts. The oil is liquid and does not separate camphor (as distinguished from the "Hon-Sho" or so-called "true" camphor oil).

Apopin Oil serves as a low-cost perfume oil in its country of origin. It is also used as a starting material for the isolation of the above mentioned three components.

Apopin Oil is not a commercial article in the European or the American perfumery business, but since the botanical material for the production of this oil is available in such tremendous quantities, it is very likely that the oil will retain its importance as a local source of the above mentioned perfume materials.

Another interesting feature is that certain fractions of Apopin Oil serve as a basis for the production of the so-called "Eucalyptus oil". This oil has recently (1958/59) appeared in significant quantities on the European market and elsewhere. This fact presents a serious threat to the production of genuine Australian, Spanish, Portuguese, African and other eucalyptus oils. Economic effects are already perceptible in several of these producing areas.

See also monographs on Camphor Oils and Eucalyptus Oil, Chinese.

Araucaria Oil.

Araucaria Oil is steam distilled from the wood of a comparatively small tree, Callitropsis Araucarioides, which grows wild and abundantly in New Caledonia (South Pacific). The tree is related to thuja, cypress and sandarac trees, but it seems to be known only in the above small area. The wood is distilled in western Australia, far away from its origin.

Araucaria Oil is solid at room temperature, but if melted, it may remain supercooled as a very viscous liquid for a considerable length of time. The solid oil is not quite homogeneous, often grainy in texture. It is very pale yellow to olive-green or of a brown color. The oil may contain some iron.

Its odor is delicately woody, but also rich and sweet (a rare combination), almost floral like nerolidol or cabreuva oil. It has notes in common with amyris oil, bois de rose, copaiba, good guaiacwood oil, and the sesquiterpene fractions from Java type of citronella oil.

Araucaria Oil is an excellent fixative among the groups of "so-called" fixatives (see monograph on Fixatives, Part One of this book). The oil is also used as a starting material for the isolation of Eudesmol, a sesquiterpene alcohol. The acetate

of this alcohol, Eudesmyl Acetate, is available and it has been used as a replacement for linalyl acetate.

Araucaria Oil is a very low-cost perfume material, but it has not yet found extensive use beyond that of a modifier-fixer in soap perfumes, e.g. mimosa, chypre, fougère, lily-of-the-valley, lilac, etc. It blends excellently with sage clary, methylionones, hydroxycitronellal, linalool, etc. The oil is not produced on a large scale, but it is freely available in smaller lots, directly or indirectly from the producer in western Australia.

Arnica Oil.

Arnica Oil is steam distilled from the flowers of Arnica Montana, a perennial plant which grows wild in many parts of Northern and Central Europe, Scandinavia, USSR, etc. It grows wild and is also cultivated in Northern India where it has been used for the skin-healing effects of its infusions and tinctures. A related plant, Arnica Cordifolia, and other species of arnica are used in the U.S.A. and are known as "mountain tobacco".

The yield of essential oil is very small, and the cultivation of the plant is highly problematic. Concequently, the oil is scarce and expensive.

It is conceivable that only a minor part of the aromatic principles of the flowers are isolated by the steam distillation. Hence, it is preferable to use a tincture or an extract (e.g. an absolute) of the flower material. A few French supply houses offer an Arnica Absolute, and a Resinoine-type is also produced. These products are more representative of the flower than are any other products from arnica.

Arnica Oil is a yellow-orange or greenish-blue colored liquid.

Arnica Absolute or Arnica Resinoine are dark amber colored, viscous liquids of intensely herbaceous-sweet, tealike, somewhat spicy, powerful and very tenacious odor. The dryout is bitter, tealike and very pleasant. The odor of the oil resembles that of chamomile with a certain woody-earthy undertone. One of the aromatic principles of the absolute is Thymohydroquinone Dimethyl-ether which is present in greater amounts in the essential oil from the roots, Arnica Root Oil. The latter is not a commercial article. The literature disagrees as to the similarity or dissimilarity in odor of the two oils. Arnica Root Oil is yellow or dark yellow in color, and is more viscous than the flower oil.

Arnica Oil (from flowers) finds occasional use in perfumes of the herbaceous (i.e. non-floral) type, e.g. chypre, fougère, "tabac", leather, colognes, etc. It is also used in certain flavors for liqueurs. The oil is produced on a very limited scale, mainly in France or Germany from locally grown material or from Belgian flowers.

The flavor is slightly bitter, but rich and herbaceous, tea-like and pleasant. Suggested use level is 0.50 to 1.00 mg%, while the Minimum Perceptible is about 0.10 to 0.20 mg% with substantial variations according to type of oil (distilled, extracted, etc.).

Artabotrys Odoratissimus.

This medium-sized tree originates in the Philippines and the Indonesian archipelago. The tree is cultivated for its very fragrant flowers which may possibly be confused with cananga flowers. The tree is related to the Ylang-Ylang tree.

Artabotrys Suaveolens.

The flowers of Artabotrys Suaveolens, also of the same genus as the Ylang-Ylang, have occasionally been admixed to the flowers of Cananga Odorata prior to the distillation of Cananga oil from the latter. The artabotrys tree is cultivated in Indonesia for the production of an essential oil by steam-water distillation. The two artabotrys oils are not commercially available, and are rarely offered outside of their countries of origin. They are mentioned in this volume for the sake of completion of the monographs on Cananga Oil and Ylang-Ylang Oil.

Artemisia Alba.

This oil is steam distilled from the whole overground part of Artemisia Alba, a wild-growing perennial from the Mediterranean countries. The plant is particularly common in Tunisia where the oil is distilled on a limited scale. The oil is shipped to France where it has been used in perfumes and flavors for over 40 years. Other species, closely related to the above plant, are found in the Mediterranean area. One is distilled in Morocco under the name of Artemisia Herba-Alba.

Artemisia Capillaris is known and used in many places all over the world, while Artemisia Mendozana grows in Argentina and serves as a source of a locally distilled and locally used essential oil.

Artemisia Alba is easily recognized by its silvergray, silky haired leaves. The plant is a close relative to the common Wormwood plant which yields Wormwood Oil, sometimes called absinth oil. (See monograph on Wormwood Oil).

The essential oil of Artemisia Alba is a dark green, rather viscous liquid of very powerful, bitter-herbaceous odor and bitter-burning flavor. The "greenness" in odor type and the peculiar bitter aroma of this oil makes it an interesting item for chypre, fougère, "forest" notes, aftershave colognes, etc. and for the flavoring of alcoholic beverages.

See also Artemisia Vulgaris and Wormwood Oil.

Artemisia Annua.

An essential oil is distilled from the whole overground parts of wild growing and cultivated Artemisia Annua plants in Yugoslavia. The plant is harvested just before the flower-buds open when the essential oil content is at its maximum.

The oil is pale yellow to greenish yellow, and has a pleasant, almost balsamic-sweet, somewhat spicy odor. There is some similarity to the odor of basil oil with a fresh-green foliage note. Oil of Artemisia Annua is used locally in the soap industry and for cosmetic preparations in the perfuming of these products. The yield by steam distillation of this plant is much higher than the yield of oil from other artemisia species. Accordingly, this is one of the most inexpensive artemisia oils. Apparently, the oil of Artemisia Annua is not regularly available outside of its country of origin.

Artemisia Vulgaris.

The artemisia plants seem to have originated in Eastern Europe and Western Asia. Most of these species are found growing wild and abundantly all over the temperate and cold-temperate zones of the world. A very common weed in Central Europe, Southeastern Europe, India, China and Japan is the Artemisia Vulgaris. An essential oil is steam distilled from the dried herb in the South of France, in Morocco, Germany, Hungary, India, China and Japan. The French oil is known as "essence d'Armoise".

The essential oil of **Artemisia Vulgaris** is a pale yellow or almost colorless liquid (as distinguished from the blue-green color of **Wormwood Oil** and of **Artemisia Alba**). The odor is powerful, fresh-camphoraceous, somewhat green and bitter-sweet, with a cedarleaf-like topnote and a sage-rosemary-like bodynote. The dryout is very pleasant, sweet-herbaceous and tealike. The flavor of **Artemisia Vulgaris Oil** is warm, almost pungent, but also bitter-sweet, showing a slightly cooling effect in higher dilution. It should be kept in mind that there are numerous types of this oil on the market, and that wide variations in odor and flavor can be expected according to the origin of the oil. Infusions of the dried herb are used in Europe for gargles in the same way as, e.g., infusions of Dalmatian sage herb.

The essential oil is used in perfumery to add freshness and warmth to lavender-colognes, chypres, fougères, pine fragrances, etc. **Artemisia Vulgaris Oil** blends excellently with oakmoss, patchouli, rosemary, lavandin, isobornylacetate, pine needle oils, sage clary, Spanish sage, coumarin, decylalcohol, etc. The oil shows great power and diffusiveness, and it is stable in soaps. The odor type is much more refined and balsamic than that of cedarleaf with which the above oil is sometimes compared.

Artemisia Vulgaris Oil finds some use in flavors, although it is conceivable that its thujone content may one day prohibit its use in food. A suggested use level in flavors is about 1.00 to 2.00 mg%, and the **Minimum Perceptible** is about 0.20 to 0.40 mg%. It is not a very powerful flavor material.

The herb is present in abundance, and the essential oil is available upon request in quite large quantities. The oil is not at all common, however, and it rarely appears in the commercial offers and price lists. The author believes that this oil deserves more attention from perfumers for its delightfully natural, herbal and refreshing notes.

Asarum Europaeum.

The essential oil of **Asarum Europaeum** is steam distilled from the entire fresh plant of the European **Hazelwort**. This plant grows wild in Poland, and is distilled locally on a limited scale. The oil is dark amber colored or almost brown, and very viscous. Old oils often show a deposit of crystals. The odor of **Hazelwort Oil** is somewhat reminiscent of that of **Canadian Snakeroot Oil**: a sharp, peppery, spicy-woody and warm, but not very pleasant odor. The flavor is burning, almost pungent and sharp, far from pleasant.

The oil could, however, still serve as an interesting item for fine perfumery and in the reproduction of other essential oils. Its penetrating and peculiar note can produce quite interesting effects in oriental perfumes and chypres when the oil is used with skill and experience. It blends well with vetiver, isoeugenol, opopanax, oakmoss, patchouli, etc.

The main constituent of **Asarum Europaeum Oil** is a phenolic ether, **Asarone**, a stereoisomer of which is found in **Calamus Oil**.

Asarone is odorless and solid, and has probably no value in perfumes or flavors. Consequently, the actual value of **Asarum Europaeum Oil** is possibly due to the minor constituents, e.g. certain terpenes. According to private communication to the author from Polish distillers, **Asarone** is not present in oils from old or thoroughly dried plant material.

Asafoetida.

Asafoetida or **Asafetida** is a natural oleo-gum-resin, exuded from roots of a big plant, **Ferula Asafoetida**, and other species of **Ferula**, a plant native to Iran and Afghanistan. The substance is a physiological product of the plant. When overground parts of the plant are cut off, a milky juice flows out and solidifies upon exposure to air. Material is also collected from the outside of the root-stem under the surface of the soil. The foliage of the plant is a local vegetable and the oleo-gum-resin is, in a way, a by-product, but it has retained a substantial interest for its peculiar odor and flavor. The annual consumption in the U.S.A. alone is about 50 metric tons.

The crude botanical is contaminated with sand, earth, gravel, vegetable fragments, etc. and it is used in the production of the following preparations:

1) **Asafoetida Resinoid** by hydrocarbon extraction.
2) **Asafoetida Absolute** or **Asafoetida Tincture** by alcohol extraction.
3) **Asafoetida Oil** by steam distillation.

The resinoid is a semi-solid, dark brown mass.

Its odor is somewhat coarse, and the product is not recommended for flavor use. By acetone-extraction, a superior resinoid is obtained.

Asafoetida Absolute or "resin-absolute" is a semi-solid reddish-brown mass of distinctly alliaceous odor. However, beneath the garlic-onion-like topnote there is an immensely rich and sweet-balsamic body of highly interesting type. The dryout reveals some vanillin or related component. Ferulic Acid is present as an ester in large quantities in Asafoetida. The acid is closely related to the flavor principle of Maple Syrup (Ferulaldehyde or 4-hydroxy-3-methoxycinnamic aldehyde). It is also related to isoeugenol and vanillin.

Asafoetida Oil is a pale yellow or orange-yellow colored liquid, having a sharp alliaceous, almost obnoxious and acrid odor. The flavor is slightly bitter, acrid and somewhat pungent. Its power and radiation is often underestimated, and the oil lacks the valuable fixation and balsamic background typical of the extracted products. The yield of essential oil by steam distillation of the crude botanical material is about 7 to 9%, occasionally much higher

Generally, the Resinoid or the Absolute, at times the Tincture, are used in flavor work in spice blends, meat sauces, pickles, etc. The use of Asafoetida in "Worcestershire Sauce" is well known. Suggested use level, based upon the alcohol-soluble matter (60 to 68% of the crude botanical), is 3 to 5 mg%, and the Minimum Perceptible is about 0.50 to 1.00 mg%. The effect of the fixative, balsamic materials in the extract is obvious.

At low concentrations, Asafoetida Absolute can introduce very intriguing notes in rose bases and heavy oriental fragrances. The alliaceous odor of asafoetida is due to large amounts of sulphur compounds in the essential oil only; there are no sulphur compounds in the non-volatile part of the extract. By steam distillation of the extract, it is possible to eliminate the alliaceous odor and produce a very interesting perfume material of great fixative value. This material is not commercially produced, but it is quite easy for most consumers to perform this partial "de-odorization" of Asafoetida.

Asafoetida is readily available and it is fairly inexpensive. The age of the crude botanical has a significant influence upon the odor and flavor of its processed derivatives.

Atractylis (Concrète) Oil.

Atractylis Oil is steam distilled from the roots of Atractylis Ovata and possibly from other species of Atractylis, native to China and India, occasionally cultivated in Japan. The small plants have been known in China for thousands of years. The oil is produced in China, but some shipments of root material arrive quite regularly in Europe, e.g. in France, where a few Grasse houses also distil the oil. Atractylis Oil is thus available all over the world on a limited scale.

Atractylis Oil is a solid, waxy-crystalline mass of dark yellow to orange-red color. It is not unlike Bruyère Absolute, Guaiacwood Oil or Araucaria Oil in consistency, all of which are also "concrète" oils. The odor of atractylis oil is strong peppery, woody-spicy, warm and dry, somewhat reminiscent of elemi, ginger, and galanga. The flavor is pungent, somewhat bitter and warm, not very pleasant.

Atractylis Oil is very useful in perfumery where its excellent fixative effect and surprising power can be utilized in heavy oriental bases, woody fragrances, spicy and dry ambra types, etc. The oil blends excellently with vetiver, ionones, phenylethylalcohol, isoeugenol, opopanax, nitro-musks, etc. Isoeugenol and phenylethylalcohol produce a distinct leather note with small amounts of Atractylis Oil. The main constituent of this oil is a solid sesquiterpene alcohol, probably identical with Eudesmol, (see also Araucaria Oil).

Atractylis Oil appeared on the European market in 1953, and is now available on a limited scale. The yield by steam distillation of the root is very good (about 8%) and the oil can be produced at a cost which is very reasonable, considering the power of this perfume material.

B

Backhousia Citriodora.

An essential oil is steam distilled from the leaves of a wild growing tree, Backhousia Citriodora, in eastern and southeastern Australia. Although the oil has been known since late in the 19th century, it has never obtained great importance.

The oil is a pale yellow or yellow mobile liquid of intensely fresh lemon-like odor with a pleasant sweet-green undertone. The main constituent is **Citral** which is present in amounts of more than 90%, occasionally up to 98%. This fact is clearly perceptible in the odor and flavor of the oil. In this respect, it bears some resemblance to the Chinese oil of **Litsea Cubeba.**

As a source of citral, the essential oil of **Backhousia Citriodora** would be excellent if the oil were freely available in 100-ton lots. Its odor is much cleaner and fresher than **Lemongrass Oil**, and there are no grassy-fatty or harsh notes at all in the Australian oil. Even the amylacetate-like fruitiness of lemongrass oil is absent in Backhousia Citriodora.

The Australian tree is not cultivated on more than an experimental scale, however, and it is inconceivable that the oil will ever become an important raw material. **Litsea Cubeba** oil may take over the job of providing a low-cost source for citral isolation if **Lemongrass Oil** is unable to keep up the competition.

Oil of **Backhousia Citriodora** could be used in flavors for its unusually clean, lemon-like aroma. But here again synthetic citral is slowly replacing the isolated natural citral. For perfumes, the **Backhousia Citriodora Oil** will hardly be able to compete with a redistilled **Litsea Cubeba Oil** or with synthetic blends.

Backhousia Myrtifolia.

Essential oils are distilled from leaves and twigs of trees of the above name in southeastern Australia. It has been disclosed recently that at least 4 different "physiological" forms of this tree grow in the area. Consequently, it is scarcely economically feasible to produce the individual oils. Only experienced botanical experts can distinguish among the various forms just by looking at the trees. Other Australian trees, e.g. eucalyptus species, melaleuca species, occur in various physiological forms. So far, the most common types of essential oil distilled from the individual physiological forms are:

1) The **Elimicin** form of **Backhousia Myrtifolia.** The main constituent is trimethoxy-allylbenzene, a sweet-woody smelling material;

2) **Isoelemicin** form of **Backhousia Myrtifolia.** This oil consists mainly of **Isoelemicin.**

3) and 4): **Methyleugenol** form and **Methyl Isoeugenol** form.

All four types of essential oil could be of considerable interest if they were produced on a large scale. They would be interesting starting materials for the isolation of the above mentioned main constituents which are either well-known and regularly used perfume materials (the latter two), or useful modifiers-fixatives for perfumes (the two former).

None of the above four types of **Backhousia Myrtifolia Oil** are produced on a commercial scale.

"Balsam Fir" Needle Oil.

Also known as **"Canadian Fir Needle Oil"**, this essential oil is steam distilled from the leaves (needles) and twigs of **Abies Balsamea**, the **"Balm of Gilead Fir"**. The tree is a fir, but the commercial name is confusing. The tree grows abundantly in Canada and the northeastern United States. It should not be confused with the tree which yields **"Balm of Gilead Buds"** (see monograph on **Poplar Bud Oil**).

Abies Balsamea also yields a so-called **Canada Balsam** which is a turpentine type of natural oleoresin. (See **Canada Balsam**).

Balsam Fir Needle Oil consists mainly of monoterpenes, e.g. l-limonene, l-beta-pinene and l-camphene, while l-bornylacetate is the main oxygenated component (15 to 18% of the oil).

The oil is a pale yellow or almost water-white mobile oil of a peculiar oily-balsamic, somewhat resinous, but also fresh and sweet odor, resembling the odor of spruce oil or pinus pumilio oil. The abies balsamea needles oil is equal in sweetness to the oil of pinus pumilio, but poorer in balsamic notes than this oil. On an overall basis, the abies balsamea oil is poorer in sweetness and tenacity than the better grades of spruce oils.

Oil of **Abies Balsamea** serves as a "pine-and-spruce" fragrance in fresh-balsamic "fir-needle" blends, Christmas-tree odors, fougères, air-fresheners, disinfectants, detergents, household cleaners, etc. The production of **Abies Balsamea Oil** is irregular, and it is rarely available in very large quantities. It is often confused or deliberately adulterated with other fir or spruce needle oils; it may be an entirely artificial composition, based upon isobornylacetate, limonene, camphene, pinene, etc.

Balsam Fir Needle Oil does not offer any unique notes, and it may eventually disappear from the market, particularly if the richer bornylacetate-types of conifer needle oils become freely available. (See also **Fir Needle Absolute** and **Fir Needle Oils, Summary**).

Balsamite.

An essential oil under the name of "essence balsamite" is steam distilled from a wild growing or cultivated herb of the family compositae. The plant is related to tansy (tanacetum) and is quite commonly grown in France as a culinary herb. The oil is distilled in the south of France on a very limited scale.

Balsamite Oil is a clear yellow or pale yellow liquid of very powerful, fresh-herbaceous and somewhat medicinal odor. The very first topnote bears some resemblance to the odor of **Evoulimba Oil** or to wild marjoram, pennyroyal terpenes, light fractions of pine oil, etc. The bodynotes have certain phases in common with basil, hyssop and savin. An almost nauseating, savin-like note is very persistent in the odor of this oil. The dryout is sweeter but resembles at times sulfate turpentine and terpinolene. All told, it is an unusual odor gamut and it is not surprising that the oil has attracted the interest of certain perfume houses.

Balsamite Oil could undoubtedly introduce piquant topnotes in fougères, pine fragrances, spicy after-shave lotions, etc. and it blends well with rosemary, bayleaf oil, sage oil, cedarleaf oil, isobornylacetate, etc.

The author has only little experience with the application of this oil in perfumes. It is hardly conceivable that the oil can find use in flavors.

Basil Oil.

Included among a large number of different types of **Basil Oils** are two which have become particularly common in perfumery and flavor work:
1) The true **Sweet Basil Oil** which is steam distilled from the flowering tops of the small plant **Ocimum Basilicum** in France and in the United States of America. Smaller quantities are produced in Italy, Hungary and Spain.
2) The **"Exotic"** or so-called **"Reunion"** type of **Basil Oil** is produced in the Comoro islands, the Seychelles, and occasionally in Madagascar.

The two oils can be distinguished by their odor characteristics in a brief description such as:
1) The **Linalool**-type,

2) The **Camphor-Estragole** type.

The former type also contains estragole, but this material is not typical of the odor of the **Sweet Basil Oil**. It does not contain camphor. The latter oil contains more estragole than No. 1), and the odor of the **"Exotic"** type is not covered up by the content of camphor in that oil. This type contains little or no linalool.

In other words, the absence of camphoraceous notes and the presence of a perfect odor balance between linalool and estragole is characteristic of true **Sweet Basil Oil**. The two oils are described in the individual monographs which follow:

1) **Sweet Basil Oil**: The oil is usually pale yellow or almost colorless. Its odor is sweet-spicy, slightly green, fresh, with a faint balsamic-woody undertone and a lasting sweetness. It is produced in very limited quantities (annual world production is less than one metric ton), and the oil ranks among the more expensive essential oils. However, its great strength makes it very useful and generally applicable in fine perfumery and in flavor work.

   In perfumes, **Sweet Basil Oil** has been a "classic" material in the **"Origan"** type of perfumes and bases for several decades. In chypres, crêpe de chines and certain modern-aldehydic and "green" perfume types, the oil can introduce very interesting notes. It blends well with the most varied types of perfume material, e.g. opopanax or bergamot oil, iso-eugenol or sage clary, methylionone or cyclam-al, lime oil or oakmoss, hydroxycitronellal, etc. **Sweet Basil Oil** finds some application in flavors, e.g. in the "chartreuse" type of liqueur, and in high-priced culinary seasonings, meat sauces, etc. The suggested use level is 0.30 to 1.00 mg%, and the **Minimum Perceptible** is 0.04 to 0.10 mg%.

2) **"Reunion"** type **Basil Oil**. This oil is usually yellow or greenish-yellow to pale green in color. Its odor is somewhat coarse-herbaceous, slightly camphoraceous in the initial notes, and displaying the intense sweetness of the estragole, a so-called "anisic" type of odor. The estragole, also known as methyl chavicol, is distinctly perceptible in the odor of **"Exotic" Basil Oil**. Although it has been claimed by authorities in the field that this "exotic" type of basil oil can be used "wherever the price of sweet basil oil prevents the use of this expensive oil", the author of the present work can

hardly consider the "exotic" type of basil oil as a replacement for the "French" type.

The trade offers basil oils under a wealth of "exotic" and "French" names, and it is not uncommon that an "exotic" oil may be "doctored", with e.g. 60% added linalool. This blend is then offered as "French" basil oil, occasionally with the addition of "pays" or some "provincial" name added on the label. This substitute is useful in soap perfumes or other low-cost perfumes as a fair replacement for the much more expensive sweet basil oil. It hardly pays, however, to substitute a sophisticated exotic basil for sweet basil oil in flavor work. There are trace components in the true sweet basil oil that make this oil much more powerful than the above "theoretical" substitute oil. The author has found the approximate use level for "exotic" basil oil to be 0.60 to 2.00 mg%. The **Minimum Percept-ible** is about 0.08 to 0.20 mg%. The sweet basil has at least twice the flavor strength compared to the exotic type. An addition of 60% of linalool to the exotic oil only lowers the flavor strength.

"**Exotic" Basil Oil** is produced in a number of countries with a tropical or subtropical climate. The plant occurs in many varieties, one of which deserves more attention:

3) The "**Methylcinnamate**" type of **Basil Oil.** This oil is produced in West Africa, East Africa, India, Indonesia, the West Indies, the Balkan States, etc. The oil is of yellow or pale yellow color, and it is much sweeter in odor than the "exotic" basil oil. It is much more fruity and not at all as fresh-green as the "French" basil oil. Its main constituent is **Methylcinnamate** which is available as a synthetic material at a very low cost. The above oil could find some use in soap perfumery, e.g. for local production of soap perfumes, provided the oil becomes available in larger quantities.

4) A fourth type is the "**Phenolic**" type of basil oil. One of these is listed in the present work under the botanical name of the plant from which it is distilled: **Ocimum Gratissimum.**

Bay Leaf Oil.

Bay Leaf Oil or **Bay Oil** is distilled from the leaves of a middle-sized tree, **Pimenta Racemosa**, earlier known as **Myrcia Acris**. The tree grows wild, but is also cultivated in various islands of the West Indies, particularly on the island of Dominica. Other important producers are Puerto Rico, Venezuela, Montserrat, St. Lucia and the tiny island of St. John, U.S. Virgin islands, formerly known as the Danish West Indies.

The leaves are distilled either with water or with steam. It is customary to add salt to the distillation water in order to increase the temperature and thus complete the distillation of oil more rapidly (compare Vetiver oil in Reunion, etc.).

Bay Leaf Oil is a yellowish to dark brown liquid. (Variations in color occur according to the type of still used and the kind of shipping container). The odor is fresh-spicy, somewhat medicinal, but it has a lasting, sweet-balsamic undertone. The odor of this oil is quite obnoxious to some people, sickly sweet, nauseating. To others, it is quite fresh and pleasant. The chief constituent is eugenol which is also present as a methylether. Myrcene, limonene dipentene and small amounts of citral bring a certain freshness to the harsh-leafy, phenolic odor. The flavor of this oil is warm, almost pungent, spicy and somewhat bitter. To the author's knowledge, this oil finds little or no use in flavor work.

Bay Leaf Oil is used very extensively in hair lotions, after-shave lotions, and other "men's line" fragrances. The old-fashioned type of "**Bay Rum**" was produced in the former Danish West Indies by distillation of **Rum** over **Bay Leaves.** Bay Rum is still available, but often produced merely by dissolving a **Terpeneless Bay Leaf Oil** (see following monograph) in diluted alcohol and rum.

Bay Leaf Oil is readily available in large quantities, but unfortunately, also in quite variable qualities. The annual production is between 25 and 75 metric tons, of which a considerable quantity is consumed in the producing areas. Adulteration of **Bay Leaf Oil** occurs quite frequently, e.g. with clove leaf oil, bois de rose terpenes, lime oil terpenes, synthetic myrcene and other terpenes, all of which are cheaper than bay leaf oil and readily available in Europe and the U.S.A. Terpenes from the bay leaf oil itself are also available where the **Terpeneless Bay Leaf Oil** is produced (see next monograph).

Bay Leaf Oil, terpeneless.

Terpeneless Bay Leaf Oil is produced from "crude"

(or "natural") **Bay Leaf Oil** by removal of the terpenes, usually only the low-boiling monoterpenes: myrcene, dipentene, pinene and limonene. Low-boiling oxygenated components, e.g. cineole and citral, may be lost in a careless vacuum distillation. The deterpenation is often carried out by this simple "topping-off" of the monoterpenes. Deterpenation is rarely, if ever, carried out on a commercial scale in the countries of origin of the **Bay Leaf Oil**.

Bay Leaf Oil contains approximately 60% of the so-called oxygenated (i.e. non-terpenic or non-hydrocarbon-) components. The loss by total deterpenation would then be around 40% of the oil. By the "topping-off" process, the sesquiterpenes are left in the oil.

Terpeneless Bay Leaf Oil is a pale straw-colored to brownish-orange colored oil, depending on the method of deterpenation. "Topped-off" oils are obviously darker than the natural oil from which they were produced. Very pale colored oils may have been steam distilled after deterpenation, or they may be alcohol-washings of the natural oil (so-called "absolutes"). The latter type of oil will be terpeneless *and* sesquiterpeneless.

Terpeneless Bay Leaf Oil has an intensely sweet, deep and mellow odor of a spicy-balsamic type. The lemon-like topnote is still perceptible, but the freshness is less pronounced compared to the natural oil. Furthermore, the terpeneless oil is more easily soluble in diluted alcohol. This is an obvious advantage since the oil is used in preparations with low alcohol percentage (hair-lotions, after-shave lotions, etc.).

The **Terpeneless Bay Leaf Oil** blends excellently with lavandin or lavender oil (e.g. in the classic "**Rondeletia**" type) and with petitgrain, citrus oils, rosemary, geraniol, citronellol, cinnamic alcohol, amylsalicylate, ylang-ylang, etc. in a wide variety of perfumes and perfume bases. Although the components of this oil are well known and readily available from other sources, there is really no suitable substitute for a good **Terpeneless Bay Leaf Oil**.

Beeswax Absolute.

Perhaps better known under its French name, **Absolue Cire d'Abeille**, this comparatively rare perfume material is an alcohol-soluble extract from crude yellow beeswax. The beeswax is cleaned of mechanical impurities by melting and subsequent straining. Extraction is usually performed as a direct alcohol-washing of the beeswax.

Beeswax is produced all over the world: in cold-temperate zones and in the hottest tropics. In a way, it is a by-product of honey production since the wax is secreted on the underside of the bee, **Apis Mellifera**. The honey is recovered from the honeycombs by slicing off the end sections of the cells, draining them, and centrifuging out the honey. The waxcombs are rinsed with water, then melted and run into pans or molds to harden while cooling. The Toilet Goods Association defines **Beeswax** as "the purified honeycomb of the bee, **Apis Mellifera**, free from all other waxes".

The main producers of beeswax are: Angola (Portuguese West Africa), the West Indies, California, Hawaii, New Zealand, Australia, Chile, Spain, North Africa, the Union of South Africa, etc. From a chemical point of view, all these beeswaxes are practically identical. A perfumer would be able to distinguish one beeswax from another because a characteristic odor is left in the wax (similar to the "brand" of special flavor imparted to various sorts of honey), according to where it has been harvested, and from what kind of flowers the bees have collected their nectar. **Benguela** wax from Angola is one of the best known waxes used in Europe for cosmetic purposes. However, in order to produce a uniform and interesting grade of **Beeswax Absolute**, the few Grasse producers often prefer a locally produced beeswax, probably derived from bees that visit the clover fields in the Grasse area or elsewhere in France.

Yellow Beeswax contains three different types of material:

1) **Cerolein,** which is carried over in the absolute since it is soluble in cold alcohol. Cerolein is a mixture of higher fatty acids. It is probably responsible for the fatty-waxy body-notes of the **Beeswax Absolute.**

2) **Cerotinic Acid,** a saturated aliphatic acid (fatty acid), soluble in hot alcohol, almost insoluble in cold alcohol.

3) a mixture of **Myricyl Alcohol** and the **Myricyl Ester** of **Palmitic Acid,** both insoluble in alcohol. Accordingly, this third part should not be present in **Beeswax Absolute,** although the **Cerotinic Acid** is present very often.

Beeswax Absolute is a solid, waxy mass of pale yellow color and a very mild, sweet, oily odor, with a haylike or coumarinic bodynote and a soft, waxy undertone. The odor is remotely reminiscent of good (not harsh) linseed oil with a trace of honey notes. Obviously, the odor of **Beeswax Absolute** is strongly dependent upon the origin of the beeswax (i.e. the hunting grounds of the bees). Various suppliers will offer quite different types of **Beeswax Absolute**. The material is usually not soluble in cold ethylalcohol.

Beeswax Absolute is useful in perfumes where similar notes occur (as a modifier), or where "rough or chemical" corners of synthetic materials must be rounded off. It blends well into jasmin, mimosa, cassie, violet, new mown hay, "tabac", etc. as well as in the so-called "cire d'abeille" perfume base, in which a meadow-like sweetness and heavy, honey-like floral notes are predominant (coumarin, cassione, phenylethyl phenylacetate, helichrysum oil, flouve oil, liatris extract, chamomile, etc.).

Beeswax Absolute could be available in sizeable quantities on fairly short notice, but it is presently produced on a very limited scale. Partly for this reason, the cost is comparatively high. Many consumers prefer to make their own beeswax absolute according to their own specifications. The quality and the uniformity of this perfume material is strongly dependent upon the producer. Actual adulteration is rare. Some producers just don't know how to make a **Beeswax Absolute** which is worth its price (often higher than mimosa absolute!).

Benzoin.

Benzoin Tincture and the various **Benzoin Resinoids**, "Resin Absolute", etc. are described under this heading. The two most important types of raw material, **Benzoin Siam** and **Benzoin Sumatra**, are described in the following monographs.

Benzoin Tincture is usually prepared only from selected "tears" of **Benzoin Siam**. Conventional strength is 20 parts by weight of **Siam Benzoin**, macerated with enough alcohol (of 90 or 96% strength by volume) to produce 100 parts by weight of finished tincture. The above quality of **Benzoin** is almost entirely soluble in alcohol, and the tincture will thus represent an approximate 20% solution of the alcohol-soluble resinoid of this benzoin. The tincture is amber colored, and has a sweet, balsamic-vanillin-like odor. The taste is somewhat bitter. **Benzoin Tincture** is used as a fixative in fine perfumery, in colognes, in alcohol

for "prefixation" prior to the preparation of colognes and lotions, etc. Benzoin tincture is furthermore used in skin preparations for its skin-healing effect and, occasionally, in certain cosmetic preparations for its antioxidant effect.

Benzoin Resinoid is produced from all grades of the crude botanical, **Siam** or **Sumatra**, often from a mixture of both. (See following monographs on the two types of **Benzoin**). Evaluation of **Benzoin Resinoid** is thus a difficult task since the customers are confused with respect to the actual standard of true resinoids. Various solvents are used for the extraction of the crude benzoin.

Benzene is the most common, but "cold alcohol" extraction is becoming more popular. It offers several advantages.

If ethyl alcohol is used directly, the resulting extract is called a **Resin Absolute** of **Benzoin**. If, in addition, heat is applied, and if the crude benzoin has not been neutralized, the free acids (benzoic acid and cinnamic acid) will esterify part of the ethyl alcohol under formation of ethyl benzoate and ethyl cinnamate. These esters are very useful perfume materials of substantial power and good fixative effect, but they do not represent the natural contents of benzoin, nor is it conceivable that a uniform odor quality of benzoin resinoid can be produced by this method. It is therefore suggested that benzoin should first be extracted with benzene, the extract be filtered and evaporated partially. The concentrated solution is then washed neutral with weak alkali, separated clear, filtered and finally evaporated under gentle vacuum. This yields a neutral resinoid which can be extracted with alcohol to yield an entirely alcohol-soluble **Benzoin Absolute**. This product is very pale in color, and has a most delicate balsamic odor, free from harsh resinous and acid notes. This true absolute is definitely superior to the direct one-step alcohol extract from the crude benzoin.

Extraction with ethyl alcohol at a maximum temperature of 40°C., subsequent filtration of the extract and evaporation under vacuum with a "skin temperature" of maximum 50°C. (the temperature of the inner side of the vacuum still, also called "pot temperature"), and prolonged "airing" under vacuum without heating will produce a very attractive, light-colored and true-to-nature "**Resin Absolute of Benzoin**". This product is not acid-free.

The yield of resinoid in the case of **Siam Benzoin** is nearly 95% for the best grades, about 85% for poorer grades. **Sumatra Benzoin** also yields up to 95% in the case of very good grades, while average commercial lots may yield as little as 65% resinoid. Among well-known **Sumatra** types are the "**Penang**" and the "**Palembang**" benzoins which usually give around 65% yield of resinoid.

The **Sumatra Benzoins** give darker resinoids, sometimes almost brown, and they can have a styrax-like odor.

As stated previously, **Benzoin Siam** is characterized by its content of **Benzoic Acid** (10 to 12%), while the major constituent is **Coniferyl Benzoate** (65 to 75%). Other resin acids are present. **Benzoin Sumatra** contains mainly **Benzoresinyl Cinnamate** and **Benzoresinyl Benzoate, Cinnamic Acid, Styrene** (characteristic odor, also found in styrax). Both types contain **Vanillin**, but since the consumers apparently expect more of this material in **Siam Benzoin** than in the Sumatra type, it is not uncommon to add up to 5% vanillin to commercial lots of **Benzoin Resinoid**. This resinoid may be prepared from a mixture of Sumatra and Siam, mostly the former, and, by the addition of substantial amounts of vanillin, it becomes a "commercial grade" of **Siam Benzoin Resinoid**, which may even be labelled "absolute". This high amount of vanillin is not natural to any benzoin, nor is it without significant discoloring effect, e.g. in soap perfumes or in perfumes which contain anthranilates, indol, etc.

Benzoin Resinoid is used very extensively in perfumery, particularly in soap perfumes (see above on discoloration) where its fixative effect is much appreciated. It is generally applicable, but it has a pronounced odor-depressing effect upon the perfumes in which it is incorporated. This effect is closely connected with the fixative effect, and it is enhanced by the rich sweetness and deep balsamic notes from the resinoid.

Benzoin Resinoid is occasionally adulterated with Sumatra benzoin extracts, doctored up with vanillin (see above), or it is "stretched" with **Acaroid Resinoid,** abietic alcohols, methyl abietate, benzyl benzoate, copaiba balsam, amyris oil, etc. The addition of smaller amounts of diethyl phthalate as a plasticizer is considered normal "for convenient handling", and when clearly labelled so.

Benzoin Siam.

Siam Benzoin is a natural gum-resin or, more correctly, a "balsamic resin" (see **Gum Resin** and definitions, Part One of this book). The resin is obtained from the small tree, **Styrax Tonkinensis,** a native of Indochina (Laos and Tonkin). Other species are known to yield similar gum-resins called Siam benzoin. The balsamic latex flows from wounds in the bark and outer wood where incisions are made deliberately. **Benzoin** is thus a pathologic product (it does not occur in healthy, unwounded trees). It is furthermore characteristic that not all of the benzoin trees will yield a latex after incisions.

The milky latex solidifies by oxidation and exposure to air and sunlight. When the benzoin is collected, it is already semi-solid, and it soon becomes hard and brittle, yellow-reddish or orange colored to pale brown, often translucent (thus differing from **Sumatra** types of benzoin). The name **Siam** is attached to this type of benzoin merely because of the fact, that the merchandise is often exported via Siam (Thailand) in transit.

Benzoin Siam comes in variable sizes of pebble-like, often tear-shaped pieces, hard and brittle, rarely agglutinated. The individual pieces are yellow-orange or yellowish-brown, and a characteristic feature is the almost white or cream-colored fracture. The odor is pleasant, sweet-balsamic with a distinct note of vanillin. When chewed, **Siam Benzoin** becomes plastic. Its taste is aromatic but somewhat acrid-bitter and biting.

There are several grades commercially available of **Benzoin Siam**. "Selected tears" or "tears No. 1" are considered superior for perfumery purposes. Lower grades of "tears" are somewhat darker, and they may have more insoluble matter. "Almonds" or "Amygdaloid" forms of **Siam Benzoin** give a very pale tincture or extract, but these grades are less aromatic than "selected tears". The best grades of **Siam Benzoin** contain 95% or even more alcohol-soluble matter. (See monograph on **Benzoin Resinoid** and **Tincture**).

Benzoin Sumatra.

Sumatra Benzoin is a natural balsamic resin, exuded from a small tree, **Styrax Benzoin,** grown extensively in Sumatra and Malaya. Incisions are made in the trunks either through the bark or after peeling off spots of bark, and a viscous balsamic substance is produced as a pathologic

7: Modern **Extraction** plant designed for oakmoss and other natural extracts.

(Courtesy of **Dragoco**, *Holzminden, Germany)*

8: All-glass liquid/solid **Extractor** for cold or hot extraction with low-boiling solvents. (Soxhlet type).

(Courtesy of Q.V.F., Ltd., Staffordshire, England)

material in the trunk. The substance flows out and solidifies on making contact with the air. The gum-resin is collected from the incisions and from the bottom of the trunk at the foot of the tree where significant quantities of benzoin accumulates. There are several grades of **Sumatra Benzoin**. The "Almond" grade is considered the most suitable for perfumery purposes. It consists mainly of white or cream-colored brittle pieces, somewhat resembling almonds. This quality obviously yields a very pale-colored resinoid or tincture. It contains about 90% alcohol-soluble matter, occasionally more. Other grades of **Sumatra Benzoin** are solid masses, dark blocks of gray or brown-gray, uneven lumps containing more or less quantities of dirt, sand, wood splinters, etc.

Sumatra Benzoin consists mainly of cinnamates (esters) of coniferylalcohol, cinnamyl alcohol, benzoresinol, phenylpropylalcohol, etc., as distinguished from **Siam Benzoin** which consists mainly of benzoates.

Lower grades of **Sumatra Benzoin**, (e.g. "Palembang" and "Penang"), have odor characteristics in common with **Styrax** (i.e. more harsh odor than "Almond" benzoin). They are darker, reddish-brown in color. The amount of essential oil or volatile constituents in benzoin is negligible, and an essential oil is not commercially available.

Benzoin Sumatra is a low-cost and readily available raw material, extensively used as a replacement for **Siam Benzoin** which is far more expensive. From a perfumer's point of view, however, the two benzoins should be considered as two different products. One can not substitute for the other. **Siam Benzoin** will find application in the more delicate fragrances. It is not possible to add the above mentioned known materials to a **Sumatra Benzoin** and convert it to anything like a fair grade of **Siam Benzoin**. The Sumatra type will remain a coarser product which can be used in perfumes of the more harsh-balsamic, sharp-floral type, e.g. hyacinth, new mown hay, etc.

Siam Benzoin is also superior with respect to antioxidative effect, e.g. in lard and other fats.

Bergamot Oil.

The economy of citrus oils in general is clearly depicted by the study of **Bergamot Oil** production. Only the expressed oil from the peels of the fruits from the small bergamot tree, **Citrus Bergamia,** are of any substantial interest. The pulp or juice is of little value beyond what can be converted into citric acid. The leaves and twigs may be distilled to yield a **Bergamot-Petitgrain Oil** (see that monograph), but the fruits are not edible.

Bergamot Oil is produced by cold expression from the peel of the nearly ripe fruit. The tree grows almost exclusively in a narrow coastal strip in the southern part of Calabria, Italy. Cultivation of bergamot trees in other areas have failed to produce bergamot oils of comparable value to that of the Calabrian oil. There is one exception, however: experimental plantations in Guinea (former French West Africa) since 1937, and more recently in Morocco have now attained some importance on the world **Bergamot Oil** market. Bergamot trees are grafted on stubs of bitter orange trees. The fruits are of the size of big oranges and almost lemon-shaped. The annual world production (over 90% of which is Calabrian) fluctuates between 150 and 250 tons.

Bergamot Oil is a green or olive green, mobile liquid of extremely rich, sweet-fruity initial odor. Although the characteristics of this topnote remain perceptible in good oils, it is followed by a still more characteristic oily-herbaceous and somewhat balsamic body and dryout. The sweetness yields to a more tobaccolike and rich note, somewhat reminiscent of sage clary and nerylacetate. The freshness in the topnote is mainly due to terpenes and small amounts of citral and aliphatic aldehydes. Absence of the "oily" note is one of the most revealing features in poor or adulterated bergamot oils. The color of bergamot oil fades on ageing, particularly when the oil is exposed to daylight. The oil turns yellow or pale olive-brown. The color is also dependent upon the maturity of the fruit at the moment of expressing. Like all other citrus oils, **Bergamot Oil** is produced in the immediate vicinity of the plantations.

The oil is used extensively in perfumery for its sweet freshness, particularly in citrus colognes, chypres, fougères, modern fantasy bases, etc. Part of the sweetness and rich bodynote is due to the presence of large amounts of linalylacetate combined with linalool and traces of methylanthranilate. It is interesting to find the presence of methylanthranilate together with aliphatic aldehydes, citral etc. in several citrus oils. In perfume creation, it is generally considered somewhat hazardous to include substantial amounts of aldehydes when anthranilates are present. The formation of "Schiff's bases" produce a very intense color which may be visible in the perfumed cosmetic product or in a soap. Other perfumers will deliberately utilize this simple chemical phenomenon to produce an increased sweetness in orange-flower or neroli types of fragrance, etc.

Unlike most other citrus oils, **Bergamot Oil** has a certain fixative effect when used in fairly high concentrations. The odor of the oil is well balanced from nature through the presence of certain coumarin derivatives, some of which are odorless and non-volatile. The quantity and composition of the evaporation residue is another important criterion in the analysis of bergamot oil.

Bergamot Oil is also used in flavors for its sweet-fruity and yet refreshing notes. It is quite popular in "hard candy" and as a modifier, along with other citrus oils. Bergamot oil forms the original flavor principle in the Continental hard candy known as "Althaea drops". Bergamot is also used in the flavoring of tobacco, particularly in the Continental types of pipe tobacco. The oil is frequently adulterated. Less than 10 years ago, when the cost of **Linalylacetate** (the main constituent of bergamot oil) was more than half the cost of the oil itself, adulteration was often done with the addition of terpinylacetate and other low-cost esters. Today, with synthetic linalylacetate available at one-fifth the old price, it is possible to cut bergamot oil directly with linalool and linalylacetate. A simple example will show how easy a $4\frac{1}{2}\%$ profit is made without any laboratory or factory facilities. An ordinary bergamot oil contains about 38% linalylacetate. To the oil is added 5% linalylacetate synthetic. The mixture has now a total of 40.85% linalylacetate which is not extraordinary. The net profit made by selling the latter mixture at the price of the former original oil is an additional $4\frac{1}{2}\%$. This adulteration is extremely hard to identify by olfactory examination alone. Other common adulterants are bitter orange oil, lime oil, citral, d-limonene, etc. Adulterations with diethylphthalate, diacetin, terpinylacetate, etc. are considered so crude that the author finds it superfluous to discuss these in detail.

The increasing and unscrupulous adulteration of **Bergamot Oil** has resulted in the establishment of the "Consorzio di Bergamotto" in Calabria. All oils which leave the Consorzio warehouses will carry the seal of the Consorzio with the guarantee for purity and genuineness. However, it is still possible to find excellent if not superior qualities of **Bergamot Oil** on the "free" market, i.e. outside the reach of the Consorzio.

(See also monographs on **Bergamot Oil, Terpeneless, Bergamot Petitgrain Oil** and **Bergamots "fallen", oil of -.**).

Bergamot Oil, terpeneless.

From among the number of various methods of deterpenation (see Part One under **Terpeneless Oils**), vacuum distillation seems to have become the most popular in the case of bergamot oil. Certain users of high-grade terpeneless bergamot oil will perform their own deterpenation, e.g. by selective solvent extraction or by the chromatographic methods. These methods result in practically colorless oils with a negligible loss of low-boiling and important oxygenated components. Occasionally, only the coarse-smelling light monoterpenes and the waxy residues are removed by simple vacuum-distillation. This yields an oil which is well suited for perfumery purposes: it will have improved solubility and intensified, rich body notes. The freshness is greatly impaired by this deterpenation. As far as concentration is concerned, the terpeneless oil is only a little "stronger" in odor effect compared to the natural oil. The terpenes hardly amount to one-third of the original oil. The conventional term "bergamot oil, terpeneless, three-fold" is not only exaggerated, but it is a fact that a true terpeneless bergamot oil barely yields twice the strength of a natural oil. The advantage of the terpeneless oil lies in an odor improvement and a better solubility, partly also in better keeping qualities. Furthermore, it is in the high-boiling constituents of the bergamot oil that we find the most interesting and important odor principles, e.g. the oily, slightly grassy dihydrocuminylalcohol (see **Perilla Oil**), etc.

Terpeneless Bergamot Oil finds use in perfumery among the high-class perfumes, better florals, etc. It blends well in "muguet", chypre, gardenia, lavender, violet and numerous other sweet florals or fantasy bases. It finds occasionally use in pear flavors and various candy flavors.

Bergamot-Petitgrain Oil.

This is also known as "petitgrain bergamier" or "essence de brouts de taille du bergamottier".

This oil is steam distilled from the leaves and twigs of the bergamot tree which is grafted upon the stubs of bitter orange trees. Distillation takes place in Calabria, Italy during the "fruitless" season when the trees are pruned. The demand for this oil is not great, and the annual production can be estimated at about one metric ton.

Bergamot-Petitgrain Oil is a green-yellow to olive-yellow colored mobile liquid, possessing a typical "petitgrain" odor: bitter-fresh, yet with a pronounced sweet-woody background. There is a strong resemblance to the better grades of South American petitgrain oil, although with an emphasis on the linalool-linalylacetate notes, and there are fewer bitter-dry notes.

All told, the **Bergamot Petitgrain Oil** does not introduce any really new or highly interesting notes in perfumery. Accordingly, this oil may never attain any importance. It is conceivable that **Bergamot Petitgrain Oil** will continue to be used in the all too well known "cutting" of true bergamot peel oil, together with the oil of "fallen" bergamots (see following monograph).

Bergamots "Fallen".

Due to weather conditions, mechanical damage, etc., a certain amount of **Bergamot** fruits fall to the ground before and during maturity. An essential oil is produced either by cold expression or by steam distillation from the peels of these "fallen" bergamots. These oils are rarely, if ever, exported as such, but they present a certain danger to the quality and reputation of the true bergamot oil because the oil of the fallen fruits is an excellent "cutting" material for the cold-pressed oil from the healthy hand-picked fruits.

Oil of **"Fallen" Bergamots** is distinguished by its very high evaporation residue (cold pressed oils from the peel) or a high linalool-linalylester content (steam distilled oil from the peel), and the latter type is easily soluble in alcohol (low content of monoterpenes).

Occasionally, the expressed bergamot peels from the production of true bergamot oil are steam distilled. They yield an essential oil which is rich in monoterpenes and low in linalool-linalyl-acetate. This oil, too, presents a threat to the quality of the true bergamot oil. Considering the fact that many tons of oil from "fallen" bergamots and "used" bergamot peels are produced every year, a certain risk is encountered in the main-

tenance of a high reputation for the true bergamot oil. Only strict control over the production of these "odd" bergamot oils can, to a certain degree, offer a safeguard against the always present possibility of "on-the-spot adulteration".

Betel Oil.

Betel Oil is also known as **"Pan Oil"**. The essential oil is produced by steam distillation from the leaves of **Piper Betle**, a vine of the pepper family. The plant grows widely over the entire area between South Arabia and Southeast China. Production of oil takes place in India, China, Malaya and Pakistan.

Betel Oil is yellow to brown, occasionally dark brown. It may discolor significantly during shipping if the container is an iron drum. The odor of the oil is distinctly phenolic, almost tar-like or "smoky". There is a great deal of resemblance to the odor of maté-leaves (or maté absolute) and to certain types of Chinese tea. The flavor of **Betel Oil** is bitter-acrid, warm and unpleasantly sharp, biting.

The peculiar odor and flavor of this oil is due to its very high content of phenols which total about 75% of the oil. The most important of these phenols are: **Chavibetol** (also called betel phenol), **Chavicol** (which is para allyl phenol), **Allyl Pyrocatechol** (hydroxy chavicol), etc.

Since **Betel Oil** is produced in Tongkin, it is not surprising that adulteration occasionally occurs with materials such as camphor oil. This addition is, however, clearly perceptible on an odor and flavor test or through a chemical analysis.

Betel Oil is primarily used in the Far East in preparations similar to the betel chew, (i.e. areca nuts, wrapped in betel leaves and spiced with various pungent botanicals. The betel leaves in this preparation represent the antiseptic part of the chew. The areca nuts are erroneously called betel nuts because of their use in this popular Eastern tonic masticatory.

Betel Oil has little or no application in European or American perfumery or flavor work.

Birch.

A number of essential oils and other perfume raw materials are produced from various species of the birch tree:

1) **Birch Bark Oil** from the bark of **Betula Lenta**,

the so-called "Southern Birch" in Canada, Eastern and Midwestern United States. Occasionally the twigs are also distilled.

2) **Birch Bud Oil** from the leaf-buds of **Betula Alba** in Germany, Finland and Denmark.

3) **Birch Tar** by destructive distillation of the bark of **Betula Pubescens, Betula Pendula** and **Betula Alba** in Finland. The tar is rectified to yield **Birch Tar Oil, Rectified.** During the past few decades, increasing quantities of birch tar have been produced from birch wood, with or without adherent bark. The wood tar is entirely different from the bark tar, and cannot replace the latter in perfumery. Birch wood tar is used in pharmaceutical preparations for its dermatological value.

The various products from the **Birch** tree are described in the following monographs:

Birch Bark Oil.

This essential oil is also known as **Oil of Sweet Birch, Cherry Birch, Southern Birch** or **Black Birch.** The tree grows wild all over the Southeastern United States up to Southern Canada. "Oil of Sweet Birch" is produced by steam distillation of the comminuted bark after it has been macerated (or, more correctly, digested) in lukewarm water for 12 hours. The essential oil is not present as such in the plant material. It is formed by enzymatic hydrolysis of the glycoside gaultherin. This process is similar to that of the formation of bitter almond oil.

It is customary to distil wintergreen leaves (see **Wintergreen Oil**) or even **Teaberry Leaves** (so-called "Indian tea", possibly identical to wintergreen) with the birch bark. This is another example of botanical material from non-related species yielding almost identical essential oils. Strangely enough, the cost of harvesting wintergreen leaves is 5 to 8 times higher than the cost of collecting the birch bark. The oil yield from the wintergreen is somewhat higher than the yield from the bark, but insufficient to make it reasonable to add wintergreen leaves in the distillation.

Birch Bark Oil is colorless or pale yellow, occasionally reddish tinted (from contact with iron). The oil smells so strikingly similar to methyl salicylate that it is hard to justify the existence of the essential oil. The flavor of wintergreen, "teaberry" and birch bark oil was popular with the American Indians, and the early European settlers

used wintergreen as a tea. Accordingly, it is not surprising that this flavor has become one of the most popular and typical American flavors. Its use in old-fashioned "**Root Beer**" beverages, later in all sorts of candies, chewing gum, toothpaste, etc., shows the well-established and lasting popularity of the methyl salicylate type of flavor in the U.S.A. **Birch Bark Oil** used to be one of the "big items" in American essential oil production (annual production was about 200 tons prior to World War I). The oil has almost completely lost its importance by now and it is merely a curiosity. What the trade offers today under the label of "**Oil of Sweet Birch**" may very well be a "touched-up" methyl salicylate from a chemical factory.

Birch Bark Oil can boast one of the highest specific gravities of all essential oils known: 1.19 at 15°C.

Birch Leaf-Bud Oil.

This essential oil is steam distilled from the leaf-buds of **Betula Alba** in Germany, Denmark and Finland. In Finland, the leaf-buds from **Betula Pubescens** are also used. The yield of oil is considerably higher than that from bark cr leaves.

Birch Bud Oil (also called) is a pale yellow or yellow very viscous oil with a pleasant woody-green, balsamic odor. The main constituents are sesquiterpenes, particularly the sesquiterpene alcohol **Betulenol**, accompanied by smaller amounts of the acetates and formates of these alcohols. One disadvantageous characteristic is the content of solid paraffins and naphthalins which causes crystallization and solidification of the oil at low temperature. These solids also decrease the solubility of the oil in alcohol.

Since **Birch Bud Oil** is mainly used in hair tonics, shampoos, etc. with a very low alcohol content, a "rectified" oil or an "absolute" of birch leaf buds is often used. A suitable absolute can be obtained by extraction of the natural oil with 80% alcohol, chilling of the alcoholic solution, filtration and subsequent evaporation of the extract under gentle vacuum.

Birch Bud Oil is, to the author's knowledge, not used as a perfumery raw material. It is used primarily for its potential skin-healing effects. Quite recently, a large German manufacturer of a well-known hair-tonic has used a hydro-alcoholic distilled tincture of birch buds in place of the steam distilled essential oil. This enables the manufacturer to use a very low alcohol percentage in his preparation and thus avoid excessive alcohol taxes.

The annual production of **Birch Bud Oil** is probably less than one metric ton. Adulteration has occurred with cedarwood oil and similar low-cost diluents.

Birch Tar.

For perfumery purposes, only the rectified oil of **Birch Bark Tar** should be considered. The tar is produced from the bark of various birch species by slow destructive distillation. This tar is oily, almost black in color, and not quite homogeneous. Flakes of carbon, oil drops, etc. separate from the liquid. The crude tar is subsequently steam distilled, and yields a rectified birch tar which is sometimes called **Birch Tar Oil, Crude.** For many years, production was concentrated in the countries along the Baltic Sea, but only little birch tar is produced in these countries now. The U.S.S.R., Germany, Finland, and occasionally Sweden produce limited quantities. Unfortunately, the present-day product is often a mixture of wood-tar and bark-tar (see below).

Rectified Birch Tar is a pale yellow to brownish yellow, clear and oily liquid. The odor description, "like Russian leather", is conventional, but somewhat incorrect. Russian leather smells of birch tar because the leather is tanned with the tar products which also preserve this special type of leather. This circle of odor association is similar to the well-known: vanillin smells of chocolate!

The odor of **Birch Tar Oil** is distinctly phenolic, very penetrating and diffusive, obviously reminiscent of tar, charred wood and smoke (all of which have their odor from components of the birch tar oil!) However, the most characteristic feature in the odor pattern of birch tar oil is the sweet-oily undertone which appears distinctly on the smelling blotter when the first empyreumatic notes have faded away. These notes caught the immediate interest of perfumers long ago, and the chemists tried to isolate these particular fractions of the oil.

A number of special "fractions" of rectified **Birch Tar** are available from the raw material suppliers; others are made by the users for their individual purposes. It seems almost certain that the typical sweet, oily and leatherlike notes are due to components in the non-saponifiable part of the rectified birch tar oil. In other words, the most interesting components are the non-phenolic ones. The tar from birch bark contains up to 80% of non-phenolic materials, while the wood tar has very little of these interesting components. Consequently, a sample of birch tar for processing into rectified birch tar oil should be chemically tested for content of non-phenolic components. The olfactory test is equally important, but it is extremely difficult to estimate the value of a birch tar exclusively by the odor of the crude tar. **Rectified Birch Tar Oil** has the additional advantage of being very pale and not discoloring with certain essential oils which would cause discoloration when mixed with phenols (patchouli, vetiver, copaiba balsam, etc.). The oil is easily soluble in alcohol, and does not impart an acid reaction to the perfume in which it is used. To the perfumer, this "heart" fraction of the birch tar oil is the true and highly appreciated sweet and powerful "leather" odor for fougères, chypres, "men's fragrances", after-shave lotions, modern fantasy bases, etc.

The steam distilled birch tar can be alkaliwashed free of phenols, and subsequently vacuum distilled to produce a pale straw-colored oil of delightful "cuir" note and tremendous diffusive power. The crude tar is used in pharmaceutical preparations, e.g. ointments, lotions, etc. for eczema and other dermatological diseases. **Birch Tar** is frequently adulterated with birch wood tar, beech tar (black and highly phenolic), pine tar (clear dark chocolate brown), juniper tar **(Cade Oil)** or even coal tar (naphthalenic odor). See also **Leather.**

Blackcurrant.

Various flavor materials are produced from the buds of the shrub, **Ribes Nigrum,** the black currant bush.

A **Black Currant Tincture** is prepared by maceration. The tincture is not a commercial article, and the flavor house will usually have to collect the flower-buds from its own plantations for this purpose. The tincture is used in the flavoring of certain types of liqueurs.

Black Currant Absolute is produced by extraction of the buds with benzene or petroleum ether. The extract is a concrete which is subsequently re-extracted with alcohol to yield an absolute. The absolute is a viscous liquid of dark green color and powerful spicy-woody odor. There is a slightly phenolic undertone and the tenacity is not outstanding. Quantitatively, the main constituents are monoterpenes and sesquiterpenes. These are not responsible for the characteristic odor of the absolute. **Black Currant Absolute** is prepared in France, occasionally in Holland.

Black Currant Oil, also known as **Niribine Oil** (by rearranging the latin name of the plant), is steam distilled from the flower-buds of the above shrub. **Ribes Nigrum** is cultivated in Northern Europe, particularly in France, Holland, Belgium, England, Denmark, Germany, and the Baltic States. The latter countries were once big producers of berries. **Black Currant Oil** is produced in Holland and France. The oil is almost colorless, mobile and of a distinctly terpenic odor, reminiscent of the terpenes in nutmeg, neroli, basil, or marjoram oils. Its high price and poor tenacity make its application rather limited, and it is doubtful whether this oil will ever attain any importance in perfumery or flavor work.

Bois de Rose Oil.

Ranking only a few years ago among the 15 "biggest" essential oils in the world, **Bois de Rose Oil** to-day is fighting for survival in strong competition with other essential oils, and particularly with synthetic **Linalool**.

Bois de Rose Oil is steam distilled, occasionally water-distilled, from the chipped wood of **Aniba Rosaeodora** and possibly other species of the genus Burseraceae belonging to the laurel family. The tree is a tropical, medium-sized, wild-growing evergreen from the Amazon basin. The wood is collected in Brazil, Peru and in the French Guiana ("**Cayenne Rosewood**"). In perfumery, the term **Rosewood** means only **Bois de Rose** of the above kind. The trade uses the term **Rosewood** for a multitude of lumberwoods, etc., e.g.:

Acacia Excelsa = Australian Rosewood

Amyris Balsamifera = West Indian Rosewood

Cordia Gerascanthus = Dominican Rosewood (fragrant)

Dalbergia Latifolia = East Indian Rosewood

Dicypellium Caryophyllatum = Brazilian Rosewood (fragrant)

Myrospermum Erythroxylon = Japanese Rosewood (see Oleo Vermelho)

Physocalumma Scaberrimum = Brazilian Rosewood (odorless)

Pterocarpus Erinaceus = African Rosewood

Thespesia Populnea = Polynesian Rosewood (fragrant; grows in Central Africa and South Pacific islands).

(See also the monograph on **Louro Brasileiro** and **Louro Nhamuy**, the latter being responsible for a high content of monoterpenes in **Bois de Rose Oil** which has been distilled from wood of "true" rosewood trees, more or less contaminated with the wood of the **Louro Nhamuy** tree). Distillation of bois de rose oil is carried out in more or less modern stills in the above three countries. During the past few decades, production has been rationalized considerably, resulting in better yields, higher quality of oil and lower prices. In post-war years, the Brazilian production has reached 500 to 600 metric tons of oil annually. Peru has produced increasing amounts of bois de rose oil since 1957. These facts have affected the market price significantly. Finally, the large-scale production of synthetic **Linalool** in the United States has resulted in a further drop in the price of **Bois de Rose Oil**.

The oil is used mainly as a starting material for the isolation of natural **Linalool**, of which the oil contains over 70%. The linalool in turn is converted into linalyl esters for many uses in perfumery and flavor work. Linalyl acetate is sometimes produced by direct acetylation of bois de rose oil, and subsequent fractionated distillation of the neutralized reaction mixture. In the years of scarcity of bois de rose oil (1940 to 1950), other essential oils were utilized as starting materials for the isolation of linalool or linalylacetate: Japanese **Ho Wood Oil**, **Ho Leaf Oil**, **Lavandin Oil**, **Spike Lavender Oil**, and even **Petitgrain Oil** from Paraguay was used for isolation of linalyl acetate.

Beyond any doubt, **Ho Leaf Oil** (see this monograph) is the major competitor of **Bois de Rose Oil**. The ho leaf oil is produced on a comparatively large scale in Japan. The oil contains more linalool (when the oil is rectified from the source), and its terpenes have a less harsh or penetrating odor. All these facts have contributed to the situation of unstable economy which presently rules in the producing areas in Brazil and Peru.

Bois de Rose Oil is a colorless or pale yellow liquid of a refreshing, sweet-woody, somewhat floral-spicy odor. The topnote varies considerably with the origin and quality of the oil. It is usually somewhat camphoraceous-peppery, reminiscent of cineole and nutmeg terpenes. It is worthwhile remembering that **Bois de Rose Oil** can dissolve considerable amounts of water (up to several percent). Some water will "fall out" of the oil during shipment, particularly if the drums are exposed to cold temperatures. The water will usually remain undissolved thereafter. **Bois de Rose Oil** is also used as such (cleaned and free from water) in soap perfumes where the strong topnotes can be utilized to advantage. The isolated **Linalool** finds very extensive use in perfumery, e. g. of the floral types: lilac, muguet, neroli, sweet pea, etc.

In respect to odor, the **Cayenne Rosewood Oil** is superior to the Brazilian and the Peruvian. Production in Cayenne has fallen below 10 metric tons per year, and the oil has little influence upon the **Bois de Rose** market. The Cayenne oil is produced mainly upon demand from a few French houses. The odor of the oil is mild, floral-woody, almost like a rectified Brazilian oil.

(See also **Linaloe Wood Oil** and **Linaloe Seed Oil** (Mexico and India).

Bois de Rose Oil is occasionally adulterated, although the tremendous drop in its price has made it difficult to find a suitable "cutting" material. Terpineol, myrcene and various fractions of pine oil have been used. More frequently, the **Bois de Rose Oil** has been contaminated with oil from admixed wood of **Louro Nhamuy**, a related and nearby growing tree (see the monograph on **Louro Nhamuy**).

Considering the development in the production of **Bois de Rose Oils** and synthetic **Linalool**, described above, it is conceivable that the essential oil will slowly lose much of its importance in perfumery, and perhaps will find its place among the fairly low-cost soap perfumery raw materials. In this respect, the essential oil remains superior to the synthetic linalool.

Boldo Leaf Oil.

The small tree, **Peumus Boldus**, grows wild in Chile, South America. Its leaves are collected for pharmaceutical purposes, and an essential oil is steam distilled from them. The oil does not seem to have found a place in perfumery. The leaves are commercially available from the larger international suppliers of botanical drugs, and the essential oil is thus also distilled in Europe and the

United States. However, the oil from dry (exported) leaves is slightly different from the oil distilled from fresh leaves on the place of origin.

Boldo Leaf Oil is yellow and has a strong, spicy-hydrocarbon-like odor, somewhat reminiscent of American wormseed oil. The oil has powerful therapeutic effects, and it can be considered harmful to the human organism even when used in very small doses.

Boldo Leaf Oil may completely disappear from the perfumer's or the flavorist's shelf (if it ever has been there) since it does not present very interesting or unique notes.

Boronia Absolute.

Boronia Absolute is a unique perfume and flavor material in more than one respect. First of all, it is one of the very few flower absolutes which is not processed into a concrète in the immediate vicinity of the growing areas of the plant. Furthermore, it is one of the few, if not the only, flower absolute which contains **Ionones**. Finally, Boronia absolute is an excellent flavor material in addition to being highly appreciated in perfumery.

Boronia Absolute is produced by petroleum ether extraction of the flowers of **Boronia Megastigma** which grows wild in abundance all along the coasts and swamplands of western and southwestern Australia. Boronia is a small shrub or bushy plant, 4 to 6 feet high. It is related to the citrus tree.

The flowers are collected and immersed in drums with petroleum ether. The filled drums are shipped by truck or train to the extraction station. In 1958, there were over 500 flower-collecting stations in western Australia. There are only a few extraction factories. The most important of these is located in Perth on the southwest coast.

The extraction process is completed in the factory. The extract is an unctuous, dark green concrète of boronia in a yield of less than 1% of the weight of the flowers. An absolute is produced by alcohol washing of the concrète. The yield is 55 to 65% of the weight of the concrète. Boronia concrète is not a commercial article, but the absolute is usually produced by the manufacturer who performs the extraction of concrète from the flowers.

Boronia Absolute is one of the few natural perfume materials which contain **Ionone** (mainly beta ionone, only a little alpha ionone). Although these ketones are present in fairly large amounts, they are not immediately detectable in the odor of boronia absolute. The odor of the dark green and somewhat viscous absolute is fresh, fruity-green, sweet tea-like, slightly spicy-herbaceous (reminiscent of cinnamon and tobacco leaf). The main body notes display a tremendously rich and tenacious floral undertone of warm, woody-sweet character.

The great distance between the producing area and the consumers is partly responsible for the unfortunate and regrettable fact that **Boronia Absolute** appears on the market in widely different qualities, some of which do not exactly encourage the perfumer to use boronia in his creations. The more important consumers of true boronia absolute will prefer to deal directly with the producer or his appointed agents.

Boronia Absolute is used in high class floral perfumes and bases, e.g. violet, mimosa, cassie, honeysuckle, sweet pea, etc., and it blends well with sage clary, bergamot, costus, sandalwood, helichrysum, amylcinnamic aldehyde, linalool, salicylates, etc. However, the high cost (about the same as for jasmin absolute from concrète) and the limited production (less than one metric ton per year) make boronia absolute an item that many perfumers entirely avoid using, or else reach for only with reluctance and scepticism.

Boronia Absolute is used in flavor work where it imparts a unique body and natural richness to many fruit essences, e.g. raspberry, strawberry, plum, peach (it blends excellently with undecanolide and nonanolide). A special application is typified by the artificial reproduction of blackcurrant flavor, a very difficult problem for the flavorist. The suggested use level is 0.40 to 0.60 mg%, and the **Minimum Perceptible** is about 0.01 to 0.03 mg%. Boronia absolute is not infrequently adulterated, "cut" or "stretched" with e.g. ionones, eugenol, methyleugenol, sesquiterpene fractions from ylang-ylang oil, benzylsalicylate, etc.

Broom Absolute.

The perfumer's "absolue de genêt", or **Broom Absolute,** is extracted from the so-called Spanish broom, **Spartium Junceum.** The small decorative shrub grows wild (and is also cultivated) in the south of France, Spain, and Italy. Production of broom absolute from petroleum ether concrète is almost exclusively carried out in the Grasse area in France. Benzene yields a much darker concrète. The original "genêt" is related to the above shrub, and it grows wild all over Europe and Western Asia, and is found even as far north as Scandinavia and Scotland. Its botanical name is **Genista Tinctoria,** also known as **Cytisus Scoparius,** the Irish or Scotch broom.

Broom Concrète is a solid, dark brown, unctuous mass of a sweet honey-rose-like, somewhat woody and haylike odor. The concrète yields about 35 to 50% of alcohol-soluble absolute.

Broom Absolute is dark brown, semi-solid or viscous liquid, with an intensely sweet, floral-haylike fragrance. The deep herbaceous-coumarinic background has great tenacity. The honey-rose notes are particularly useful in certain types of rose bases, tuberose, cassie, mimosa, violet, honeysuckle, etc. It blends excellently with ionones, vetiver, castoreum, etc. in "tabac" notes, and it is generally useful in modern aldehydic perfume types, green notes, etc.

Little is known about the constituents of **Broom Absolute.** The annual production can be estimated at 50 to about 150 kilos.

Broom Absolute is used in flavors of the deep-sweet "preserve" type, e.g. plum, fig, raisin, date, etc. where it lends a rich body and naturalness. It is one of the most generally applicable of all the floral absolutes since trace amounts will yield perceptible improvement without being noticeable as a "perfumey" note. Suggested use level is 0.40 to 0.70 mg%, and the **Minimum Perceptible** is about 0.07 to 0.10 mg%.

Bruyère.

A perfume material is extracted from the roots of various species of heather shrubs (Ericaceae), and the extract is sold under the name of **Bruyère Absolute** (absolu de bruyère). A similar product is obtained by steam distillation of the comminuted roots. The French term, "bruyère", actually refers to all kinds of shrubs growing on barren, arid, uncultivated plains. However, certain species have distinguished themselves by their ability to grow to a considerable size and substantial age.

Erica Arborea grows all over the Mediterranean countries, and it is particularly common in Algeria, Corsica, and in the Canary Islands. This plant may grow to an age of several hundred years and a height of 60 feet (18 metres). The roots of such old species are collected for the purpose of carving shag tobacco pipes ("Briar" wood). The unusually high content of ashes in the wood prevents it from "burning through" in a pipe.

Waste wood from the pipe carving factories and workshops used to be discarded, but it is now occasionally used for the production of **Bruyère Absolute**. This absolute is a greenish-yellow to pale yellow or brownish-yellow, solid but soft mass, resembling guaiacwood or araucaria oils. The odor of bruyère absolute is very mild, woody-green and pleasant-balsamic, slightly spicy-aromatic. In rose perfumes, chypre bases, crêpe de Chine, oriental-woody bases, etc., bruyère absolute lends a delightful undertone and excellent fixative effect. It blends well with olibanum, ionones, sage clary, oakmoss, labdanum absolutes, etc.

Bruyère Absolute is produced by a few French houses on a very limited scale. The comparatively low cost of this material can do nothing to expand the application or increase the popularity of this rare perfume material.

Buchu Leaf Oil.

This essential oil is steam distilled from the dried leaves of **Barosma Betulina,** a herb which grows wild and abundantly in South Africa. Tinctures, oleoresins and other extracts are produced for pharmaceutical purposes. Only a small fraction of the total amount of harvested buchu leaves are used for distillation of essential oil. Distillation takes place almost exclusively in Holland, England and the United States of America, rarely in the growing areas.

Buchu Leaf Oil is a yellow to brownish-yellow liquid, oily or somewhat viscous, depending upon the age of the oil and the dryness of the plant material prior to distillation. The odor is very peculiar: strong, bitter-sweet, minty-camphoraceous, rootlike, penetrating and somewhat medicinal, reminiscent of cough preparations. One of the main constituents of the oil is **Diosphenol,** a terpenoid phenol. It is responsible for the antiseptic effect of **Buchu Leaf Oil.** A significant percentage of menthone in the oil is probably the cause of the minty odor and somewhat cool flavor of the oil.

Buchu leaf oil is occasionally used in chypre bases, certain types of colognes, etc. for its power, diffusion, and freshness. In flavors, it may find some application for gooseberry and other "tart" fruit essences. On account of its very penetrating odor-flavor, this oil will always be limited to being a "low-percentage-item" in the formula. It serves no purpose to mention a use-level since the flavor of this oil changes significantly on dilution. Although quantities of up to 1000 kilos of **Buchu Leaf Oil** have been available at times, its production fluctuates and is presently decreasing. Interest in the essential oil is failing, and only limited quantities of leaves are available since the plant is not cultivated on any significant scale. **Buchu Leaf Oil** ranks among the more expensive essential oils. During 1959, its price was about 2 to 4 times that of geranium oil.

C

Cabreuva Oil.

The wood of various species of wild growing **Myrocarpus** trees in Brazil, Paraguay and Argentina is highly appreciated as an ornamental lumber and furniture wood, although it is extremely hard to cut or saw. The wood is known as **Cabureicica** or **Cabreuva** wood; it is extremely resistant to moisture and mold growth.

Since the tree is related to the trees which yield **Peru Balsam** and **Copaiba Balsam** it is not surprising, that also the **Myrocarpus** yields a "balsam" when the trunk is deliberately damaged. This kind of "balsam" formation is known as a pathological one in contrast to the "voluntary" or physiological products (copaiba or turpentine).

However, the essential oil of **Cabreuva** is now produced by distillation of waste wood from the lumbermills. Chippings and sawdust of **Myrocarpus Fastigiatus** are steam distilled in Brazil. They yield a pale yellow, somewhat viscous essential oil of sweet-woody, very delicate and slightly floral odor. Its tenacity is one of its greatest virtues. Certain lots of **Cabreuva Oil** may display dry topnotes similar to those found in cubeb oil or in the sesquiterpenes from clove leaf oil. Although very delicate and apparently faint, the odor of **Cabreuva Oil** is often under-estimated in its effect of freshness and suave-floral notes. In rose, lily-of-the-valley, cassie, ambre and in woody-oriental perfumes, **Cabreuva Oil** lends tenacity and distinct notes of "precious wood" with a background of slightly green, dry floralness, a combination rarely found in synthetic perfume materials.

The oil is produced by a few Brazilian distillers only, and in very modest quantities. It served for some time as a starting material for the isolation of the sesquiterpene alcohol, **Nerolidol,** the main constituent of cabreuva oil. This sesquiterpene alcohol is now produced synthetically at a reasonable cost. Adulteration or contamination of **Cabreuva Oil** with **Oleo Vermelho** (see this monograph) is possible. See also monograph on **Melaleuca Viridiflora,** variety "A".

Cabreuva oil, as such, has found very little use in perfumery in spite of the above mentioned excellent effects of the oil.

Cade Oil.

Strictly speaking, **Cade Oil** is identical to **Juniper Tar** (also called juniper tar oil), obtained by destructive distillation of the wood from **Juniperus Oxycedrus,** a shrub related to the common juniper. Three other oils are obtained from this shrub: 1) From the fruits ("berries"), 2) from the twigs and leaves (needles), 3) from the wood—all by steam distillation. None of these three oils have obtained any interest from the perfumery or flavor industry (see **Juniper Wood Oil**).

The **Cade Oil,** used in perfumery is usually a rectified oil, obtained by rectification (steam distillation or vacuum distillation) of the crude juniper tar oil. The latter consists of the upper layer of the entire mass of tar which is obtained by destructive distillation of the wood.

The juniperus oxycedrus is quite common all over the Mediterranean countries, particularly in Spain and North Africa. Production of **Cade Oil** is concentrated in Spain, France, and Yugoslavia. The annual output is quite substantial: 125 to 200 metric tons, most of which is used in veterinary medicine and for the treatment of various human skin diseases.

Rectified Cade Oil is a clear, orange-brown to dark brown, oily liquid with an intense "tar-like", smoky-phenolic odor. Its use in perfumery is limited to situations where a smoky-leathery, woody-phenolic, dry and warm note is called for: forest notes, leather-bases, fougères, pine for "men's fragrances", etc., and in the imitation of certain essential oils, oakmoss, etc.

Cade oil has certain disinfectant properties for which it can be utilized in soap perfumes, for example combined with thyme, origanum, clove and similar phenolic oils, if the discoloration creates no serious problem, and with cassia oil, melaleuca alternifolia, ocotea pretiosa, etc. **Cade Oil** finds occasionally use in the flavoring of meat and seafood to which it imparts the "smoke"-note previous obtained in a regular smokehouse.

Cajuput Oil.

Cajuput oil or cajeput oil is steam distilled from the fresh leaves and twigs of a medium-sized tree, **Melaleuca Minor** and possibly other species of **Melaleuca.** The botanical source was earlier known as **Melaleuca Leucadendron.** The tree was planted many years ago in Florida, U.S.A. and grows now wild in abundance in that state. It is locally known as **"Punk Tree".** No essential oil is produced from the American cajuput trees.

The cajuput tree is occasionally named "tea-tree" or "ti-tree" on the islands between Australia and Malaya, the Indonesian archipelago, in the Philippines, etc. where the tree grows abundantly. In Malaya and in the Philippines, the name "kaju-puti" means "white wood", referring to the color of the lumber from this tree.

The essential oil is distilled from material collected from wild-growing trees in the Moluccas in the eastern part of Indonesia. A large number of primitive, native stills produce between 75 and 200 metric tons per year of cajuput oil. Only a small fraction of this production reaches Europe and the U.S.A. Local consumption is quite substantial since great medicinal effects are attributed to the oil among the Eastern people.

Cajuput Oil is a colorless, pale yellow, greenish or turquoise-colored, mobile liquid of powerful, fresh, eucalyptuslike, camphoraceous odor and a burning-aromatic taste. Characteristic are the almost fruity-sweet body notes and the soft tones in the dryout. The green color is not an indication that the oil is genuine. This was earlier assumed, and many price lists emphasized that the green color was synonymous with genuineness.

Apart from its use as a general household remedy for colds, throat diseases, pains, headaches, etc. in the Far East, the **Cajuput Oil** has found very little use in Europe and America. Its main constituents are identical to those of the pharmaceutical eucalyptus oils; thus, cajuput oil does not present any advantages over eucalyptus, save for the slightly milder-sweeter odor and flavor. In throat lozenges, gargles, etc., where the oil is often used in combination with other flavoring materials, it could easily be replaced by the cheaper eucalyptus oil or a combination of eucalyptus oil (pharmaceutical) with small amounts of terpinyl acetate, terpinyl propionate and higher esters of terpineol.

See also **Niaouli Oil.**

Calamintha Oil.

An essential oil is steam distilled from the wild growing herb **Calamintha Clinopodium**, also known as **Calamintha Nepeta**. The oil is occasionally offered under the name of **"French Marjoram Oil"** or **Wild Basil Oil.** However, this oil has little or no importance beyond the above mentioned. It cannot be considered as a replacement for sweet marjoram oil in general. See monographs on **Marjoram Sweet** and **Marjoram Wild.**

Numerous species of nepeta and similar Labiatae grow wild in the Mediterranean countries. The **Nepeta Cataria** is harvested for the production of essential oil in Yugoslavia. The oil is obtained by steam distillation of the flowering tops of the plant. The same plant has been introduced in the northern United States where the oil is distilled from fresh plant material for the purpose of preparing a wildcat lure. The oil is effective as an attractant for cats, pumas (American mountain lions) and other wild beasts. This essential oil is known as **Catnip Oil.** A lactone which is present at 3 to 5% in the oil, is known to be the active cat-attractant in the **Catnip Oil.** The oil contains furthermore between 80 and 90% of odorless substances.

American catnip oil has found no use in perfumery. Its odor is almost pungent, intensely herbaceous, somewhat woody, but it also displays a rich, sweet-spicy undertone.

The European (mainly Yugoslavian) **Nepeta Oil**, often called **Calamintha Oil,** may be distilled from a different species. Its odor seems to reveal a great variety of components, such as citral, nerol, citronellol, limonene, etc., often a typical "fresh" odor. Certain oils from Poland contain substantial amounts of citral. **Calamintha Oil** is mainly used in the various countries of origin and it has attained little importance elsewhere.

Calamus Oil.

Calamus Oil is steam distilled from the rhizomes (underground stems) of the wild growing or cultivated **Acorus Calamus,** a perennial plant which is known in the U.S.A. as **"Sweet Flag"** or **"Sweet Root", "Sweet Myrtle", "Sweet Cinnamon", "Sweet Cane",** etc. The very decorative plant grows wild all over the swampy areas of the temperate zones in Europe, Asia, and America, along brooks, rivers, lakes, etc. The rhizomes can be dried without a substantial loss of essential oil provided they are kept unpeeled. Distillation may thus take place far away from the origin of the rhizomes.

The principal producers of calamus rhizomes are: Hungary, Poland, Yugoslavia, Bulgaria, USSR, India, Holland, U.S.A. and Japan. Japanese rhizomes produce an essential oil with a more medicinal odor, and these rhizomes are less popular for the production of flavor and perfume oils.

Polish and Yugoslavian oils are often pale colored and they display a delightfully sweet and uniform, lasting odor. **Calamus Oil** is generally a pale yellow to pale brown, viscous liquid of a warm, woody-spicy and pleasant odor with increasingly sweet afternotes and great tenacity. Poorer oils show more or less pronounced camphoraceous or cineolic notes. The odor of good oils bears some resemblance to the odor of dried milk or sweet leather, slightly creamy-nutty. Typical laymen-expressions for the odor of calamus oil at the first experience with this oil are: "milk-truck odor" or "shoe-repair shop odor", etc. These expressions, whether the perfumer agrees or not, can often be more helpful in an odor description than any of the usual professional phrases.

The flavor of **Calamus Oil** is equally warm-spicy, yet slightly bitter with a slowly growing, pungent aftertaste. The suggested use-level is 0.10 to 2.00 mg%. The **Minimum Perceptible** is 0.04 to 0.10 mg %. Calamus oil is usually a minor component in flavor or perfume compositions.

The main constituent of **Calamus Oil** is a phenolether, **Asarone,** which is odorless and tasteless. As we could expect, a "de-asaronized" calamus oil has been prepared experimentally. The author has no personal experience with this concentrated oil.

Calamus oil is occasionally adulterated with amyris oil, copaiba balsam, d-limonene, cedarwood fractions, sesquiterpene fractions from various essential oils, etc. However, the greatest variations in the quality of calamus oil are often due to difference in the botanical starting material. Dried roots produce a distinctly different type of oil, but the essential oil from fresh roots is not nearly as common. From a perfumery point of view, the author would definitely prefer the oils from fresh roots, particularly those of Polish or Yugoslavian origin. They can not substitute oils from dried roots in a perfume or flavor formula, but they offer a much wider field of application to the perfumer and the flavorist.

Calamus Oil is useful in perfumes of the woody-oriental type, in leather-bases, ambres, etc. It blends excellently with cananga, cinnamon, costus, labdanum, olibanum, patchouli, ionones, and methylionones, cis-para-tertiary butylcyclohexanyl acetate, nitromusks, grisambrol, and cedarwood derivatives, etc. In flavors, the oil finds some application with cardamom, angelica, ginger, etc. in spice blends and flavors for alcoholic beverages.

The annual production of Calamus Oil is adjustable to demands. It is estimated that more than one metric ton is produced annually in India. The European production may be slightly smaller at the present time. The botanical material is abundantly available.

Camellia.

Among the many known species of Camellia only a few are sufficiently fragrant as to obtain any interest in perfumery. One of these is Camellia Sasanqua which grows in China and Japan. It is mainly cultivated for its fragrant flowers as a decorative garden shrub. Extraction of the flowers with volatile solvents has been undertaken in China during the 1950's. The extraction products are not commercially available although samples have reached some parts of the outside world. The author has no personal experience with the use of Camellia flower extracts.

A fatty ("fixed") oil is produced from the seeds of the above camellia species and from the related Camellia Drupifera. This oil has a faint odor, but it is not an essential oil and it has no application in perfumery. The leaves of the two species of camelia are occasionally used to be mixed with tea on account of their pleasant fragrance. The Camellia shrub belongs to the same family as Thea Sinensis, the tea shrub (also known as Camellia Sinensis).

Camphor Oil.

The group of Camphor Oils ranges high in quantity produced among the "upper ten" of all the essential oils in the world, but their use in perfumes and flavors is limited.

Among the many types of so-called Camphor Oils, only the most important ones should be mentioned in this work:

A crude essential oil is produced by steam distillation of the wood from a number of varieties of the camphor tree, Cinnamomum Camphora. Distillation takes place locally, often in primitive apparatus.

In Japan and Formosa, the individual varieties of the above tree yield either "True" Camphor Oil or Ho Oil (see monographs).

In China, the most common variety of Cinnamomum Camphora will yield an essential oil which consists mainly of cineole, and which accordingly is rectified and sold as "eucalyptus oil" at a price that makes competition from Australia, Africa, and Spain hopeless. Terpineol is a by-product of the oil from this Chinese camphor tree, and Chinese (isolated) terpineol is now appearing on the world market in increasing quantities (see Apopin Oil).

In the following monograph, only true camphor oil will be described. (Ho Oil is described under its proper name, and the cineole-terpineol type of Chinese camphor tree oil is mentioned under Eucalyptus Oil, "false", or Chinese).

The three varieties of Camphor Oils could be distinguished as follows:

> Formosan Camphor Oils = camphor-linalool type and camphor-safrole type.
> Japanese Camphor Oil = camphor-safrole type.
> Chinese Camphor Oil = cineole-terpineol-camphor type (see Apopin Oil).

In Formosa, the camphor-safrole type as well as the camphor-linalool type are produced, the former being the largest in quantity.

Camphor Oil, "True":

An essential oil is produced by steam distillation from the wood, rootstumps, and branches of the variety of Cinnamomum Camphora known as Hon-Sho, growing in Formosa and Japan.

Along with the crude oil comes a solid, partly crystalline mass of crude Camphor. The oil is separated from the crude camphor by filterpressing. This yields the **Crude Camphor Oil.** The crude oil is subsequently rectified under vacuum, and yields another 50% of crude camphor. The remaining 50% of the filterpressed crude camphor oil is now free of camphor. It contains light terpenes, cineole, safrole, terpineol, sesquiterpenes and sesquiterpene alcohols. These materials are separated in various fractions known as:

> **White Camphor Oil,** the light fraction, contains **Cineole** and monoterpenes;
>
> **Brown Camphor Oil,** the medium-heavy fraction which contains up to 80% **Safrole,** and some terpineol;
>
> **Blue Camphor Oil,** the heavy fraction which contains sesquiterpenes, etc. of minor interest in perfumery.

The white and the brown camphor oils both amount to about 20% of the crude total distillate from the wood, or each about 40% of the filterpressed, camphor-free oil.

The three oils will be discussed individually in the following monographs. Annual world production (Japan and Formosa) of crude (liquid) camphor oil is estimated at 5000 metric tons or even more (1959).

Camphor Oil, Blue.

This is the heaviest (=highest boiling) fraction, distilled in vacuum from the crude camphor oil from which the camphor has been removed. (See monographs on **Camphor Oil White, Camphor Oil Brown,** and **Camphor Oil "True").**

Only a small part of the annually produced 50 tons (approx.) of this fraction is exported. The oil has little importance in perfumery, although it may serve locally for the perfuming of low-cost soaps, detergents, etc.

Blue Camphor Oil is a viscous, dark bluish-green or bluish-brown liquid. It consists mainly of sesquiterpenes and sesquiterpene alcohols of weak odor, but with fair masking effect and good fixative value. It finds some use as a drying solvent in porcelain paints. **Blue Camphor Oil** is produced in Formosa and Japan only.

Camphor Oil, Brown.

This is the medium-heavy fraction from the vacuum-distillation of the camphor-free oil. (See **Camphor Oil, White).**

The **Brown Camphor Oil** amounts to 6 or 7%

of the total oil, or 20 to 22% of the de-camphorized oil.

Brown camphor oil is produced almost entirely in Formosa and Japan from the **Hon-Sho** type of **Cinnamomum Camphora,** the camphor tree.

This fraction is the most interesting from a perfumer's point of view. Its main constituent is safrole, and the redistilled brown camphor oil can be used directly in soap perfumes for its magnificent masking effect. The safrole can be isolated from the oil and it then serves as a starting material for the production of heliotropine, vanillin, and other perfume materials. Terpineol is separated during the safrole-isolation, and serves as is, or it may be transformed into terpinyl esters.

An artificial sassafras oil, **"Oil Camphor Sassafrassy",** is also produced from the brown camphor oil by rectification and adjusting of the safrole content, terpenes, etc. The Formosan artificial sassafras oil was the most important replacement for North American (true) sassafras oil until the appearance of the Brazilian **Ocotea Pretiosa Oil** (see this monograph).

Brown Camphor Oil is produced in quantities exceeding 1000 metric tons per year.

Camphor Oil, White.

This oil is produced by fractional distillation of the camphor-free oil, filterpressed from the crude camphor oil. The latter is a natural oil, steam distilled from the wood of the **Hon-Sho** camphor tree in Formosa and Japan. The white camphor oil fraction amounts to about 6% of the total oil, or 20% of the camphor-free ("de-camphorized") oil.

White Camphor Oil is hardly used as such in perfumes, but it serves as a starting material for the isolation and production of a great number of perfumery chemicals: cineole, pinene, terpineol, para-cymene, menthol, thymol, etc.

The oil itself is used as a solvent in the paint and lacquer industry, and certain synthetic perfumery chemicals are produced locally from this oil. Fractions of white camphor oil find application in the compounding of artificial essential oils (eucalyptus, thyme, rosemary, Spanish sage, lavandin, etc.) as well as for the perfuming of detergents and low-cost household products, technical odor masking, industrial products, disinfectants, insecticides, etc. A less decent application of white camphor oil is the one as an adulterant in the above mentioned essential oils.

The annual world production (Japan and Formosa) of this fraction of camphor oil runs into nearly 1000 tons. The true figure may be still higher since the major part of the oil is used locally in the chemical industry.

Canada Balsam.

Canada Balsam is a physiological product exuded from the spruce, **Abies Balsamea**, which grows extensively in Canada and the northern and northwestern U.S.A. According to our definitions (see Part One of this book), Canada balsam is a **Turpentine**, a special type of **Oleoresin**. It consists of a monoterpene-type of essential oil and a resin; it is not a true balsam.

The hemlock spruce **(Tsuga Canadensis)** which grows all over the northern and midwestern U.S.A. also yields an exudation, sold under the name of **"Canada Balsam"**.

Canada balsam is a very viscous, non-pourable (except when very fresh), honeylike and crystal-clear mass of pale yellow color, occasionally with a greenish tint. Its odor is fresh, sweet-balsamic with an almost fruity-floral topnote reminiscent of the odor of iso-propyl benzoate, but fresher, at times lemon-like rather than turpentine-like. The dryout bears some resemblance to the dryout notes of Atlas cedarwood oil. On exposure to air, **Canada Balsam** slowly solidifies to a glass-like, brittle, transparent lacquer. This ability of Canada balsam is exploited in microscopy and in optical instruments where the "balsam" is used to glue lenses into systems, and to glue coverglasses to objectglasses. **Canada Balsam** contains more than 20% essential oil. The balance is odorless resin. The essential oil consists almost entirely of mono-terpenes and has little perfumery value.

Canada balsam is used to a limited extent as a fixative in finer pine needle fragrances to which it also lends a certain freshness. Its high price and limited availability prevents extensive use of this material.

The so-called **"Venetian Turpentine"** is used in Europe in place of Canada balsam in low-cost perfumes. Venetian turpentine is derived from a larch tree which grows in central and southern Europe—see: **Larch Turpentine**.

See also **Oregon Balsam**.

Cananga Oil.

The true **Cananga Oil** of today is the total essential oil, water-distilled from the flowers of **Cananga Odorata** (forma macrophylla) in the northern and western parts of Java (Indonesia). There are several qualities of **Java Cananga Oil**, but they are all distilled by the so-called direct-fire method (flowers in water, fire under the pot, and no heating jacket). This method is used for a great part of the ylang-ylang oil production in Nossi-Bé and in the Comoro Islands, but not in Réunion (see **Ylang-Ylang Oil**).

Although cananga oil is essentially a "complete oil", the yield obtained in Java is considerably poorer than the yields of ylang-ylang oil (same tree) in the Comores, Nossi-Bé, etc. This is due to a very primitive distillation, and to poorly selected flower material; it is also partly due to the fact that the cananga flowers are crushed when packed in the still, while ylang-ylang flowers are not. The flower is extremely delicate, and easily loses its fragrance when damaged. Since World War II, production of cananga oil in Java has increased rapidly, while production in the Philippines (earlier home of the ylang-ylang tree) is negligible. The annual world production of **Cananga Oil** is about 20 metric tons (1959) which is almost as high as the pre-war figure.

Java cananga oil is a yellow to orange-yellow or slightly greenish-yellow, somewhat viscous liquid of sweet-floral, balsamic and tenacious odor. The initial notes are woody-leathery with a fresh-floral undertone, a characteristic combination. The odor type is much "heavier" than that of ylang-ylang and it is also more tenacious than the first and second grades of that oil.

Cananga oil is useful in soap perfumery and for the popular "leathery" notes in men's fragrances where it combines well with castoreum, calamus, birch tar oil rectified, cyclamal, creosol, copaiba oil, isobutyl cinnamate, isoeugenol, labdanum products, guaiacwood oil, nerol, para-cresyl salicylate, oakmoss products, etc. and with fougère bases, violet bases, etc. The superior stability and tenacity of the odor of cananga oil makes this material interesting for soap perfumes where ylang-ylang oil is of comparatively little value.

The fact that far more cananga oil is available than the 10 to 20 tons annually produced indicates that some kind of large-scale adulteration takes place. The most obvious one is most likely a "false denomination of merchandise", rather than plain adulteration. A mixture of high-boiling fractions ("tails") from the distillation of ylang-

ylang oil in the Nossi-Bé—Comoro area will inevitably end up under the label of **Cananga Oil —Java**! The principal difference lies in the fact that canara oil is truly a complete oil, not a fraction of an oil. This, of course, leads certain suppliers to perform a number of manipulations with the ylang-ylang fractions in order to introduce the "missing notes", e.g. by adding synthetic perfume materials, perfume compounds, terpenes, fractions of other essential oils, etc. Very crude adulteration may take place locally (in Indonesia), but this has become rare. In most cases, these adulterations are easily detectable by olfactory analysis.

A contamination may occur locally when flowers of **Anona Suaveolens** are admixed to the true cananga flowers prior to distillation.

See also **Artabotrys Odoratissimus**.

Canella.

Apart from the two "big" **Cinnamon** types (Ceylon and cassia), several others are known. The so-called **Saigon-Cinnamon** comes from the Indo-chinese tree **Cinnamomum Loureirii** while the **Padang-Cinnamon** comes from the tree **Cassia Burmannii** in India and Indonesia. The bark of a small tree, **Canella Alba**, from the West Indies is occasionally marketed under the name of **White Cinnamon**. The tree is also cultivated in the Union of South Africa where it is sometimes called **"Wild Cinnamon"**. The tree **Canella Alba** was formerly known as **Canella Winterana**.

The dried bark of this small tree is exported and used in spice blends. However, the greater part of the production is consumed in local household. An essential oil is very rarely distilled from this bark. It is generally believed that essential oils under the name of **Canella Alba** or **Canella Winterana** are not true distillates from the bark of this tree. These oils are presumably compounded spice oils from cinnamon bark, clove leaf, etc. The author has no experience with the true essential oil of **"White Cinnamon"**.

Cangerana.

The essential oil of **Cabralea Cangerana**, often called **Cangerana**, is steam distilled from the bark of the root of a Brazilian tree of the above name. The tree belongs to the genus of Meliaceae among which we also find **Cedrela Odorata** (see that monograph) and **Swietenia Mahagony**, the "true" mahagany tree.

The name **Cabralea** is derived from the famous portuguese navigator and explorer Pedro Alvarez Cabral, who found Brazil in A.D. 1500. To be more correct: he found the east coast of South America and when he saw the wealth of trees in the new land, he particularly admired those with a beautiful, red-colored wood. Accordingly, he named the land: Brazil (= the red woods).

The peel or bark of **Cabralea Cangerana** root is used in local medicine. The essential oil finds its way as a perfume for soaps, floorwaxes and other perfumed household articles in the local market. The annual production of this oil is hardly more than a few metric tons.

Cangerana Oil is a viscous liquid of pale olive-green to pale turquoise color. Its odor is distinctly woody, very dry and earthy, spicy-peppery, reminiscent of cubeb oil, cyperus oils, carrot seed oil, clove leaf sesquiterpenes, etc. It blends well with clove oils, lavandin, oakmoss, olibanum, petitgrain, pine needle oils, vetiver, etc., and with borneol, cedarwood derivatives, coumarin, iso-bornylacetate, methyl anthranilate, nitromusks, etc. The oil could no doubt find use outside of its country of origin for the creation of pine needle fragrances, fougères, Oriental perfume bases, violet bases, "men's fragrances", spice blends, etc. and it is particularly interesting for use in the construction of artificial essential oils.

The oil is also known locally as **Oleo de Madeira**, which is a mutual name for a number of essential oils from trees along the Brazilian Madeira River.

Capé Oil.

Although hardly available except upon demand well in advance, the oil of **Popowia Capea** deserves some attention. It represents one of the many results of the botanical research expeditions which were sponsored by some of the larger Grasse perfume raw material houses long ago. More recently, the well-known French botanist, author, engineer, and coffee-expert, R.-L. Joly, has explored the West African area for the purpose of finding new perfume plants. But even his visits and reports did not seem to call **Capé Oil** to life.

The plant is a semi-climbing vine which grows wild in the jungles of Guinea and the Ivory Coast, formerly French West Africa (A.O.F.) The leaves are extremely fragrant, and the natives use them to perfume their baths and to scent their vegetable oils.

Capé Oil is an olive-green liquid of strong, woody-floral and deep-sweet odor with a somewhat minty-sharp topnote. The tenacity is excellent and this oil would blend well with Oriental and woody-herbaceous bases, floral bases, hyacinth, lilac, ylang-ylang, etc. Very little is known about the constituents of the oil. The plant belongs to the same family as do the ylang-ylang, but its flowers are not particularly fragrant.

The best method of production of this oil is by steam distillation of the leaves, after which the condensate is collected in a hydrocarbon solvent (see also Manevoro Oil). The heavier fractions of the oil contain cinnamic alcohol and esters of this alcohol. These are not only heavier than water but also slightly soluble in the distillation waters. The difficulties encountered in the collection of the leaves in the jungle and the complicated distillation make the production of this oil unrewarding unless there is a strong demand for it. The plant has not been found elsewhere.

Capsicum.

Under the name of Capsicum, the fruits of various species of the family Solanaceae (nightshade family) are used extensively as pungent food additives in pickles, spice blends, etc.

There are two main sorts of Capsicum of interest to flavorists:

1) The large pepper from Capsicum Annuum or Capsicum Longum,
2) The small pepper from Capsicum Frutescens or Capsicum Fastigiatum.

1) The large "cayenne" pepper is known in many varieties, some of which are free from pungent constituents and, accordingly, are used unripe in green salads. This type of capsicum fruit is particularly rich in vitamin C. Perfumers will inevitably recall the odor of galbanum or certain lower olefinic aldehydes when they enjoy fresh green peppers in a salad bowl.

The more original types are all pungent, i.e. in the ripe and orange-red fruits, we find the seeds located on a central stand inside the inflated, hollow pepper. Only the seedstands which are very juicy, contain pungent materials. The best

known of these has been identified as Decylene Vanillylamide, also known as Capsaicin. The content of capsaicin determines the pungency of the pepper. In some of the varieties, capsaicin is also found to a minor extent in the seeds.

The dried fruits are known as "Spanish pepper" or "paprika". They are cultivated extensively in central and southern Europe. The orange-red powder of the fruits, from which the most pungent parts have been removed, is known as "Rosenpaprika" and is a Hungarian specialty. It is used in numerous dishes and recipes as well as in many variations of the so-called "Indian curry powder". Originally, this called for the small capsicum fruits (see below).

Since the content of pungent matter is much smaller in the "large" capsicum, than in the "small" varieties, the latter is frequently used for extraction to Oleoresin Capsicum, etc. Although capsaicin is a solid material, it is somewhat volatile, and this may explain the fact that other parts of the fruit have a slight pungency when the fruit is mature. However, capsicum fruits yield no essential oil on ordinary steam or water distillation.

2) The "small" capsicums are derived from:
Capsicum Frutescens, e.g. the "African chiles" (originally: chillies), or from
Capsicum Anuum, var. conoides, known as "Tabasco pepper" or "Tabasco piment".
The latter term has caused some confusion concerning origin, since the Spanish word "pimienta" refers to the pungent taste, and should not refer to the botanical name of the plant (the Mexican Pimenta Officinalis has been mentioned as parent of the Tabasco spice, but apparently is merely an allspice variety with little or no pungency).

"Tabasco pepper" is also known as "Cayenne pepper". These "small" capsicums are cultivated extensively in tropical zones all over the world, and have become everyday additive to native food in India, Indonesia, China, Central America, etc. They also enter the spice blends, curry powders, pickles, seasonings and table sauces, partly as comminuted fruits, partly as extracts (usually oleoresins). The "small" capsicums contain up to 20 times as much capsaicin as do the "large" European capsicums.

Capsicum Oleoresin is a prepared oleoresin, but the term oleoresin is a little out of line of our definitions. The extract consists of resinous matter and a liquid phase which is not volatile with steam.

9: Modern equipment for continuous **Concentration** of fruit juices, etc. for **Flavors.**

*(Courtesy of **Dragoco**, Holzminden, Germany)*

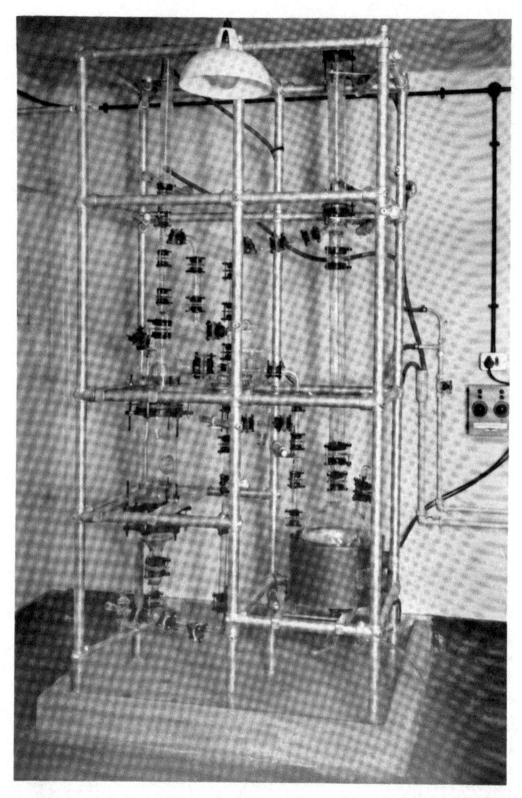

10: All-glass liquid/liquid **Extraction** apparatus. Heat-resistant essential oils can be **deterpenized** in this type of apparatus. *(Courtesy of Q.V.F., Ltd., Staffordshire, England)*

Extraction is usually carried out with ethyl ether, and the evaporation residue will separate into an oily-fatty part and a liquid, rather mobile oleoresin which is collected as the yield.

Capsicum Oleoresin is a dark red or orange-red to brownish-red liquid, soluble in ethyl ether, hydrocarbon solvents and most vegetable (fixed) oils, but not in alcohol. If the fruits are extracted with alcohol, the oleoresin will be darker, more viscous and contain less pungent matter per weight unit. If the ether-extracted oleoresin is extracted with ethyl alcohol, the oleoresin will yield an **Absolute of Capsicum** which contains the pungent material. The absolute is soluble in alcohol and is easier to use in flavors where hydrocarbon solvents are rarely used or wanted. **Capsicum Absolute** has an interesting tobacco-like, sweet-herbaceous odor which could be utilized in jasmin bases, cassie, mimosa, modern fantasy bases, etc. A pungency-free and non-irritant capsicum absolute should be prepared for use in perfumes which inevitably come in contact with the human skin.

Capsicum Oleoresin is used in place of the botanical drug with the advantage that the strength can now be standardized since the pungent material is known and synthesized. Also, the fruits are fully utilized: fruits of poor appearance may be used for extraction; fruits of various crops and quality can be extracted together. The taste or mouthfeel—(flavor is out of the question) —of **Capsicum Oleoresin** is characterized by an extreme pungency: With a dilution of one part of oleoresin capsicum in five million parts of a 9% sugar water at $10°C$. (i.e. a concentration of 0.02 mg%), a distinct burning effect in the throat and rear parts of the inside mouth is still produced. The above test is obviously very subjective and strongly dependent upon the eating habits of the taste panel. At such extreme dilutions, it is impossible to distinguish between the pungency of capsicum and that of ginger; this is why capsicum extracts are used to adulterate ginger oleoresins, to make them "stronger" for use in "ginger nuts", "ginger ale", etc. A well known test is to heat the extract with a weak sodium hydroxide solution. Only the ginger extract will lose its pungency; capsicum remains unaffected. Besides, the flavor of ginger oleoresin is not present in capsicum extracts, and the ginger flavor would be impaired by any addition of capsicum oleoresin.

Capsicum Oleoresin and **Capsicum Tincture**, the latter usually produced from European capsicum fruits, are still used in pharmaceutical preparations as rubefacients and skin irritants (stimulants).

Caraway Oil.

This oil is steam distilled from the dried, crushed, ripe fruit of **Carum Carvi**, a small herb which grows wild in Asia, Europe, North Africa and in the northwestern United States. The plant is cultivated in Holland, Denmark, Poland, USSR, Hungary, Yugoslavia, Germany, England, Spain, Tunisia, India, and Pakistan. The four first-named countries are main suppliers of the fruits; Holland is the largest producer of the essential oil. The annual production in Holland may exceed 40 metric tons. Other countries supply smaller quantities, and the Dutch oil is considered superior, although the scarce English distilled oil (partly from foreign fruits) is also of high flavor quality.

Caraway Oil is offered on the market in at least two grades:
1) "crude" or "natural" caraway oil—and
2) "double rectified" or "redistilled" caraway oil.

Crude caraway oil is the direct distillate. It is a pale yellow to brownish, mobile liquid, possessing a strong and peculiar odor typical of the fruit, but with a fatty-harsh undertone. The taste is similar, but quite burning, warm, biting.

Rectified caraway oil is colorless or very pale yellow. The odor is stronger, less fatty. The flavor is warmer, less sweet and more biting than that of the crude (natural) oil.

When presenting a "blind" sample of caraway oil to an odor panel, one may often hear that "it smells of rye bread". This is another example of the difficulties one faces in logical odor description. Rye bread is flavored with caraway oil (or with other carvone-containing flavor material). To the same panel was shown with several weeks interval first a "blind" sample of **Carvone**, later one of spearmint oil. In all three cases, the description "rye bread" came up as the most frequently used by the panel.

Characteristic of crude caraway oil is an initial note of a nauseating, almost amine-like type. This note is found in a number of "seed"-oils, particularly those from the family of umbelliferae (caraway, carrot, celery, coriander, fennel, etc.), and the unpleasant note may be due either to decomposition of proteins in the germ of the seed, or to the presence of glycosides or alkaloids. Black pepper oil presents an ammoniacal odor when fresh out of the still, conceivably a decomposition product from the nitrogen components of the fruit.

The above odor is not present in redistilled (rectified) caraway oils. See also **Cumin Oil.**

Caraway Oil is used primarily in flavors: in bread, cheese, meat, pickles, sauces, and seasonings. It is the main flavor ingredient in the Scandinavian "snaps" (a caraway-brandy), or the German "kümmel". It is used in mouth wash or gargle preparations, toothpaste flavors, chewing gum, candy, and as a masking agent in bad-tasting pharmaceutical preparations. Combinations with cinnamon or cassia oils are frequently encountered.

The suggested use level of rectified caraway oil is about 2.00 to 5.00 mg% and the **Minimum Perceptible** is 0.30 to 0.50 mg%. In perfumery, the use of caraway oil is restricted to soap perfumes where it is often combined with cassia oil or similar notes. Minute quantities of caraway oil may be used in jasmin bases, tabac perfumes, etc. Caraway oil has a pronounced odor-masking effect upon some of the most common insecticidal chemicals and has occasionally been used for the purpose of covering the obnoxious odor of the active principles.

Since the main constituents of caraway oil, **Carvone** and **Limonene** (both in the dextro-rotatory form) are available as synthetic chemicals, the use of caraway oil has been decreasing considerably during recent years. Apart from the two materials mentioned, however, trace amounts of other ingredients actually decide the characteristic odor of true caraway oil. It is interesting to note that spearmint oil also consists mainly of carvone and terpenes (in laevo-rotatory form), but the "traces" of odor-flavor materials which characterize the typical spearmint odor and flavor are more than mere traces (several percent of certain materials).

An olfactory analysis of caraway oil will usually reveal any substantial adulteration. In the crude oil, sulfide compounds often occur naturally, causing a putrid odor, but these notes soon disappear completely on ageing or after rectification. A similar odor is noted in true cumin oil (see monograph). Such observations may help in the evaluation of samples of caraway oil. It is believed that the sulfides should only exist in the distillation waters from the oil, not in the oil itself. Most distillers cohobate the distillation water, others extract the water with volatile solvent in order to recover this special fraction of the crude caraway oil.

Adulteration takes place on an increasing scale with synthetic d-carvone and d-limonene, particularly since the former is now produced at a competitive cost (see also **Spearmint Oil**). Adulteration can also take place with **Caraway Chaff Oil,** distilled from the waste material from the threshing of the caraway fruits. This oil contains more terpenes and less carvone; it is of poorer grade than true caraway fruit oil

Cardamom Oil.

Cardamom Oil is one of the oldest essential oils known. In the reports of Valerius Cordus dated 1540, cardamom oil is described, and its distillation is outlined.

The oil is produced by steam distillation of the seeds of **Elettaria Cardamomum,** a plant of the ginger family. This plant grows wild, and is also cultivated in Ceylon, India (Malabar coast, Travancore, Canara and other provinces), in Guatemala, and lately in El Salvador, Central America.

The seeds are enclosed in husks (hulls), and should not be removed from the almost odorless hulls until immediately prior to distillation. The so-called "green" cardamom, e. g. "Green Aleppy", which gives a high yield of essential oil (in rare cases up to 8%, usually 4 to 6%), is preferred as distillation material. The essential oil from "green" types of cardamom smells more of cineole than does an oil from the bleached or pale yellow, straw-colored cardamom (fruits). Until recent years, all cardamom oil was produced in Europe and in the U.S.A., but in the 1950's, distillation took place on an increasing scale in India and Ceylon. India is, by far, the largest consumer of cardamom spice in the world. It is estimated that India uses between 50 and 65% of the total world production.

Guatemala is the second largest producer of cardamom, but still comes nowhere near the quantities produced by India and Ceylon. A very good cardamom oil is distilled locally in Guatemala. It compares favorably with any other cardamom oil on the market in respect to odor and flavor.

Numerous varieties of cardamom, useful as spice, grow wild or semiwild, and are cultivated in Madagascar, east and west Africa, central

Africa, China, Siam and Indonesia. These have little or no importance as a source of essential oil.

Cardamom Oil is an almost colorless or pale yellow to light brownish liquid. It darkens when exposed to daylight. The locally distilled oils are generally darker than those distilled in Europe or the U.S.A. Guatemalan oil is distilled in comparatively modern equipment and under experienced technical supervision. It is also light colored. The odor of cardamom oil is warm-spicy, aromatic (in the author's opinion it is the most "aromatic" of all the oils from "aromatic" seeds), at first penetrating camphoraceous-cineole-like or somewhat medicinal, reminiscent of eucalyptus. Later, it becomes balsamic-woody, increasingly sweet and almost floral on the dryout. The odor is extremely tenacious with a delightful, warm spiciness and balsamic-floral undertone.

The main constituents of cardamom oil are cineole, terpinylacetate, terpineol, borneol and terpenes. All of these can be and are produced synthetically at a fraction of the price of cardamom oil. Obviously, adulteration takes place on a really big scale, and only a good experience with genuine oil, for example of his own distillation, will enable a perfumer to judge successfully between a true oil and an adulterated one. Spanish sage oil, pine oil fractions, etc. are also used in the above fraud. The flavor of cardamom oil is rich-aromatic, warm and spicy, somewhat burning or pungent at high concentration, and faintly bitter unless well diluted. The use level of this oil in food is strongly dependent upon the further processing of the food (high temperatures for baked goods, etc.) but it would be about 0.20 to 0.50% while the **Minimum Perceptible** is 0.04 to 0.05 mg% for a good and true cardamom oil.

The spice itself is one of the "musts" in the genuine east Indian curry powder. Apart from its use as a spice in blends, cardamom oil replaces the spice in the canning industry for pickles, meat sauces, seasonings, etc. where uniform quality and constant effect are of paramount importance. In certain areas, e.g. the Scandinavian and north European countries, cardamom is a very popular addition to bread and all baked goods, while the spice is hardly known at all to the American housewife.

In perfumery, the oil will not only impart spiciness, but also a warm, sweet note which fits into floral bases such as muguet and rose. Card-

amom oil blends well with bergamot, olibanum, ylang-ylang, labdanum products, nerol, methyl-ionones, cedarwood derivatives, etc. or with heliotropine, cassione, isoeugenol, hydroxycitronellal, etc. Coriander oil is an extremely fine modifier for cardamom oil in perfumery (and in flavors, too!). The oil imparts warmth in Oriental perfume bases, chypres and face powder perfumes.

Recently, a few European and American spice houses started production of **Cardamom Oleoresin** which reproduces the organoleptic virtues of the true spice even more closely than does the oil. The oleoresin is produced by extraction of the seed with ethylether, petroleum ether or other volatile solvent. The extract will contain about 10% of a fixed oil which is odorless. Extraction with hot alcohol produces a very dark extract which is free from fixed oil. The ether extract is an orange-brown or greenish-brown liquid of rich and "true-to-nature" odor. An **Ultrasonic Extract** of **Cardamom** is also available.

The annual world production of cardamom oil seems to adjust itself to the demand. The oil is comparatively expensive, but this is not due to scarcity of raw material.

Carnation Absolute.

Known in France as "absolue d'œillet", **Carnation Absolute** is produced by extraction of the flowers of **Dianthus Caryophyllus,** the common garden carnation. The plant is grown for the purpose of cutting the flowers (for decorations, etc.), but at the end of the season, the flowers are extracted with petroleum ether to yield a hard, green concrète.

Cultivation takes place in most European countries and in the U.S.A. Production of the concrète and absolute, however, is carried out only in France, Holland, Germany, and Italy. An absolute is produced by the usual alcohol washing method (see Part One in this book: **Absolute**).

Carnation is an olive green to green or orange-brown, viscous liquid of very sweet, honeylike, somewhat herbaceous, heavy and tenacious fragrance, reminiscent of the odor of the live flowers only to a certain degree and only in high dilutions (5% or weaker). The yield of absolute from concrète is very small (about 10 to 25%), and since the yield of the concrète itself is also poor (0.2 to 0.3% of the weight of the flowers), the production of **Carnation Absolute** is a costly one. Consequently, adulteration occurs quite frequently, mainly in the form of "cutting", and it may be difficult to detect. Synthetic materials such as isoeugenol, methyl eugenol, benzyl benzoate, methyl salicylate, etc. or small amounts of everlasting absolute, flouve oil, clove bud absolute, etc. can be added, and these can make the odor of the "sophisticated" absolute even more similar to that of the flower.

Carnation Absolute is used sparingly in certain modern perfumes, and it can add interesting notes to rose, lily, narcissus, etc. It blends well with lavender, ylang-ylang, sage clary, castoreum, etc. The annual production of carnation absolute has diminished considerably, and is now estimated at 20 to 30 kilos.

Carob Bean.

The carob bean or **"Locust Bean"** is also called **"St. John's Bread"** since it was believed that St. John, as referred to in the New Testament, took nourishment from locust and from the syrup of these fruits during his stay in the desert. But since the tree, **Ceratonia Siliqua**, from which the fruits are derived is not a desert tree, it is not conceivable that St. John really had these pods. The honeylike juice which can be expressed from the fruits is nowadays fermented locally and it produces an alcoholic beverage.

The flowers of the carob bean tree can be extracted to yield a concrète of a very interesting mimosa-cassie type of odor. The perfume type "locust flower" was originally intended to call this fragrance in mind. It is very likely, however, that the flowers from the carob bean tree are used accidentally or intentionally with cassie or mimosa flowers in the extraction of concrète. The trees grow in the same areas of the Mediterranean countries.

Ceratonia Siliqua is a small tree which probably originates in the Middle East. It grows abundantly in Cyprus Island in the eastern Mediterranean. The bulk of St. John's bread is, however, produced in Spain and Italy. Greece, Turkey and Lebanon produce smaller quantities.

A syrup of about 50% sugar content is found in the tissue around the seeds of the fruit. The fruit also contains some butyric acid, etc. which gives the syrup a cheese-like, almost rancid odor.

Some people dislike St. John's bread just for this particular reason.

The five to eight inches long pods (fruits) are used in flavor work in the form of an extract. The menstruum for the extraction is very weak alcohol or water. Strong alcohol would not extract the sugar which seems to be accompanied by a certain amount of the peculiar aroma. This aqueous extract of St. John's bread is used in tobacco flavors, in imitation rum flavors and in many types of caramel or nut flavors.

A tincture made with strong alcohol is prepared specially for use in perfumes. It is pale colored and has a faint odor of the bean. This tincture finds occasionally use in the creation of certain floral notes, where it seems to introduce naturalness and roundness in spite of the unquestionable cheese-note.

The cultivation of the **Carob Bean** tree has found renewed interest since the dried and powdered endosperm from the seeds produce a most useful gum, known as **"Locust Bean Gum"**. Under the brand name of **"Rexer"** (Spanish product) and other brand names, this endosperm powder has become a serious competitor to tragacanth and other gums. The locust bean gum is in several respects superior to tragacanth. The waste fruits, known as "kibbles", from the production of the endosperm-flour are used as cattle feed. Locust bean gum is used extensively in cosmetic preparations, but its greatest outlet is in the textile industry as a thickening agent in the printing of fabrics (also for "apprêtage", etc.).

Carrot Seed Oil.

This oil is steam distilled from the dried seed (fruit) of the common carrot, **Daucus Carota**. Production of the essential oil is almost entirely concentrated in France, although Holland and Hungary produce minor quantities. In France, it is customary to crush the seed prior to distillation, but not all distillers do so. Like celery seed, carrot seed can be distilled without crushing, and this will minimize the carry-over of odorless fixed oil (palmitic acid, etc.) in the distillate. Superannuated seed which has lost its germinating power can also be used for distillation. This makes the distillation more economical.

Carrot Seed Oil is a yellow or amber-colored to pale orange-brown liquid of peculiar dry-woody, somewhat root-like, earthy odor. The initial notes are sweet and fresh, but the tenacious undertone and dryout is very heavy, weset-earthy, fatty-oily, slightly spicy. The flavor is warm-spicy, slightly biting at high concentration, but sweet and piquant. The suggested use level is 0.10 to 0.20 mg% and the **Minimum Perceptible** is 0.02 to 0.04 mg%. The oil contains large amounts of terpenes, particularly monoterpenes, but the characteristic odor and flavor is probably due to certain components related to those found in calamus oil and to certain materials with ionone-like odor.

Carrot Seed Oil is occasionally adulterated with d-limonene (although it should be l-limonene) or with oil from siftings, etc. The oil is used in France quite extensively for culinary purposes, e.g. in spice blends, seasonings, etc., and also in alsoholic beverages. In France and other countries, **Carrot Seed Oil** is used in perfumery for its fatty-woody notes which blend well with chypres, citrus oils, costus oil, cassie and mimosa, fougères, geranium oils, ionones and methylionones, cedarwood derivatives, etc. Many Oriental perfume types, modern aldehydic or fantasy type perfumes, etc. contain traces of carrot seed oil. For certain artificial essential oils, **Carrot Seed Oil** lends unique and indispensable notes.

The oil could be produced in amounts of several metric tons per year in France alone should the demand continue to increase. Its low price and great power makes it useful and economical in a great variety of perfumes and flavors.

Cascarilla Oil.

This oil is steam distilled from the dried bark of **Croton Eluteria** and possibly other **Croton** species, small trees which grow in the West Indies, probably originally from the Bahama Islands. The Bahamas are the main producers of cascarilla bark on a commercial scale. Smaller amounts come from Cuba. The bark is dried and freed from any adherent sapwood or heartwood, but it is not distilled locally. The bark is sold to the large botanical houses and drug store suppliers. Alcoholic tinctures or extracts are prepared pharmaceutically, and are used as flavor materials, as a tonic additive or as a so-called "bitter".

In Europe, mainly in France and England, and also in the U.S.A., small quantities of essential oil are produced from the imported cascarilla bark. **Cascarilla Oil** is a pale yellow to greenish-

yellow or dark amber colored liquid of strong spicy-aromatic, warm-woody, slightly peppery odor reminiscent of nutmeg, myrtle, melaleuca alternifolia, hyssop and other spices or culinary herbs. Its topnote is not exactly pleasant, but the unusual diffusiveness and power of this oil places it among the "trace" components in perfumes. The flavor of the oil is somewhat bitter, burning but pleasantly spicy and quite powerful. Suggested use level is 0.10 to 0.50 mg% and the **Minimum Perceptible** is 0.02 to 0.04 mg%.

The very complex note of spiciness and the warm, woody undertone has intrigued many perfumers to use **Cascarilla Oil** in high-class perfumes. It was even claimed that "l'origan" contained this oil as one of the "key" materials (if one can use such an expression at all about a creation). But the oil does present interesting notes in chypre bases, "tabac"-types, Oriental perfumes, "men's fragrances", fantasy colognes, etc. It blends well with nutmeg, pepper, pimenta berry oil, sage oil dalmatian, oakmoss products, quinoline derivatives, cedrenol, coumarin, etc. Its power is often underestimated.

In flavors, the oil has found use in tobacco-aromas, in liqueurs as a "piquant" additive and in tonic wines and bitters. The oil is produced on a very limited scale only, and its high price and limited area of botanical origin create problems of meeting the demand when significant quantities are called for.

Cassia Oil.

Cassia Oil, or **Chinese Cinnamon Oil**, is steam distilled from the leaves of **Cinnamomum Cassia**, large slender trees which grow in the southeastern parts of China and, to a minor extent, in Viet-Nam and India (Cochin). The bark of this tree is known all over the world as "cinnamon bark" or "cassia-cinnamon", not to be confused with the true Ceylon cinnamon bark which is derived from a different species (see **Cinnamon Bark Oil**).

The bark is distilled together with the leaves and the stalks, twigs and waste material from the collection of the bark of the **Cassia** tree. After proper drying of the plant material, the distillation is carried out in local stills, primitive, but quite ingeniously constructed. The distillation is, in its principle, a water-distillation. Accordingly, the oil is very crude, and appears as a dark brown liquid of strong, spicy, warm and woody-resinous odor with an intensely sweet, somewhat balsamic undertone. The bark contains significant amounts of tannin and this material causes a certain darkening of the oils from iron or copper stills.

For various reasons, however, true **Cassia Oil** hardly reaches the American consumers any more. First of all, this oil has been subject to "local" adulteration for several decades, and the adulteration was quite skilfully made. Thus, very few buyers ever knew how a true oil looked or smelled. Next, the political disturbances and subsequent ban on goods from Red China have blocked off this material from the U.S.A. although smaller lots still reach Europe (but these may very well be adulterated oils!). All told, these circumstances have been well-nigh disastrous for the future of **Cassia Oil,** and artificial oils have already been accepted by the consumers for many years. The result is that the oil is not available any more in the U.S.A., and what is available in Europe, Africa and South America may very well be a "compounded" oil. The chief constituent, **Cinna-mal** (or **Cinnamic Aldehyde**) is available as a low-cost synthetic chemical. Several other synthetic chemicals have cinnamon-like odor and flavor: alpha-methyl cinnamic aldehyde, alpha-methyl furanacrolein, etc., and with the addition of balsamic fixatives such as Sumatra benzoin, methyl isoeugenol, etc. it is possible to reproduce the odor and flavor of cassia cinnamon satisfactorily. Acaroid resinoid has also been used as a balsamic fixative. Its dark color is only an advantage in this case.

However, for those who may still have the opportunity of working with (more or less) "true" **Cassia Cinnamon Oil** ("cassia leaf oil"), a brief description will follow. The description is partly based upon the author's personal notes from the 1930's, partly upon more recent studies of small, true samples obtained by supervised distillation of cassia leaves and stalks. The botanical material, too, was checked and found genuine by the author.

Crude, locally distilled cassia oil is a brownish yellow to dark brown liquid from which a resinous matter may deposit after ageing. Rectified (redistilled) cassia oil is a pale yellow or dark yellow, clear liquid, less viscous than the crude oil. Its odor is somewhat sweeter but less tenacious. The flavor is also similar: warm, spicy, slightly woody, balsamic and intensely sweet. The suggested use level is 1.00 to 4.00 mg% (with wide variations in concentration according to type of flavor,

modifier, etc.). The **Minimum Perceptible** of the redistilled oil is about 0.10 to 0.20 mg%. A certain degree of water-solubility seems to place this oil among the "medium-strong" materials and not, as one should expect from its odor-masking ability, among the very strongest of our flavor materials.

Because of its intense and dark color, crude cassia oil is rarely used in perfumes as such. It may easily cause not only coloring but also discoloration of soaps and other perfumed products when incorporated in the perfume in modest concentration. For flavors, it often pays to use the crude oil which has a tremendous odor-tenacity, thanks to the significant amount of resinous matter. As a modifier with benzaldehyde in liqueur-flavors, in cherry flavors or "wild cherry" flavors, flavors for baked goods, candy, mouthwashes, etc., a true **Cassia Oil** lends power, sweetness and a popular spicy-warm note. Certain bactericidal effects are also attributed to this oil on account of its high content of **Cinnamic Aldehyde.**

It was customary to ship crude cassia oil in lead-lined containers, and this occasionally caused not only discoloration of the oil, but also formation of the lead salt of cinnamic acid. The latter is produced by air oxidation of the main constituent in the cassia oil, **Cinnamic Aldehyde.**

Annual production of **Cassia Oil** is estimated to fluctuate between 175 and 250 metric tons, but since the western world has become accustomed to an artificial replacement, it is conceivable that production will diminish significantly. It is worthwhile noting that a large part of the "cinnamon" which goes into the spice blend in "apple pie with cinnamon" in the U.S.A. and other countries, is derived from the bark of **Cinnamomum Loureirii,** an Indochinese tree which is related to the cassia tree. This bark is recognized by authorities in many countries as "cinnamon bark". See the monograph on **Canella.**

Cassie.

A valuable and scarce perfume material is extracted from the flowers of **Acacia Farnesiana,** a small tree or shrub which grows in warm-temperate and semi-tropical areas all over the world. The tree is cultivated for the purpose of extracting the flowers in Lebanon (near Beyrouth), in Morocco, Egypt (near Cairo) and in the south of France. Algerian plantations and flower extraction installations are practically abandoned. Flowers are collected on a commercial scale for extraction in India (Himalaya) where a local type of pommade is made ("attar" of cassie). The tree grows abundantly in the West Indies and in the South Pacific Islands. Other species are found in Central Africa, Belgian Congo, Australia, etc. but these locations are prohibitive for an economical extraction of the flowers. Insignificant quantities of flower extracts (concrètes) are produced in Italy, Israel and Bulgaria.

The flowers are extracted with petroleum ether to yield **Cassie Concrète** which is a solid, waxy mass of dark yellow or brown color, usually much darker than mimosa concrète. The cassie concrète is rarely used as such. It is processed further to **Cassie Absolute** by alcohol extraction of the concrète. The concrète yields only about one third of absolute by weight.

Cassie Absolute from Concrète is a dark yellow or pale brown, viscous liquid, clear at room temperature but separating waxy flakes at reduced temperatures. Its odor is extremely warm, powdery-spicy, at the same time herbaceous and floral with a deep and very tenacious cinnamic-balsamic undertone.

The absolute is used in high-cost perfumes where it lends a unique warmth and woody-floral note. It blends well with all the ionones and methylionones, heliotropine (not to speak of its well-known derivative, **Cassione**), anisalcohol, cyclamal, etc. and with bergamot oil, costus, mimosa, orris products, olibanum, ylang-ylang absolute, etc. in ambre bases, oriental bases, etc. **Cassie Absolute from Concrète** is occasionally used in flavors; it gives a delightful naturalness and body to a raspberry flavor when used with extreme discretion. Being a typical "bouquet" material in flavors, **Cassie Absolute** should be used at a concentration only slightly above the **Minimum Perceptible**, which is about 0.04 to 0.08 mg%.

A different type of cassie absolute is made by the enfleurage method (see **Pommade** in Part One of this book). The alcohol-extract from the pommade is known as **Cassie Absolute from Pommade**. This absolute is a very viscous, dark green or olive green liquid. Its odor is distinctly different from that of the absolute from concrète. The former has a fresher, almost narcissus- or violet-leaf topnote and a much lighter body-

note. Its tenacity is by far inferior to that of the absolute from concrète. **Cassie Absolute from Pommade** is an extremely scarce perfume material and must be considered as an individual material, not a substitute for the absolute from concrète.

Cassie Absolute from Concrète is produced in very limited quantities. The annual production is hardly more than 100 kilos. It is estimated that about 80% hereof is derived from Lebanon. The Egyptian producers send their concrète to France for processing into absolute. **Cassie Absolute** is adulterated with mimosa absolute, isoeugenol, artificial cassie bases, etc. or it can be contaminated with extracts of carob bean flowers (see **Carob Bean**) or flowers from related Leguminosae.

Castoreum.

Castoreum is a secretion from the male or the female beaver. It is collected in a gland which produces an oily substance in which the beavers rub themselves in order to protect their fur from being soaked in water. **Castoreum** is a term normally used for the entire gland. The contents of the gland turn dark and hard when it is sun-dried. One gland weighs up to 100 grams. Thus, it is much less expensive than civet.

Castoreum is collected in Canada (Hudson Bay in particular) and in the U.S.S.R. (Siberia, etc.).

Canadian castoreum is pear-shaped, wrinkled on the surface, somewhat flat, 5 to 17 cms. long, 2½ to 5 cms. wide. Siberian castoreum is egg-shaped and smooth on the surface, almost the same size as Canadian castoreum, but not flat. Siberian castoreum is considered inferior to the Canadian castoreum.

Castoreum is used in perfumery in the form of various processed materials: **Tincture, Resinoid, Absolute.**

Castoreum Tincture: See **Tincture** in Part One of this book.

Castoreum Resinoid: is prepared from the animal tissue and the exudation inside. Accordingly, it should not be called a resinoid, but more truly a concrète. Castoreum contains no true resins. Benzene extraction of castoreum yields about 20% of a brown "resinoid". However, it is customary to prepare an alcohol-resinoid by direct extraction with hot alcohol.

Castoreum Absolute: The above mentioned alcohol-"resinoid" is not a true absolute and it is not clearly soluble in cold alcohol. It can be prepared in a way that will cause it to be fairly soluble (chilling before evaporation). The yield by hot alcohol-extraction is about 75 to 80% of a dark brown, soft unctuous mass.

Castoreum Anhydrol is available. It offers certain notes of the castoreum gamut in an almost colorless liquid.

Castoreum (the tincture in particular) is used extensively in perfumery. Its warm, animal, leather-like sweet odor makes it an interesting item in "men's perfumes", fougères, chypres, Oriental bases, leather notes, tabac bases, etc. A frequent "smoky" note in castoreum is not a natural odor, but is due to the drying of the glands over smoking fires. This curing or processing of the raw material may also be responsible for the so-called "birch-tar" note of castoreum.

Castoreum products blend particularly well with ambra notes, calamus, cananga, cedarwood Atlas, chamomile moroccan, creosol, labdanum products, isoeugenol, oakmoss products, sandalwood oil, veratraldehyde, zingerone, etc.

In flavor work, it has long been known that castoreum extracts or tinctures were useful in vanilla flavor compounds. One very well known vanilla specialty from a European house reveals this quite perceptibly. Conversely, vanilla extracts can be used to smooth down the coarseness of higher concentrations of castoreum products in fougères, leather bases, etc.

Castoreum is readily available in quantities sufficient to meet the normal demand. One cannot say that the material is cultivated, but increased production would be possible. However, the use of castoreum has decreased during the past few decades.

Cedarleaf Oil.

Cedarleaf Oil, which is also known commercially under the name of **Thuja Oil,** is actually not distilled from the most well known cedar. Its name is thus somewhat confusing. The American **Cedarleaf Oil** is distilled almost exclusively from the leaves and twigs of **Thuja Occidentalis,** in the U.S.A. called **Eastern** or **Northern White Cedar.** Leaves and twigs of **Juniperus Virginiana** are occasionally admixed to the above material prior to the steam distillation of cedarleaf oil (see **Cedarwood Oil, Virginia**). The white cedar is botanically related to the cypress and it grows abundantly in the northeastern States of the U.S.A. and in eastern Canada. The essential oil is distilled mainly in New York State, in Vermont and in the Quebec province of Canada. Leaves and twigs are collected and distilled in the growing areas. Canadian oil is derived exclusively from white cedar. Cedarleaf oil (thuja oil) is a colorless to pale greenish-yellow, mobile oil of an intensely sharp, but quite fresh, camphoraceous odor. It bears great resemblance to the flowering tansy herb, artemisia herb, dalmatian sage herb, etc. with a sweet undertone reminiscent of bitter fennel.

The annual production of **Cedarleaf Oil** is quite substantial and the interest in this oil has not decreased lately. It is a low-cost and powerful perfume ingredient for room-sprays, disinfectants, insecticides, paints, household and industrial cleansers, etc. Its green, sweet-herbaceous, although medicinal and camphoraceous-minty note blends well with pine needle oils, citrus oils, lavandin and rosemary in chypre or fougère bases. The oil has even been used as a "piquant" topnote in high-class perfumes.

The chief constituent, **Thujone,** is a ketone which is considered skin-irritant and poisonous to a certain degree. At the normal use-level of cedarleaf oil in perfumes, however, it seems inconceivable that the oil could be responsible for any harmful effects.

Apart from occasional adulteration with pine oil fractions or turpentine fractions, **Cedarleaf Oil** is rarely adulterated. The oil serves, on the other hand, as an adulterant for tansy oil, artemisia oil and dalmatian sage oil. See these monographs. See also **Thuja Plicata Oil.**

Cedarwood "Atlas" Resinoid.

A concrète can be produced by benzene extraction of the wood from **Cedrus Atlantica** (see **Cedarwood Oil, Atlas**). The concrète is commercially known as **Atlas Cedarwood Resinoid** (compare: vetiver resinoid). Although not produced regularly on a large scale, this material is made available upon demand, and it maintains some interest on account of its magnificent fixative effect and fine odor.

Resinoid of **Atlas Cedarwood** is a dark amber to brownish mass of high viscosity. The **Cedarwood "Atlas" Absolute,** produced from this resinoid by the conventional alcohol washing method, is a brownish-yellow, very viscous liquid. The two materials will usually carry some solvent odor (benzene), due to their tremendous fixative power, but they do not present the camphoraceous-cresylic, or ketonic-sharp topnote which is usually found in the essential oil from this wood. To those who have had the opportunity of smelling the Atlas cedarwood in the local lumbermills or in the shape of various handcarved articles of art from Morocco, the **Resinoid** and the **Absolute** of **Atlas Cedarwood** present a very true-to-nature fragrance.

The above products are used in perfumery along with bois de rose oil, boronia absolute, calamus oil, cassie absolute, cistus oil, mimosa absolute or concrète (excellent in soap perfumes!), olibanum, sage clary, vetiver, ylang-ylang, etc. in certain types of woody, woody-oriental, woody-floral or violet bases.

A so-called "absolute" of atlas cedarwood is also prepared from atlas cedarwood oil by fractionated distillation under vacuum, see **Cedarwood Oil, "Atlas"**.

Cedarwood Oil, "Atlas".

This essential oil is also known as **"Moroccan" Cedarwood Oil.** The oil is entirely different—chemically and olfactorily—from the American Virginia or Texas cedarwood oils. The tree, **Cedrus Atlantica,** is a pine, not a cypress (such as the American and East African cedars). It is believed that the Atlas cedar is originated from the famous Lebanon cedars which grow wild in Lebanon and in the island of Cyprus, now protected from being felled for essential oil distillation and lumbering. The Atlas cedarwood oil may occasionally be offered as **Lebanon Cedarwood Oil** (see **Cedarwood Oil, Lebanon**).

Atlas Cedarwood Oil is steam distilled from either the wood and stumps—or from sawdust—of the above tree which grows abundantly in the Atlas mountains, particularly in Morocco and in the northwestern parts of Algeria. Distillation takes place almost exclusively in Morocco. The annual production of this oil fluctuates between 15 and 35 metric tons. It is one of the most inexpensive essential oils entering the European market.

Atlas Cedarwood Oil is a yellowish to orange-yellow or deep amber-colored, viscous oil, occasionally somewhat turbid. Its odor is very peculiar and not exactly pleasant when undiluted: slightly camphoraceous-cresylic with a sweet and tenac-

ious, woody undertone, reminiscent of cassie and mimosa. However, it does not present the delicateness or depth of these floral oils. The mimosa-like note is typical of the essential oil of atlas cedarwood and it is not present in the so-called resinoid of the same wood. The odor characteristics can vary significantly. Certain lots of Atlas cedarwood oil are produced by other methods than the direct steam distillation, e.g. high-pressure steam distillation or alkali-treatment (so-called "pulping") prior to distillation. Concequently, the essential oil may contain certain odorous materials which are not present in the wood.

Atlas Cedarwood Oil is widely used in perfumery for its fixative effect and unique odor which seems to blend so well with labdanum products and with all the woody and woody-floral types of perfume materials.

Although large quantities of the oil are consumed locally as a household medicine of almost universal application, the oil finds its way into a wealth of European and American soap perfumes and other perfumes.

The oil is rarely adulterated, but it may be confused with cedarwood oils from other species or areas. The only essential oil which has some similarity to **Atlas Cedarwood Oil** is the Himalayan **Deodar Cedarwood Oil.** This oil is derived from a close botanical relative (see **Cedarwood Oil, Himalaya**).

Atlas Cedarwood Absolute (or cedrus atlantica absolute) is a name given to two entirely different types of perfume materials:
1) The absolute from concrète of Atlas cedarwood (see **Cedarwood Atlas Resinoid**) and
2) The heart fractions of Atlas cedarwood oil, redistilled under vacuum. This is not a true absolute.

Cedarwood Oil, East Africa.

The term "it smells like the pencil sharpener" is frequently encountered when various cedarwood oils are presented to laymen for odor description. The above term is particularly suitable for the essential oil of **Juniperus Procera,** a cedar, or rather a cypress, botanically related to the "Texas cedar" from Texas and Mexico and to the "Virginia Cedar" of the northeastern U.S.A. The east African cedarwood oil is furthermore olfactorily related to the Texas cedarwood oil.

East African Cedarwood Oil is steam distilled from the waste wood in the saw mills of Kenya,

East Africa where the trees are exploited for various purposes, e.g. lead pencils, boxes, hand carved figures, etc. The oil is a brownish-yellow or orange-yellow to reddish, usually very viscous liquid, occasionally showing a considerable deposit of crystals. The odor is very dry-woody, somewhat earthy and quite strong with a slightly cade-like topnote. The dry notes yield to an increasing balsamic sweetness as the oil dries out on a perfume blotter. Overall, it is less balsamic than the Virginia cedarwood oil, more reminiscent of the odor of **Cedarwood Oil, Texas** (see that monograph).

The annual production of **East African Cedarwood Oil** is quite impressive, usually between 55 and 100 metric tons. The major part of the production goes to the United Kingdom. Here, it serves as a starting material for the isolation of its main constituents: **Cedrenol** and **Cedrol**, production of cedryl esters, cedrenyl esters and other chemical derivatives of cedrenol, etc. The oil is also rectified and fractionated for perfumery use in Europe. The rectified oil is almost colorless. An almost cedrenol-free fraction (consisting mainly of sesquiterpenes) is used as a low-cost ocor-masking agent in household products, for industrial perfuming, etc. This oil is a water white mobile liquid which does not deposit any crystals even on cooling. Its odor is dry and woody, quite typical of cedarwood, but virtually deprived of balsamic notes and with little fixative power.

Kenya (or "east African") cedarwood oil is a good fixative for soap perfumes, pine fragrances, wood notes, etc., and it blends well with rose notes, Oriental bases, moss notes, etc. In violet, fougère and chypre bases, and even in modern, woody-aldehydic perfume types, it may well modify the notes of vetiver, patchouli or sandalwood.

It is believed that the **Cedrol** and **Cedrenol** content of this oil is dependent upon the exposure of the waste wood to the sun prior to distillation. Due to the great similarity of this oil to the (American) Texas cedarwood oil, the **East African Cedarwood Oil** has little importance for the American perfume industry.

See also **Cedarwood Oil, Texas**.

Cedarwood Oil, Himalaya.

Himalayan cedarwood oil is also called **Deodar Cedarwood Oil**. It is steam distilled from the wood of **Cedrus Deodara** which grows at high altitude in the mountains of Himalaya, toward northern India, Afghanistan and Pakistan. Distillation takes place locally, and the trees are felled exclusively for the production of the essential oil since the wood is of little or no use as a lumber. The tree is very closely related to **Cedrus Atlantica** and **Cedrus Libani** (see **Cedarwood Oil, Atlas** and **Cedarwood Oil, Lebanon**). The **Deodar Cedar** tree has been introduced in Europe as a decorative plant. It grows now in English countrysides, in central Europe and other places unusual for this mountain tree.

The interest in essential oils and in the local production of same in India has increased enormously since World War II. **Deodar Cedarwood Oil** is one of the oils which probably will be produced regularly on a comparatively large scale (50 to 200 metric tons per year).

Deodar Cedarwood Oil is a yellowish to brownish-yellow oil (when crude), somewhat viscous and of rich, sweet-woody, almost balsamic odor, closely reminiscent of Atlas cedarwood oil. It presents similar cresylic-camphoraceous topnotes, but it also becomes delicately sweet-woody on its lasting dryout.

It is conceivable that this essential oil will be produced mainly for the purpose of supplying the Indian soap industry with a perfume material which otherwise had to be imported. **Deodar Cedarwood Oil** can replace the **Atlas Cedarwood Oil** is almost any soap perfume formula.

Cedarwood Oils, Japanese.

Various essential oils, derived from Chinese and Japanese trees belonging to the genus cupressaceae, appear occasionally on the perfume market under the name of **Japanese Cedar** or **Japanese Cypress** oil.

Hiba Oil, Hinoki Oil and **Sugi Oil** are three of the most important essential oils in this group. They constitute the cedarwood-like and pine-like raw materials for the Chinese and the Japanese perfume industry where they find use in soap perfumes, industrial perfumes, etc.

Hiba Oil—see monograph on **Thujopsis Dolobrata** (var. hondai).

Hinoki Oil—see **Chamaecyparis Obtusa**, root oil and leaf oil.

Sugi Oil—see monograph on **Cryptomeria Japonica**.

Cedarwood Oil, Lebanon.

The world famous and antique, perhaps thousand-year-old cedars of Lebanon are finally protected by law against felling or any kind of exploitation. The tree, **Cedrus Libani**, grows wild in the mountains of Lebanon and in the nearby island of Cyprus. Although the wood—and thereby indirectly the essential oil—from this tree is one of the oldest known perfume materials, the oil is no more available. There are to-day only a few—if any—perfumers who have ever seen and smelled a true Lebanon cedarwood oil; however, the oil is mentioned here for the sake of honor and veneration to this distinguished old material.

The oils which are offered to-day under the name of Lebanon cedarwood oil are most likely oils, distilled from the wood of **Cedrus Atlantica,** Manetti. This tree is known as the **Atlas Cedar** and it grows in great number in Morocco and Algeria (the Atlas mountains). The essential oil is produced regularly, see monograph on **Cedarwood Oil, Atlas.**

According to 50-year-old descriptions, the true Lebanon cedarwood oil was a yellow liquid of a strong, cedarleaf-like, grassy odor. If this is true, then the oil must have been quite different from other cedarwood oils, including to-day's Atlas cedarwood oil. However, the technique of distilling high-boiling essential oils has improved significantly during the past half century, and it is likely that the oil would turn out to-day with an odor altogether different from what the above description says.

The author is not old enough to have any personal experience with true **Lebanon Cedarwood Oil**, but he owes his thanks to a very high authority for information on this subject.

Cedarwood Oil, Port Orford.

This oil is steam distilled from the sawdust and other waste of the wood of the "Western White Cedar", **Chamaecyparis Lawsoniana,** a tall and very decorative cypress which grows wild and abundantly in a limited area of Oregon and California states, U.S.A. The tree is cultivated for ornamental purposes all over Central Europe and in other parts of the world.

Between the two world wars, the sawmills in Oregon and California produced this oil in tremendous quantities. Interest in the oil has now almost disappeared, and it is not produced on a large scale any more, if produced regularly at all.

Port Orford Cedarwood Oil is a mobile liquid, colorless to pale yellow or straw yellow, darkening and thickening on ageing. The odor is moderately sweet-woody, pine-oil-like, bitter fennel-like, substantially different from the odor of other cedarwood oils. Its odor could remind of the odor of a mixture of pine oil and Virginia cedarwood oil, but the dryout of the Port Orford oil is almost herbaceous-woody, long lasting and anisic or fennel-like sweet.

Since the odor type does not present any unique effect beyond its peculiar complexity of fragrance, it is most likely that this oil will slowly disappear from the perfumer's shelf. Probably the most interesting thing about the oil is the extraordinarily high content of borneol (10 to 20%). This material is sometimes hard to obtain as a synthetic chemical in the U.S.A., free from isoborneol. See also **Wormwood Oil,** section: **Mugwort,** Chinese.

Cedarwood Oil, Texas.

Practically unknown 30 years ago, the oil of **Juniperus Mexicana** to-day ranks among the "over 100-tons-a-year" oils, and it enjoys the steady interest of perfumers and an increasing interest of the manufacturers of aromatic chemicals. The tree, which is a small and poor-looking relative of the cypress, grows abundantly in the southwestern parts of Texas, toward the south in Mexico and Central America. The oil is steam distilled from the heartwood of this tree which is felled exclusively for the purpose of producing the essential oil. Distillation takes place mainly in Texas, U.S.A. However, the crude oil is often rectified by the large essential oil and perfume houses in New Jersey, U.S.A.

Crude **Cedarwood Oil, Texas** is a dark orange to brownish, turbid or clear, somewhat viscous liquid. Considerable amounts of crystals deposit from the oil on standing. In cold weather the oil may become entirely solid. The odor of the crude oil is pleasant, sweet-woody, yet somewhat tar-like or cade-like, smoky. On drying it becomes increasingly balsamic-sweet and it shows great tenacity with a uniform, sweet-woody dryout.

Rectified (redistilled, steam-redistilled, etc.) oil of **Juniperus Mexicana** is pale yellow or almost colorless. Its odor is less tar-like, less cade-like or smoky than that of the crude oil. The dryout is clean, sweet-woody with the typical "pencil-sharpener"-odor. This type of rectified oil is not the most common of the Texas cedarwood oils. It is customary to fractionate the crude oil during the re-distillation. A "light" fraction consists mainly of sesquiterpenes and it presents the dry-woody part of the cedarwood notes. It has only poor fixative effect but great odor-masking ability. The "heavy" fractions consist mainly of cedrenol and cedrol. These sesquiterpene alcohols can be isolated in a more or less pure state. They are solid materials of weak, but very pleasant, woody-balsamic odor. It has been claimed that these materials are virtually odorless when absolutely pure. The commercial grades do have pleasant odors and are not always white, dry crystals.

The sesquiterpenes can be chemically converted into some highly interesting perfume materials while the solid cedrenol serves as is or in the form of its acetate (usually liquid). The crude oil as well as the rectified oil are used extensively in perfumery. The rectified oil is generally preferred when dark perfume color may be a problem. As a blender for ionones and methylionones, cinnamic alcohol, nitromusks, ambre bases and leather bases, patchouli, pine, spruce, vetiver oil, etc., the oil of **Juniperus Mexicana** (Texas cedarwood oil) is a most versatile material for the creative perfumer. The oil is readily available, and at a very attractive cost.

See also **Cedarwood Oil, East Africa.**

Cedarwood Oil, Virginia.

One of the most important cedarwood oils from the United States of America is the oil of **Juniperus Virginiana**, known as Virginia cedar or "Southern Red Cedar" (see also **Cedarwood Oil, Texas**). The so-called "Eastern White Cedar" is now used only for the production of cedarleaf oil. At present, the wood of that tree is not distilled (see **Cedarleaf Oil** = "Thuja oil"). The Virginia cedarwood oil is also known in the U.S.A. as "**Bedford Cedarwood Oil**".

Juniperus Virginiana is a shrub or a tree; it occasionally grows to a considerable size, and is found growing wild all over the southeastern United States. The wood from these trees is highly appreciated for the manufacture of cabinets,

chests, etc.; the essential oil is steam distilled from the sawdust and other waste wood from the lumbermills. Older trees are preferred since they contain more of the reddish heartwood which not only gives a beautiful surface when polished, but also yields much more essential oil than the wood from young trees or sapwood (which is white). The annual production of **Cedarwood Oil, Virginia** amounts to 200 or 300 metric tons, and it has been steadily increasing since World War II.

Virginia Cedarwood Oil is a pale yellow to slightly orange-yellow colored oil which, on rectification, will yield a water-white, oily liquid. It is slightly less viscous than Atlas or Texas cedarwood oils and it does not deposit crystals at ordinary temperatures. The odor of Virginia cedarwood oil is at first oily-woody and almost sweet, mild and pleasant, somewhat balsamic and typical of cedarwood (lumber). The odor becomes drier and more woody, less balsamic as the oil dries out on a perfume blotter (Texas cedarwood oil smells sweeter as it dries out).

The odor of Virginia cedarwood oil is well known to many eastern American owners of cedar chests, cabinets, boxes, etc. On the unpolished surface of such wood, one can often see small crystals. The oil, too, may deposit crystals on cooling or prolonged standing. The crystals are cedrol crystals and their appearance in the oil is to a certain degree a sign of high cedrol content or a sign of age—or both. According to Schimmel, an absolutely pure cedrol, recrystallized, is odorless. The content of cedrol in Virginia cedarwood oil is usually rather small, and this oil is not a good source for the isolation of cedrol.

Cedrol, like camphor and menthol, is comparatively volatile, and the odor of very old cedarwood chests could not be due to this material which may disappear completely on ageing. However, the main constituent of the oil, **Cedrene**, a sesquiterpene, is slowly converted to **Cedrol** and **Cedrenol** during ageing of the oil. Due to the fact that Virginia cedarwood oil is usually rectified, various fractions are also commercially available:

1) **Cedarwood Oil, Light Fractions,** consist mainly of the sesquiterpene **Cedrene** which represents the very dry topnote in the odor of various cedarwood oils. Cedrene can be converted into interesting chemical derivatives of great value in perfumery.

2) **Cedarwood Oil #1025** consists of high-boiling materials and it represents the balsamic-woody

parts of the "cedarwood odor". It is conceivable that the typical sweet part of the cedarwood odor is mainly due to **Cedrenol** and similar constituents, present only in the high-boiling fractions, and found in the total oil only in a small percentage. However, some chemists claim that a chemically pure **Cedrenol** is virtually odorless (see above).

Virginia Cedarwood Oil is used extensively in perfumery, particularly in soap perfumery, as a fixative and cost-reducer for vetiver oil, sandalwood oil, patchouli oil or even in the comparatively cheap guaiacwood oil. The dry-woody character and the fixative effect of cedarwood oil, Virginia, make it almost universally applicable. The oil is frequently used as the only active perfume ingredient in room sprays, disinfectants, insecticides, cleansers and other industrial products, household products, etc. Mixed with Ceylon citronella oil, it was once a popular mosquito-repellent, but it has now been replaced by more active chemicals.

Virginia Cedarwood Oil is also found quite frequently as an adulterant in the above mentioned essential oils as well as in numerous others. For the isolation of **Cedrol** and **Cedrenol** and for the production of **Cedryl Acetate, Cedrenyl Acetate** and other esters (or "acetylated cedarwood oil"), the oils from **Cedarwood East Africa** and **Cedarwood Texas** are far superior. See these monographs. Virginia cedarwood oil is a good source for the isolation of **Cedrene** which is a starting material in the production of various interesting perfumery chemicals.

Cedrat Oil.

As a result of private communication with earlier producers and suppliers, the author is convinced that the true **Cedrat Peel Oil** is no more produced. Oils which are offered on the market under that name, are most conceivably compositions of lemon oil, lime oil, citral, etc.

The **Cedrat** fruit is the original and classical citrus fruit which is known in English speaking countries as **Citron**. But since this name is generally applied in Europe to the **Lemon**, the name **Cedrat** has been preferred by the author to describe the above classical citrus fruit.

The **Cedrat** tree, **Citrus Medica**, var. bajoura, grows in the southern part of Italy where the peel is preserved, usually in sugar syrup or salt

brine. Salt brine removes the bitter taste from the peel and makes it edible.

The very thick cedrat peel may be boiled in sugar syrup for several days to prepare the **"Sucade"**, a well-known topping or filling for baked goods, plumcakes, fruitcakes, etc. Most of the European "sucade" is derived from the cedrat tree. In the Pacific Ocean Islands, the **Citrus Decumana** (the French "pampelmousse") is used for a similar purpose. The "pampelmousse" is the largest of all citrus fruits. Single fruits may weigh as much as 10 kilos. The American grapefruit is presumably a hybrid of the above "pampelmousse" with the sweet orange.

True **Cedrat Oil** was used in the early part of the 20th century as a modifier in citrus colognes, etc.

Cedrat Petitgrain Oil.

See also **Cedrat Oil.**

The essential oil from the leaves and twigs of the tree, **Citrus Medica**, var. bajoura, possibly a local sub-variety, is occasionally steam distilled in some of the French islands in the south Pacific (Samoa and other islands) upon demand from European perfume houses.

Cedrat Petitgrain Oil has been recommended for use in various perfume types ever since the name of the oil appeared in various published perfume formulas.

The oil is a greenish-yellow to olive-yellow or pale yellow mobile liquid of sweet and fresh, floral-woody, leafy "petitgrain"-type of odor, somewhat reminiscent of lemon-petitgrain oil, however, not nearly as powerful as that oil.

There would be quite a problem in producing a uniform quality of cedrat petitgrain oil, due to the scarcity of true cedrat trees and due to the great number of varieties of these trees. Thus, it is unlikely that the cedrat petitgrain oil which has only little news to offer to the perfumer, will ever become a regularly produced item.

See also **Combava Petitgrain Oil.**

Cedrela Odorata.

From the wood of a large tree indigenous to the West Indies, Central and South America, an essential oil is steam distilled under the above name. The wood is collected for the purpose of making cigar boxes, closets, cabinets, book-shelves, etc. or for plywood. The wood is also known as "Cigarbox-Wood", "Indian Mahogany" or "Sugar-Crate Wood". It is a fragrant wood, and from the waste materials produced in the lumbering of the boards, the essential oil can be produced at a fairly low cost.

The main supplier is Brazil. Occasionally, lots of Cedrela Oil are offered from Cuba or Jamaica, where cigarboxes are also made from locally grown Cedrela Odorata and similar species.

Oil of Cedrela Odorata is a greenish-yellow to olive-colored liquid of pleasant, dry-woody and powerful odor, reminiscent of cedarwood oil, Texas and cubeb oil or clove leaf oil sesquiterpenes with an undertone like carrot seed oil, however, without the fattiness of this. The odor bears some resemblance to the odor of the Cyperus oils. Cedrela oil blends well with cedarwood oil (Texas) and its derivatives, with ionones and methylionones, pine needle oils, isobornylacetate, isobutylquinoline, oakmoss, rosemary oil, etc. The oil is used mainly in soap perfumes of the woody types, Oriental types, etc., and in the perfumes for disinfectants, insecticides, air-freshener sprays, etc. in industrial perfumes, etc. Up to the present, the oil has been given very little attention, but it is constantly available in modest quantities.

In northern India, another species of the tree is grown, Cedrela Toona. The wood of this tree is fragrant, but the yield of essential oil by steam distillation is extremely small, perhaps due to the very high boiling point of the constituents of this oil. Experimentally, a two-step extraction of the wood with hydrocarbon solvents yielded a viscous, orange-colored oil. However, this Cedrela Toona Oil is not commercially available, and the oil may be of very little interest to the perfumers. The author has no personal experience with the so-called Cedrela Toona Resinoid which is extracted from this wood.

The tree, Toona Calanthas grows in the Philippines and is used locally for the production of cigarboxes.

See also monograph on Cangerana.

Celery Seed Oil.

This oil is produced by steam distillation of the fruits (seed) of either wild or cultivated Apium Graveolens, the celery plant. This plant is cultivated in France, India, Holland, Hungary, and China, and, to a smaller extent in the U.S.A. Distillation takes place in all these countries, Indian seed being freely available on the market and frequently preferred for distillation.

It is customary to crush the seed prior to distillation, but some distillers do not comminute the seed prior to distillation. Celery seed, like most other fruits of the umbellifer family, contain substantial amounts of palmitic acid and related fatty acids. These are volatile with steam and may withhold some essential oil in solution and emulsion.

The annual production of celery seed oil has increased considerably, and is estimated to be between 10 and 50 tons. Most of this is used in the spice industry where all kinds of foods and food additives are flavored with celery: soups, meats, sauces, pickles, vegetable juices, etc. The oil substitutes for the spice in many cases. More recently, the Celery Oleoresin (see next monograph) has replaced the essential oil in food flavors, particularly in meat sauces, canned foods and juices, etc.

Celery Seed Oil is a pale yellow to orange yellow liquid. Its odor is spicy-warm, sweet and rich, "soup-like", longlasting and powerful, slightly fatty, typical of the odor of the seed (fruit) but less fresh than the odor of the celery plant. The flavor is equally warm and spicy, somewhat burning and very powerful. Celery seed oil is one of the most diffusive odors and one of the most penetrating flavors. The average use level of this oil in flavors would be somewhere between 0.05 and 0.50 mg%, but the Minimum Perceptible is incredibly low: 0.001 to 0.002 mg%. In other words, the typical celery flavor is perceptible in a dilution of one part of celery seed oil in one hundred million parts of a neutral liquid medium. Minor quantities of selery seed oil are used in pharmaceutical preparations where the oil is said to exert a sedative effect. Consequently, the most important ingredients in celery seed oil are named Sedanolide and Sedanolic Acid Anhydride. Although present only to the extent of one percent or less of the oil, these materials actually determine the power of the odor and flavor of celery seed oil. The two materials are available as synthetic chemicals. The main constituents of celery seed oil is the monoterpene, d-limonene, and the sesquiterpene, selinene. The former is the most common adulterant or diluent found in commercial lots of celery seed oil (in a too high percentage). **Maraniol** (4-methyl-7-ethoxy cumarin) and **Cyclotene** (2-hydroxy-3-methyl-2-cyclopenten-1-one) are occasionally found in celery seed oil. These materials are not natural constituents of the oil, but they are added to fortify or enrich poorer oils (e.g. limonene-diluted oils).

In perfumery, celery seed oil is used very frequently, but only in very small amounts. Used skilfully, it can impart warm notes in floral and Oriental compositions, in lavender bouquets, in modern fantasy and aldehydic perfumes, etc. Carelessly used, it may easily ruin a perfume. Its diffusive power and great odor tenacity should not be underestimated.

Various oils distilled from other parts of the celery plant are also available on the market under the name of **Celery Seed Oil** or **Celery Oil.** However, the true seed oil is the one with the highest content of the above mentioned "key" materials which give celery seed oil its particular effectiveness in perfumes and flavors. All other celery oils have less of this special effect.

An oil distilled from the entire plant, **Celery Herb Oil,** is also available, but should be considered as another spice oil or a "culinary herb oil", representative of the flavor of the entire plant; it can not be regarded a replacement for celery seed oil. The herb oil has less strength or power, but more freshness than the seed oil. The latter being more expensive, it may be adulterated with the herb oil or with an essential oil distilled from the waste material from the cleaning of the seed (so-called **Celery Chaff Oil.**)

Celery Seed Oleoresin.

Celery Seed Oleoresin is a prepared oleoresin. It is produced by extraction of celery seed (see **Celery Seed Oil**) with petroleum ether or other hydrocarbon solvents or with ethyl alcohol. The latter solvent would yield an ordinary extract from a pharmaceutical point of view. The alcoholic extract has the advantage of a lower terpene content and, accordingly, a better flavor and solubility than the hydrocarbon solvent extracts.

Celery Seed Oleoresin is a dark green or brownish green, viscous liquid of a very powerful odor and flavor, typical of the aroma of the seed: warm, fatty-spicy and rich, intensely sweet-herbal, radiant and tenacious.

The extract is used in food products where it reproduces the aroma of the celery seed even better than does the essential oil. The oleoresin also presents the advantage of containing more of the important highboiling odor- and flavor principles, some of which are hardly distillable with steam at all. Steam distillation of celery seed is combined with significant problems.

The average use level of **Celery Seed Oleoresin** in flavors is strongly dependant upon the nature of the end product. In straight celery flavors, the concentration of the oleoresin may be as high as 0.60 mg%; when used as a "bouquet" flavor material, its concentration in the finished product should be close to the **Minimum Perceptible** which is about 0.001 mg%.

The oleoresin is only rarely used in perfumery. Its dark color is a disadvantage in many compositions. However, the great diffusive power and the outstanding odor-tenacity of this product makes it possible for the perfumer to obtain good effects from very low concentrations of celery seed oleoresin.

This interesting perfume material blends very well with lavender absolute, oakmoss absolute, opopanax resinoid, deertongue or melilotus extracts, tobacco leaf absolute, melaleuca alternifolia oil, etc. and with isoeugenol, anisaldehyde, coumarin, etc. It is related olfactorily to lovage and opopanax and the synthetic materials maraniol (7-ethoxy-4-methyl coumarin) and cyclotene (2-hydroxy-3-methyl-2-cyclopenten-1-one).

The oleoresin gives delightful effects in fougères, pine needle fragrances, "forest" notes, spice blends, etc.

The annual production of **Celery Seed Oleoresin** is steadily increasing and is easily adjusted to the demand.

Cestrum Nocturnum.

This small shrub belongs to the same botanical genus as do the potato and the tobacco plants. It is grown as an ornamental and fragrant shrub in many parts of India, in China and in other parts of the Far East. The local name for the shrub in India is "rajanigandha" which means "night queen", not to be confused with the famous cactus of the same nickname.

The flowers of cestrum nocturnum are, like many other long-tubed flowers, particularly fragrant at night in order to attract certain night-butterflies and moths who are able to reach the honey with their very long trunk. The flowers are white with pale green tubes.

The author has no experience with the use of this oil in perfumery since the samples which the author received during the past 6 years have been either too small, too old or, in cases, they were merely "attars" and not true essential oils. Judging from the extremely heavy isoeugenol-like, faintly carnation-like, woody-warm, yet strongly floral odor, the essential oil of **Cestrum Nocturnum** could find use as a "new note" in many modern "warm-spicy" or aldehydic-floral perfume types.

"Attars" of cestrum nocturnum flowers are prepared in India by co-distillation with sandalwood oil or by distilling the essential oil of cestrum nocturnum into a receiver with sandalwood oil or with a vegetable (fixed) oil. These "attars" find use in East Indian perfumery.

Essential oils, absolutes or "attars" of **Cestrum Nocturnum** are not regularly available outside of the countries of origin.

Chamaecyparis Obtusa.

Two important essential oils are distilled from the cypress-like tree, **Chamaecyparis Obtusa**: **Hinoki Root Oil** and **Hinoki Leaf Oil**. The tree grows abundantly wild and replanted in the southern parts of Japan and in Formosa.

1) **Hinoki Root Oil** used to be distilled in substantial quantities. Prior to World War II about 600 metric tons were distilled annually. Production has now dropped to about 30 tons in Japan per year. The oil is produced by steam distillation of the roots which are chopped but not always dried prior to distillation. **Hinoki Root Oil** is a pale yellow liquid of dry, woody, camphoraceous odor with a peculiar warm-sweet, almost spicy undertone. The oil consists almost entirely of terpineol, monoterpenes and sesquiterpenes. The presence of isoborneol should have been proved according to some scientists. This would be one of the very rare cases where isoborneol is identified in nature.

Hinoki Root Oil is used locally for low-cost soap perfumes, for industrial perfumes, insecticides, etc. It is also widely employed for mineral flotation in the local mining industry.

There are two distinctly different types of **Hinoki Root** oils or, more correctly there is an extracted **Hinoki Wood Oil** which is pro-

duced in a similar way as described under **Pine Oil**. The Formosan **Hinoki Root Oil** is more important since it contains significant quantities of terpineol. The two oils are rarely exported in quantity and they do not offer new or unusual perfume effects to the perfume industry in other parts of the world.

2) **Hinoki Leaf Oil** is steam distilled from the leaves of the above mentioned cypress-like tree. The yield of oil is much smaller than that from the roots. The 1958-production in Japan was about 20 metric tons. The oil is also produced in Formosa where a related tree yields another essential oil. The latter is occasionally called **Hayata Oil**, see monograph on **Machilus Oil** (from leaf). There seems to be some confusion of the two oils outside of the country of origin.

Hinoki Leaf Oil is a yellowish liquid with an intensely strong, camphoraceous, fresh pine-like and somewhat green odor. The odor is distinctly fresher than that from the root oil but also "lighter" of type. The leaf oil resembles the root oil in its heavy-sweet undertone. **Hinoki Leaf Oil** has no importance in perfumery outside of its countries of origin where it finds use in soaps, detergents, industrial perfumes, etc.

Chamomile Oil, "German".

Also called "**Hungarian**" **Chamomile Oil** or "**Blue**" **Chamomile Oil**, this oil is distilled from the true pharmaceutical chamomile, **Matricaria Chamomilla**, which grows all over Europe, particularly in central and northern Europe. It is cultivated in Hungary, Yugoslavia, Czechoslovakia, Bulgaria, U.S.S.R., Germany, Belgium, and Spain. Hungary is the main producer of the plant material. The name "German" chamomile may refer to the fact that the plant is cultivated in Germany, but more likely because the bulk of essential oil used to be distilled in Germany (from Hungarian flower material.

The ligulate florets are collected, dried and steam distilled. It should be mentioned at this point that at least one large supplier of **Chamomile Oil** produces his oil by extraction of the flower material and not by distillation. This product is a **Chamomile Absolute**, not an essential oil. The extraction method is also responsible for the extraordinarily high content of **Azulene** in this

11: Wild growing **Broom** shrubs near Seillans, Var (France).   *(Fot. S. Arctander, 1960)*

12: Flowering top of a **Broom** shrub in the harvest season. Seillans, Var (France).

(Fot. S. Arctander, 1960)

particular German oil which has an intense, deep ink-blue color and a high viscosity. The odor is indirectly affected also since Azulene and other hydrocarbons tend to impart a "rubberlike" note in the odor of this chamomile oil.

Steam distilled chamomile oil is, when fresh, a deep ink-blue, somewhat viscous liquid of intensely sweet, herbaceous-coumarin-like odor with a fresh-fruity undertone. In a pure and undiluted state, the sweetness and odor-intensity of this oil is almost sickening, nauseating. The dryout of a mellow and aged oil is pleasant, sweet tobacco-like and warm, but in freshly distilled oils there is often an obnoxiously animal-sweet, amine-like note. The flavor is warm, but somewhat bitter and strongly herbaceous.

Extracted Chamomile Oil (could be called **Chamomile Absolute**) is produced from the flower heads by extraction with alcohol or chloroform. This method will yield the highest content of **Chamazulene**, the blue hydrocarbon, in the extract. Interesting dermatological effects are attributed to this constituent, but it has little or no direct influence upon the odor of **Chamomile Oil**. Upon ageing, the color of the oil changes to brown, but apart from telling the perfumer that the oil is not of a recent production, this color change is not directly connected with the odor of the oil.

True Chamomile Oil is used in very small percentages in high-class perfumes to introduce a warm, rich undertone which lasts through all stages of evaporation. The "topnote-effect" of the "blue" chamomile oil is less pronounced than that of the "English" or "Roman" chamomile oil, see **Chamomile Oil, Roman**. It should also be remembered that distilled chamomile oil is much less tenacious in its odor performance than the extracted chamomile oil, the latter having a superior fixative effect. The unpleasant off-odors in certain extracted chamomile oils can sometimes be traced back to the solvent used in the extraction. If the solvent contains as much as 0.01% of an odorous, high-boiling impurity, there is a good chance that the chamomile extract may contain up to 10% of this material since the total amount of solvent in the process is up to 1000 times the yield of extract.

However, the extracted chamomile oil is so common on the market that some perfumers even refuse to believe that they have a true oil in front of them when presented with a distilled chamomile

oil, which is obviously less viscous, paler blue and often clear.

In flavor work, **Chamomile Oil** is used, like the Roman chamomile oil, in certain liqueurs, etc., particularly in those of the D.O.M. or the Benedictine type. In this respect, chamomile oil blends well with angelica root oil, artemisia oils, calamus oil, etc. or with the fruity flavor types, such as banana, peach, strawberry, etc.*

Since the main constituents have recently been synthesized (see monograph on **Chamomile Oil, Roman**), chamomile oil may be more and more cleverly adulterated. Even the blue hydrocarbon, **Chamazulene**, has now been produced synthetically, and is available.

The **Extracted Chamomile Oil (Chamomile Absolute)** is a semi-solid mass or very viscous liquid, often grainy and not homogeneous; it may separate solids at low room temperatures. The odor is similar to that of the distilled oil, but less fresh, more heavy-nauseating.

The very common weed, **Matricaria Suaveolens**, may occasionally contaminate the flower material from which the essential oil is produced. The presence of minor proportions of this wild flower in the botanical material does not affect the odor of the produced oil seriously.

The annual production of **Chamomile Oil** and **Chamomile Absolute** is very limited (at times below 200 kilos), and the price is comparatively high (about one-third to one-half the price of jasmin absolute). But only a small fraction of the total world production of the chamomile flowers is used for distillation or extraction, the bulk being consumed by the drug stores as a medicinal tea.

See also **Chamomile Oil, Moroccan** and **Chamomile Oil, Roman**.

Chamomile Oil, Moroccan.

Related to "German chamomile" botanically but not at all resembling this plant, is **Ormenis Multicaulis**, a good-looking plant, 90 to 125 cms. high, with very hairy leaves and tubular yellow flowers, surrounded by white ligulets, the typical construction of a composite species. The plant is probably a native of northwest Africa, and evolved from a very common **Ormenis** species which grows all over the Mediterranean countries.

* (Suggested use level is 0.50 to 2.00 mg% and the Minimum Perceptible is about 0.10 to 0.20 mg%.)

Distillation is carried out locally where the plant is most common, i.e. in the northwestern parts of Morocco. The flowering tops, harvested at the beginning of the inflorescence, are steam distilled.

The oil of **Ormenis Multicaulis** is a pale yellow to brownish yellow, mobile liquid. It seems that light-colored oils are obtained at the beginning of the inflorescence (better perfume oils), and darker oils come jn poorer yields at the end of the inflorescence. The odor of the pale oils is fresh-herbaceous, slightly camphoraceous, but soon changes into a sweet, cistus-like and rich-balsamic undertone which is very tenacious and pleasant, almost ambra-like.

Moroccan Chamomile Oil blends well with artemisia oils, cypress oil, labdanum products, lavandin and lavender, vetiver oil or derivatives of cedarwood oils, oakmoss products, olibanum, etc. Chemically and olfactorily, the oil is distinctly different from the "German" or the "Roman" chamomile oils, and cannot be considered as a replacement for them. Ormenis multicaulis oil deserves its own place in perfumery on account of the above mentioned valuable notes and effects. The oil finds application in citrus-colognes, ambre-, chypre-, fougère-bases, as well as in a multitude of other bases where a fresh modification of ambre-herbaceous notes are called for (lavender, pine, etc.). Even trace amounts of the oil may introduce a delightful topnote in a herbaceous or floral-herbaceous fragrance. Moroccan chamomile oil has occasionally found use as an adulterant in cistus oil (distilled from labdanum "gum").

Ormenis Multicaulis grows wild, and is available in quite substantial quantities, but the oil is not yet a common article although it has been produced for at least 30 years.

Chamomile Oil, "Roman".

Occasionally called "chamomile oil", the **Roman Chamomile Oil** is distilled from the ligulate florets of **Anthemis Nobilis,** a plant which is related to the "true" chamomile (see monograph **Chamomile Oil, "German"**), but which looks more like the wild chrysanthemum.

Anthemis Nobilis is cultivated in England, Belgium, France, and Hungary for the purpose of collecting flowers (flower heads). Distillation is by steam and takes place mainly in England.

Other flowers are sold to pharmaceutical houses. The yield of essential oil is very small.

Roman Chamomile Oil is a pale blue, mobile liquid (when fairly fresh) of sweet herbaceous, somewhat fruity-warm and tealeaf-like odor. The odor is extremely diffusive but it has little tenacity. The flavor of the oil is somewhat bitter, chemical or medicinal, but also fruity-herbaceous, warm. **Roman Chamomile Oil** and **German Chamomile Oil** are, if distilled in the same way, somewhat similar, and they do contain the same odor and flavor principles. The oils are distinguished analytically by the fact that they present the highest ester value of all essential oils known (the ester value is about 300). This is due to a very high content of the butyl-, amyl- and hexyl esters of tiglic and angelic acids. The ester content is about 85%. These esters are responsible for the peculiar odor of the chamomile oils. The pale blue color of **Roman Chamomile** oil is due to the presence of a hydrocarbon, **Chamazulene** which is high boiling and thus present only in traces in the **"Roman"** chamomile oil. See also **Chamomile Absolute** under **Chamomile Oil, "German"**.

"Roman" chamomile oil is rarely used in flavor work (occasionally in certain types of alcoholic beverages), but more frequently, although very sparingly, in perfumes. It imparts a warm, yet fresh note and a natural depth which is difficult to obtain by other means. Roman chamomile oil blends well with amyl cinnamic aldehyde, bergamot oil, jasmin bases, labdanum products, neroli oil, sage clary oil, or absolute, oakmoss products, etc., but it is mainly a trace additive, independent of the "body" materials in the perfume. The oil is sometimes preferred over the "german" chamomile oil because of the much paler color of the "Roman" oil. However, both oils fade on ageing. This color change will tell the perfumer about the age of the oil, but it has no direct connection with the odor of the oil.

Roman Chamomile Oil is produced in limited quantities only. Some years, the production has been lower than 100 kilos. It rarely exceeds 500 kilos.

Champaca Absolute.

Champaca Absolute is obtained by extraction of the beautiful deep-yellow flowers of **Michelia Champaca,** a medium-sized slender tree, related to the magnolias. The tree is a native of the

Philippines and the Indonesian islands, but, similarly to ylang-ylang, has been brought along by the Melanesian people to places far west of its origin.

Apart from its native area, the champaca tree grows in the Ganjam and South Orissa districts of India, in southeastern China, in Réunion and on the tiny island of Nossi-Bé off the northwest coast of Madagascar.

Practically all of the **Champaca Concrète** which reaches European and American perfume houses to-day is produced in Nossi-Bé. In Réunion, the trees are no longer exploited, but they decorate the sinuous highways and mountain roads. In India and Indonesia, partly in the Philippines, the flowers are treated differently for local use: the mature flowers are extracted with vegetable (fixed) oil, and the perfumed oil is used as an "attar" in floral bouquets in the local perfume industry. Recently, the production of petroleum ether extracted concrète and an alcohol soluble absolute has been investigated by the Forest Research Institute in India. It is conceivable, that **Champaca Concrète** will be regularly produced in India, at least for local use.

In China, the rapidly growing perfume industry has already started exporting the **Champaca Concrète** produced in that country. The author has had a few chances to study the Chinese product and he is inclined to believe that it is derived from the flowers of **Michelia Alba**, not from the "true" **Michelia Champaca**. The chinese growers also produce an essential oil from the leaves of this tree. The so-called **Michelia Leaf Oil** is a pale yellow to pale olive yellow or greenish yellow liquid. Its odor is sweet oily-grassy, reminiscent of perilla oil but less pungent, more delicate. The odor also reminds of the fragrance of freshly cut stems or leaves of tulips. After this interesting fresh-grassy topnote the odor changes into a delicately sweet, tea-like or hay-like fragrance with an undertone of sage clary and rose leaf absolute. Indeed an interesting oil.

The total world production of **Champaca Flower Concrète** is thus somewhat variable and difficult to estimate, but probably runs about 100 to 200 kilos per year.

Champaca Concrète is a dark yellow to orange-brown, solid, waxy mass of delightfully sweet and delicately floral fragrance.

An **Absolute** of **Champaca** is produced by the usual method (see **Absolute**, Part One of this book). The absolute is produced in France. It is a dark yellow or a brownish-orange colored, somewhat viscous liquid. Its odor is quite unique: delicately dry-floral, at the same time reminding one of orange flowers, ylang-ylang, carnation and tearose. There are notes which resemble those of sage clary, methyl eugenol and "the good old type" of guaiacwood oil. But since guaiacwood oil has been used as an adulterant, or, more frequently to produce the so-called "**Champaca Wood Oil**", it might be confusing to use guaiac wood oil as an odor comparison.

Being produced right in the areas where ylang-ylang is cultivated, it is not surprising to find that champaca is often "cut" with this material, e.g. by co-extraction of the two kinds of flowers.

But a true **Champaca Concrète** is produced (in Nossi-Bé), and its odor is distinctly different from that of ylang-ylang concrète. The latter is a liquid while champaca concrète is a solid waxy substance.

An essential oil is not produced. The constituents of the fragrance would not be justly represented in a steam distilled oil. Besides, phenyl ethyl alcohol is an important constituent in **Champaca Concrète** and this alcohol would not be found in the distilled oil at the same percentage. Phenyl ethyl alcohol is comparatively soluble in water and the loss of this material would be quite significant.

Champaca Absolute is used in certain high-class perfumes where it may produce a unique, warm, floral-leafy note which is often compared to that of a fine grade of tea. The absolute blends excellently with lily-of-the-valley bases, carnation, rose, violet, etc., and it is almost generally applicable in this respect. However, its effect is not perceptible unless the absolute is skilfully backed up with rich, but weak-smelling blenders and modifiers. Sandalwood oil is an excellent fixative for the champaca fragrance, and so is isoeugenol, benzylsalicylate, etc. It is most unfortunate that there are so many poor champaca-reproductions on the market, and it is even more regrettable that the name champaca absolute is unscrupulously applied to such products. This fact has greatly impaired the interest in champaca absolute which seems to remain a very scarce and rare perfume material through several generations.

Chenopodium Ambrosioides.

This plant is closely related to the parent plant of

"American wormseed oil". The latter is distilled from **Chenopodium Ambrosioides**, var. anthelminthicum. See **Wormseed Oil, American.** This oil is by far the most important of the two.

Chenopodium Ambrosioides is a plant similar to the American wormwood. It grows wild in Brazil and Mexico and it is cultivated in Brazil, India, and Indonesia. Smaller quantities are harvested in France, Central and Eastern Europe.

The essential oil is steam distilled from the dried plant which is harvested just before the flowerbuds open. At that moment the essential oil will have the highest content of **Ascaridol** and related therapeutic ingredients. The oil is used exclusively in medicine as a specific anthelminthicum (worm exterminator). Since the oil has no application in perfumery or flavor work, it will not be described in detail here. The oil is, like American wormseed oil, toxic and hazardous to administrate without the advice of a physician.

The above brief description of **Chenopodium Oil** was adopted in this work exclusively to enlighten the subject of **Wormwood** oil and to prevent confusion with this oil. See monograph on **Wormwood Oil.**

Cherry Laurel Oil.

Cherry Laurel Oil is produced by water distillation or water-and-steam distillation of the enzymatically decomposed macerate of powdered leaves of the cherry laurel tree, **Prunus Laurocerasus.** The tree grows commonly in the western parts of Asia, in Asia Minor, the Middle and Near East, the Mediterranean countries and in southern Europe. Distillation takes place in France, Italy, Yugoslavia, U.S.S.R. and occasionally in other countries. The oil has lost most of its former importance as a flavor additive to pharmaceutical preparations and foods.

Cherry Laurel Oil is not a true essential oil according to our definition since it does not occur "in natura" in the leaves. A glucoside has to be decomposed just as in bitter almond kernels, apricot kernels, black mustard seed, etc., before any steam distillable matter appears. The glucoside prulaurasin in cherry laurel leaves is decomposed in lukewarm water under the presence of the enzyme prunase. The enzyme is brought about with an infusion of the powdered leaves. When this infusion is added to the macerate of cherry laurel leaves in the still, decomposition takes place

at moderate temperature and the "essential oil" can be distilled off.

Cherry laurel oil is an almost colorless liquid of strong and sweet bitter almond odor. The oil consists almost entirely of benzaldehyde and hydrocyanic acid. The latter is usually eliminated by neutralization and washing of the oil. **Cherry Laurel Oil** has nevertheless been largely replaced with the non-poisonous benzaldehyde which is obtained synthetically. Cherry laurel oil has previously found some use in liqueur flavors, baked goods, etc., but the oil is now hardly more than a curiosity.

See also **Almond Oil, Bitter.**

Chimonanthus Fragrans.

Various exotic or foreign plants have from time to time been introduced in the south of France for the purpose of supplying the perfume industry with new and interesting items. One such plant is the **Chimonanthus Fragrans**, a shrub from China and Japan where the decorative plant has drawn the attention of certain manufacturers of perfume materials.

An absolute is produced from the flowers of this shrub by petroleum ether extraction and subsequent alcohol washing of the concrète extract. This absolute has never attained any significant interest in perfumery and the production remains very occasional, although the absolute has been known for over 30 years. It is not a regularly produced, commercially available item.

The odor of **Chimonanthus Fragrans** absolute is generally described as "resembling jasmin, jonquil and orange peel" (mostly quotations from a 1931 publication in a no more existing French perfumery periodical). The constituents which have so far been identified in the absolute of chimonanthus fragrans would confirm the likelihood of such an odor complex (unless the odor description was based upon these findings).

Considering a yield of little more than 0.1% of absolute, based upon the weight of flowers, it is conceivable that this absolute is comparatively expensive. Materials which are occasionally offered in the perfume raw material market as **Absolute** of **Chimonanthus Fragrans** may very well be compounded perfume bases. The author has no personal experience with the use of this material.

Chloranthus Spicatus.

An absolute is produced from a benzene- or a petroleum ether extracted concrète of the flowers of this Chinese shrub. The flowers are also distilled with steam to yield an essential oil, but the yield is extremely small.

Originally, the flowers were used together with the flowers of jasmin, orange tree or mandarin tree for the perfuming (scenting) of tea. See also **Champaca Absolute** and **Camellia, Nyctanthes Arbortristis** and **Chimonanthus Fragrans**, etc.

The concrète and the absolute from concrète of **Chloranthus Spicatus** are not regularly available outside of China at the present moment. Small commercial lots of the essential oil occasionally arrive in Europe.

Absolute of chloranthus spicatus is a yellow to dark amber colored viscous liquid of delightfully soft, woody-floral odor. The overall odor has a striking resemblance to that of boronia absolute (see monograph). The topnote is somewhat dry-woody, but it becomes increasingly sweet-balsamic and floral like Peru balsam oil, cassie absolute, boronia absolute, etc.

The essential oil is a straw colored or amber colored, somewhat viscous liquid of light-woody, delicately floral and extremely tenacious odor, reminiscent of the above mentioned materials.

Chloranthus Spicatus Oil blends excellently with "violet-leaf-green" materials such as amyl heptine carbonate (so-called), beta-gamma-hexenyl acetate, methyl nonylenate, dibutyl sulfide, sec.-nonyl acetate, 2,6-nonadienal, etc., and with methylionones, cardamom oil, cassie absolute, mimosa absolute, sage clary, heliotropine, cassione, beta-ionone, cinnamic alcohol, etc.

It is very conceivable that this essential oil may become a popular and well known item on the perfumer's shelf, once the oil becomes available in other parts of the world.

Cinnamon Bark Oil.

True **"Ceylon" Cinnamon Bark Oil** is steam distilled, occasionally water-distilled, from the dried innerbark of the shoots of coppiced, cultivated bushes (would-be trees) of **Cinnamomum Zeylanicum**, preferably the variety grown in Ceylon.

The cinnamon tree is a native of East India and Indonesia, and grows wild in Ceylon, India, Burma, Indochina, and on several of the islands of the Indonesian archipelago. In most of these areas the tree is cultivated for the purpose of producing cinnamon bark. Climatic conditions, soil conditions, pruning or coppicing of the trees, curing (scraping) of the bark, and the age of the trees (bushes) strongly affect the quality of the cinnamon bark. The essential oil of the bark was not distilled in its countries of origin until quite recently when distillation commenced in Ceylon, the Seychelles, and in India and Indochina. The best grades of cinnamon bark oil are still produced in Europe and in the U.S.A. Distillation technique and knowledge of the botanical raw material play paramount roles in the production of really outstanding qualities of cinnamon bark oil (and many other spice oils). Many of these spices, and the above in particular, contain volatile aromatic materials which are more or less soluble in water. Native distillers in the growing regions and inexperienced European and American distillers frequently overlook this very important problem which can be solved only through extraction of the distillation waters (cohobation is not sufficient), and by subsequent addition of the evaporated extract from the distillation waters to the water-distilled oil. Olfactory and organoleptic tests show that such "complete" oils outperform any ordinarily distilled cinnamon bark oil by far.

Cinnamon Bark Oil "Ceylon" is a pale yellow to dark yellow or brownish-yellow, somewhat oily liquid of extremely powerful, diffusive, warm-spicy, sweet and tenacious odor. The undertone and dryout notes reveal a persistent dryness which is very unique in combination with the distinct sweetness. Characteristic is a dry powdery-dusty, but warm, uniform and lasting dry-out note. In the very first topnotes, one may find a certain fruity freshness, similar to the sweet candy-like freshness in a good clove bud oil. The flavor is distinctly sweet and spicy, and a correctly produced oil will show a tremendous flavor power, five or ten times stronger than ordinary grade cinnamon bark oils ("commercial" quality or "pharmacopoeia-grade").

The main constituents of Ceylon cinnamon bark oil are cinnamic aldehyde, eugenol, acet-eugenol, and trace amounts of various aldehydes. Together with methyl-n-amyl ketone, the latter are probably responsible for the power and the characteristic notes in *good* oils. As in clove bud oil, the content of aceteugenol in cinnamon bark oil may be dependent upon the method of distillation. Steam distillation will decompose most of the aceteugenol. Water distillation is less detrimental to the natural aromatics in the bark. Thus, an **Oleoresin of Cinnamon Bark** would more truly represent the natural aromatic constituents in a concentrated form.

Ceylon Cinnamon Bark Oil is used extensively in flavors for food and candy, baked goods and beverages, pharmaceutical and dental preparations, mouth rinses, gargles, etc. where smaller amounts give pleasant bouquets to peppermint type flavors, while larger concentrations of cinnamon bark oil exert an antiseptic affect. Tinctures and infusions of Ceylon cinnamon bark have been used for centuries as germicidal gargles etc., and the essential oil ranks among the most powerful of all known natural antiseptics. From available literature, publications, etc., it appears that cinnamon bark oil is far more effective than cassia oil and clove oil. If this is correct, we do not know yet what causes cinnamon bark oil to be such a powerful germicide, unless the explanation can be found in the combination of eugenol and cinnamic aldehyde and perhaps certain substances with a synergistic effect in this respect.

In perfumery, the oil blends well with Oriental-woody notes, and the combination with olibanum is known and often utilized. The warmth and dry spiciness, the immediate sweetness and tremendous diffusive power (or "radiation") induced by the addition of fractions of one percent of this oil in a perfume composition, is highly appreciated by certain perfumers. The oil is even more interesting for the flavorists, since cinnamon flavor ranks among the most popular and generally applicable flavors. The oil has a magnificent masking power, and is frequently used in flavors for pharmaceutical purposes where an unpleasant medicinal taste is a common problem. In combination with sweet orange, lime oil, cola extract and de-cocainized coca-extract, the cinnamon flavor is an important part of the Coca-Cola type flavor complex. The cinnamon note is even more pronounced in the Pepsi-Cola type. An average use-level for the cinnamon bark oil would be about 0.30 to 0.80 mg% (where a distinct cinnamon flavor is wanted) while the **Minimum Perceptible** is 0.05 to 0.10 mg%. The author wants to emphasize that these figures are based on experiments with exceptionally fine cinnamon bark oil from one English distiller (expert in spice oils) and one French distiller. As a comparison, similar experiments were carried out with various "ordinary,

commercial grades" of oils, labelled "cinnamon bark oil" or "Ceylon cinnamon bark oil". The figures for these oils were as follows: average use-level: 1.50 to 2.50 mg%, and **Minimum Perceptible:** 0.60 to 0.90 mg%. The effect of the high-grade oils is about five to ten times higher than that of the "commercial grades". For the sake of completeness it should be mentioned that the high grade oils were about two to two-and-one-half times as expensive as the ordinary grades. Which still leaves everything in favor of using a very high grade of cinnamon bark oil.

Since the main constituents of cinnamon bark oil are very common low-cost materials which are partly available as synthetic chemicals (partly isolated from inexpensive essential oils), it is not surprising that **Cinnamon Bark Oil** (Ceylon) is very frequently adulterated or "cut". A knowledge of the market price of cinnamon bark will enable the buyer of cinnamon bark oil to calculate roughly the cost of the essential oil: 120 to 150 times the price of choice bark material (not necessarily the best-looking material). Add to this a reasonable overhead for distillation, etc., and you can be sure that any oil which is offered significantly below this cost is adulterated or "cut". A high price is, of course, no indication that you have a genuine oil. Olfactory and organoleptic tests will usually reveal the actual value of the oil. Cinnamon leaf oil, canella bark oil, clove leaf oil, eugenol, cinnamic aldehyde, etc. are the most common additives.

True Ceylon **Cinnamon Bark Oil** is produced on a limited scale only. The production is steadily increasing, and is estimated at a figure of between five and ten metric tons annually. By far, the majority is European distilled.

The oil produced in the Seychelle islands from the Ceylon type of cinnamon bark is somewhat different from the "true" Ceylon cinnamon bark oil. The odor of the Seychelles oil is harsher, probably due to camphene and other terpenes, and to camphor which has not yet been identified in the bark oil from cultivated Ceylon cinnamon bark. In the Seychelles, wild trees are used since the cinnamon tree grows all over the islands' 100 square kilometres, thanks to the talking mynah bird (the East Indian acridotheres tristis) who has chosen the cinnamon fruits as its favorite dish. The islanders benefit from this activity in their "Garden of Eden", as the Seychelles are generally named. It is, furthermore, the only area in the world where white people and their descendants, down through the centuries, have lived and walked around all day without any sort of footwear. Indeed an interesting place!

As mentioned above, the label "cinnamon oil" or "cinnamon oil Ceylon" or "cinnamon bark oil", often encountered in price lists and market reports, does not specify the quality of the oil; it is not surprising then to see **Cinnamon Oil** offered at prices of from $16.— per kilo up to more than $200.— per kilo. Occasionally, even artificial cassia leaf oil is offered under the **Cinnamon Oil** label, with the addition of some Pharmacopoeias's name.

"Ultrasonic" extracts of cinnamon bark (Ceylon) are known and used in flavors.

Cinnamon Leaf Oil.

This oil is steam distilled locally from partly dried leaves and twigs of **Cinnamomum Zeylanicum**, the same tree which yields the Ceylon cinnamon bark (see previous monograph). The tree grows wild, and is cultivated in Ceylon, South India, Indonesia, Indochina and in the Seychelles, a tiny island group midway between Zanzibar (east Africa) and Ceylon. Recently, small scale distillation has commenced in Zanzibar, too. The main producing centers are Ceylon (south) and the Seychelles. In Madagascar and the nearby Comoro Islands, small quantities of a good cinnamon bark are produced, and occasionally the leaves are distilled on the spot.

During the recent years of steep decline in the clove leaf oil price, however, there has been less interest in the production of cinnamon leaf oil. The two oils both contain about 80 to 90% eugenol, and the cheapest oil will serve as a starting material for the isolation of this important perfume material. Eugenol, isolated from different natural oils, displays certain small variations in odor type. Due to its fresher note, eugenol from **Bay Leaf Oil** (see monograph) has recently become more popular than eugenol from clove leaf oil or from cinnamon leaf oil. If isolated in a gas chromatograph column, all the eugenols would smell exactly alike, but traces of "impurities" (those which "create odor and natural nuances", the perfumer would say) result in different types of eugenols when these are isolated on a large scale.

Since **Cinnamon Leaf Oil** is now more expensive than clove leaf oil, the latter presents a possible means of adulteration for cinnamon leaf oil. The two oils are produced in rather primitive stills (some of the Seychelles installations are, however, quite good: of large capacity and fairly up-to-date design), and being produced in neighboring areas, there is always a strong possibility of "coupage" ("cutting" of the cinnamon leaf oil with clove leaf oil). Apart from that, only the usual crude diluents, such as alcohol, fuel oil, kerosene, petroleum, etc., might come into consideration.

Cinnamon Leaf Oil is a yellow to brownish-yellow oil of warm-spicy, but rather harsh odor, lacking the rich body of the bark oil. It has some resemblance to the odor of clove leaf oil and clove stem oil. The flavor is somewhat bitter, slightly pungent, irritant-burning, but very spicy and powerful.

The oil is used in perfumery for its spicy notes and its warm and woody-Oriental type. In the chemical industry, it is used for the isolation of eugenol (from which again vanillin and other derivatives are produced), and in flavors, as a modifier in spice blends, as a "warm" note in certain fruit essences, e.g. cherry, raspberry and prune, in chocolate and liqueur flavors, in soft drinks and candy, etc. It blends well with benzaldehyde, anisaldehyde, anisalcohol, vanillin, ethylvanillin (so-called), peppermint oil, nonanolide and undecanolide, many glycidates, ionones (and ionone-glycidates), cinnamic alcohol, etc.

The annual world production of cinnamon leaf oil is, as mentioned, somewhat dependent upon the demand for eugenol and the production of clove leaf oil. An average of 150 metric tons of **Cinnamon Leaf Oil** is estimated. Up to 90 tons annually has been produced in the Seychelles alone.

Cistus Oil, so-called.

Cistus Oil (so-called) is the essential oil which is steam distilled from the crude "gum" labdanum, collected almost exclusively in Spain. More recently, the oil has been obtained by a two-step extraction with benzene/ethyl alcohol or with ethyl ether/ethyl alcohol. The product is then, according to the definitions in Part One of this book, an **Absolute from Resinoid of Labdanum** (spanish). Distillation of the crude "gum" labdanum takes place in Spain and France. For details of the plant from which the crude labdanum is boiled off, see monograph on **Labdanum.**

Cistus Oil (so-called) is an amber-colored or dark yellow, viscous liquid having a very powerful and tenacious odor: warm and sweet, yet dry and reminiscent of ambra in its somewhat animal notes. The oil is used in modern aldehydic or ambre types of perfumes, in Oriental bases, and in numerous "fantasy" bouquets where it will lend tenacity, warm tonalities and an intriguingly spicy-animal note. It has the advantage of yielding the main odor effects of the labdanum resinoid, concrète, or absolute, but it does not have the intense color of these products. Its greater solubility makes it interesting for colognes where it blends extremely well with citrus oils, sage clary and oakmoss products. Cistus oil also blends well with cinnamic alcohol, juniperberry oil, ionones and methylionones, heliotropin, lavandin oil, pine needle oils, opopanax, etc. Artificial musks are frequently rounded off with **Cistus Oil** if the formula permits the comparatively high cost of this oil. Little is known about the chemical composition of the so-called cistus oil, and adulterations are most often of the "artistic" kind rather than the "scientific".

Cistus Oil is used quite frequently in trace amounts as a "bouquet" material in certain essential oils (sage clary and others). The annual production of so-called **Cistus Oil** is steadily increasing, but has probably not yet exceeded 300 kilos. The residue of exhausted labdanum "gum" from the distillation of this type of cistus oil unfortunately presents good possibilities for adulteration of labdanum "resinoids" or even for the crude labdanum "gum".

Steam distillation of the entire plant is carried out in Spain. The plant is known under the name of **Cistus** ("ciste") in France, and the essential oil from the entire plant is described in the following monograph.

Cistus Oil, true.

An essential oil which is truly a **Cistus Oil** is produced in Spain by steam distillation of the entire herb (leaves and stems with flowering tops) of **Cistus Ladaniferus.** A product derived from this oil by rectification, has been sold by a well known French perfume house for many years. The product is marketed under a brand name.

The same Spanish producer has also placed a **Terpeneless Cistus Oil** on the market.

True Cistus Oil is a pale orange colored liquid of a very peculiar, warm-herbaceous odor. The odor bears some similarity to that of Roman chamomile, to decaying fruits, to certain methacrylates, etc. The tenacity is much inferior to that of the so-called cistus oil (see above monograph), but the true cistus oil has an immense power in its topnote. It produces interesting effects in lavender bouquets, colognes, spicy after shave fragrances, etc. The oil is produced on a very limited scale only.

Citronella Oil, Ceylon.

Ceylon citronella oil is steam distilled from the leaves (grass) of the so-called **Lenabatu** variety of the citronella grass. This variety is cultivated in Ceylon only. It can be considered a variety of **Managrass,** the only wild growing citronella grass which is also found in Ceylon. Cultivation of **Lenabatu** grass is concentrated in a comparatively small area on the southernmost tip of Ceylon.

The grass is dried prior to the distillation which is carried out locally in primitive stills. Annual production has been surprisingly stable, between 500 and 800 metric tons during the past 50 years. Until 1926, the Ceylon type of citronella oil was the most important and the largest one. But the production of Java-type (see monograph: **Citronella Oil, Java**-type) has increased steadily because of its better yield and higher content of "total-geraniol" (see below).

Ceylon Citronella Oil is a yellow to brownish yellow or even olive-brown liquid, occasionally hazy due to a water surplus. The odor is very peculiar, warm-woody and yet fresh, grassy and somewhat reminiscent of wet leaves. Geraniol and citronellal are the main constituents, but they are not predominant in the odor of this oil. The camphene-borneol-methyleugenol complex seems to characterize the odor of Ceylon citronella oil.

The oil is used extensively in low-cost perfumes for soap-flakes, detergents, floorwaxes, cleansers, insecticides and other household products. Its great masking power makes it an effective and universally applicable material for technical products, industrial perfumes, etc. Mixed with cedarwood oil "Virginia", it has been a popular remedy against mosquito attacks for many years prior to the appearance of DDT and other modern insecticides. In the chemical industry, it serves as a starting material for the production of geraniol, citronellol, citronellal and menthol. For these purposes, however, the Java type oil presents definite advantages and may completely replace the Ceylon type. In spite of its extremely low cost, Ceylon citronella oil has been subject to very serious adulterations for many decades. Only quite recently, the Ceylonese authorities attacked the problems caused by a series of disastrous adulterations of the locally distilled oil by instituting thorough control measures which should now guarantee the customers against future "on-the-spot" adulterations and contaminations.

Commercial lots of poor grade oils are still appearing on the market, some with considerable amounts of water, others with precipitate, etc. But the "old" type of adulteration with coconut oil, kerosene or rice alcohol is becoming rare. On its way to consumers through transithouses, the oil may be adulterated with more skill, e.g. with fractions from geraniolproduction, with orange terpenes, lemon oil terpenes, camphor oil fractions, etc. An olfactory test will usually reveal such additions.

See also **Citronella Oil, Java**-type, following monograph.

Citronella Oil, Java-type.

Among all the essential oils which find direct application in perfumery, Java-type citronella oil is one of the largest in quantity, surpassed only by turpentine, pine oils and camphor oils. Seventy years ago, it was unknown; to-day it is produced from cultivated grass in practically all the tropical and semitropical areas of the world except Australia.

Citronella Grass, Java-type, so-called **Maha-Pengiri** grass, is cultivated in Formosa (Taiwan), China (Hainan island), Java, Malaya, Guatemala, Honduras, and to a lesser extent in Ceylon, Argentina, Brazil, Ecuador, east and central Africa, Madagascar, Comoro islands, Seychelles, the West Indian Islands, in Mexico and in Salvador. It is cultivated for local use in numerous islands of the Pacific Ocean and in the Indonesian Archipelago. In many of these areas, however, the grass which is cultivated under the local name of "citronelle" is actually lemongrass (e.g. in central Madagascar where it is served as a tea, according to the author's personal experience).

Chinese production is concentrated on the island of Hainan, and the production here in 1959 surpassed 2000 metric tons. Very little, if any at all, of this oil reached consumers outside of Asia.

The **Maha Pengiri** grass has the advantage over the Ceylon type grass in that it yields up to twice as much essential oil. The Java-type oil contains more of the components important for the production of synthetic or semi-synthetic perfume materials than does the Ceylon type oil. Java-type oil (maha pengiri oil) is distilled either from fresh grass or from partly dried grass. **Java**-type **Citronella Oil** is almost colorless or pale yellow. This is mainly due to the fact that the oil is generally distilled in equipment which is more modern than that used for distillation of Ceylon citronella oil. The equipment used by the citronella oil industry in Formosa, Hainan, Guatemala and Honduras is particularly and completely new and of modern design.

The odor of **Java**-type citronella oil is fresh and sweet, revealing the high content of citronellal and geraniol + citronellol. The oil does not present at all in its odor the camphene-borneol notes characteristic of the Ceylon citronella oil. The dryout of the Java-type oil is also sweet, but somewhat woody; this is probably due to the sesquiterpenes and sesquiterpene alcohols (**Elemol**, etc.).

The oil contains from 30 to 45% geraniol or related alcohols. Furthermore, it contains from 40 to 50% citronellal (in good oils). **Java**-type citronella oil, now mainly produced in Taiwan (Formosa) finds extensive use in perfumery, both directly and indirectly. Soaps, soapflakes, detergents, household cleansers, technical products, insecticides, etc. are often perfumed exclusively with this oil. The oil itself, or certain of its isolated components may serve as starting materials for the production of numerous important perfumery materials:

Java-type citronella oil may be treated with aluminium-propoxide in the so-called **Meerwein-Ponndorf-Verley** reaction (reduction without affecting the double bonds), or directly condensated with acetone. The citronellal may be transformed into menthol by means of several steps. One French manufacturer of synthetic menthol used to consume about 10% of the total world production of citronella oil, Java-type, for this purpose. Citronellal is used for the production of hydroxycitronellal. Geraniol is used either as such, or it may be processed further to geranyl esters, etc. Citronellol (sometimes labelled "rhodinol") and esters of this alcohol are also produced from citronellal.

The commercial labelling of citronella oil, Java-type, is often expressed in terms of "totalgeraniol" and "citronellal", e.g. 85/35, which means that this oil contains a minimum of 85% geraniol + citronellal + various alcohols, and a minimum of 35% aldehydes, calculated as citronellal. A good oil should contain at least 40 % citronellal and it may contain up to 95% "totalgeraniol".

The oil is not frequently adulterated. The large-scale production in Formosa, Java, Guatemala and elsewhere, and the fairly modern setup seem to insure uniform quality. Recent years have not been very interesting from the producers' points of view since the price of citronella oil Java-type has reached an ultimate minimum. Adulteration may take place in "transit" if large consumers of citronella oil also happen to be suppliers of citronella oil to smaller industries. Fractions from the isolation of geraniol or citronellal (foreruns or afterruns, etc.) may be added to the natural oil which accordingly changes composition and odor effect. The "old" type of adulteration with fatty vegetable oils, etc. is hardly found any more.

The annual world production of Java-type citronella oil is significantly in excess of 5000 metric tons, distributed as outlined below:

Formosa: 3000 tons (best of recent years)
China-Hainan: 1000 to 2500 tons (1957-58-59)
Java: 800 tons (and increasing)
Other areas produce more than: 1000 tons.

It is noteworthy that a conciderable percentage of the world production is not freely available in all overseas areas outside of the producing regions.

Civet.

Civet is a glandular secretion collected from various species of the **Civet Cat**, male and female, preferably the male. The Abyssinian variety, **Viverra Civetta**, is the most important supplier of this animal perfume raw material. Smaller quantities of civet are collected from other species of the civet cat in India, Indonesia, Malaya, China, Belgian Congo, Somali, Kenya, and occasionally in Haiti. The total annual world production runs into several tons, and with respect to value, **Civet** ranks among the 20 most important perfume raw materials.

The crude civet arrives in Europe and the U.S.A. in Zebu horns, containing about 500 to 1200 grams of the buttery yellowish paste which turns darker and more solid on age. The contents of one average Zebu horn represents the production from one civet cat in **Four Years.** During this period, the animal will consume something like the raw meat from 50 (fifty) sheep, and the poor cat, frequently teased in its narrow cage, will have undergone 400 to 800 painful "scrapings" of its glands. The raw meat, the narrow cage and the teasing are all means of increasing the production of the civet secretion which is scraped off with regular intervals while the cat is caged. It is no wonder that **Civet** is one of the most expensive perfume raw materials! But, thanks to the outstanding power of civet, its price does not prohibit its use by any means.

From the crude natural civet, a **Concrète** of **Civet** is produced by hydrocarbon extraction. In turn, the concrète is usually further processed to an absolute by the conventional method. The yield of **Concrète** is about 50 to 60% of the crude secretion, and the larger part of the concrète is alcohol-soluble **Civet Absolute.**

Civet Absolute dilutions, or **Civet Tincture,** are very commonly used perfume materials. They not only present excellent fixative value, but, most important, they lend a distinct natural-animal note when used with care and with an experienced touch. Overdoses produce obnoxious notes, and it should be kept in mind that civet products tends to "grow" in a perfume. A mellow and well aged civet tincture is less capricious in this respect.

Civet Tincture may be produced directly from the crude civet by maceration with 95% ethyl alcohol. It is customary to use either 5 or 10 parts by weight of alcohol to one part by weight of civet. The tinctures may be prepared with or without the application of heat. In any case, the tincture must be well chilled prior to filtration which can take place after a maceration time of several months. The tinctures are labelled **Civet Tincture** 20% (respectively 10%). See also the monograph **Tincture** in Part One of this book.

It seems to be a general conception among older perfumers that civet is no longer what it used to be. This suspicion is not uncommon. Similar worries are expressed about opopanax, guaiacwood oil, patchouli oil, etc. In a few cases these worries can be traced back to the very human tendency of glorifying the "good old times". Among other reasons, one of the most frequently given is the fact that the exotic perfumery raw materials come to the consumer much more quickly today than they did 20 or 30 years ago. But this excuse certainly does not cover all the obvious differences.

Civet products are used in a great variety of perfume types, particularly in the better lotion perfumes of the rose-type, Oriental types, "honey"-notes, narcissus bases, ambre types, etc. It blends well with the nitromusks, coumarin derivatives, quinoline derivatives, vanillin and related materials, etc. and many commercial fixative specialties are based upon such mixtures. The use of civet extracts or tinctures in muguet and other delicate floral bases may seem surprising to the layman, but this application of civet is well known and highly appreciated. The "lift" and radiation (diffusive power) derived from minute quantities of civet tincture in certain types of perfumes is quite unique and this effect can only be adequately understood through long experience with good grades of civet.

The odor of Civet extracts (tinctures, absolutes, etc.) and of crude civet, too, should be typically animal-sweet, free from faecal notes, urine notes or the like. The undertone bears some resemblance to that of ambrette seed oil and of a well cured goat skin. The odor of civet preparations appears not immediately powerful, but it is very tenacious, an upon dilution the true richness becomes quite apparent.

The recently developed synthetic materials Civettone and Civettol represent individual notes from the civet complex, and cannot fully replace the natural civet or its extracts. The main advantage of the synthetic materials is in the total absence of faecal notes, and in the constant availability in a uniform quality and cost. An Anhydrol of Civet has been prepared by molecular co-distillation of a civet extract with a high-boiling, odorless solvent. Civet Anhydrol is a viscous, almost colorless liquid. Its odor is free from faecal notes, but it is not typical of the entire gamut of odor principles in natural civet.

Civet is frequently adulterated (mainly before shipping out of Africa) with "ghee" butter (another product of the zebu!), honey, beeswax, soybean oil, baby excrements, etc. Some of the most experienced importers of civet actually *taste* the unctuous substance from the horns, before they pay for it. Honey can be detected this way, but the other adulterants – –!.

Clausena Anisata.

An essential oil is locally distilled from the leaves of a small tropical tree, Clausena Anisata, related to the citrus trees. The tree is cultivated in Indonesia and in East Africa (Tanganyika and Somali), but it is particularly popular in the Philippines where the essential oil is distilled and used for a local brandy, equivalent to the French "anisette".

The oil of Clausena Anisata is almost colorless or pale yellow and its odor is very similar to that of star anise oil or "true" anise oil (see monographs on Anise Oil and Star Anise Oil). Frequent attempts have been made to promote the interest in this oil which, after proper rectification, could become a good and low-cost replacement for anise oil or star anise oil.

The appearance on the market of synthetic Anethole from large-scale production in the U.S.A. in the early 1950's and the rapid improvement in the flavor of this synthetic product almost completely wiped out the interest for anise, star anise and similar essential oils in the U.S.A. or other countries where these oils were unavailable due to the fareastern troubles.

Clausena Anisata Oil is produced in the Philippines and in East Africa exclusively for local use and for the purpose of releasing scarce foreign currency for more important articles. The oil is not regularly available in Europe or in the U.S.A.

The annual production of clausena anisata oil is adjusted to the local demand but in view of the abundance of the tree it seems conceivable that this oil could—in case of emergency—cover a good part of the world's demand for the anise-type oils at a reasonable cost.

Clavel Moena.

Oil of Clavel Moena is not produced on a commercial scale but it represents one example among the hundreds of essential oils which have been produced experimentally and which, in case of significant interest, could be produced on a larger scale with little or no notice and at a very reasonable cost.

The oil is also called "Peruvian Spice Oil" (or Peruvian spicewood oil). It is steam distilled in

Peru from the wood of a tree of the genus lauraceae (possibly myrtaeceae). The Spanish name for clove (or carnation) is **Clavel.**

Oil of **Clavel Moena** is an almost colorless or pale yellow, mobile liquid of a warm-spicy, nutmeg-like, cinnamon-leaf-like odor. The undertone and the dryout are distinctly dry-woody, less spicy and it is strongly reminiscent of the odor of clove leaf sesquiterpenes (caryophyllenes).

Clavel Moena oil could, in view of its peculiar composition, possibly find use in perfume work on artificial essential oils (clove, cubeb, nutmeg, black pepper, etc.) or the oil could be used in perfumes of the woody-Oriental and spicy type.

The flavor of **Clavel Moena** oil is far from attractive. It merely represents a high concentration of the dry-bitter notes which are so carefully avoided in the selection of a good clove bud oil for flavor use.

It has been claimed that the essential oil from the leaves of the above tree consists almost exclusively of **Myristicin.** The leaf oil is not a commercially available article.

Clove Bud Absolute.

Clove Bud Absolute is produced from **Clove Bud Concrète.** The concrète is produced by hydrocarbon solvent extraction of the dried and comminuted flower-buds of **Eugenia Caryophyllata** (see monograph on **Clove Bud Oil**). Petroleum ether, benzene or gasoline is used in the extraction. Gasoline yields a superior concrète in respect to odor. The color and general appearance, too, varies according to the solvent used.

Clove Bud Concrète is a semi-solid mass or a viscous liquid of dark brown, yellowish brown or pale olive green color. The author has prepared extracts with all the above mentioned solvents. The extracts were in all cases clear and viscous liquids of pale brown to olive color. Several commercially available concrètes are waxy and semi-solid masses.

The odor of clove bud concrète is oily-sweet, intensely rich and spicy, slightly sour-fruity and refreshing. The odor is very closely reminiscent of that of the dry clove buds.

Clove Bud Oleoresin is a commercial name for various extracts of clove buds. The direct extraction product from the buds with boiling ethyl alcohol is quite common. It is a viscous brown liquid, occasionally separating waxy particles on standing. Its odor is often perceptibly affected by the presence of small amounts of solvent (ethyl alcohol). A "wine"-like note develops upon ageing but the overall fragrance is very typical of the spice itself. The alcohol-extracted "oleoresin" is generally a more powerful perfume and flavor material than any of the other types of extract. It is less refined or delicate in odor and it is considerably darker in color than the hydrocarbon solvent extracts or the corresponding absolutes. True **Clove Bud Oleoresin** should be prepared by hydrocarbon solvent extraction, preferably by room-temperature percolation.

Clove Bud Absolute is prepared by alcohol extraction of the concrète (sometimes called oleoresin). The absolute from a gasoline extracted material is usually superior in respect to odor. The yield is somewhat smaller than that from benzene extraction. Absolute from petroleum ether extracted material is very pale of color (olive green) and of a more "piquant" odor than the absolute from benzene extracted material. The latter is richer in odor body.

Clove Bud Absolute is usually an olive-green, greenish brown or orange brown, viscous or oily liquid which may solidify at reduced temperatures to a semi-solid mass. The absolute is soluble in alcohol in all proportions. The odor of the absolute is not only a very close approach to the odor of the botanical material. It presents a floral and refined type of this fragrance, also resembling the balsamic, sour-sweet and immensely rich fragrance of clove flowers in full bloom.

Clove Bud Absolute (and other cold-extracted products from clove buds) contains apparently only those aromatic principles which are present in the buds from nature's side. There is no trace of a dry caryophyllene-type of odor (such as found in clove leaf oil). It seems beyond doubt, that these unwanted off-notes in odor and flavor are formed during the distillation of the buds, particularly when the distillation is performed at temperatures beyond 100°C. (see monograph on **Clove Bud Oil**).

Clove bud absolute is particularly useful in perfumes where the non-phenolic notes of cloves are wanted to impart a spicy, yet fresh-floral and intriguing note of great diffusive power. The absolute can be used with surprisingly good effects in many floral bases and it lends interesting twists to ylang-ylang, carnation, rose, cassie, narcissus and other floral perfume types.

The absolute is occasionally used in flavors to bring the true fragrance of the clove buds to life in a delightful topnote. The use level for **Clove Bud Absolute** from **Gasoline Concrète** would be about 0.80 to 2.50 mg% and the **Minimum Perceptible** is 0.08 to 0.12 mg%. It is noted that the flavor strength of the absolute is about twice the strength of an average quality of clove bud oil.

Oleoresin of **Clove Buds** (various direct extraction products) is used quite extensively in table sauces, baked goods, etc. in place of powdered clove buds.

Clove Bud Ultrasonic Extract is available in limited quantities but the recent development in this technique of extraction may result in improved capacity and consequently in more attractive cost of these extracts.

Clove Bud Oil.

Clove Bud Oil is water distilled (rarely steam distilled) from the dried flower buds of **Eugenia Caryophyllata**, a slender, medium-sized, tropical tree, originating in the Moluccas, particularly the island of Amboyna in the eastern Indonesian archipelago. The original wild clove tree from the Moluccas does not produce a eugenol-containing essential oil at all. This wild tree still grows in the islands among plantations of cultivated trees. The cultivation of clove trees is at least 2000 years old.

Clove Bud Oil is the largest of the essential oils produced from "stable" material which is brought to European or American distilleries thousands of miles from the areas where the cloves grow. No clove bud oil is produced in the clove growing areas. Madagascan, Zanzibar or Comoro clove buds are used for the distillation. Amboyna clove buds are usually sold as the highest grade of the whole spice. The yield of essential oil by water distillation of the clove buds is about 15%. Up to 20% of the world production of clove buds is used for distillation, but the figure fluctuates with the immediate cost of the cloves.

The clove buds are comminuted prior to distillation. During the water distillation of clove buds, certain materials are formed in the essential oil which do not exist in the clove bud in natura, e.g. **Caryophyllene** and possibly other sesquiterpenes. The same happens during steam distillation, but not during a low-temperature hydrocarbon-extraction of the buds (see monograph on **Clove Bud Absolute**). If the cloves are steam distilled, hydrolysis takes place, and most of the natural acetyl eugenol (aceteugenol) is converted to eugenol. Since this hydrolysis takes place only to a minor degree during water distillation, the latter method is accordingly preferred. Water distilled clove bud oil has a very high content of "total eugenol" (usually over 92%), but a substantial part of this is aceteugenol (10 to 15%) which is partly responsible for the characteristic odor of clove bud oil. The author wishes to extend his acknowledgements to a well known English distiller and expert in spice oils for this simple and handy test on clove oils:

"add a few drops of the clove oil sample to an aqueous paste of magnesium hydroxide, stir well, and leave overnight in a closed beaker. The eugenol is then fixed as an odorless magnesium salt while esters of eugenol, methyl-n-amyl ketone, etc. are not affected by the magnesium hydroxide. If pure clove bud oil was used in the experiment, the odor of the mixture the next day will be a strong, pure clove odor". This experiment emphasizes the importance of trace elements among the odor principles in essential oils. The quality of a clove oil can not be judged by the eugenol content of the oil (unless the oil is purchased for the purpose of isolating eugenol).

Trace amounts of lower aliphatic ketones lend this oil a peculiar fruity-fresh topnote, and a touch of an acetic odor makes it quite refreshing and distinctly different from clove stem oil which may even have the same content of "total eugenol". The acetic note could very well derive from traces of acetic acid, produced from the aceteugenol which even in a gentle water distillation hydrolyzes to some degree. The eugenol note in a good clove bud oil is distinctly subdued, sweetened and freshened by the presence of the above mentioned materials in the bud oil. **Clove Bud Oil** is used frequently in perfumery for its sweet-spicy note, but the largest part of all clove bud oil by far is used in flavor work.

In perfumes, clove bud oil blends well with its derivatives, e.g. aceteugenol, methyl eugenol, isoeugenol, vanillin, "ethyl-vanillin", etc. to form part of the well-known "carnation" base. In rose, honeysuckle and certain deep-sweet florals, clove bud oil lends a unique note of natural richness and body. The classic "*rondeletia*" perfume type is based upon the combination of clove and lavender oils. Modern variations include the use of lavandin, sage clary, bergamot, bay leaf oil, pimenta berry oil, etc. The oil blends excellently with ylang-ylang and cananga oils, and Oriental types of perfumes often contain significant amounts of clove bud oil.

Clove Bud Oil is used extensively in flavors in a large variety of food products: spice blends, seasonings, pickles, canned meat, baked goods, powdercakes, ready-made mixes etc. Due to its well-known antiseptic effect, the oil finds its way into numerous mouth washes, gargles, dentifrices and pharmaceutical and dental preparations. Candy, particularly chewing gum, is also flavored with clove bud oil in combination with other essential oils. The suggested use level for a high-grade clove bud oil is 1.00 to 3.00 mg%, while the **Minimum Perceptible** is 0.15 to 0.30 mg%. Wide variations in the figures for the use level must be expected according to the specific use of the oil in each case.

The annual world production of clove bud oil fluctuates according to the price of the buds. 300 to 500 tons has been the annual output in recent years. This corresponds to 2100 to 3500 metric tons of clove buds distilled, or: 10 to 15 percent of the annual clove bud production. This huge progress in clove bud oil production has brought the price down to an all-time low, a fact which is interesting to study along with the fact that eugenol has not yet been synthesized on a commercial scale.

The fluctuating production of clove bud oil is not a true picture of the demand for clove bud oil. The price of the buds is strongly dependent upon the demand for clove buds in Indonesia. That country is the largest customer for the clove bud growers. Comminuted clove buds are used to the extent of up to 8% in Indonesian cigarette tobacco. If this peculiar need for "spicy smoke" should fade away, there will be an enormous surplus of clove buds on the market. The price will drop, and clove bud oil can be produced at a fraction of its normal price. The spice houses can keep clove bud oil for many years, and a large stock does not require much space.

The adulteration of clove bud oil could be described in immediate connection with the above remarks of demand for clove buds. At the present moment (1960) there is only little profit in the "cutting" of clove bud oil with clove stem oil or rectified clove leaf oil. Eugenol and caryophyllene, two of the main constituents of all clove oils, are not produced synthetically on a commercial scale.

Accordingly, there is no reason for adulteration of clove bud oil until its price increases twice or three times, and that is not very likely.

Clove Leaf Oil.

From the whole leaves and twigs of the clove tree (see **Clove Bud Oil**, previous monograph), an essential oil is distilled in the clove growing areas of northeastern Madagascar. The distillation is a so-called "direct-fire" distillation and corresponds to a type of water-distillation. The stills are mostly of an extremely primitive kind. Almost inevitably a certain amount of clove stems are found among the leaves and twigs, but the stems will obviously appear only during and right after the clove bud harvest (there is only one bud harvest per year in Madagascar). It is estimated that, out of Madagascar's annual 1000 metric ton-production of clove oil, about 80% is derived from leaf material and 20% from clove stems. The oil is usually bulked, but lots of oil of high eugenol content, sold separately, may derive from distillation of "high-stem-content" material. Clove leaf oil is not produced outside of Madagascar, but production can be expected in the near future from the Comoro islands where extensive plantings of young clove trees (seedlings from Madagascar) are growing up since 1952.

When crude and natural, **Clove Leaf Oil** is a dark brown, often violet- or purple-brown oil which may show some precipitate or cloudiness. Madagascan-French bulk-producers make an effort to strain and dehydrate the oil before it is exported, and they usually obtain oils with very high eugenol content. The crude oil is usually rectified (steam distilled or vacuum-distilled) in Europe or in the U.S.A. before it is used in perfumes or flavors. However, the major part of all clove leaf oil is used in the chemical industry for the isolation of eugenol of which the oil contains 82 to 88%. The oil also contains significant amounts of the sesquiterpene **Caryphyllene** which is isolated during the production of eugenol. Caryophyllene finds some use in perfumery, particularly in the reproduction of certain essential oils, e.g. cubeb oil, black pepper oil, etc. (skilful adulteration!). More recently, caryophyllene has been used as a starting material in the production of new and interesting perfume materials, e.g. certain related ketones, etc. Neither eugenol nor caryophyllene have yet been produced synthetically on a commercial scale. The odor of crude clove leaf oil is somewhat harsh, phenolic, only slightly sweet, with a "burnt" breadlike note, and distinctly different from the odor of eugenol, and different also from the odor of clove bud oil. Woodiness and dryness probably are the most typical notes of clove leaf oil.

Rectified (sometimes called redistilled) clove leaf oil is pale yellow and clear; it smells sweeter than the crude oil, less harsh and burnt, but still somewhat dry-woody. The odor is much closer to that of eugenol. Rectified clove leaf oil may find use in all types of spicy perfumes, particularly in "low-cost" types and soap perfumes. In the case of the latter, however, the risk of discoloration at higher concentrations should be kept in mind. Alkali will produce a brown, iron and purple-violet discoloration in the presence of significant amounts of clove oils. On the other hand, only eugenol itself gives the typical spice odor. None of the non-phenolic derivatives (methyl eugenol, aceteugenol, etc.) will produce a similar spicyness in a perfume. Thus, there is no substitute for clove oil or eugenol, if the hydroxyl group ($-$OH group) is occupied or "inactivated" in the eugenol molecule. Accordingly, there are no stable white soaps containing significant amounts of eugenol or clove oil on the market. Spicy smelling soaps are usually colored dark amber or brown ("Windsor", etc.), whereby the discoloration is camouflaged.

In flavor work, the clove bud oil and, occasionally, the absolute from clove buds are preferred since these products reproduce the true clove flavor to a higher degree, and they are far more than being merely "eugenol"-flavor materials. The **Minimum Perceptible** of clove leaf oil (crude) is only one-third of the figure for a high-grade clove bud oil. The flavor type of the crude leaf oil is, however, inacceptable for use in foods. It does not reproduce the flavor of the clove bud such as it is known by many consumers. The apparent power in the clove leaf oil flavor is probably derived from traces of lower aldehydes, furfural, etc. which are often present in essential oils from leaves and other green plant material.

The isolated eugenol from clove leaf oil is used in pharmaceutical and dental preparations, in the synthesis of vanillin, for the production of eugenol derivatives, etc. Eugenol is not produced synthetically on a commercial scale, and clove leaf oil is the cheapest starting material for the isolation of this important aromatic chemical. The switch to "lignin-vanillin" during recent years has caused decrease in the clove leaf oil price, and the oil is now (in 1959/60) hardly profitable to produce. A series of devastating cyclones in March, 1959 on the Madagascan east coast destroyed portions of the clove plantations, and this caused a temporary increase in the price of the leaf oil. In respect to quantity produced, **Clove Leaf Oil** ranks among the 12 largest essential oils in the world.

Clove Stem Oil.

This oil is steam distilled from the stems upon which the clove buds grow (see **Clove Bud Oil**). Prior to distillation, the stems are sun-dried but not pulverized; the distillation takes place only in Zanzibar. The entire output of clove stems (3000 to 5000 metric tons per year) is distilled on the spot at the Clove Growers Association's modern distillery in Malindi, a Zanzibar port. There are 12 stainless steel steam stills which operate in shifts of 6, around the clock every day of the year. The exhaust stems are mixed with coconut shells and used as fuel in the fireplaces under the steam generators. All clove stem oil on the market is derived from this distillery. Accordingly, clove stem oil is one of the most uniform of all the essential oils on the market. Since the stems are distilled and then destroyed by law, there is no possibility of producing an experimental, water-distilled clove stem oil. It would be interesting to see, if this oil should have odor qualities similar to those of a water distilled clove bud oil.

Zanzibar **Clove Stem Oil** is—when fairly fresh and well stored—a pale yellow to straw yellow colored liquid of strong spicy, somewhat woody, but quite pleasant odor. The odor is not very different from that of eugenol (which is sweeter and less woody). The annual production is about 225 to 250 metric tons, all of which is exported, mainly to Europe and the U.S.A. Part of the oil is redistilled by the buyers, part is used as such in perfumery and flavor work. Some clove stem oil is used for the isolation of eugenol, production of eugenol-derivatives, vanillin, etc. Freshly redistilled clove stem oil is almost colorless. It finds use in perfumery for its spicy note in Oriental bases, spicy after-shave fragrances and other "men's odors", and in flavor work as a low-cost replacement for the more delicate and true-to-nature clove bud oil. Redistilled clove stem oil contains 90 to 96% eugenol, but does not present the sweet-floral, fruity-fresh notes found in the water-distilled clove bud oil. The exceptionally low **Minimum Perceptible** of the redistilled stem oil (0.04 to 0.06 mg%) may be due to the absence of the odor-depressing caryophyllene. The redistilled stem oil then performs almost like a pure eugenol. It has power, but no bouquet, no typical clove nuances.

Coconut Absolute.

Coconut Absolute is one among a great number of natural perfume materials which are not commercially available but nevertheless are used and appreciated by many perfume houses. The material may accordingly serve in this book as an example of the group of raw materials which are "made on our own premises", as the individual perfume houses would probably say. See also **Linseed Oil Absolute, Cypress Absolute, Lemon Aroma Distillate, Lupulin Distillate**, etc.

Coconut Absolute is produced by extraction of the comminuted endosperm of **Cocos Nucifera,** the coconut. Flaked or "grated" coconut meat may be used, but in order to obtain the full and natural gamut of volatile and alcohol extractive matter, it is adviseable to start from the "de-oleated" coconut.

When coconut meat is expressed hydraulically the oil will contain the volatile substances. The crude coconut oil is subsequently steam distilled in order to recover these odorous components. An essential oil of coconut is produced this way. However, the so-called **Coconut Absolute** is produced by alcohol extraction of the crude coconut oil. The alcohol is distilled off under gentle vacuum. A somewhat different coconut absolute is obtained by alcohol extraction of the press-cake of "de-oleated" coconut meat. This type of coconut absolute has a "heavier", more nutty type of odor and a darker color.

Coconut Absolute is usually a pale yellow, dark yellow or brownish yellow colored viscous liquid or a low-melting solid, waxy mass. It has a peculiar fruity-fatty, very fresh and light, yet tenacious odor. Only upon extreme dilution (about 1.0 mg% or lower) the nutty and typical fragrance appears.

Coconut Absolute is an interesting material in

the hands of the experienced and artistic perfumer for his work in unconventional perfumery. Floral fragrances such as jasmin, lily-of-the-valley, lily, lilac, ylang-ylang, etc. and in particular gardenia as well as fruity notes may be excitingly lifted or modified with this unusual perfume material. It blends well with ambrette seed oil, clove bud oil, cognac oil, neroli oil, sweet orange oil, etc. and with amyl cinnamic aldehyde, decylpropionate, cyclamal, isoeugenol, linalool, methyl nonyl acetaldehyde, trimethyl undecylic aldehyde, etc.

. Coconut absolute is rarely, if ever, used in flavors although it definitely has a delicate mellowing effect upon synthetic coconut flavors; its flavor strength is comparatively small and it has only little diffusive power. Besides, natural coconut meat flakes or "grated" coconut meat is used extensively "as is" in the candy industry, for baked goods, foods, etc.

Cognac Oil.

Cognac Oil, also known as **Wine Lees Oil** or **Weinhefeoel** (in German), is a by product from the distillation of Cognac (Brandy). It is present in cognac to the amount of about 2 mg%. The aromatic substances contained in cognac oil derive partly from the activities of the particular yeast fungus used, partly from the type of grapes fermented.

An oil can be obtained by steam distillation of the residue of grape tissue and fungus precipitate after fermentation (and distillation) of the alcoholic beverage. Water distillation is also applied directly to a slurry of the yeast residue in water. The aromatic principles in **Cognac Oil** are generally higher boiling esters of ethyl and iso-amyl alcohols, and they do not distil readily with the hydro-alcoholic mixture which is known as **Cognac** after proper maturing and ageing.

The crude cognac oil may be redistilled to yield a very powerful aromatic which represents the maximum concentration of high-boiling esters from the cognac yeast precipitate. **Cognac Oil** is a pale yellow or greenish yellow, somewhat oily liquid of intensely strong, almost harsh-fruity, oily-fatty, yet green-herbaceous odor of outstanding tenacity and great diffusive power.

The rectified oil is used in flavors and perfumes in trace amounts to give "lift" and fresh-fruity, natural notes, e.g. in liqueurs, fruit flavors,

(Fot. S. Arctander, 1960)

13: Majestic **Cedar** trees tower among small, husky **Sandaracs** (Atlas-thuja) at 8000 feet altitude in central Morocco.

14: Ornamental young **Araucaria** tree in Rabat, Morocco. At the age of 100–200 years the tree may have grown to a height of 150 feet. *(Fot. S. Arctander, 1960)*

15: **Champaca** flowers on a cultivated tree near an extraction factory in Nossi-Bé (Madagascar).

(Fot. S. Arctander, 1956)

16: Young Ceylon **Cinnamon** shrub with its characteristic leaves.　　　*(Fot. S. Arctander, 1960)*

colognes, fougères, after-shave fragrances, etc. It blends excellently with ambrette seed oil, amyl salicylate, bergamot, coriander, galbanum, lavender, linalool, sage clary, styrax, ylang-ylang, etc. The average use level in flavors would be about 0.50 mg% (in aqueous medium) and the **Minimum Perceptible** is 0.05 to 0.08 mg%. In cognac proper, the flavor of the 2 mg% of **Cognac Oil** is partly masked by the presence of 45 to 56% of ethyl alcohol. When the cognac is diluted with water, it smells stronger of cognac oil.

See also **Rum.**

Cola.

The **Cola** "nut" is one of the most important of all the essential-oil-free—and practically odorless—natural flavor materials. The botanical material which we call cola "nuts" are embryo-leaves from the seeds of the cola fruit. The fruit is obtained from a large tree, **Sterculia Acuminata** (or other **Sterculia** species) originating in west Africa. The cola trees are now cultivated extensively in other tropical regions since it is too difficult to transport the fresh "nuts" over long distances. The fresh cola "nut" has been the indispensible tonic of the west African people from time immemorial. It can be packed in green banana leaves and kept fresh for many days during exhausting travels through jungles or across deserts. The active ingredient in the cola "nut" is **Caffeine** which also lends an intensely bitter taste to the "nut" when it is chewed. The "nut" is about the size of a walnut, purple colored on the outside, white inside when it is fresh. The cola "nuts" are usually halved during the drying process. They become chocolate brown, hard as wood, and they lose part of their stimulant effect.

Dried cola "nuts" are shipped all over the world. They are used in pharmaceutical preparations, in mild tonics, in non-alcoholic beverages and for the extraction of **Caffeine.** The ground or coarsely comminuted cola "nuts" are extracted with a weak ethyl alcohol or with hot water. In the latter case, a mild alkali is added in order to transform the caffeine into a less bitter substance, and to make it easier soluble in the aqueous extract. The extract is evaporated to a standard strength (one part of extract to be equivalent to one part of dry cola "nut"), or the extract is evaporated completely to a dry extract which is approximately five times stronger than the crude botanical material.

For the use of **Cola** in flavors it has certain advantages to add an edible, non-volatile solvent, such as propylene glycol to the extract during the evaporation which should be carried out under vacuum. By this method it is possible to produce a concentrated **Cola**-extract (two-fold or more) which is miscible with other flavor materials or with alcohol of reduced strength.

Cola Glycol Concentrates are dark brown, clear and viscous liquids of bitter-woody but not unpleasant taste. The odor is typical of the amine-like or "animal" odor of the wet and pulverized cola "nuts". This "proteine" type of odor is also found in certain fractions of Atlas cedarwood oil. It vanishes completely when cola extracts are used in acid media and it is conceivable that this unpleasant odor is due to an alkaline substance.

Cola Extracts are used in the **Coca-Cola** type of carbonated beverages in the flavor complex of coca, lime, cinnamon, ginger, orange peel and other natural materials.

The **Coca** flavor is characterized by methyl salicylate, the main flavor principle in the decocainized **Coca**-leaf extract which is also used in the above popular beverage.

Combava Petitgrain Oil.

Among the numerous varieties of edible citrus fruits, many are known only in small or isolated areas where they have become not only a local variety, but also a local delicacy. A certain citrus tree in the Comoro islands northwest of Madagascar and in other nearby islands and in Madagascar itself produces large and very delicate fruits, locally known as combavas.

It was not until recently that the perfumery industry became interested in this tree, **Citrus Hystrix**, varietas **Combava.** For obvious reasons the essential oil of the peel of these edible fruits of the tropics is rarely expressed or distilled. Fruits are used as part of everyday food.

But when a local essential oil distillery undertook steam distillation of the leaves and twigs of this citrus variety, a new petitgrain oil was discovered: **Combava Petitgrain Oil.** The oil is distinguished by its very delicate sweetness and freshness which is distinctly different from bitter orange petitgrain or other well-known petitgrain oils. Still more interesting is it, that this oil contains laevo-**Citronellal** as one of its main constituents. It was hoped that the oil could thus become a new starting material for the production of laevo-**Citronellol** (by reduction), a perfume material sometimes called rhodinol. It is not possible at the present moment to predict the future of combava petitgrain oil, but the next decade will no doubt tell us.

Combava Petitgrain Oil is a pale yellow to greenish yellow, mobile liquid of fresh-leafy, sweet-rosy odor, somewhat reminiscent of the odor of Guinea lemon petitgrain oil and eucalyptus citriodora oil. The flavor is, contrary to that of most other petitgrain oils, sweet and pleasant, fresh lemon-lime-like and when sufficiently diluted, it is without the perfumey note which one could expect from the known constituents of this oil. The **Minimum Perceptible** is about 0.02 to 0.05 mg%, but at a suggested use-level of 0.50 mg% there are still little or no woody-perfumey notes perceptible in the flavor. The oil could possibly find application as a freshener-modifier in citrus type flavors, etc., or in trace amounts as a bouquet material for raspberry, apple, etc.

In perfumes the oil would probably be needed in larger concentration since it appears well fit for the soap and detergent type of fragrances. It could also find use as a modifier in citrus colognes and, generally, as a new topnote ingredient.

The annual production of **Combava Petitgrain Oil** is still at the "upon demand" scale, but considerable quantities of botanical material is available for an increased production of the oil.

The presence of **Citronellol** in certain other varieties of citrus leaf oils and peel oils is not uncommon. The essential oil from the peel of **Citrus Hystrix**, varietas torosa, contains a significant percentage of laevo-**Citronellol** although not enough to make an isolation economically attractive. This tree grows in the Philippine islands and may be the ancestor to the combava tree. Many of the utility trees and plants of the Philippines and Melanesia (ginger, lytchie, pepper, ylang-ylang, etc.) have been brought along by the immigrants to Madagascar, Nossi-Bé and the Comores. The essential oil from the peel of **Citrus Hystrix**, var. torosa, is known in the Philippines as **Colobot Oil** and it is used locally for the perfuming of cosmetic preparations, etc. The author has no personal experience with the odor of Philippine **Colobot Oil**.

Copaiba Balsam.

Copaiba Balsam, also known as **Copahu Balsam** is one of the most "natural" (unprocessed) of all the natural perfume materials. It is used in perfumes exactly as it comes out of the tree, exactly as it occurs in nature. It is not a balsam according to the definitions given in Part One of this book (see **Balsam**).

Copaiba Balsam is a natural oleoresin which occurs as a physiological product in various **Copaifera** species. These are large trees which grow wild in the northeastern and central South America. The chief producer is Brazil, and smaller amounts come from Venezuela, British Guiana, Surinam and Colombia.

The oleoresin flows abundantly from large cavities in the trunks of these trees when holes are drilled for collection of the copaiba "balsam".

Copaiba "Balsam" is a more or less viscous, brownish-yellow or grayish-greenish yellow liquid which dries to a hard and brittle resin upon exposure to air. The oleoresin is not always clear or translucent, but may be hazy due to its water content or to the continuous resinification of the essential oil part of the oleoresin, a process which starts already inside the trunk. The odor of the oleoresin is very faint, mild-woody, slightly spicy-peppery and modestly tenacious. The flavor is bitter and irritant.

Since copaiba "balsam" is mainly used for its fixative properties, it is reasonable that the "balsams" with a low content of essential oil are preferred for this purpose ("Maracaibo balsam"). These copaibas contain about 30 to 50% of essential oil. "Balsams" with high (60 to 80%) content of essential oil are used for the distillation of essential oil (see following monograph). The resin which is left when the essential oil has been removed is odorless, and has no perfumery value beyond that of a fixative. Its high acid number is a drawback.

Copaiba "Balsam" blends well with cinnamic alcohol, styrax, amyris oil, coumarin, lavandin oil, cedarwood oils, ionones and methylionones, nitromusks, and numerous other common perfumery materials. It is often used as a fixative in low-cost violet and wood perfumes, for lavender or fougères in detergent perfumes, industrial perfumes, etc.

The "balsam" is also used in the adulteration or "reproduction" of essential oils, and in the "cutting" of guaiacwood oil, amyris oil, patchouli oil, etc. (see also **Gurjun Balsam**). Copaiba "balsam" is produced in quantities of 50 to 90 tons annually, and it is one of the most inexpensive natural fixatives.

Copaiba Balsam Oil.

An essential oil is obtained by direct distillation (dry, in vacuum) of **Copaiba "Balsam"** (see previous monograph). It is customary to select the copaibas which contain a very high percentage of volatile oil for this purpose (Para balsams). Such balsams are less appreciated as commercial copaiba balsam since they dry out more slowly and yield less resin. For the same reason, they are poorer fixatives in perfumery, and thus the low-oil copaibas find their way into perfumery and porcelain-painting, etc., while the high-oil copaibas are distilled. Brazilian copaibas are in the latter category, Venezuelan copaibas in the former.

Copaiba "Balsam" Oil (or **Copaiba Oil**) is a colorless or pale yellow to yellow-green or bluish, very mobile oil. The odor is similar to that of the "balsam", but much milder, sweeter, almost creamy-balsamic with a faint peppery-spicy undertone. There are notes which resemble furfuryl alcohol and cadinene, others may remind of the notes in Peru balsam oil. A very peculiar and complex, but very faint odor.

Copaiba Oil finds some use in perfumery, but its fixative value is negligible and its contribution to the overall odor of a fragrance is quesitonable. Its main use is that of a blender-modifier. It blends well with cananga, ylang-ylang, heliotropine, hydroxy-citronellal, isoeugenol, vanillin, ionones and methylionones, sandalwood oil, jasmin absolute (!), amylcinnamic aldehyde, etc. The oil is used in pine fragrances, woody bases, violet perfumes, spice fragrances, etc., and its low cost and good availability makes it popular for some of these purposes. However, it is still missing from many a perfumer's shelf, and it is unlikely that the oil will ever arouse any particular interest. Only its low price will keep it from becoming completely obsolete.

Copaiba "Balsam" Oil can be used in the "reproduction" of certain essential oils and to "correct" the physico-chemical properties of such oils. In this respect, **Gurjun Balsam** has been even more outstanding.

Coriander Oil.

Coriander Oil is steam distilled from the dried fully ripe fruits (seed) of **Coriandrum Sativum**, a small herb native to southeastern Europe. The fruits are crushed immediately prior to distillation. The coriander herb grows not only wild, but is cultivated extensively all over the world: U.S.S.R., Hungary, Poland, Czechoslovakia, Germany, Holland, France, Italy, Morocco, Spain, Yugoslavia, Roumania, Turkey, Norway, England, India, Mexico, Guatemala, Argentina, etc.

Distillation takes place mainly in the U.S.S.R., Poland, Hungary, Holland, France, and England. Fruits from India and Morocco are distilled in the U.S.A. by a few companies which specialize in such work. Consequently, it is difficult to estimate the actual production of **Coriander Fruit Oil.** But with an annual production of more than 20,000 metric tons of coriander fruit, and an estimated use of 15% for distillation, a rough figure of 20 metric tons of annual world production of coriander fruit oil seems conceivable. It must be kept in mind that a tremendous amount of coriander seed (fruit) goes into certain classic spice blends, particularly those of the "Indian Curry" type, and this spice blend has not yet been replaced by any liquid essential oil mixture. The distillation of **Coriander Fruit Oil** presents at least two kinds of problems: a physical and a chemical problem:

Physical problem: The seed contains 0.7% essential oil if it is the correct quality of coriander. In addition, it contains 25% fixed oil (fatty, vegetable oil). In other words, the crushed mass of fruits in the still contains 25% oil, of which only 3% is volatile. The aromatic seed is rather bulky. One metric ton of crushed coriander in a 4500 litres (1200 U.S. gall.) still will yield 7 kilos ($15\frac{1}{2}$ lbs.) of coriander oil, and this amount of oil requires many thousand kilos of steam to be liberated. Furthermore, coriander oil is slightly soluble in water.

Chemical problem: The principal constituent, dextro-linalool, is a tertiary terpene alcohol which also occurs as an acetate in the oil. Linalylacetate is easily hydrolyzed, and linalool readily undergoes a molecular rearrangement, particularly when exposed even to very weak acids.

Coriander Fruit Oil is a colorless or pale yellow liquid with a pleasant sweet, somewhat woody-spicy, aromatic-candylike odor. The floral- balsamic undertone and peppery-woody, suave topnote are characteristic features of this delightful fragrance.

The flavor of coriander fruit oil is mild, sweet and spicy-aromatic, yet somewhat warm, very slightly burning. In flavor compositions, it blends well with anise, cardamom, bergamot, clove, sage clary nutmeg, etc., or with sweet-fruity bases such as peach, cherry, plum, etc. The combination with bergamot oil is well known from hard candy flavors. The oil is used extensively in flavors for alcoholic beverages, candy, tobacco, pickles, meat sauces, seasonings, etc. A suggested use level would be around 0.30 to 1.00 mg%, and the **Minimum Perceptible** is 0.05 to 0.10 mg%. These figures are based upon true and genuine, good coriander oils. Poor grade oils may easily show four times higher figures. In perfumery, its warm and sweet notes blend equally well with sage clary and bergamot in colognes, with floral notes in jasmin, lilac, appleblossom, honeysuckle, etc., and with olibanum and Ceylon cinnamon, it may produce highly interesting effects in perfumes of the "Oriental" type. The oil blends well with neroli, petitgrain, citronellol, nerol, sandalwood oil, cananga oil, calamus oil, ginger oil, cypress oil, pinus pumilio oil, decylalcohol, decylpropionate, aliphatic aldehydes, citral, etc. The use of coriander oil in tobacco flavors has also brought the oil into a position as an interesting modifier in "tabac" type perfumes.

The main constituents of **Coriander Fruit Oil** are readily available as synthetic chemicals. Consequently, the oil is frequently adulterated. Certain essential oil houses even make it a rule to "cut" their coriander oil with 20% synthetic (or isolated) linalool prior to resale. Small amounts of bouquetting materials are added: decyl aldehyde, decyl alcohol, linalylacetate, phellandrene, limonene, etc. Only a thorough olfactory investigation and knowledge of the true oil (or of the botanical proper) will enable the perfumer to judge between true and false oils. An organoleptic test is particularly useful for the flavor chemist in detecting even minor additions of natural or unnatural constituents. The author has yet to see an artificial or adulterated coriander oil which displays a more powerful flavor (in respect to coriander flavor) than a true, good grade coriander oil.

Adulteration with **Coriander Herb Oil** may occur, but since the pure herb oil consists almost entirely of **Decylaldehyde**, only small amounts can be used for the cutting of the fruit oil where this aldehyde occurs in traces. However, the herb oil could very likely find use in perfumery because of its interesting and powerful odor. But decylaldehyde is now produced synthetically at a very low price, and the herb oil cannot serve as an economical source of this perfume material.

Costus Absolute.

Costus extracts have been manufactured on a smaller scale in France and a few other countries for several decades. The raw material is the **Costus** root, see description under **Costus Oil.** Substantial quantities of the root are still exported from the Himalayan areas to perfume houses all over the world for distillation or extraction.

The **Costus** root contains certain very high boiling aromatic materials. Accordingly it requires a lengthy distillation which is harmful in general to most constituents of essential oils. Extraction with hydrocarbon solvents (benzene or petroleum ether) at modest temperature will produce a concrète of a rich and true-to-nature odor. An absolute is produced from the concrète by the conventional alcohol extraction method. The **Concrète** is commercially called **Costus Resinoid.** The costus root which has been steam distilled for essential oil is occasionally extracted with a volatile solvent. This second extraction yields a resinous and faintly aromatic material which unfortunately is used as a "cutting" agent for true **Costus Resinoid.** Other so-called **Costus "Resins"** are merely residues from the rectification of costus oil. An **Anhydrol** of **Costus** is commercially available. It is a molecular distillate of costus root extract. A neutral solvent is co-distilled with the extract.

Costus Absolute is a semi-solid mass or very viscous liquid of pale amber or brownish-amber color. Its odor is similar to that of the essential oil but it appears at first much weaker and less harsh. The odor of the absolute is strikingly similar to that of the root itself—to those who have had the opportunity of smelling the root material. The odor of the absolute is soft, sweet-woody and fatty without any unpleasant "harsh" or "rancid-fatty" notes. The tenacity of this odor is tremendous and its fixative value can hardly be overestimated.

Costus Absolute is available at a quite attractive cost thanks to the fact that the yield of alcohol-soluble absolute by extraction of the concrète (or "resinoid") from costus root is almost the same as the yield of essential oil by steam distillation. However, only an increased demand will bring the price of the absolute down near the cost-level of the essential oil. The trend in perfumery raw material production is steadily going toward the extracted products rather than the distilled ones. This is particularly true when the problem is "expensive" perfume materials. Several Grasse factories specialize in extracting practically any natural raw material to produce a perfume material.

Costus Absolute and Costus Concrète (costus "resinoid") are used in similar perfume combinations as those described under Costus Oil.

Costus Oil.

Costus Oil is steam distilled from the comminuted, dried roots of Saussurea Lappa, a large impressive plant which is found growing wild in the Himalayan highlands at high altitude. The plant has been introduced in the southwestern parts of the highlands, and is found also in southern China, i.e. on both sides of the Himalaya. Only recently, the roots have been submitted to distillation in India. Earlier, the oil was produced in places outside the origin of the plant.

Prior to distillation, the roots are not only comminuted, but also macerated in water. The distillation is then a combination of water- and steam-distillation. This is similar to some vetiver distillations. The oil does not separate well from the condensed water, partly because of the fact that its specific gravity is almost the same as that of water, partly because of water-solubility of certain components of the oil. The oil is actually extracted from the distillation waters by means of hydrocarbon solvents, usually benzene. (See also Manevoro oil and certain other oils which are produced in a similar way).

Costus Oil is a pale yellow to brownish yellow, very viscous liquid. It has a peculiar soft, but extremely tenacious odor, reminiscent of old, precious wood, orris root, fatty (but not rancid) acids, vetiverol, etc., with a distinctly animal or sebaceous undertone. The odor has been compared to that of human hair, fur coats or "wet dogs". The latter description is often heard from people who smell costus oil for the first time. It is certain that not all people will like this odor.

In surprisingly small concentrations, Costus Oil will induce warm, woody and "natural" notes to a perfume; however, this is limited to certain

perfume types, e.g. Oriental bases, chypres, violet bases, certain floral fragrances, etc., and many types of the "modern-aldehydic" theme. The oil blends well with alpha-decanolide (various isomers), cinnamic alcohol, flouve oil, isoeugenol, methylionones, decylpropionate, nitromusks, patchouli, opopanax, oakmoss, etc. Overdoses of costus oil may easily produce obnoxious effects, and the power of this oil is often under-estimated. Similar in effect to angelica root oil, Costus Oil has the peculiar ability of producing diffusive power and intriguing topnotes, and at the same time it works effectively as a fixative of unusual tenacity.

Only a good knowledge and experience, including knowledge of the botanical raw material, will enable the perfumer to choose a genuine costus oil from among the many poor ones which are offered. Although the selection of raw materials— and natural materials in particular—for the use in perfumes and flavors is mainly a matter of esthetics, it is still an advantage to know when a natural raw material is genuine and unadulterated. (See monograph Adulteration in Part One of this book).

Costus Oil is quite expensive, and accordingly subject to frequent and extensive adulteration. Elecampane root oil, distilled from the roots of a related plant, is available in most parts of the world, and it presents certain notes which can be compared to those of costus oil. However, it does not have the typical fatty-sebaceous, animal-like notes. Elecampane Oil, in turn, is also adulterated (see monograph on this oil). The selection of a good costus oil thus becomes quite complicated and problematic.

In spite of all this, Costus Oil is regularly produced in substantial quantities, estimated at 6 to 12 metric tons per year. India is the main producer, but good oils in considerable quantities are also distilled in Europe, particularly in Grasse, from Indian roots. Occasionally, the oil from Indian roots is distilled in the U.S.A. Large quantities of Indian costus root are shipped to China and other countries in the Far East for use among the population as a "factotum" remedy and house-scent.

Elecampane and other, similar plants grow in China and are distilled locally. This is another source for the "on-the-spot" adulteration of costus oil.

The constituents of costus oil are mainly very high boiling sesquiterpenes and sesquiterpene alcohols. Among a number of ketones found in costus oil are alpha- and beta ionone, which occur in nature very rarely (see **Boronia, Cassie, Chloranthus Spicatus,** etc.). Ketons and lactones are held responsible for the peculiar odor of costus oil.

See also **Costus Absolute,** previous monograph.

Cryptomeria Japonica.

Cryptomeria Japonica Oil is occasionally known as **Sugi Oil** or **Japanese Cedarwood Oil,** see also the monographs on **Cedarwood Oil, Japanese** and **Chamaecyparis Obtusa.**

Various essential oils can be obtained from the cypress-like Japanese tree, **Cryptomeria Japonica:**

Root Oil, Bark Oil and **Leaf Oil.** Only the **Root Oil** has obtained any significant interest for the perfume industry. The roots are readily available since the fragrant wood of the above tree is used extensively in the local production of beer-barrels. The bark oil and the leaf oil have been produced experimentally in Japan.

Sugi Root Oil is produced in quantities of about 5 to 10 metric tons per year, and only in Japan (figures from 1958). The oil is colorless to pale yellow or pale olive-green. Its odor is woody-cedarlike with a faint peppery undertone, not unlike **Atractylis Oil** (which is much more pungent) or **Araucaria Oil** (which is much milder). The oil consists almost entirely of sesquiterpenes and sesquiterpene alcohols.

Sugi Root Oil is used locally in soap perfumes for its good fixative value, equivalent to the use of cedarwood oils elsewhere. Little, if any, **Sugi Root Oil** is exported and the oil has no importance for the perfume industry outside of Japan.

See also **Machilus Oil.**

Cubeb Oil.

Cubeb Oil is steam distilled from the unripe, dried, crushed fruits of **Piper Cubeba,** a climbing vine similar to the pepper plant. The plant is a native of the greater Sunda Islands (Indonesia) where it is commonly grown on coffee and cocoa plantations. Cubeb is also cultivated in Ceylon, on the Malayan peninsula and on a number of Far Eastern islands. The fruits are harvested before they are ripe; this explains the wrinkled surface of the dried fruits. A short piece of stem is usually

left on the fruit which also bears the name of "Tailed Pepper".

Distillation takes place almost exclusively in Europe and the U.S.A. Considerable quantities of cubebs are locally consumed as a spice, and a great number of other species of this family are also cultivated in the same areas, mainly for local use as spice. This fact, however, has lead to very frequent contamination, not to speak of adulteration, of the berries as such. It takes quite a bit of experience to distinguish between true cubebs and the many false varieties, etc. The so-called "Singapore-seed" is generally preferred for distillation.

Importers of cubeb will be very disappointed after an initial trial distillation if their cubeb lot was false or a poor mixture. Not only is the essential oil from these cubeb-resembling varieties of very little value, but the yield of oil from most of these false cubebs is usually much lower than the yield from the genuine berries.

Cubeb Oil is a pale greenish-yellow to bluish-yellow, occasionally almost colorless, somewhat viscous oil. The presence of blue or greenish-blue color usually indicates that the distillation has been carried through to the very highest boiling constituents of the oil (azulenes and related hydrocarbons). During the distillation, one can observe a distinct ammoniacal odor in the condensate. This is also observed during the distillation of black pepper, allspice, ginger, and numerous other oils. Although this phenomenon has not been officially explained, it seems conceivable that proteins (which are amines) in the plant material may be hydrolytically decomposed during the distillation, probably due to the presence of certain activators in these particular botanicals. The annual world production of true cubeb oil is difficult to estimate, but probably does not exceed 10 metric tons.

The odor of **Cubeb Oil** is very dry-woody, but simultaneously warm-camphoraceous, spicy-peppery. The odor should be free from the very light pepper-like characteristic found in black pepper and elemi oils, and it should rather present the heavy-woody peppery notes found in guaiacwood, atractylis, araucaria, schinus molle, etc. The closest approach to the cubeb oil odor in a single perfume material is probably found in the oil of **Cedrela Odorata.** The flavor of cubeb oil is warm, but bitter, hardly pungent at all. Accordingly, cubeb oil is only rarely used in flavors, occasionally in spice blends. **Cubeb Oleoresin** (see following monograph) is preferred in flavor work.

Cubeb Oil, consisting mainly of sesquiterpenes, sesquiterpene alcohols and minor quantities of monoterpenes, etc., is useful in soap perfumes where it may lend "peppery" undertones and warm-woody character. Black pepper oil would be almost wasted if thus used. Cubeb oil is also very useful in the creation of woody-peppery perfume bases, carnation perfumes, and in the "construction" of artificial essential oils. The oil blends well with cananga oil, cinnamic alcohol, clove stem oil, coumarin, eugenol, galbanum, isoeugenol, lavandin oil, rosemary oil, etc.

Cubeb Oil itself is frequently subject to adulteration, e.g. additions of clove leaf oil sesquiterpenes, cedrela oil, copaiba oil, schinus molle oil, etc., and fractions of other essential oils. False cubebs, e.g. **Piper Crassipes** (see monograph) are, however, the most frequent cause of a poor grade of **Cubeb Oil**.

Cubeb Oleoresin.

Cubeb Oleoresin is a prepared oleoresin for flavor use. It is produced from the dried, unripe, coarsely powdered cubeb fruit (see **Cubeb Oil**) by extraction with a hydrocarbon solvent or with ethyl alcohol. According to the definition in Part One of this book, the alcohol extract is a **Resin Absolute**. In pharmaceutical terms it is an extract of unusually high essential oil content. Alcohol is usually preferred as a solvent since it is quite difficult to remove the solvent quantitatively—even under good vacuum. The extract is used in flavors and should not have any trace of hydrocarbon solvent. Prolonged exposure to heat and reduced pressure will inevitably cause a loss of aromatic components of the oil in the extract.

Cubeb Oleoresin is produced almost exclusively in Europe (particularly in England) and in the U.S.A. The most recently developed extraction methods are applied to cubeb (and other spices) in Grasse factories. This includes the **Ultrasonic** extraction method, see **Ultrasonic Extracts**, Part One of this book.

When alcohol is used as a menstruum for the extraction of cubeb fruits, the resulting oleoresin will be free from waxes and fatty oils. Upon standing for 24 hours this alcohol extract will deposit a crystalline mass and some waxes. The crystalline mass consists mainly of cubebin, a bitter principle. A clear, viscous oleoresin in then obtained by draining the extract through a funnel with absorbent cotton. The cubebin and the waxy deposit are of no value to the flavorist. Good alcohol-oleoresins of cubeb are accordingly clear, homogeneous and viscous liquids. Hydrocarbon extracts tend to deposit very slowly a grainy, waxy substance.

The odor of **Cubeb Oleoresin** is warm-spicy, peppery-camphoraceous with a rich, herbaceous undertone. The flavor is equally warm and spicy, peppery but not very pungent. Hydrocarbon solvent extracted oleoresins are usually bitter of taste. The oleoresin produces slowly a burning mouthfeel. It is primarily a flavor material and it finds some application in spice blends for pickles, meat sauces, etc. It is also used in certain countries for the flavoring of shag (pipe) tobacco along with many other flavor ingredients.

Cubeb Oleoresin is not produced on a large scale but it seems to be available in sufficient quantities as to cover the small demand. The main constituent of cubeb oleoresin is **Cubeb Oil** which is present to the amount of 50 to 55% (see monograph on **Cubeb Oil**). The oleoresin blends well with oleoresin of black pepper, clove, allspice etc. in combination spice blends. It has little or no use in perfumery.

Cumin Absolute.

From **Cumin** fruits (seed) an **Oleoresin** can be prepared the usual way (see **Oleoresin**, Part One of this book), and by alcohol-washing of the oleoresin an **Absolute** of **Cumin** is produced.

Cumin Absolute is a dark olive-brown or dark yellow, viscous liquid of a powerful, but delicately mellow and round, green-spicy odor, very closely reminiscent of the odor of the crushed seed from which it is derived. The absolute has a striking resemblance to curry powder in its complex and exciting fragrance. Cumin seed is an important ingredient in curry powder.

The extracted product seems to contain more of the sweet notes from the extractive plant matter than does the essential oil. This fact makes the absolute superior to the oil in flavor work. The essential oil is extremely volatile and of tremendous diffusive power, while the absolute displays a richer, softer, true-to-nature cumin seed character.

The suggested use level for **Cumin Absolute** is

132

about 0.20 to 1.00 mg%, and the **Minimum Perceptible** is 0.05 to 0.10 mg%. The figures are somewhat higher than those for the essential oil.

Cumin absolute is produced on a very limited scale only, but the advantage of its use in flavor compositions, particularly in extracts for pickles, etc., is obvious. It is very conceivable that cumin absolute will be a common item in future price lists. In perfumes, the intense color of the absolute is only a minor drawback, considering the minute amounts necessary for obtaining "green-spicy" effects. The absolute needs less fixation than does the essential oil, and cumin absolute blends excellently with oakmoss absolute, lavandin absolute, galbanum resinoid, etc. in lavender-fougères, chypres, aldehydic bases, etc.

For details of botanical origin, etc., see **Cumin Oil.**

Cumin Oil.

This oil is distilled from the dried, ripe fruit (seed) of **Cuminum Cyminum,** known as **"Roman Caraway",** a small herb originating in the Middle East. The cumin seed belongs to the group of very old spices whose history of use can be traced back thousands of years. To-day it still is one of the important ingredients in the ever-popular "Indian Curry Powder".

The plant is cultivated in its native area, in Cyprus, Lebanon, Morocco, Malta, Turkey, Spain, U.S.S.R., China and, on a small scale, in Central America. Distillation is performed in India, in Europe and in the U.S.A. The fruits are crushed immediately prior to the steam distillation. The problems connected with the distillation of **Cumin Oil** are similar to those encountered in the production of other essential oils from fruits of umbellifer species:
1) a high content of fatty (fixed) oil which is partly distillable and forms emulsion,
2) proteins which are decomposed and produce putrid odors,
3) an essential oil which is partly water-soluble. Cohobation of the distillation waters is necessary.

The yield, however, is quite encouraging in the case of **Cumin Oil. Cumin Oil** is a pale yellow to brownish yellow liquid; it occasionally displays a greenish tint. Dark-colored oils may have been stored in iron containers or under poor conditions. The oil is quite sensitive to daylight, air, moisture and metals as well as to alkali. Its odor is extremely powerful, diffusive, green-spicy, slightly fatty, but at the same time not sharp or pungent, almost soft and mellow. This softness is one of the main features of a true oil, and is very hard to duplicate when making an artificial oil with a similar content of **Cumin Aldehyde** (the main constituent of cumin oil). The synthetic aldehyde has a very sharp odor of cumin type, far from mellow or pleasant. The characteristic odor and flavor of cumin oil is probably due to its minor constituents such as **Dihydrocuminaldehyde** and various monoterpenes.

The flavor of cumin oil is spicy-herbaceous, faintly pungent and fatty-green, not pleasant in high concentrations. The suggested use level is 0.20 to 0.50 mg%, and the **Minimum Perceptible** is 0.02 to 0.05 mg%. A powerful flavor material.

As previously noted, a freshly distilled **Cumin Oil** presents a peculiar, putrid odor, recalling sulfides and/or amines on top of its true fragrance. Similar topnotes are encountered in freshly steam distilled fruits of other umbellifers and in black pepper oil (ammoniacal odor), etc. It is conceivable that such odors represents trace amounts of decomposition products from proteins, etc., in the endosperm of the seeds. However, most cumin oils offered in the market do not possess this type of odor. Obviously, such oils have been "treated" somehow, or "doctored up" to eliminate or mask the off-odor. For those who have observed an actual distillation, however, the presence of these typical by-odors is often a valuable criterion in determining whether or not an oil is genuine.

Cumin Oil is used in perfumes in trace amounts to introduce green-spicy and green-woody topnotes, particularly in the woody-floral perfume types, Oriental bases, mimosa, cassie, violet, etc. It is also used for "special effects" in modern-aldehydic fragrances, etc. and for its unusual diffusive power. The oil blends well with lavandin, rosemary, galbanum, oakmoss, bois de rose oil, etc. and it performs well in soap although it may discolor a white soap tablet visibly after a few months of ageing.

In flavors, the oil may replace the fruits (except in curry powder), and it is generally used for seasonings, pickles, meat sauces, etc. **Cumin Oil** is very frequently adulterated with or even substituted for by artificial cumin oil, based upon **Cuminaldehyde,** cymene, etx. Only a thorough olfactory and organoleptic analysis will reveal such adulterations to the experienced perfumer-flavorist. See also **Cumin Absolute.**

Curacao Peel Oil.

The essential oil which is generally offered under the above name is the hand-pressed oil from the peel of green (immature) bitter oranges. The green peels are also dried and sold to botanical and pharmaceutical houses under the name of **Jacmel** or **Jacmal** orange peels (quartered or halved). These peels are produced in the West Indies, particularly in Jamaica where also the ordinary bitter orange oil is produced (see **Orange Oil, Bitter**). The true **Curacao** peel is derived from a variety of the bitter orange tree, the so-called "varietas curassaviensis". This tree is cultivated in the tiny island of Curacao, off the north coast of South America. The island is part of the Dutch West Indies. The true Curacao peel is slightly smaller than the jacmal peel and the Curacao peel is much stronger in aroma. It is doubtful, however, if any essential oil at all is produced from the true Curacao peel. The larger part of the production of Curacao and Jacmal peels are shipped to Europe and the U.S.A. for preparation of tinctures and flavor extracts. These are used in flavor compositions for liqueurs of the "Curacao" type, "Triple Sec", "Grand Marnier", etc.

True **Curacao Peel Oil** is an olive-green, mobile liquid of powerful, fresh and rich, grapelike citrus-peel odor reminiscent of expressed lime oil, petitgrain oil and bitter orange oil, however, the odor of the curacao oil is slightly sweeter, almost perfumey. The essential oil of the peel is justly replaced by an alcoholic tincture which is more stable and which contains less terpenes. The purchase of true Curacao peel requires great experience. The author was unable to confirm any local production of **Curacao Peel Oil** in 1959 in the Dutch West Indies, and it is conceivable that the oil is not produced on a commercial scale, if the true oil is produced at all any more.

Curcuma Oil.

The plant, **Curcuma Longa**, is related to the ginger plant which it also resembles. Curcuma is a native of the south Asian countries where it has been known and used for thousands of years

as a spice and as a common house medicine. The plant is now cultivated extensively in India, Indonesia, southeast China, Formosa, the Philippines, Indochina and Japan. Distillation of oil takes place in India, China, Japan in or near the growing areas. Imported rhizomes of the curcuma plant are distilled in Europe and the U.S.A.

Curcuma Oil is produced by steam distillation of the dried, comminuted rhizomes ("tubers") of the curcuma plant. The finely powdered rhizome is also used directly as a spice which is known under the name of **Turmeric.** This ingredient is responsible for the intensely yellow color of the world famous "Indian Curry Powder". This yellow color is particularly visible when moisture or water is present (in gravies, etc.). Curry powder is usually made up from capsicum (or paprika), black pepper, ginger, coriander, cardamom, clove, allspice, cinnamon, nutmeg, etc. This spice blend is used all over the world in hundreds of international or local dishes, but above all the Indonesian "rijstafel" is spiced with curry powder and numerous other pungent additives. At wedding ceremonies in Indonesia the bride and groom tint their arms and waists with a dye of curcuma.

Curcuma Oil is a yellow to dark orange-yellow liquid which occasionally shows a faintly blue fluorescence. The odor is usually spicy and fresh, reminiscent of sweet orange, ginger and galanga. The flavor is slightly pungent and bitter except in extreme dilution. The odor of Japanese curcuma oil is warm, dry-woody, powdery, camphoraceous and slightly peppery-spicy with a peculiar undertone reminiscent of the odor of Atlas cedarwood oil. The flavor of the Japanese oil is bitter, spicy and slightly burning. **Curcuma Oil** finds comparatively little use in flavor work since curry powder has not yet been replaced by a mixture of the respective essential oils or oleoresins.

Curcuma oil can be used in certain types of perfumes where it introduces warm-woody, dry-powdery tonalities in Oriental bases and fantasy fragrances, etc. The oil blends well with cananga oil, cistus oil, elecampane, ginger, labdanum, orris "resin", etc. and with heliotropine, ionones, methylionones, nitromusks, etc. Although the spice itself is so extremely widely known, the essential oil seems to have failed to catch the interest of most perfumers and flavorists. The annual world production of **Curcuma Oil** is adjusted to the modest demand, which is estimated at not more than a few metric tons.

A **Curcuma Absolute** is produced on demand by various Grasse houses and by a few internationally known specialists in spice extraction. See also **Curcuma Oleoresin.**

Curcuma rhizomes are known in Europe under various names which can be translated as "yellow root". This name should not be confused with the American "yellowroot" which unfortunately also bears the name of "Indian turmeric" (note: *American*-Indian!). The American plant has the botanical name **Hydrastis Canadensis.** The rhizome of this plant contains two alkaloids of doubtful therapeutic effect. The plant which resembles the wind-flower (anemone), was used by the American Indians as a stomachic tonic, etc., and it is still used in world-wide medicine for its dubious hemostatic effect.

Curcuma Oleoresin.

This flavor material is produced from the **Curcuma** rhizome (see **Curcuma Oil**) by extraction with a volatile solvent, usually petroleum ether, ethyl ether or, in special cases with diluted ethyl alcohol. The hydro-alcoholic extract can be considered as similar to the conventional pharmaceutical extract of curcuma.

The hydrocarbon-solvent extracts of curcuma are not soluble in water. The hydro-alcoholic extract is soluble in diluted alcohol but not in concentrated alcohol, nor in water. A well-known hydro-alcoholic extract is marketed under the brand name of **Tumerol** (not to be confused with the sesquiterpene alcohol turmerol. The extract contains mainly **Turmerone** which is the ketone corresponding to turmerol).

Curcuma Oleoresin is a dark yellow to brownish-yellow, viscous mass of faint odor reminiscent of the odor of the spice. Solvent odor should not be perceptible. The oleoresin is used in flavor work as a replacement for the powdered rhizome. It is by far superior in this respect to the essential oil of curcuma. The flavor of the oleoresin is richer, more woody-sweet, free from terpene-like notes, resembling ginger oleoresin but less pungent than this.

An **Absolute** of **Curcuma** has been produced from the oleoresin by the usual alcohol-washing method. The absolute is a viscous, brownish-yellow liquid. Its odor resembles that of the oil but the absence of terpenes in the absolute is distinctly perceptible in its odor: a soft, spicy-woody, warm and mellow, tenacious fragrance. It blends excellently with cassie, mimosa, methylionones, cedarwood derivatives, sage clary, heliotropine, etc.

Curcuma Absolute is not a regularly produced flavor and perfume material.

Cymbidium Virescens.

The essential oil of **Cymbidium Virescens** is a comparatively recent product in the Chinese perfume oil industry. The oil is not yet available all over the world. It is used in southeastern China for the perfuming of cosmetic preparations.

The plant is a multiflowered orchid from tropical China and from the Philippines. It represents one of the comparatively few examples of fragrant orchids. See also **Sulpitia Orsuami** under the monograph of **Perilla Oil.**

The author has no personal experience with the essential oil of **Cymbidium Virescens.**

Cymbopogon Connatus.

The east African grass **Cymbopogon Connatus** is related to citronella, gingergrass and inchigrass (see these monographs). The plant is locally known as "sar saharu" which means something like: "desert grass". It grows in the western parts of north-Abyssinia (formerly called Erithrea) and into the eastern parts of southern Sudan (Kassala province).

A great deal of research was carried out on the agricultural aspects of these areas during the Italian occupation of the Abyssinian area. Encouraging remarks on the above essential oil can be found in the reports which are now more than 30 years old. Experiments have been recommenced lately and the perfumery industry has also shown an increasing interest in essential oils which can supply new notes for creative perfumery. The presence of about 40% of **Dihydro Cuminyl Alcohol** in the essential oil of **Cymbopogon Connatus** makes it immediately interesting as a source for the isolation of this alcohol which is also known as **Perilla Alcohol.**

The odor of cymbopogon connatus oil is intensely fatty-green, spicy-fresh with a sweeter dryout and a strongly herbaceous undertone. The oil is olive-green to yellowish green and mobile, but its viscosity increases on ageing.

During the author's visit to the above mentioned

areas in 1956, he had the impression that a confusion between two or more species of Cymbopogon was very possible. A related plant, Cymbopogon Schoenanthus, subspecies nervatus, grows abundantly in the Kordofan province alongside and east of the blue Nile. This area is adjacent to the above mentioned home of Cymbopogon Connatus. The cymbopogon schoenanthus subspecies nervatus produces an essential oil of very similar composition (it consists mainly of dihydro cuminyl alcohol and laevo-limonene). This oil smells almost exactly like the sample of Cymbopogon Connatus Oil which was submitted to the author later on.

Being unaware of the above facts at the moment of his study trip, the author would prefer now to avoid a definite statement in respect to the possible confusion between the two oils.

However, the fact remains that we have at our possible disposal a highly interesting source of a powerful perfume raw material. The essential oil of Cymbopogon Connatus could furthermore find some use "as is" in perfumery. It lends a certain naturalness and freshness together with its outstanding diffusive power. In the reproduction of "missing" notes in artificial essential oils, the oil would no doubt attract the perfumer who works on artificial bergamot oil, ylang-ylang, jasmin, etc.

The essential oil of Cymbopogon Connatus can be produced at a low cost and in large amounts.

See also Inchigrass Oil.

Cyperus Oil.

Various essential oils from the roots of certain tropical grasses appear on the perfumery market under the above name. The greater part of these oils are used locally, but one seems to have obtained more than local interest:

The essential oil of the rootlets of Cyperius Scariosus (or cyperus scariosus) is marketed under the brand name of Cypriol in India. The oil has been known for many decades in its home country where the roots are used in the same way as vetiver roots for the scenting of sari's and other women's clothing. The grass is locally known as Nagar Mustaka.

Cypriol is produced by steam distillation of roots and rhizomes after proper washing, drying and comminuting, similar to the treatment of vetiver rootlets. The distillation is a lengthy process since all the volatile constituents of this botanical material are high-boiling: sesquiterpenes, sesquiterpene alcohols, sesquiterpene ketones, etc. —a composition very similar to that of vetiver oil.

Oil of Cyperus Scariosus ("Cypriol") is an amber colored or light brown viscous liquid of woody-earthy and very tenacious odor. The very first impression of the odor of this oil bears great resemblance to the odor-impression of the "Oriental" cinnamon-olibanum complex: diffusive, dry, woody, slightly spicy. The overall body-note resembles that of Virginia cedarwood and vetiver oils, but toward the dryout there is a strong similarity to vetiver in sweet-woody and rich undertones. Apart from the excitingly fresh topnote this oil is distinguished by a firm uniformity in odor throughout all stages of evaporation.

Cypriol blends well with bergamot, labdanum, patchouli, sage clary, etc. for dry ambre notes which can be further enhanced by the addition of very small amounts of "fixateur 404" or the complex "grisambrol", etc. Cypriol is useful in perfumes or bases of the woody, Oriental or dry-ambre types, in heavy fougères, in hyacinth (along with galbanum resinoid), in forest notes and in general as a fixative. In higher concentrations it will display its peculiar, soft-woody note and intriguing topnotes. The relatively low cost of this oil makes it attractive even in soap perfumery where its odor-tenacity and stability come to their right.

Cypriol is produced on a limited scale by one producer in India. The annual production is perhaps in excess of 2 metric tons, but this figure could easily be increased since the natural raw material is abundantly at hand.

Among the other Cyperus species which grow in tropical and semi-tropical regions all over the world, only a few have caught the perfumer's interest:

Oil of Cyperus Rotundus (in French: "souchet rond") is steam distilled from the rootlets of a grass which grows in China, India, Japan and scattered over parts of Sudan south of Sahara. The African Cyperus Rotundus is, to the author's knowledge, not distilled locally. Shipments of the rootlets arrive irregularly in Europe where an essential oil is distilled upon demand for certain perfume houses.

Cyperus Rotundus Oil is a yellowish or amber-colored to dark orange-brown (locally distilled oil) or pale yellow-brown (European distilled) viscous liquid. Its odor is quite interesting. The topnote is almost floral-woody, resembling cassie and boronia with a violet-like or tea-like warmth. The odor becomes drier and more woody, borneole-like, camphor-like but it remains faintly floral throughout the long-lasting dryout. The oil blends well with mimosa absolute, cassie, costus, methylionones, isoeugenol, oakmoss absolute, sage clary, etc.

There are some facts which confirm the possibility of confusion of this oil with vetiver oil from certain parts of Africa. Small shipments of southwest African vetiver oil arrive occasionally in Europe. These oils often display quite abnormal physical constants, such as strong laevo-rotation and very high ester number. Some of the **Cyperus** oils are naturally laevo-rotatory and they do have odor types similar to that of vetiver oil, however, more to the dry, cedarwood-like type.

The grass **Cyperus Rotundus** is very abundant in certain of the above mentioned areas, but the production of root oil is still very occasional and irregular. Accordingly, the oil of cyperus rotundus is not a regularly available or commercial item in Europe or in the U.S.A.

Cyperus Longus is a west-Sudanese grass. Its rootlets are collected by the natives in West Africa (formerly A.O.F.) for the purpose of scenting their clothes, etc. The roots smell woody-violet-like, reminiscent of alpha-Ionone, but the author has no personal experience with the essential oil of **Cyperus Longus**, if this oil is produced at all. In respect to odor, the roots resemble the wood of the Australian **Acacia Homalophylla**, the so-called Australian **Violetwood**.

The foliage of various **Cyperus** species in China and Japan are twined into ropes which are commercially known as "sea-grass" and used for seats, baskets, etc.

Cypress Absolute.

The yield of essential oil by distillation of the leaves and twigs of **Cypressus Sempervirens** is comparatively small (0.2 to 0.3%). The steam distillation is quite time-consuming since it is necessary to continue the distillation until the high-boiling and more valuable constituents are carried over (12 to 18 hours at low steam pressure). It is therefore not surprising that hydrocarbon

solvent extraction of the plant material was considered already long ago.

Concrète of **Cypress Leaves** has been produced by benzene extraction. The yields are 5 to 8 times higher than the yields of oil by distillation. **Cypress Concrète** is a semi-solid, dark green to brownish-green mass of powerful balsamic-fatty, sweet and pine-like odor. The concrète yields 65 to 75% of alcohol-soluble absolute which is only slightly more liquid, unctuous and greener of color. The odor of **Cypress Absolute** is lighter and more powerful than that of the concrète. Apart from the components which are found in the essential oil, the **Cypress Absolute** contains large amounts of alcohol-soluble resin acids. The absolute could accordingly be classified as a prepared oleoresin. **Cypress Oleoresin** is one of the commercial names for this product.

Cypress Absolute is produced in very small quantities and usually only upon demand. However, this product is far more interesting for ambre perfumes, chypres, colognes, pine fragrances etc. than is the essential oil. The absolute blends well with amyl salicylate, cedarwood derivatives (vertofix, etc.), cistus oil, isobutyl-cinnamate, etc. The intense green or brownish-green color of the absolute is a certain drawback unless it is used with oakmoss, etc. It is not conceivable that **Cypress Absolute** will ever become an important perfume raw material. The limited amount of botanical raw material available for its production seems to scare the larger consumers from including cypress absolute in their current formulae.

Cypress Oil.

Cypress Oil is distilled from the leaves (needles) and twigs of the evergreen, **Cypressus Sempervirens,** and possibly from other species of **Cypressus.** However, only oils distilled from the sempervirens species should be accepted as **Cypress Oil.** The tree presumably originated in the eastern Mediterranean countries, and now grows both wild and cultivated (primarily as a windbreaker) along the coasts of southern France, Italy, Corsica, Sardinia, Sicily, North Nfrica, Spain and Portugal, and, to a lesser degree, in the Balkan countries.

Distillation is concentrated in the South of France. It is customary to collect and distil the material which is obtained by the annual pruning of the trees, perhaps together with twigs, etc. torn off the trees during the winter mistral, the violent storm. This is why **Cypress Oil** is usually available only in very limited quantities and only at certain times of the year. This quantity could easily be increased to 3 or 5 metric tons annually, perhaps more, provided the distillers were notified of the demand well in advance. Unfortunately, other varieties of **Cypress** are distilled with the "true" one, and branches and other woody material are not always screened away prior to distillation. Thus, the various lots of **Cypress Oils** which are offered present themselves in a very unattractive manner, exhibiting a far from uniform quality. An essential oil, distilled exclusively from **Cypress Fruits** has also been available, but this oil is now only produced on demand.

Cypress Oil is a pale yellow, pale olive-greenish or almost colorless, mobile liquid of sweet-balsamic, yet refreshing odor, reminiscent of pine needles oil, templin oil, juniper berry oil, carda-mom oil (without the cineole-note), and with a unique dryout of delicate and tenacious sweetness, often compared to that of ambre (labdanum-ambre). For this reason, **Cypress** Oil is frequently submitted to fractionated distillation under vac-uum, or simply to a "topping-off" under vacuum. The high-boiling fractions or, in the case of "topping", the residue in the still, usually 40 to 45% of the natural oil, are particularly useful.

This "partially deterpenized" cypress oil is used in perfumes of the ambre-labdanum type in combinations with cistus oil or other labdanum products, delta-methylionone (so-called), lavender oil, mandarin oil, sage clary, musk ambrette or macrocyclic musks, styrax products, moroccan chamomile oil, etc.

Cypress Oil (natural oil) is occasionally used as a modifier in pine needle fragrances, in citrus colognes, fougères, chypres, and in the modern-aldehydic type of perfumes.

The main constituents of the oil are mono-terpenes (60 to 70%), pinene and camphene in particular, but these are not responsible for the above-mentioned sweet and tenacious ambre-notes.

Cypress Oil from areas other than the Med-iterranean countries are distilled from different species (e. g. Brazil, Japan, Kenya, etc.). Adulter-ation of cypress oil is effected with these oils, and with the addition of pinene, camphene, juniper-berry oil, juniperwood oil, pine needle oils, etc.

In spite of its scarcity, **Cypress Oil** is in no way an expensive material. The cost level is usually slightly higher than that of a good "Siberian" pine needle oil.

D

Dacrydium Elatum.

An essential oil can be produced by steam dis-tillation from the wood of this conifer.

This essential oil seems to have disappeared from the world market since 1952, like so many other products from the former French Indochina. The tree grows in the northern parts of that country, previously known as Tonkin, and this particular species does not seem to be known outside of that area. A number of related conifers from neighboring areas yield other interesting essential oils, see **Huon Pine Wood Oil** and **Siam Wood Oil.**

The essential oil of **Dacrydium Elatum** is a dark, yellow-brownish liquid of dry-balsamic, woody odor, reminiscent of crude Virginia cedarwood oil. The yield by steam distillation is very good and it is most likely that the oil still serves as a soap perfume and household article perfume ingredient on the local market.

The author has no recent experience with the essential oil of **Dacrydium Elatum.**

Davana Oil.

This oil is obtained by steam distillation of the overground parts of the flowering herb, **Artemisia Pallens.** The plant grows in the same parts of southern India where also sandalwood is grown.

Davana Oil is very dark green or brownish green (similarity to several other artemisia oils). Its odor is sharp, penetrating, bitter-green, foliage-like and powerfully herbaceous with a sweet-balsamic, tenacious undertone.

The oil is a comparatively new item resulting from the activities of the world-known research institute in Dehra Dun, India. It is still too early to predict a future for this oil and the production of it remains on a small scale. The oil will no doubt find use in local flavor and perfume work in compositions where similar artemisia oils are used in European or American formulae. The intense color is a certain drawback but the oil blends well with most chypre and fougère materials which also include strongly colored products (oakmoss, labdanum, etc.).

See also **Artemisia Alba, Artemisia Vulgaris** and **Wormwood Oil.**

Deertongue.

Various species of the genus **Liatris**, particularly **Liatris Odoratissima**, grow wild in the southeastern United States, and have been known for their medicinal effects for a long time. The roots were extracted or infused to prepare a medicine of diuretic effect, etc. The leaves of this plant become very fragrant when they are dried. This is similar to the observations one can make with hay, everlasting, woodruff, melilotus, etc. Apparently the aromatic substances are combined (e.g. glycosidically) into odorless materials in the live plant. (See also **Flouve Oil** and the above mentioned oils).

The leaves of **Deertongue**, as the composite plant is called in the U.S.A., do not yield any essential oil when they are distilled, but a highly aromatic extract, called **Oleoresin** of **Deertongue**, is prepared from the dried leaves with a volatile hydrocarbon solvent. After removal of the solvent in vacuum, the oleoresin appears as a dark green, very viscous liquid or semiliquid mass, possessing a heavy-sweet, coumarin-like, rich herbaceous odor. The immediate odor-similarity to shag tobacco is probably a reflection of the fact that the extract has been used since long ago for the flavoring of tobacco. It is interesting to note that extraction has mainly been carried out in Europe, particularly in England and France.

Under the name of **Deertongue, Lacinaria** or **Liatris Oleoresin,** the extracts have been used for many decades in the food flavoring industry also, until the coumarin ban in 1952. The extract is still used in tobacco flavoring, which is, for some inexplicable reason, considered as "exterior use".

In perfumery, however, **Liatris Oleoresin** or **Liatris Absolute** (prepared from the "oleoresin") are used frequently in chypre, moss, new mown hay, Oriental, and similar sweet or coumarinic bases. Its high content of coumarin and related compounds makes it an excellent fixative, but its intense color is a drawback in certain creations and uses. With synthetic musks, it produces very

interesting, dry-perfumey powder-notes, particularly in combination with heliotropine, "gamma"-methyl ionone, cinnamic alcohol, etc. It blends well with oakmoss, labdanum, lavandin, olibanum, clove bud oil, amyl salicylate, patchouli, etc. In odor type, it is very similar to **Flouve** and **Melilotus,** both of which are prepared in Europe, the former also as an essential oil.

As previous mentioned, there are several species of **Deertongue**, and they present various modifications of the coumarin-type of fragrance: from green-sharp herbaceous to intensely vanilla-sweet and candylike. The plant is very common in the southeastern U.S.A., where it is also known as **Prairie Pine** or **Blazing Star,** these names referring to the shape and the flowers of the fair-sized composite plant.

Although it is not a very expensive perfume material, **Liatris Oleoresin** is used in comparatively small quantities, and the annual production hardly amounts to more than a few metric tons. The designation "oleoresin" is stubbornly applied to the commercial product although it contains no volatile oil and very little resinous matter. According to the definitions in this work, it is a *concrète* (which happens to be a pourable, viscous liquid).

Dictam Oil.

Dictam Oil is steam distilled from the flowering tops of **Dictamnus Hispanicus**, a small plant which belongs to the same family as the rue plant. **Dictam** herb has been a common drug store item for many decades and the fragrant leaves were previously used as a culinary herb and as a house medicine.

The essential oil is distilled on a very small scale in Spain and only upon demand. The plant grows wild in several countries in southern Europe and north Africa. The production of **Dictam Oil** could be increased considerably in case of more interest from perfume of flavor houses.

Dictam Oil is a pale yellow mobile liquid of very fresh, sweet and anisic odor, reminiscent of Texas goldenrod oil. The odor also resembles that of estragon but it is less green-herbal than this. There is finally some resemblance to the odor of dill weed oil which has a slightly burning taste, while dictam oil has a milder, intensely sweet taste.

Dictam Oil could be used in perfumes to introduce topnotes or modifying notes in fougères, chypres, colognes, in lilac and ylang-ylang bases, narcissus and other floral bases, etc. In flavors the oil blends well with mild spice oils, such as anise, basil, dill, goldenrod, hyssop, estragon, etc. It may find use in seasonings, table sauces, pickles, etc. The suggested use level is 0.50 to 1.50 mg% (perhaps higher in acid media) and the **Minimum Perceptible** is about 0.03 to 0.08 mg%.

It has been mentioned that **Dictam Oil** is occasionally used as an adulterant for sweet (French) **Basil Oil**.

Dill Seed Oil.

Of little interest to the flavorist, and holding hardly any interest for the perfumer, is the essential oil from the fruits (seed) of **Dill** (see **Dill Weed Oil**, following monograph, the more important of the two oils). Dill seed oil is also known as **Dill Fruit Oil**. Although chemically almost identical to **Caraway Fruit Oil**, there is a distinct difference in the odor and flavor of the two oils. However, caraway oil is the one which is produced on a large scale, and is thus available regularly at an attractive price; dill seed oil is a small item, produced by only a few specialists in Europe, mainly in England, rarely in the U.S.A. Lately, the essential oil of the fruits of **Anethum Sowa** (see monograph) has been subjected to more extensive investigation in India where the plant is cultivated quite commonly. The oil of anethum sowa is somewhat different from dill seed oil. **Dill** is cultivated in the U.S.A., Hungary, Holland, Italy, England, Germany, India, and Pakistan (see **Dill Weed Oil**).

Dill Seed Oil is steam distilled from the crushed, dried, mature fruit of **Anethum Graveolens**. One distiller in England, however, insists upon water-distillation, and his oil is unquestionably superior in flavor to any other dill seed oil on the market. Dill seed oil is pale yellow or almost colorless (when fresh) and very mobile. Its odor is light and fresh, warm-spicy and reminiscent of caraway and spearmint, although less sharp. The taste is warm, slightly burning, but pleasant and powerfully aromatic-sweet. The suggested use level is 2.00 to 6.00 mg%, and the **Minimum Perceptible** is 0.40 to 0.60 mg%. Dill seed is extremely popular in Sweden where many types of bread are flavored with the seed (or with anise or fennel seed). The American "rye bread" is flavored with caraway oil or carvone. Hence the popular odor-description "it smells like rye bread" for **Carvone.**

Dill Seed Oil is produced in modest quantities only, but there is usually available a plentiful supply for those who want to use this oil.

Dill Weed Oil.

Also known as **Dill Herb Oil**. The dill plant, **Anethum Graveolens**, is one of the many umbellifers which supply us with aromatic seed or culinary herb material. The plant grows wild in most parts of Europe, the Middle East up to southern Russia, all around the Mediterranean Sea widely in India and Fareast Asia, in Italy and in Kenya. In most of these areas, it is harvested for use as dry botanical material. In England and Hungary, it is cultivated for the purpose of distilling the seed oil (see monograph), and in the U.S.A. and Hungary, distillation of the entire Herb (the "weed") is effected on locally grown cultivated dill. Smaller quantities are cultivated and distilled in Germany and Holland (weed oil). The plant is distinguished by having yellow flowers (like the pimpinella plant) in contrast to the white flowers of most other umbelliferes.

Dill Weed Oil is distilled from the partially dried, fully grown herb which is harvested immediately prior to maturity of the seed (fruits). The herb is steam distilled on the growing spot, and the yield of dill weed oil per acre is slightly less than the yield of oil from spearmint (which is concentrated in the midwestern area where harvesting is mechanized, thus making the production more economically attractive. Practically all of the American dill weed oil is used in the American pickle industry. Pickles are the largest quantity canned food item in the U.S.A.

Dill Weed Oil is an almost colorless or pale yellow mobile liquid with a powerful and fresh, sweet-spicy, peppery and aromatic odor, reminiscent of elemi oil, spearmint oil, citrus oils, etc. with a sweet, nutmeg-like undertone. The taste is warm and slightly burning, but pleasant and not pungent although very peppery and spicy, with a faint anisic undertone. The suggested use level is (measured in a neutral medium; the figures should be significantly higher in acid medium, e.g. vinegar): 3.00 to 8.00 mg%, and the **Minimum Perceptible** is 0.40 to 0.80 mg%. A comparatively mild tasting oil.

Although it is used in this large industrial product (canned pickles), **Dill Weed Oil** is used very little in other cases, mainly those connected with sauces, seasonings, etc. The production of the oil is not impressive, and outside the U.S.A., the herb itself is still widely used for the flavoring of pickles, vinegar, etc. With the rapid growth of the canning industry, it is conceivable that the oil will be introduced in other countries, too, as a replacement for the herb.

From the related plant, **Anethum Sowa** (see monograph), another *seed* oil is distilled which differs slightly from the oil distilled from **Anethum Graveolens**. Anethum sowa oil is mainly used in the Far East where the plant is cultivated and is also found as a native, wild-growing plant.

Douglas Fir Needles Oil.

The essential oil from the leaves (needles) of the "**Douglas Fir**" or "**Oregon Fir**" (see **Oregon Balsam**) is briefly mentioned in this work, although the oil is not regularly produced.

The tree, **Pseudotsuga Taxifolia**, is not only very abundant in the northwestern United States but it has been introduced in many European countries for its useful lumber. Accordingly, there is ample leaf material at hand whenever a distillation may seem interesting enough for the lumbermills.

Douglas Fir Needles Oil is a pale yellow liquid of very rich, woody-balsamic, sweet pine-needle type odor. Oils from various sources show quite wide differences in odor, but the main characteristic seems to be a softness and a sweetness, a very rich bodynote and a great odor tenacity which is exceptional for a "pine needle oil".

The oil could find use in all kinds of pine fragrances and it would make a good supplement to the so-called Siberian pine needle oil which regularly floods the market but in most cases never saw Siberia. **Douglas Fir Needles Oil** would undoubtedly perform better in soap and in other products where a natural fixative is essential.

Unfortunately, the oil of **Douglas Fir Needles** is not regularly available in quantities sufficient to attract the interest of the soap perfume manufacturers.

E

Elderflower Absolute.

The flowers of **Sambucus Nigra** or other species of **Sambucus** yield on extraction with benzene, gasoline or petroleum ether a solid, dark green or olive-green concrète. The concrète is brownish-yellow in the case of petroleum ether extraction.

Elderflower Concrète yields an absolute when treated as described under **Absolutes** in Part One of this book.

Elderflower Absolute is a solid, waxy mass only slightly lighter colored than the parent concrète. The odor varies according to the solvents used but it is in general intensely sweet-herbaceous, honey-waxy, faintly anisic-floral or spicy. The odor of elderflowers does not please many people and the elderflower absolute presents a very concentrated edition of the nauseating sweetness of these flowers.

Elderflower Absolute lends, however, interesting warm-floral effects in suitable dilution and in the trace amounts where it is useful at all in perfumes. It blends well with bergamot, boronia, oakmoss, ylang-ylang, anisalcohol, ionones, isoeugenol, etc. in carnation bases, lilac, tabac bases, etc.

The eldertree grows wild or is planted as an ornamental shrub in most European countries including France, and the yield of absolute from the flowers is far better than the yield of essential oil by distillation. Therefore, several Grasse houses and at least one German producer make regular extractions of this flower material. The annual production is probably less than 100 kilos but it could be increased significantly in case of increased interest.

Elderflower Absolute is occasionally used in flavors where it can lend interesting bouquet notes to honey, blackcurrant and cherry flavor compositions.

Elderflower Oil.

This perfume and flavor material is only very rarely offered on the market. The concrète and the absolute (see the previous monograph) are generally preferred by the producers because of the better yield and by the consumers because of the more versatile application of the extracted material.

The small tree or shrub, **Sambucus Nigra,** grows

17: **Clove Buds** with stems and leaves at harvest time near Soanierana-Ivongo, northeast Madagascar.
(Fot. S. Arctander, 1955)

18: **Clove Buds** drying on mats in the sun of Zanzibar.   *(Fot. S. Arctander, 1955)*

19: **Elder**-bush in full bloom near Roskilde Cathedral, Denmark.
(Fot. S. Arctander, 1960)

20: A wealth of creamy-white **Elderflowers** exhaling their nauseatingly sweet, honeylike fragrance. Roskilde, Denmark.
(Fot. S. Arctander, 1960)

all over Europe wild or planted. It is appreciated for its flowers which are used in medicine for their mild diuretic effect, for their berries which serve as a food (soup) or a preserve (syrup), and finally for the soft marrow which finds use in certain carvings and for industrial purposes (insulation, etc.).

The dried flowers are steam distilled in Hungary, Germany and France. The essential oil is known in France as "essence de sureau". The oil is solid at room temperature and it has a very peculiar, intensely sweet, honeylike, faintly animal and unpleasantly nauseating odor. The fact that the odor of this oil does not immediately remind one of the suave, sweet-balsamic fragrance of the flowers (at a distance) may be due to the very low content of essential oil in the elderflowers. Hence, the oil is very concentrated as compared to the volume of flower material. On extreme dilution the odor of the oil becomes more pleasant.

Elderflower Oil is available in modest quantities and only upon demand.

Elecampane Absolute.

An oleoresin or a concrète can be produced by volatile solvent extraction of the roots of **Inula Helenium** (see **Elecampane Oil**). The concrète is rarely used as such in perfumery, but it is further processed to an alcohol-soluble absolute by the conventional method (see **Absolute**, Part One of this book).

Elecampane Absolute is a dark olive-green or brown, semi-solid mass which is hardly pourable at room temperature. Its odor is very soft, woody-rootlike, slightly fatty-sweet or "oily", extremely tenacious. The material blends well in perfumes with ionones, methylionones, heliotropine, sandalwood, bergamot, orris products, cistus oil, labdanum products, cypress oil, etc.

Elecampane Absolute produces interesting notes in ambre bases, woody-floral or oriental bases, heavy fragrances, etc. such as mentioned under elecampane oil. The absolute has a less earthy, more tenacious and rich odor than the essential oil.

The absolute is produced in France from imported or locally grown roots. Experimental batches of elecampane absolute have been produced lately in China. The annual world production of this absolute is probably less than 100 kilos.

The author has, however, some suspicion as to the genuineness of the samples and shipments of **Elecampane Absolute** which form the basis of the information in this monograph (in respect to odor description). On the other hand, if only a few producers offer this material, one must consider the product arbitrarily as a "perfume material" and not as a "guaranteed 100% pure extract of elecampane root". One meets this problem quite frequently when dealing with rare perfume materials.

Elecampane Absolute is presumably used as an adulterant in costus oil and perhaps in other expensive essential oils.

Elecampane Oil.

The roots and rhizomes of **Inula Helenium,** a tall plant related to the sunflower, have been known and used in medicine for many centuries. The roots contain an essential oil which can be isolated by steam distillation. The extraction products of elecampane root are described under **Elecampane Absolute** (previous monograph).

Elecampane Oil is produced from the dried comminuted roots which are collected from cultivated plants in Belgium, Germany, France, and southeastern Europe, or from wild-growing plants in southeastern Europe and Asia, in particular India and China, the countries in which the plant originated. Distillation takes place mainly in France from imported roots.

"Essence d'Aunée", as the oil is called in France, is a semi-solid mass or a viscous liquid which often displays a mass of crystals. The color is dark yellow to brownish-yellow, occasionally pale yellow and turbid. It is dry-woody in odor, but also sweet, somewhat anbre- or honeylike with a fatty undertone. The odor has some resemblance to those of calamus, costus and cedrela. The flavor is warm, woody-rootlike, slightly bitter, nauseating, reminiscent of calamus oil and manevoro oil.

Elecampane Oil is useful in perfumery for heavy-woody, Oriental or ambre-like bases, and it blends well with cananga, cinnamon, labdanum, lavender, mimosa, olibanum, orris, tuberose, violet, cedarwood, patchouli, nitromusks, etc. It has been found as an adulterant in **Costus Oil** where it can be quite difficult to trace olfactorily. The tenacity and soft woodiness of the odor of elecampane oil makes it an attractive fixative in perfumes. It has very little application in flavors.

Chinese **Elecampane Oil** has a somewhat

harsher topnote than have the European oils. The annual production of elecampane oil is less than one metric ton at present, and the oil is still comparatively expensive.

Elemi.

Elemi "gum" is a natural oleoresin in the sub-group of turpentines. It consists almost entirely of resin and essential oil. The term "gum" is thus a misnomer. Elemi is an exudation of a pathological product from the tree, **Canarium Commune**, and other species of **Canarium** which grow wild and, to a lesser degree, cultivated in the Philippine islands. The tree belongs to the same family as do those which yield myrrh, olibanum, opopanax and Indian linaloe. A mutual feature of these plants is that each of them is known or cultivated in only a comparatively small part of the world and never widely distributed.

Elemi, however, is quite abundant in the Philippines, and it is one of the most inexpensive sources of fixative resinoids. The annual production (harvesting) of Elemi runs into several hundred metric tons, most of which ends up in perfumes, etc.

Crude Elemi is a semi-solid, pale-yellow, waxy-honeylike mass, usually containing numerous woodsplinters, bark pieces, insect debris, dirt and earth, etc. Elemi is graded on the bulking place (locally), and it is possible to get lots which are quite clean, dirt-free and almost water-free. The odor is very fresh, terpeney, peppery-lemony, with a woody-balsamic background note. The odor bears some similarity to that of dill weed oil.

Elemi Resinoid is prepared by extracting the crude elemi with a volatile solvent, and removing the latter in vacuum after proper filtration. Acetone gives a very high yield and is a very good solvent for elemi. The acetone-resinoid is pale yellow, and soon shows white masses of crystals separating in the soft, slowly solidifying resinoid. Benzene gives a lower yield, and the odor of this solvent is more difficult to remove from the resinoid. Ethyl alcohol is a comparatively poor solvent for elemi, but some perfumers prefer to extract only once with one or two parts of ethyl alcohol. It will be necessary to filtrate the extract before it cools off. A smaller yield of resinoid is thus obtained, but it presents the heart of the fragrance of elemi in a more concentrated form: fewer monoterpenes, resin acids, sesquiterpenes,

etc., and higher concentration of the rare but important oxygenated components of elemi. One could call this product **Elemi Resin Absolute.** This is a very interesting fixative for artificial bergamot, lemon, lime, etc., as well as for the various verbena compositions, e. g. eau de verveine bases and other cologne types. In lavender-colognes, fougères, spicy colognes, etc., it simultaneously introduces freshness and fixation. For many of these purposes, one can omit evaporating the alcohol and use the concentrated extract ("tincture") as is.

The very high content of essential oil in **Elemi** is not always an advantage, and the factories that produce *elemi oil* (see following monograph) will have a useful pot residue when they have distilled the essential oil out of the crude elemi.

Various specialties are based on this residue.

Elemi Oil.

This is steam distilled from the crude **Elemi** (see previous monograph). Distillation takes place almost exclusively in Europe and the U.S.A. It is not advisable to dry-distil or vacuum-distil the oil. Its high content of unstable monoterpenes which tend to form peroxides presents a hazard of explosion at comparatively modest heating of the elemi (oil).

Elemi Oil is responsible for the fresh-lemony, peppery odor of crude elemi and of elemi resinoid. The main constituent of the oil is **Phellandrene**, a very unstable terpene, widely distributed in the plant kingdom. Small amounts of high-boiling, oxygenated components lend character and interesting dry-out notes to this oil which is found in amounts of 25 to 28% in elemi.

Elemi oil is colorless or pale yellow, mobile, and possessing a light, fresh, lemon-like, peppery odor which later dries out into a balsamic, slightly green-woody and sweet-spicy, pleasant note. The oil is not very stable, but antioxidants can retard decomposition of the phellandrene and dipentene. Peroxide-free oils can be "topped-off" in vacuum, whereby the bulk of the monoterpenes are removed (see **Elemol** below).

However, the natural **Elemi Oil** is very useful as a freshener and topnote material in various perfume compositions, e.g. fougères, chypres, colognes, and even in the heavy-sweet floral bases. The partially deterpenized elemi oil will prove particularly interesting in the Oriental bases, muguet, orchid, etc. It blends well with cinnamon bark oil, olibanum, labdanum products, rosemary oil, lavandin, sage oils, etc.

Elemi Oil is freely available, but should be freshly prepared from acceptable crude elemi; since the oil tends to resinify and polymerize, the odor can accordingly become disagreeable. Because of its main constituent and its optical rotation, elemi oil is frequently used as an adulterant or in the "constructing" of artificial essential oils which "conform to the specifications of this or that Codex or Pharmacopoeia". The oil has been found as an adulterant in lemon oil, black pepper oil, dill weed oil, angelica seed oil and numerous other essential oils.

Elemol is the commercial designation for a processed elemi oil from which the lower boiling terpenes have been removed. **Elemol** is a yellow or pale yellow, somewhat viscous liquid of peppery-balsamic odor and good stability.

Erigeron Oil.

Among the comparatively few essential oils which are produced exclusively from wild growing plants is the oil of **Erigeron Canadensis.** The plant is a weed and its original habitat is unknown to the author.

The plant is known in the U.S.A. as **Fleabane** and it is also common in other parts of the world, except in the tropical zones. The fleabane is almost a nuisance in the corn fields in the midwestern United States and it also causes trouble in the peppermint and spearmint fields there. One fleabane plant will produce about $\frac{1}{4}$ million seeds in one season. Accordingly, the plant is considered a weed and not a utility plant.

The entire overground part of the fleabane plant is steam distilled in the spearmint growing area of the midwestern United States (Michigan and Indiana). To the author's knowledge, there is no production of this oil on a commercial scale outside of the U.S.A. The annual production runs into a few tons of this oil.

Erigeron Oil is a water-white or pale yellow liquid of a sweet, but very fresh-spicy, herbaceous, basil-like odor. The dryout note is peculiar, winey-herbaceous and sweet, resembling the odor of powdered licorice root. The odor also resembles that of moroccan chamomile oil (ormenis multicaulis) in its verbena-like freshness and the herbaceous, ethereal-sweet, ambra-like undertone. The

taste is acrid, burning, somewhat sweet but unpleasantly biting, leaving a bitter aftertaste. The author has no experience with this oil in respect to use in flavors. The oil becomes darker and more viscous on ageing.

The oil of **Erigeron Canadensis** is occasionally used in perfumes where its peculiar and quite powerful odor may contribute interesting modifications in various types of colognes, fougères, chypres, aldehydic fantasy bases, etc. The oil blends well with cardamom oil, citrus oils, coriander oil, decyl aldehyde, hydroxy-citronellal, linalool, etc.

Erigeron Oil is occasionally adulterated. This is particularly true about oils which are offered in Europe where erigeron oil is frequently "doctored up" with synthetically prepared components of the oil: terpinyl acetate, d-limonene, etc. or even with cajuput oil, eucalyptus oil, etc. All these additives tend to decrease the characteristic fresh-herbaceous background notes in the odor of the natural oil.

Estragon Oil.

Also known as **Tarragon Oil.** In contrast to most other **Artemisia** oils, the essential oil of **Artemisia Dracunculus** is a sweet-smelling, spicy oil. The plant is a small member of the Compositae family, growing wild in many European and Asian countries. It is widely cultivated as a culinary herb or household spice for its sweet-anisic, somewhat celery-leaf-like and fresh-green flavor for use in vinegar, pickles, seasonings, meat sauces, etc. Distillation of the estragon herb is accomplished almost exclusively in France, although smaller quantities are produced in Holland, Hungary and the U.S.A. The whole overground part of the herb is steam distilled immediately prior to the inflorescence. **Estragon Oil** is a colorless or very pale yellow to greenish-yellow liquid with a sweet-anisic, green-spicy, slightly celery-like odor, very similar to that of the fresh herb. Like anise and basil oils, estragon oil tends to resinify on ageing; it becomes dark yellow and sticky, viscous, and loses its fresh green note and pleasant aroma. The flavor of the oil is sweet and slightly spicy-aromatic, reminiscent of anise and basil with a faint celery-note. A suggested use-level for **Estragon Oil** would be 0.20 to 0.50 mg%, and the **Minimum Perceptible** about 0.06 to 0.12 mg%. It is interesting to compare the flavor strength of this oil with that of synthetic **Estragole** (= methyl chavicol or para-methoxy allyl benzene). Estragole is the main constituent of estragon oil, and it is found in pine oil and in American turpentine oil. It is also prepared synthetically. The use level of **Estragole** is then 0.30 to 0.60 mg% and the **Minimum Perceptible** is 0.06 to 0.12 mg%. These figures do not reveal the wide difference in flavor type between estragol and estragon oil, but they do show that the natural oil with about 65% estragole compares favorably with pure estragole in flavor strength. Estragole is not, as we might expect, one-and-one-half times as strong as the essential oil.

Estragon Oil is useful in trace amounts in chypre, l'Origan types, fougères, lilac bases, green floral bases, etc., where it blends well with galbanum, lavender, isoeugenol, methylionones, vanillin, cinnamic alcohol, oakmoss products, etc. The oil finds extensive use in flavors where it replaces the herb in the canning industry (pickles, etc.) and for certain types of liqueur flavors.

Estragole (synthetic or isolated from pine oil) presents a serious threat to the unexperienced buyer of estragon oil. Fifty percent of estragole can easily be added to a good estragon oil (along with small amounts of phellandrene and other terpenes). The adulterated oil will show a "shorter life" on a perfume blotter, a too "clean" dryout, a lack of herbaceous undertone. A thorough olfactory and organoleptic evaluation will tell the experienced perfumer or flavorist whether or not he has a true estragon oil in front of him. Adulteration and "cutting" of this oil is extremely common. The annual production of the true oil is barely more than one metric ton.

Eucalyptus Australiana.

Of the almost 700 known **Eucalyptus** species, several hundred have been subject to thorough investigation, including experimental distillation of their essential oils. But only a small number of the species have proved interesting with regard to their oils. This book will deal with about one dozen of the eucalyptus oils, and the author hopes that this selection will cover all oils which are of interest to those in the fields of perfumery and flavor, and which are produced regularly, or made available upon demand.

The oil of **Eucalyptus Australiana** exists in several "forms" apart from the so-called "type"

tree. We shall describe only the "type" and the variety called "B". The two oils are produced in sizeable quantities in southern Australia, and the trees have lately been introduced in the Union of South Africa. The oils are produced locally by steam-distillation of fresh or semi-dry leaf material. Both oils are colorless or pale yellow, mobile liquids.

1) **Eucalyptus Australiana** "type" is a **Cineole**-type of oil, slightly different from the common "pharmaceutical" eucalyptus oils (see also **Eucalyptus Globulus**), however, it has a peculiar sweet dryout, and has less of the unpleasant "low-aldehydic" topnote, characteristic of most of the "pharmaceutical" cineole-type oils.

2) **Eucalyptus Australiana**, variety "B" is also called **Eucalyptus Phellandra.** It is a phellandrene-cineole type of oil, not suitable for pharmaceutical purposes, but of some interest to perfumery because of its great masking effect and low cost. This oil is produced on a large scale in Australia and on a small scale in Belgian Congo. Its odor is fresh, very powerful, peppery-camphoraceous, and it has a pleasant dryout but little or no fixative effect.

These two oils are both produced in large quantities, i.e. from 50 to 200 tons per year, particularly the latter which is used in the mining industry and as a solvent or hardener in paints and lacquers. It finds some use as a perfume material in the so-called industrial perfumes.

Eucalyptus, Chinese.

Before World War II, large quantities of fractions from **White Camphor Oil** (see monographs on **Camphor Oils**) were exported all over the world under the name of Japanese eucalyptus oil. A significant amount of this oil came from Formosa.

After World War II, the distilleries in Formosa seem to have discontinued the production of "eucalyptus oil" from the cineole fraction of **Camphor Oil, White** produced on that island. However, the world market has seen substantial quantities of so-called **"Chinese Eucalyptus Oil"** during the late 1950's. As a matter of fact, this eucalyptus oil (which is available at an all-time low cost) has made production of true eucalyptus oil uneconomical in a number of other countries, including the Belgian Congo and Spain. The latter country still has the advantage of being geographically close to the European consumers, and Red China does not sell its oil all over the world.

In China proper, the **Yu-Sho** ("Oil Camphor Tree") is the predominant "camphor tree", and this variety yields an oil that is rich in **Cineole** (about 50% in the de-camphorized Yu-Sho oil).

The cineole is isolated from the cineole-terpineol fraction; certain terpenes are added, etc., and the oil is brought "up to specifications" on physico-chemical properties to be presented as a pharmaceutical eucalyptus oil. In view of the number of camphor trees in China (an astronomical figure which reminds us of the expression "—all the tea in China" or of the number of inhabitants in Red China), it is conceivable that the so-called "Chinese eucalyptus oil" will continue to show up on the market in the future. At present, it is not possible to give exact data or information on this "artificial" oil.

Eucalyptus Citriodora.

Although scarcely yet in the 100-tons-per-year class, the essential oil from the leaves of **Eucalyptus Citriodora** has become one of the most interesting eucalyptus oils.

Like all other eucalyptus species, the citriodora is originally from Australia. The tree gives a very good and useful lumber and is therefore popular in the tropics. Today, it is cultivated—and also grows wild from old plantings—in Brazil, Belgian Congo, the Seychelles, the Union of South Africa, Southern Rhodesia, Tanganyika, Indonesia, Morocco, the U.S.S.R. and Guatemala. The aforementioned countries are listed approximately in order of importance as producers of the oil. Brazil has produced 50 to 80 metric tons per year lately, while Belgian Congo turns out 10 to 15 tons. However, the all-time low in citronella oil prices during 1958–1959 has been quite detrimental to the further development of citriodora distillation in the Belgian Congo and other areas. Brazil is a large country with sizeable needs for perfumery materials, and they can probably maintain their production for local consumption in perfumes and menthol-syntheses.

Steam distilled on local, but often quite modern stills, the oil is a colorless to pale yellow, mobile liquid which has a strong and very fresh, rosy-citronella-like odor and a sweet, balsamic-floral dryout note. As a source of natural citronellal, it is unsurpassed. The very high content of this oil in the best of the Belgian Congo oils (up to 82% in natural oils), and the fact that the balance consists of foreruns of a pleasant odor (light monoterpenes) and short tail fractions of geranyl acetate, etc. makes isolation of a high-grade citronellal from this oil a very attractive operation.

During the shortage of Fareastern citronella oils in the early 1950's, citriodora came into the limelight and its production increased tremendously. A large European company based their entire Brazilian menthol production upon locally distilled citriodora oil. By itself, eucalyptus citriodora oil is not much used in perfumery although it offers very attractive notes for low-cost soap perfumes, soap flakes, detergents, sprays, etc. This can be due to several facts:

1) the oil was "reserved" for many years for the menthol producers; 2) citronellal is not very stable in soaps or alkaline medium; 3) the really large soap manufacturers might hesitate to introduce this oil in their perfumes for detergents or soap flakes because they might be unable to get sufficient quantities of the oil (if it forms a major part of the fragrance, by weight). Furthermore, they generally try to avoid using large quantities of raw materials from countries over whose future development they have little or no "control"; 4) citriodora oil will, in many other cases, be only a minor ingredient in a soap perfume as a freshener, "lifter", etc.

Eucalyptus Citriodora Oil also serves as a starting material for the production of certain acetone-condensation products; the isolated citronellal is further processed to an excellent grade of hydroxycitronellal. The citronellal can be reduced with hydrogen in the presence of a catalyst. Various "special rose-alcohols" are produced by similar methods.

The 1960's will tell us about the future of citriodora oil, but it is obvious that Congo and Brazil producers are uninterested in producing, let alone exporting, this oil at the same price as Formosa citronella oil (1959 price fell below 8/- sh. engl. per kilo for oils of less than 45% aldehyde content!). This kind of competition is not exactly conducive towards improving the level of living among the native producers or the settlers in the growing areas. At the present price level, it is hardly possible to adulterate the essential oil of **Eucalyptus Citriodora** at all. Even "synthetic" citronellal (from American turpentine) would be too expensive to use as a "cutting" agent. Belgian Congo citriodora oils have usually shown the highest citronellal content (over 80% in oils from the Ituri district) and superior overall quality.

Eucalyptus Dives.

Of this species, we must mention three varieties:

1) **Eucalyptus Dives**, var. "C" which is the "pharmaceutical" type whose composition is almost identical to that of **Eucalyptus Australiana** "type" (see monograph). The oil is produced in sizeable quantities in southeastern Australia, and the tree has been introduced in South Africa. The oil from Australia is usually sold as "eucalyptus oil" and not as "dives" variety since it is marketed as a pharmaceutical eucalyptus oil. It is a colorless or pale yellow liquid whose odor is almost indistinguishable from that of the **Eucalyptus Australiana** "type" oil.

However, what is usually marketed under the name of **Eucalyptus Dives** oil is the essential oil, steam distilled from the leaves of 2) **Eucalyptus Dives**, var. "A", or from the leaves of 3) **Eucalyptus Dives** "type". The latter has captured the most interest during the late 1940's and early 1950's when synthetic menthol saw a rapidly increasing market all over the world. This oil (3) contains a large amount of laevo-**Piperitone** which can be converted into menthol. The balance of the oil will yield **Phellandrene**, another useful material in perfumery and in the reproduction of essential oils. laevo-**Piperitone** forms the starting material for the production of synthetic **Menthol** in a very large Australian factory.

Eucalyptus Dives var. "A" (2) contains less laevo-**Piperitone** and more **Phellandrene**, and is mainly used as a solvent and for technical perfumes, insecticides, etc.

All three types are produced on a large scale in Australia, and the oils 1) and 3) will probably soon be distilled in the Union of South Africa, possibly later on in Brazil.

See also **Evoulimba Oil**.

Eucalyptus Globulus.

Some decades ago, a pharmacist wouldn't think of buying a eucalyptus oil unless it was a genuine **Eucalyptus Globulus** oil. And this surname has remained in many price lists of today, even in cases where the **Globulus** has long since been replaced with other oils of very similar constitution. Pharmaceutically, it is the most important (type) of all the eucalyptus oils, and if we consider all the **Cineole**-types of eucalyptus oil as one big "pharmaceutical eucalyptus oil", this will be the largest in quantity by far. Various producers actually speak of **Eucapharma Oils** when they market oils of high-**Cineole** type.

The essential oil of **Eucalyptus Globulus** is scarcely produced in its homeland at present. The tree originated in Tasmania, but no oil has been exported from Australia or from its small neighbor island for many years.

However, the **Globulus** tree is planted practically all over the world in temperate and semi-tropical regions and in tropical highlands or swamps. The tree is found in France, Spain, Portugal, Algeria (and North Africa in general), Brazil, Colombia, Ecuador and India. There are more eucalyptus trees in Brazil than in any other country outside of Australia. To a minor extent, it is planted in California and in numerous African and European countries. In the Belgian Congo, the **Globulus** tree has now been replaced with **Eucalyptus Smithii** (see this monograph).

Eucalyptus Globulus oil is steam distilled from the fresh or partly dried, long and narrow leaves of this large beautiful tree. Distillation is carried out locally. In Algeria and a few other countries, the leaves are also dried completely and sold to drug houses, but these leaves are not distilled. They would yield little and poor oil. The oil is colorless and quite mobile when rectified. It is pale to dark yellow when old or poorly stored. Rectification or "redistillation" is often carried out on the spot since this operation improves the keeping qualities of the oil. Lower aliphatic aldehydes in the foreruns are partly removed, together with resinified terpenes in the tail fractions; the oil becomes a "Codex" or Pharmacopoeia-quality with a higher **Cineole** content, and thus easier to export. Incidentally, the lower aldehydes are usually held responsible for a cough-provoking effect which is not exactly wanted in the eucalyptus oil used in cough-drops, etc.!

The total annual production of **Eucalyptus Globulus** and other **Cineole**-type oils ("**Eucapharma Oils**") is in excess of 1000 metric tons, thus placing the **Eucapharma Oils** among the "upper ten" in quantity. The approximate distribution of the production is:

Australia:	60% of world production (mainly **Polybractea, Smithii** and **Leucoxylon** oils)
Brazil:	15% of world production (mainly **Globulus**)
Spain:	10% of world production (mainly **Globulus**)
Belgian Congo:	8% of world production (mainly **Smithii**)
Portugal:	2% of world production (mainly **Globulus**)

Other countries: 5% of world production.

The main use for **Eucalyptus Globulus** oil is in the pharmaceutical preparations, flavoring of cough drops, vaporizers, mouth-gargles, toothpaste, etc., as well as a rubefacient and general germicide. The germicidal effect is not very outstanding. In perfumery, the oil enters numerous formulas for low-cost perfumes, industrial perfumes, in the masking of various odors, and as a replacement for other essential oils. It is comparatively stable in soap and it has a powerful radiation or "lifting" effect upon the other ingredients in the soap perfume.

Fractions from the rectification of eucalyptus globulus oil are frequently used in the unethical "art" of "cutting" essential oils such as rosemary, spike lavender, thyme, spanish sage, etc. More artistically, certain fractions can be used as perfume ingredients of special effect. The literature gives full information of such isolates from various types of crude eucalyptus oils. **Eucalyptus Globulus Oil** is no longer the most common of the pharmaceutical eucalyptus oils, but it remains the largest of those grown and distilled in Europe. See also **Eucalyptus Australiana, E. Leucoxylon, E. Polybractea, E. Sideroxylon** and **E. Smithii** which are the "large" sources of the **Eucapharma** oils of today.

Eucalyptus Leucoxylon.

Although the oil which is distilled from the leaves of this tree is hardly ever encountered outside Australia under the above name, it is very likely that significant quantities of this oil are actually sold elsewhere under various names as a pharmaceutical eucalyptus oil.

It belongs to one of the larger "**Eucapharma**"

oils (see **Eucalyptus Globulus, E. Polybractea, E. Smithii**, etc.), and consists mainly of **Cineole**. In appearance, odor and flavor, it is quite similar to the **Globulus** oil. It has furthermore been claimed that the oil of **Eucalyptus Leucoxylon** is never produced in a "pure" state since the tree grows along with two other quite similar species (E. elaeophora and E. sideroxylon). The leaves of these two trees also yield a **Eucapharma** oil, or the three oils are frequently distilled as one from a mixture of all three sorts of leaves. With this possibility kept in mind, the mixed oil can be considered as being the largest eucalyptus oil in Australia, amounting to about 50% of all the **Eucapharma** oils of Australia.

Distillation takes place in eastern Australia only (Victoria province). The oil (or the oil mixture) is a pale yellow liquid, having a somewhat harsh topnote and a prolonged, sweet-terpeney dryout. As described above, the **Cineole** body-note of this oil is similar to that of other eucapharma oils.

See also **Eucalyptus Sideroxylon.**

Eucalyptus Macarthuri.

Among the comparatively few eucalyptus oils which have found use exclusively in perfumery, we find the steam distilled oil from the leaves of **Eucalyptus Macarthuri**, a native of southeastern Australia. The tree is cultivated in that area, and was introduced in the 1950's into the Iswete and east Transvaal provinces of the Union of South Africa. Earlier, it had been introduced into Brazil and Belgian Congo where the oil was experimentally distilled in the 1940's.

The yield of essential oil from these leaves is very small, usually far less than one percent. This fact, among others, is responsible for the farmer's reluctance and failing interest in the distillation of this oil.

Oil of **Eucalyptus Macarthuri** is a yellowish to pale orange colored oil with an intensely fresh, fruity-rosy initial odor, sweet-rosy and fruity-woody body notes and a pleasant, sweet, faint-woody dryout. There is considerable difference in odor characteristics between a crude (natural) oil, and a rectified oil. Like many other eucalyptus oils, the **Macarthuri** oil too contains lower aliphatic aldehydes in the "foreruns" of the redistillation. The foreruns are usually removed prior to use of the oil in perfumery. A rectified oil may contain as much as 70 to 80% natural geranyl acetate.

The main constituent being such a well-known perfume "chemical", oil of **Eucalyptus Macarthuri** has nothing in particular to offer the perfumer beyond the fact that it is Nature's best source of natural geranyl acetate. Instrumental investigations of essential oils of recent years have also affected this oil. There are alcohols other than geraniol in this oil, too. Pure geraniol (i.e. unaccompanied by other "rose" alcohols) seems to be extremely rare in steam distilled essential oils.

Still produced, although on a limited scale only, the oil of **Eucalyptus Macarthuri** may slowly disappear from the market.

Eucalyptus Numerosa, "Type".

For purely industrial purposes, various varieties of the above tree serve as raw material in the production of essential oils. Of the two best known oils, **Eucalyptus Numerosa** "Type" and **Eucalyptus Numerosa**, var. "A", we shall discuss only the former. The latter is almost identical to the oil of **Eucalyptus Dives** "Type" (see monograph).

Oil of **Eucalyptus Numerosa** "Type" is steam distilled from the leaves of this Australian tree in the southeastern parts of the continent. The yield of oil is very good, but the oil itself is of no particular interest to perfumers or flavorists. Recently, the tree has been introduced in the Iswete and east Transvaal provinces of the Union of South Africa where the mining industry can absorb significant quantities of the oil for flotation (i.e. screening of the particles of powdered ore in a foaming mixture of light oil, water and fine air bubbles).

Occasionally, the laevo-**Phellandrene** is isolated from this oil. This monoterpene finds some use in the "reconstruction" of essential oils (the "art" or rather *science* of composing artificial oils from their known and identified constituents).

Oil of **Eucalyptus Numerosa** "Type" is a colorless to pale yellow mobile liquid, possessing a fresh-peppery, spicy and minty odor with a bitter-terpeney, rather unpleasant undertone. There is little or no dryout note. The oil is readily available, but it is rarely offered to the perfume industry. Local (Australian) factories produce various isolates from these oils, and these isolates are made available to the perfume industry.

See also **Evoulimba Oil**.

Eucalyptus Phellandra.

This essential oil is also known under the name of **Eucalyptus Australiana**, var. "B", under which name it has already been discussed in this book. Being a **Cineole-Phellandrene** type of oil, it holds a more important place for the solvent and mining industry. See monograph on **E. Australiana**, var. "B".

Eucalyptus Polybractea.

The leaves of this tree give a very good yield of an essential oil which contains up to 92% **Cineole**. Thus, the oil is of the pharmaceutical type (here named **Eucapharma** oils). It is the most important of all the exported Australian eucalyptus oils. It is furthermore distinguished by the fact that it does not contain the unpleasantly smelling lower aldehydes found in **Globulus** and other **Eucapharma** oils; thus, a well distilled **Polybractea** oil may not require redistillation.

Distillation is undertaken only in southeastern Australia. Oil of **Eucalyptus Polybractea** is a colorless to pale yellow mobile liquid of strong but somewhat sweet-camphoraceous and fresh-cooling odor, and it has a similar taste. Its dryout on a perfume blotter is distinctly different from that of a **Globulus** or similar oil: it is not woody-sweet or heavy, "paint"-like; as a matter of fact, there is hardly any dryout note at all, but just a clean fadeout.

The main use of this oil is in pharmaceutical preparations, cough-drops, gargles, mouth-washes, toothpaste, etc. as is the case with all the other eucapharma oils.

Oil of **Eucalyptus Polybractea** is readily available in large quantities, but since it is produced in Australia only, there may be a considerable shipping delay for certain customers.

This oil is an excellent starting material for the isolation of **Cineole**, also called eucalyptol. This material is simply frozen out of the oil (cineole congeals at about $+1°C.$).

Eucalyptus Sideroxylon.

See also **Eucalyptus Leucoxylon**. Together with this and the oil of **E. Elaeophora**, a pharmaceutical eucalyptus oil is produced from a mixture of leaves of all three trees in the eastern and southeastern parts of Australia.

However, the **E. Sideroxylon** is mentioned here

because significant plantings of this tree have been under cultivation in the Dundee-Carolina provinces of the Union of South Africa for several years. Eucalyptus oil is also distilled in these plantations. Australia is the main supplier of the mixed oil.

As for the oil itself, it is of little interest to the perfumer or the flavorist. The oil is quite similar to the earlier mentioned oils of Eucalyptus Globulus and E. Smithii, (next monograph). A number of other eucalyptus species are also distilled in Australia and yield similar Eucapharma oils, but these oils are either used locally or exported as pharmaceutical eucalyptus oils, or even as Eucalyptus "Globulus", a designation still demanded by many customers.

See also monographs:

    Eucalyptus Australiana
    Eucalyptus Dives, var. "C"
    Eucalyptus Globulus
    Eucalyptus Leucoxylon
    Eucalyptus Polybractea
    Eucalyptus Smithii

Eucalyptus Smithii.

For several and weighty reasons, this tree has become more popular than the Globulus among the planters and distillers. The Smithii grows faster and its leaves yield more oil on steam distillation. The oil contains as much—or more—Cineole as does the oil of E. Globulus.

Plantations of E. Smithii are found in the Belgian Congo, Nyasaland, Rhodesia, Union of South Africa (Iswete and east Transvaal provinces), Uruguay, Argentina, etc. This oil is the most important eucalyptus oil of the Belgian Congo. Since the 1958/1959 appearance on the market of the so-called Chinese eucalyptus oil, however, the competition has been so fierce that the future prospects for Eucalyptus Smithii in the Belgian Congo are debatable. Production there has been near 100 tons per year in good years.

The oil is either rectified on the plantation or sent to nearby Goma, center of the essential-oil producing eastern Belgian Congo, and rectified there in modern stills by Belgian specialists. All essential oils in the Belgian Congo are produced by Belgians (till now, 1960).

Oil of Eucalyptus Smithii is a colorless or very pale yellow, mobile liquid with a fresh Cineole-type of odor, quite similar to the odor of other Eucapharma oils. Its use is similar to that of other cineole-types of eucalyptus oils as described under the E. Globulus.

Eucaluptus Staigeriana.

From the leaves of this tree, an essential oil is obtained by steam distillation and sold under the above name. This oil is one of the few eucalyptus oils produced exclusively outside Australia, although the tree originates in this "home of all eucalyptuses". Distillation is undertaken on plantations in Brazil, in the Union of South Africa (Dundee and Carolina provinces), the Seychelles and in Guatemala. The yield is excellent, far better than the yield from E. Citriodora which is an even cheaper oil.

Oil of Eucalyptus Staigeriana is (according to age and resinification) a pale yellow to dark yellow, somewhat oily liquid of sweet and fresh, fruity-lemony odor. The particular odor of this oil makes it immediately interesting for use in fresh-rosy types of soap perfumes, detergent fragrances, etc. But its stability in soap is not very good. The main constituents, Citral and geranyl acetate are not exactly noteworthy for stability in soaps unless very skilfully fixed. By various means of chemical stabilization, e.g. partial reduction, condensation with acetone, etc., this oil can be transformed into more generally useful soap perfume materials in the same way as described under citronella oil, eucalyptus citriodora oil, etc. As a source of isolated Citral, the staigeriana is of little or no interest: the content is too low (35 to 45 percent), and citral is now produced synthetically in a beautiful quality at an attractive price.

Oil of Eucalyptus Staigeriana is presently produced in quantities of 15 to 35 metric tons per year, but the production may slowly diminish in the future in view of the above competition. There are only few actual producers of this oil, and they are all earnest settlers, growers and distillers. Adulteration is practically out of the question.

Eugenia Jambolana.

The oil of Eugenia Jambolana is hardly known outside India. It is steam distilled from the leaves of the above tree of the genus Myrtaceae. Distillation is carried out in various places all over India where the tree is known as Jamun.

Eugenia jambolana oil is a yellowish to greenish-olive, blue-olive or brownish, fairly viscous liquid. Its odor is dry, woody, strong and spicy-earthy like a very poor patchouli oil (cade-like topnote). There is an undertone with some similarity to clove leaf oil, but a strong and heavy terpene note covers the sweet spicy odor. The dryout is terpinolene-like, somewhat spicy-woody, rather dry. There is a peculiar "bitterness" through all the stages of evaporation of this oil.

Eugenia Jambolana oil is used locally in India as a mild antiseptic and as a perfume material in low-cost soap perfumes, etc. It blends well with cedarwood, citronella, safrole, rosemary, thyme, isoeugenol, amylsalicylate, etc.

The author has but little information in respect to the annual production of this oil. It is not conceivable that the oil will become a "steady" item on the perfumer's shelf in other parts of the world.

Everlasting Absolute.

Widely known in southern Europe as **"Immortelle"**, **"Everlasting"** or **"St. John's Herb"** is the small plant **Helichrysum Angustifolium**. The plant has attracted perfumers for quite some time. It should not be confused with **"St. John's Wort"** which is an entirely different plant (hypericum perforatum) of no use in perfumery and little use in cosmetic preparations.

Many attempts have been made to produce an essential oil by steam distillation of the entire overground plant or of the flowers alone. All efforts have either failed or shown an extremely small yield. For those who have seen the plant, this cannot come as a surprise: it is hardly possible to visualize anything drier than the mature plant. It appears to be simply dehydrated or ovendried, but the flowers still keep their beautiful colors, hence the name—**Everlasting**. However, an essential oil is produced in Yugoslavia and France from various species of **Helichrysum**, particularly from **Helichrysum Orientale**, which is originated in Asia Minor and the neighboring Mediterranean countries and islands. The essential oil is listed in this work under **Helichrysum Oil**. It was not until extraction began to be practised on a large scale in Grasse and other perfume centers that this flower became available for the perfumers in the form of concrètes and absolutes.

Concrète of **Immortelle** is prepared from the flowers by extraction with benzene, gasoline or petroleum ether. The concrète is an olive-green (benzene-extracted) to dark brown, semi-solid mass of waxy consistency. Its odor is entirely different from that of the essential oil, although there are certain mutual features: it is intensely sweet-herbaceous, coumarinic, honeylike, slightly woody-floral with a peculiar licorice-like undertone. The heavy and fruity sweetness is sometimes compared to that of blackcurrant preserve and to the odor of elderflowers. The concrète usually carries some odor of the solvent.

Absolute of **Immortelle** is a semi-liquid oil or a very viscous liquid, olive-green to dark brown in color. The odor is as above described, but less waxy than the odor of the concrète, more refined-sweet and extremely tenacious. The yield of absolute from the concrète is very good, and this fact makes the material even more interesting from the economic aspect. As a peculiarity, it should be mentioned that **Absolute** of **Immortelle** usually contains significant amounts of tannin, a material rarely found in flower extracts. Tannin is liable to discolor in contact with iron and other metals which are present in trace amounts in many essential oils, etc. (e. g. copaiba, patchouli, vetiver).

Everlasting Absolute is used in perfumery for its deep-sweet, honeylike, tobacco-like notes, and for its great fixatice effect. Although it cannot possibly exert a true physical fixation at the normal use concentration (fractions of one percent in the perfume oil), the absolute has an extraordinary ability of rounding off and "bouquetting" a fragrance which may need life and naturalness. It blends well with coumarin, flouve, lavender, lavandin, sage clary, citrus oils, linalool, rose bases, phenylethyl alcohol, Peru balsam oil, clove bud oil, etc. Its effect in rose bases and heavy-floral Oriental fragrances can be quite unique and successful. It is used in certain fruit flavors and tobacco flavors.

Everlasting Absolute is produced in France, Italy, Yugoslavia and Spain. The three former countries often extract two or more species of helichrysum, while Spain mainly extracts the **Helichrysum Stoechas** which gives a sharper, more fruity-rosy smelling absolute, probably due to the presence of nonyl acetate. The annual world production of **Everlasting Absolute** is about 100 to 150 kilos.

See also **Helichrysum Kilimandjarum** and **Helichrysum Oil**.

Evoulimba Oil.

For those who are familiar with the Swahili language, it can hardly be a secret that this oil must be produced somewhere in an area where eucalyptus trees grow ("evoulimba" = eucalyptus tree) and where the Swahili is spoken. This kind of detective work leaves us with only two possibilities:

Eucalyptus Numerosa "Type" and Eucalyptus Dives "Type". The two oils are almost identical in chemical composition and they present great odor similarity.

Evoulimba Oil is steam distilled from the leaves of Eucalyptus Dives "Type" in the eastern Belgian Congo. The oil was once used as a topnote ingredient in a comparatively fashionable perfume. Consequently, a number of competitive perfume houses started an investigation in order to identify the "new and unknown" material which gave such an unusual effect in this perfume. The French supply house managed to keep the origin and the identity of the material quite secret for many years, although it should seem quite tempting to draw conclusions from the "native" name of the oil.

Evoulimba Oil is a pale yellow, mobile liquid of strong peppery-terpeney odor, reminiscent of dillweed and elemi, and with a camphoraceous-phellandrene-like dryout note, not exactly pleasant. The odor bears some resemblance to that of Balsamite. To the author's knowledge, eucalyptus dives "type" oil is no more distilled in Belgian Congo. However, the Numerosa oil is available from the Union of South Africa. A production of Dives oil can be recommenced in Belgian Congo with short notice.

In view of its peculiar odor, the oil of Evoulimba may not ever become a common perfume material.

See monograph on Eucalyptus Dives.

F

Fennel Oil, Bitter.

The Fennel Oils can be classified in two groups:
a) The oils from Bitter Fennel and
b) The oil from Sweet Fennel.

Bitter fennel can be derived from the cultivated herb or from the wild growing herb. The fruits of the two herbs will yield essential oils of different composition.

1) The Bitter Fennel Oil from wildgrowing herb is steam distilled from the upper part of the plant when the fruits just begin to ripen (compare with dill weed oil). Distillation takes place only in the areas where the bitter fennel grows wild: France, Spain, Portugal and North Africa, particularly in Morocco. This oil is not the bitter fennel oil as it is known commercially (see below). The total annual production hardly exceeds 10 metric tons.

Bitter Fennel Oil from wildgrowing fennel herb is a yellowish to pale orange-brown, mobile liquid which has a sharp peppery-camphoraceous odor and a spicy, faintly sweetish dryout note. The oil finds some use in the flavoring of pickles, etc., but it is mostly used in the perfuming of industrial products, so-called technical perfumes, etc. because of its excellent masking effect and great odor power.

Bitter Fennel Herb Oil (1) is occasionally contaminated (rather than adulterated) with the oil from "harvest fennel", a smaller umbellifer which grows wild and abundantly in Morocco and the Mediterranean countries and is found in the fennel fields, too.

2) Bitter Fennel Oil from Cultivated bitter fennel is the bitter fennel oil commercially offered. It is steam distilled from the crushed seed (fruit) of the cultivated Foeniculum Vulgare (and the variety vulgare of the subspecies capillaceum). The plant is identical to the above mentioned plant which grows wild.

Bitter Fennel is cultivated in Argentina, China, Czechoslovakia, France, Germany, Hungary, India, Italy, Japan, Roumania, Spain, U.S.A., U.S.S.R. and, on a limited (domestic) scale, in a great number of other countries. Distillation takes place mainly in France, Germany, Hungary, Italy and India.

Bitter fennel oil (from fruits of the cultivated plant) is a pale yellow or almost colorless liquid of a somewhat sharp and warm-camphoraceous odor, initially earthy, but later on sweet, anisic and spicy. Its flavor is distinctly bitter, slightly burning, but it tones out in a sweet aftertaste, still carrying, however, a warm-camphoraceous or earthy note. This is typical of its difference from the flavor of Sweet Fennel Oil (so-called "Roman" fennel oil, se following monograph).

Bitter Fennel Oil has become particularly

popular in Germany and other central European countries where the bitter fennel herb has been known and used for many centuries: in medicine, cooking, and last but not least, in the flavoring of liqueurs. The essential oil has largely replaced the herb for this purpose. The oil is used in minute amounts in a number of fruit flavors, but the bitter note and the camphoraceous-earthy taste prohibits its extensive use in fine flavoring. The suggested use level is 1.00 to 5.00 mg%, and the **Minimum Perceptible** is about 0.2 to 0.4 mg%. The oil is frequently used as a masking agent, as a perfume ingredient in technical preparations, room-sprays, insecticides, etc. It is perhaps the largest in quantity of the fennel oils. The annual world production fluctuates between 25 and 75 metric tons. However, fennel belongs to those aromatic seeds which have already seen their best years. Its popularity reached its peak hundreds of years ago, and fennel is slowly but steadily on the downgrade.

Bitter Fennel Fruit Oil (2) is frequently adulterated with synthetic anethole, synthetic or isolated estragole, fenchone, phellandrene and other monoterpenes. It can be quite difficult to distinguish between a natural and an artificial oil, but if an organoleptic examination is in favor of the sample, there is little reason for not preferring the oil whatever the origin (see chapter on **Adulteration**, Part One of this book). Synthetic anethole may contain the toxic isomer cis-**Anethole**, see monograph on **Star Anise Oil,** and care should be taken that such material is not used in the composing of artificial fennel oils.

Fennel Oil, Sweet.

Of little importance—and steadily decreasing in interest—is the essential oil that is steam distilled from the crushed fruits of cultivated **Sweet Fennel**, also known as **"Roman Fennel"**, **Foeniculum Vulgare,** varietas dulce.

The plant exists only cultivated, and is grown in France, Italy and Greece (Macedonia). The plant was probably originally from the island of Malta where—in turn—it might have been introduced by monks or crusaders nearly a thousand years ago.

Distillation takes place in many countries— where the oil is used—from imported or locally grown seed. France and Italy are main producers, but the oil lost its importance during the same period when anise (seed) oil almost disappeared from the market.

Synthetic anethole is now produced in such a pure and organoleptically acceptable quality that the anethole-carrying essential oils have little to offer in the countries where synthetic anethole is produced or readily available. In rough terms, **Sweet Fennel Oil** is hardly more than an anethole, modified with limonene, phellandrene and trace amounts of other components which exercise surprisingly little influence upon the odor and flavor of the oil. Synthetic anethole is known to have contained a significant amount of cis-anethole, a toxic isomer of anethole. Natural anethole is trans-anethole. This fact is known by all producers of synthetic anethole, and it is conceivable that future batches of synthetic anethole will contain little or no cis-anethole. See also **Star Anise Oil.**

Sweet Fennel Oil is a colorless or pale yellow liquid with a very sweet, but slightly earthy or peppery-spicy odor and a clean, sweet-aromatic dryout. There is a hint of a fruity-fresh topnote in fresh oils. The flavor is warm-spicy, aromatic, then sweet and only faintly burning.

The oil is still used in some perfume types, e. g. chypre, fougère, etc., but it is used more extensively in flavor work, e. g. liqueurs, licorice candy, cough drops, lozenges, etc. The annual production in France has been as high as 500 tons, according to information from suppliers to the French "anisette" brandy industry.

Sweet Fennel Oil is the pharmaceutical ("Codex") fennel oil. It is frequently adulterated—or it may be entirely artificial— in the same way as is the oil of bitter fennel fruit (see previous monograph).

Fenugreek.

From a far Eastern bean comes a seed which has attracted the attention of perfumers and flavorists increasingly during the past three decades. **Trigonella Foenum Graecum** is a sizeable herb, probably originated in Iran or India, now widely cultivated in Arabia, China (Kwangsi and Yunnan), Egypt, Greece, India, Iran, Morocco, and Tunisia.

The uncrushed seed emits only a very faint odor. However, the comminuted seed releases an intensely sweet, spicy, proteinlike, "soup-like" and caramellic odor. Steam distillation of the seeds has been tried although with very poor yields of oil. Extraction with volatile hydrocarbon solvents or with weak alcohol will yield products of various appearance, odor and flavor. The hydro-alcoholic extract is very dark and resinous in appearance; it has an intensely sweet, rootlike odor. The petroleum ether extract of the crushed seeds is lighter of color but less sweet of odor. The characteristic odor of **Fenugreek Extract** is a celery-like spicyness, a coumarinic-balsamic sweetness and an intense, almost sickening and strong, lovage-like or opopanax-like note of extreme tenacity. The diffusive power of the odor of this material is usually underestimated by far. Traces of fenugreek extract can ruin a perfume or a flavor if the extract is used in "wrong" combinations; but equally minute concentrations of fenugreek extract can do wonders in certain compositions: Oriental bases, aldehydic-herbaceous topnotes, chypres, fougères, lavender compositions, new mown hay bases, etc.

Fenugreek Extract is very useful in flavors such as maple (for maple syrup, "burnt sugar", caramel notes, etc.), vanilla compositions, butterscotch, rum (excellent fixative for the low-boiling esters), licorice, pickles, cheese, seasonings, etc. The extract blends excellently with cyclotene (2-hydroxy-3-methyl-2-cyclopenten-1-one), hepta-lactone, maraniol (4-methyl-7-ethoxy-coumarin), anethole, safrole, undecanolide, etc. and with celery seed oleoresin, lovage oil or oleoresin, licorice extract, etc. The crushed **Fenugreek Seed** is used in certain types of the so-called Indian curry powder, see **Curcuma Oleoresin.**

The annual world production of **Fenugreek Seed** runs into thousands of tons but only a fraction hereof ends up in perfumes and flavors. The seed serves as a cattle feed on account of its content of proteins and vegetable (fatty, fixed) oil. The seed can be deodorized for this purpose. If cows are fed with fenugreek seed which has not been deodorized, the cows' milk will smell and taste of fenugreek.

The suggested use-level of a hydro-alcoholic **Fenugreek Extract** in flavors is 0.20 to 1.00 mg%. For straight "maple" flavoring the figure will be somewhat higher. The **Minimum Perceptible** of this type of extract is about 0.10 mg%.

Fern.

Fern Extract is used very rarely, if used at all, in perfumery although the material is well known and available as a pharmaceutical drug. True fern absolutes do exist but they have been replaced by complex perfume bases ("fougères") in which oakmoss (see this monograph) and certain salicylates play a major role in respect to odor type.

The foliage of certain ferns is fragrant, but the commercially available extract is produced from the rhizomes of the "male fern", **Dryopteris Filix-Mas,** also known as **Aspidium.** The most commonly available extract is an oleoresin which is used in medicins as a teniafuge. It is a poison and should only be used as part of a complex cure, as prescribed by a physician.

Oleoresin of **Aspidium** is a dark green, viscous liquid which on standing deposits a crystalline substance. The oleoresin is soluble in alcohol and perfume oils and it can be used in perfume compositions if so wished. The odor of true **Fern Extract** (oleoresin of aspidium) is sweet-woody, somewhat earthy, very rich and tenacious but of comparatively poor strength (low odor yield) in perfume compositions. The inevitable solvent note is distinctly perceptible and often ruins the impression of the light, green-bark-like or cambial-like notes which are so characteristic of true, freshly prepared **Fern Extract** (or fresh, broken rhizomes). The plant from which the rhizome is obtained is known widely in Europe; other varieties are found all over the world. In a few remote islands one can find "leftovers" of prehistoric fern-trees of an appearance which is presumably unchanges through millions of years. Réunion Island, now a famous perfume island, is one place where you can still find fern trees 10 to 12 metres high and with a trunk measuring up to 40 cms. in diameter. Sections of these trunks are hollowed out and made into flower-pots in which the islanders plant orchids without any soil. The orchid can extract nutrition from the coarse fibres of the pot for more than a year until the pot is literally "digested" by the orchid.

In view of the fact that methyl salicylate was recommended for use in **Fougère** perfume bases many decades ago, it is interesting to note that this ester has been identified as a natural constituent of the stems of various ferns. Methyl salicylate is present as such, not glycosidically combined (in contradistinction to wintergreen and other plants).

A description of the classical perfume complex which is known by the name of **Fougère** falls beyond the scope of this work. Some of the materials which are frequently used in **Fougère** perfume compositions are: amyl salicylate, bergamot oil, coumarin and coumarin derivatives, heliotropine, ionones and methyl ionones, isobornylacetate, iso cyclo citral, isoeugenol, flouve oil, geranium oil, labdanum products, lavender or lavandin oils, nitromusks and other synthetic musks, methyl salicylate (traces) or benzyl salicylate, isobutyl salicylate, etc., rose de mai absolute, rosemary oil, sandalwood oil, sage clary oil, oakmoss products, patchouli oil, vanillin and derivatives, vetiver oil, ylang-ylang oil, etc. Characteristic of the **Fougère** perfume type is it, that the basic "fougère" note is obtained by two or three items alone: Oakmoss, coumarin, amyl salicylate—or: oakmoss + amyl salicylate.

Fig Leaf Absolute.

This comparatively rare perfume material has attained some interest among perfumers during the past decades. A few of the Grasse factories specialize in extraction of botanical drugs, etc. and some of these factories are more research-minded than others. Thus, there is hardly any botanical raw material within reach of the extraction factory which has not been subject to a thorough investigation. Fig leaves is one example.

The leaves derive from **Ficus Carica,** one of the oldest of all the cultivated plants in the Mediterranean area. Growing wild as a shrub it is cultivated as a small tree in most of the countries around the "blue sea". This cultivation is, however, mainly conducted for the purpose of producing the edible "fruits" (swollen receptacles) which we call **Figs.**

Algeria, Greece, Turkey and Spain are main producers of sun-dried figs but the tree is also cultivated in the south of France for local, partly private consumption. Accordingly, there is leaf material available for the present small-scale production of **Fig Leaf Absolute** in Grasse. The leaves are extracted with petroleum ether and the resulting concrète is washed with alcohol to produce the absolute (see **Absolute,** Part One of this book).

Fig Leaf Absolute is a dark green to brownish green, semi-solid mass or a heavy, viscous liquid of a delicately sweet-green, herbaceous and somewhat woody odor with a mossy undertone. The absolute is used in various perfume creations, mostly those of the fougère, moss, chypre or meadow-type. It is also an interesting modifier in green-leafy "foliage" bases, etc.

The annual production of **Fig Leaf Absolute** is probably less than 200 kilos but it could easily be adjusted to a higher figure in case of increased interest.

Fir Needle Absolute.

A fairly recent addition to the materials on the perfumer's shelf is the extract of one or more kinds of pine needle, spruce needle, etc. Concrètes as well as absolutes are available, and the botanical raw material varies from one supplier to another. In France, the main source is **Abies Alba,** a silver fir, while in the U.S.A., **Abies Balsamea,** the balsam fir, or **Tsuga Canadensis,** the eastern hemlock spruce, are the main suppliers of needles and twigs for the extraction.

The materials are extracted with benzene, ethyl ether, acetone or petroleum ether, and a concrète is produced. The concrète is sometimes called **Oleoresin of Balsam Fir Needles.** It is not a true oleoresin, and it is rarely extracted exclusively from one botanical species. The concrète is a very dark green paste, often grainy, and after standing, it displays white, needleshaped crystals of an intensely sweet odor, reminiscent of the odor of strawberry jam and caramellized sugar.

The concrète can be used as such in soap perfumes as it is soluble in most perfume oils. The intense green color is a drawback and prohibits the use of this concrète in perfumes for white soaps, even at the low concentration in which the concrète is used in soap perfumes (often less than one percent in the perfume). Its odor power is easily underestimated, and the apparent suave sweetness has a tremendous penetration in most fragrances. Obviously, this material is particularly useful in pine and spruce fragrances, "Christmas-tree"-odors, etc., but the real pleasure of such a material is primarily obtained when it is used in the more unusual places, e. g. chypre, fougère, muguet (!),, cologne bases, violet bases, opopanax, hyacinth, carnation, etc.

Fir needle concrète is further treated with alcohol to produce an **Absolute** of **Fir Needles** which when it comes from American suppliers is a dark green, semi-liquid or syrupy mass of sweet-coumarinic, somewhat fruity and intensely balsamic odor; briefly, it is very true to nature.

The absolute of fir needles from French suppliers is usually a syrupy, amber-brown, clear liquid which has an odor more balsamic and sweet than pinelike and of great tenacity. It is conceivable that the French extracts are made from dry or partly dried material which would not produce a green color in the extract.

Attempts to produce a decolorized fir needle absolute have so far failed or resulted in only a slight color change from deep green to brownish green. Molecular distillates of fir needle concrète with high-boiling, co-distilling solvents have been produced experimentally. These products are almost colorless, viscous liquids, but their odor is significantly different from that of the green extract of fir needles (or spruce needles).

The alcohol-soluble Fir Needle Absolute is obviously stronger in odor than the concrète (it is free from resins and waxes), and it should be used with utmost care, particularly in perfumes other than the pine types. Additions far below one percent in the perfume oil are often sufficient to introduce the wanted "naturalness" to a pine fragrance, and much smaller concentrations can be used to obtain warm and "special effects" in many other perfume types. The absolute blends well with amyl salicylate, bergamot oil, coumarin, cypress oil, labdanum, lavandin oil, linalool, linalyl acetate, nerol, oakmoss products, rosemary oil, sage clary oil, thyme oil, etc.

There is a great difference between the odor and effect of the extracts from various suppliers. The French extracts reproduce the fragrance of the fallen needles in a forest of conifers, e.g. on a hot and dry summer day. The American extracts resemble in odor the refreshing scent of young spruces and firs in a plantation after a heavy rainfall. Their odor is more "juicy" and it also reminds of the fragrance from recently felled conifers, Christmas trees, etc. A general description of Fir Needle Absolute as such is well-nigh impossible.

At present, these materials are produced regularly, but larger quantities are available only upon request and a reasonable notice. An estimated 1000 kilos are produced annually in the United States, and somewhat less in France. The absolute is from 4 to 8 times as expensive as the essential oil from same botanical source. An increased interest may bring this ratio down, and make the use of these highly interesting perfume materials even more popular in the future.

"Fir" Needle Oil.

Before entering on a brief discussion of the various "fir" and pine needle oils, it may be practical to give a brief summary of the oils which generally are offered under one or the other label:

1) Siberian Fir Needle Oil, in the United States called Siberian Pine needle oil is derived from the leaves (needles) of a true fir, Abies Sibirica, see monograph on Fir Needle Oil, Siberian following this monograph.

2) Japanese Fir Needle Oil, also called pine needle oil, is derived from the leaves and twigs of Abies Mayriana and Abies Sachalinensis, see monograph: Abies sp. in this book.

3) Silver Fir Needle Oil, is derived from the leaves and twigs of the European Abies Alba, known in Germany and Austria as "Edeltanne" and "Weisstanne". See monograph on Abies Alba under which also the oils of Abies Excelsa, Abies Picea and Abies Pectinata are mentioned.

4) Balsam Fir Needle Oil is derived from the leaves and twigs of the Canadian and northeast American "balsam fir", Abies Balsamea, (see monograph).

5) Scandinavian Fir Needle Oil is best known as oil of Pinus Sylvestris (see monograph). Botanically, it is truly a Pine Needle Oil. See also 10).

6) Picea Excelsa—see monograph under this heading.

7) Spruce Oils—see Spruce (including Tsuga Canadensis and other species distilled with it to yield Spruce Oil).

8) Canadian or White Pine, see Pinus Strobus (monograph). See also Pinus - - - oils.

Oils that are steam distilled from leaves and twigs of various Abies-, Larix-, Picea-, and Pinus species are sold under the name of Fir Needle Oil (translated from various European languages).

9) Canadian Black Pine is a spruce, Picea Nigra which yields a needle oil of up to 50% bornyl acetate, the highest of all pine needle oils. This oil is not produced commercially but the tree is lumbered, and there is a huge amount of leaves and twigs available for distillation in case of any interest in this oil.

10) **Dwarf Pine Needle Oil,** which is steam distilled from the needles of **Pinus Pumilio** (see monograph). This tree is also known as **Pinus Montana,** and, in Yugoslavia, the dwarf pine needle oil is marketed as **Pinus Montana Oil.**

Fir Needle Oil, Siberian.

Commercial name: Siberian pine needle oil (truly a **Fir**). This essential oil is steam distilled from the twigs and leaves (needles) of **Abies Sibirica,** a tree that grows abundantly in the northeastern parts of the U.S.R., Mongolia, and has been introduced into various European countries, particularly Finland. Smaller amounts of the oil are produced in Tyrol (Austria), Germany, Poland, Sweden and, occasionally, in Norway.

Siberian Fir Needle Oil is undoubtedly the most popular type of "fir" needle oil in Europe, and one of the most pupolar in the U.S.A. also. It is a colorless to very pale yellow or pale olive-yellow, oily liquid, occasionally turbid or opalescent. Its odor is refreshingly balsamic, slightly fatty or oily with a powerful pine-forest odor, and a peculiar fruity-balsamic undertone.

The oil is probably produced in quantities of several hundred metric tons annually, but the amount of adulterated and out-and-out artificial oils sold under the same name is overwhelming. Furthermore, the majority of all genuine lots of this oil derive from the U.S.S.R., and these factors make it difficult to give more than an approximation of the actual production figures. Apart from the high amount of bornyl acetate (about 40%), the oil contains a number of terpenes. It is conceivable that camphene, myrcene and phellandrene play a more important role in the particular fragrance of this oil than does the pinene which was once considered its main monoterpenic constituent. Bisabolene, a sesquiterpene, may also contribute to the tenacious, balsamic-sweet dryout notes in this oil on a perfume blotter. Trace amounts of certain aliphatic aldehydes (dodecanal, etc.) may be responsible for the freshness of this odor, and possibly one or more compounds related to larixinic acid (commercially known under the brand name of "palatone", etc.) contribute to the balsamic and "jam"-like, fruity sweetness of the odor of this oil. The latter material has been identified in the bark from this tree and from other conifers. The presence of dodecanal is

perhaps more surprising, but it is certainly characteristic of the odor of **Siberian Pine Needle Oil.**

The oil blends well with other pine or "fir" needle oils, amylsalicylate, coumarin, oakmoss products, nitromusks, diphenyl oxide, citrus oils, rosemary oil, juniper berry oil, labdanum extracts, patchouli oil, lavandin oil, etc. The particular odor and aldehydic topnote of this oil makes it an interesting material for use in "unconventional" perfumery.

Flouve Absolute.

From the flowering tops of a grass which is known in France as **Flouve Odorante,** various perfume and flavor materials are produced. It is conceivable, but not known to the author from his own experience, that the botanical material is the withering tops including the ripe grass seed, and that this material is dried, perhaps slightly fermented, prior to distillation or extraction. The plant is related to the grass which is used as cattle feed when dried, also called **Hay.** See also **Hay Absolute** and **Hay Oil.**

Flouve Absolute was for many years produced by only one house in Grasse, France. They originally produced an essential oil, **Flouve Oil** (see following monograph).

The product sold today under the name of **Flouve Absolute** is very dependent upon this single producer and supplier. Since it is such a highly interesting and quite unique item, several other producers recently have put a similar material on the market under the same label.

Flouve Absolute is a viscous, greenish-amber to brownish-yellow liquid, having a very sweet, herbaceous, tobacco-like and coumarinic odor. The odor is so rich and so complex that one can keep on finding notes in it. However, the overall fragrance is a sweet, licorice-like, root-like, somewhat mossy-herbaceous like wet underforest and meadows, of exceptional tenacity and high penetrating power. The author has heard some quite interesting comments on the odor of the absolute or the oil from people when they smell these materials for the first time. The odor is described as being "like the steam from a pot of hot cereal (porridge)",—"bread",—"a beer brewery",—"an emptied beer glass", etc.

The flavor is similar: very sweet, reminiscent of tobacco, i.e. the flavored shag tobacco or cigarette

21: A large field of young **Estragon** plants in northern Morocco.   *(Fot. S. Arctander, 1960)*

22: A branch with leaves, flowers and fruits of **Eucalyptus Citriodora** in northeastern Belgian Congo (Ituri district).   *(Fot. S. Arctander, 1955)*

160

23: A primitive but efficient jungle still for rectification of locally produced **Eucalyptus Smithii** oil in eastern Belgian Congo (Kivu district).

tobacco. This description may not be a very good one because the absolute (and the oil) is actually used in certain tobacco flavors. Furthermore, **Flouve Absolute** is a fine modifier in maple, licorice, root-beer, licorice-anise, caramel, hazelnut and numerous other flavor types. However, it must be kept in mind that the power of this absolute is very easily underestimated. The **Minimum Perceptible** in a 9% sugar water at 10°C. is about 0.03 to 0.05 mg%. The essential oil (see next monograph) has an even greater flavor power. The absolute has flavor effects in common with **Cyclotene** (2-hydroxy-3-methyl-2-cyclopenten-1-one) and 6-methyl coumarin, but none of these synthetic materials can offer such a rich body and naturalness as that obtained from **Flouve**.

In perfumes, **Flouve Absolute** is useful in chypre, fougère, pine, Oriental bases, and in traces as a sweetener for dry-woody notes which can be modified in a very pleasant way with flouve absolute. It blends excellently with oakmoss products, labdanum extracts, pine needle oils or fir needle absolute, chamomile oils, cypress oil, lavandin and lavender oils, petitgrain oils (the terpeneless in particular!), etc. The usual concentration of **Flouve Absolute** in a perfume base should be well below one percent, and effects are often perceptible below the concentration of 0.1% in the perfume oil. Thus, cost is no serious drawback although **Flouve** belongs to the "medium"-priced raw materials (about three to four times the cost of geranium oil).

The annual production of flouve absolute fluctuates according to immediate demand, but is usually estimated at less than 200 kilos. The botanical raw material exists in fairly large quantities, and the absolute could be available in larger amounts if needed. Since it is a kind of a "specialty", there is little reason to discuss adulteration. The author is not convinced, however, that this product is derived exclusively from the extraction of one botanical material with no addition whatsoever. Still, it must be noted that **Flouve Absolute** (and **Flouve Oil**) is unquestionably one of the most interesting "natural" perfumery materials which have come up during the past decades.

Flouve Oil.

From the dried upper part of the grass, **Flouve**

Odorante, harvested during or after the inflorescence, an essential oil can be produced by steam distillation under certain circumstances. Originally produced by only one company in Grasse, little is known of the details of production for this oil. It is conceivable, however, that an ordinary steam distillation is insufficient to produce an oil of appearance and composition like the **Flouve Oil**. One peculiarity of the oil is its abnormally high specific gravity. But whatever the physico-chemical properties are, this oil can offer quite unique effects in perfumes and flavors.

Flouve Oil is a light amber colored or pale orange-yellow, viscous oil of intensely sweet, coumarinic-haylike and heavy herbaceous odor. In contrast to the absolute (see previous monograph) the oil has no mossy notes, but it has a certain fatty-rootlike undertone reminiscent of elecampane and mimosa. It is not floral, however, but it presents part of the fragrance of a meadow with flowering herbs and grasses.

The flavor is also sweet: somewhat licorice-like, tobacco-like, slightly malty-herbaceous, reminiscent of beerwort, roots and sweet wood, and it is extremely powerful. The suggested use level is about 0.08 to 0.20 mg%, while the **Minimum Perceptible** is 0.01 to 0.03 mg%. It is even superior to **Cyclotene** (see previous monograph) in respect to threshold flavor perception. Cyclotene is probably the closest approach among the synthetic materials to the odor-flavor type of **Flouve Oil**.

The oil has been used for the flavoring of a famous brand of cigarette tobacco, and it finds extensive use in the flavoring of candy, carbonated waters (root-beer types), chocolates, caramels, etc., where it acts as an intensifier and modifier of vanillin, anethole, palatone, fenugreek extracts, cyclotene, maraniol, etc. It has an outstanding masking effect to cover unpleasant flavors and odors. The oil blends well with amylsalicylate, acetanisole, anisaldehyde, cassie, lavender, lavandin, oakmoss products, linalool, sage clary, nerol, alpha-terpineol, mimosa, costus, etc. It is used in perfumery in fougères, chypres, new mown hay bases, Oriental bases, ambres, etc.—although always at a very low concentration. It often accompanies chamomile, tansy, artemisia oils, galbanum and other essential oils in trace amounts to produce "special effects", topnotes, etc. The oil is thus almost generally applicable.

The annual production of **Flouve Oil** is limited to a few hundred kilos, but could possibly be

162

increased upon demand at a fair notice. The oil is presumably composed of several items of which the distillate of the grass forms the major part.

See also **Flouve Absolute** (previous monograph).

G

Galanga Oil.

Also known as "**Galangal Oil**" or "**False Ginger Oil**". The oil is steam-distilled from the comminuted rhizome of **Alpinia Officinarum**, a relative to ginger and cardamom. The plant is a native of **Hainan,** southeast Chinese island, and of the peninsulas **Pak-Hoi** and **Lei-Tchou** where it is widely cultivated. Galanga is also cultivated in Indonesia, Siam, and Japan where many varieties of **Alpinia** have been cultivated experimentally. The above plant, however, gives the highest yield of essential oil by far, and the most interesting oil, too. The above **Galanga Oil** should not be confused with the essential oil of **Kaempferia Galanga** (see monograph). It should also be kept in mind, that in the beginning of the 20th century, **Galanga** rhizomes were derived from a different plant which was cultivated in China and east India: **Alpinia Galanga**. The essential oil from the rhizomes of this plant is substantially different from the galanga oil of today. It seems however, that **Alpinia Officinarum** is the only plant whose rhizomes are used in the production of galanga oil today.

Galanga Oil is a yellowish to olive-brown, occasionally pale olive or pale yellow liquid of fresh-camphoraceous and spicy-woody odor reminiscent of laurel leaf oil, cardamom oil, ginger oil, etc., with a distinct cineole-like topnote and a warm undertone of rich and spicy body. The flavor is somewhat bitter at high concentration, but warm and spicy, leaving a faintly cool aftertaste. The suggested use level is about 2.00 to 4.00 mg%, and the **Minimum Perceptible** is 0.50 to 1.00 mg%. In respect to flavor power, it is inferior to all the common spice oils.

Galanga Oil is used in flavor work as a trace additive in spice compounds where it acts as a modifier for cardamom, ginger, nutmeg, etc. It blends well with Moroccan chamomile, Dalmatian sage, cinnamon, allspice, etc. in flavors for baked goods, meat sauces, etc. It finds some use as a

modifier in flavors for soft drinks, e.g. ginger ale and root beer types, and in certain types of candy flavors. The galanga rhizome itself is occasionally used in Indian curry powder blends. See also **Galanga Oleoresin**, next monograph.

Galanga oil is rarely used in perfumery, but it could introduce interesting notes in Oriental bases, woody fragrances, spicy perfumes, etc. It blends well with lavandin, pine needle oils, citrus oils, rosemary oils, patchouli oil, myrtle oil, opopanax oil, etc.

The oil is produced in very limited quantities mainly in Europe and the U.S.A. from imported rhizomes. Recently, China has started production of the essential oil from locally grown material. The oil is not regularly available yet.

Galanga Oleoresin.

Galanga Oleoresin is a prepared oleoresin. With the definitions of this book it is either a concrète or a resin absolute (concentrated tincture). It is very rarely offered from the usual suppliers of perfume or flavor materials but it is occasionally prepared by the flavor houses for their own use, or it is produced upon demand by one of the extraction specialists in Grasse or elsewhere (England or Holland).

Galanga "Oleoresin" is produced from the comminuted rhizomes of **Alpinia Officinarum**, see **Galanga Oil.** The solvent is either acetone, benzene, petroleum ether or, in certain cases, ethyl alcohol. Benzene is avoided when the product is intended for use in flavors. Ethyl alcohol produces a very dark but easily soluble extract. The resinoid varies in color and consistency according to the solvent used. The color is orange-red to dark, red-brown and the resinoid is usually a viscous, non-pourable mass of a spicy-balsamic, warm, yet fresh odor and a warm, somewhat biting, spicy-woody flavor with a characteristic, faintly cooling aftertaste. The flavor bears some resemblance to that of curcuma or ginger.

Galanga Oleoresin finds now and then use in flavors as a modifier for ginger, cardamom, allspice, nutmeg, etc. with which it blends favorably. The "oleoresin" represents the closest approach to the odor and flavor of the rhizome itself and it offers obvious advantages over the old-fashioned tincture in this respect. The "oleoresin" remains, however, a rarity and a specialty which is hardly ever offered from the regular supply houses.

Galanga rhizomes have since long been used as a non-pungent additive in the production of Chinese "preserved stem ginger" which is exported in the very decorative "bojans" (artistically hand-painted and ornamented clay or china jars).

See also **Ginger Absolute, Ginger Oil, Ginger Oleoresin.**

Galbanum.

Galbanum is a natural oleo-gum-resin (see definitions in Part One of this work). Speaking strictly in accordance with our definitions, galbanum should be listed as a natural oleo-resin since the perfumery grade of galbanum contains very little gum.

Galbanum is one of the typical examples of a botanical which has "changed" appearance, composition and odor during the past five decades. This is apparent when we look into literature from 1939, 1936, 1926 or even further back: the description of galbanum in these works is out-dated. A few, more modern authors suggest that more rapid transportation to the user is the main reason for the significant change, but it seems inconceivable that this should be the only reason. The author of this book has seen various African and Middle-eastern "gums" arrive at the original shipping stations after harvesting, and it appears that the time which elapses between harvesting and the arrival of the merchandise on board ship in the nearest export harbor, has not changed significantly. Only the transportation from the port of origin (departure) to the destination (user) has been slightly shortened.

Galbanum is collected from not one, but several different species of **Ferula** (big umbellifer plants). These grow wild in Iran and in the countries toward Asia Minor, e.g. Lebanon. There are still—as the literature correctly says—two types: a hard and a soft galbanum offered commercially. For perfumery, only the soft variety has interest. The hard galbanum is used in pharmacy and for various industrial purposes.

Soft Galbanum is a dark amber-colored to yellowish-brown or grayish-green, olive-brown, very viscous liquid whose consistency is like fresh honey. It is usually contaminated with wood splinters, sand, gravel, plant fibres, insects, etc., and it will separate a "foot" of a grayish mass on the bottom of its container. This precipitate contains water, sand, some dissolved gum, etc., and it has no perfumery value. It is often possible to eliminate it when emptying a container, since the precipitate is not pourable, while the useful galbanum is just pourable at room temperature (over 20°C.).

The odor of crude galbanum (soft type) is powerful, green-woody, almost balsamic-resinous, reminiscent of oleoresins from conifers. The leafy-earthy, green note is often referred to in terms, such as: "like green peppers" or "tossed green salad", etc. There is a distinct resemblance to the odor of hyacinth leaves. For a further odor description, see **Galbanum Resinoid.**

The "hard" galbanum will be discussed here only with respect to its physical description: it is a dry, solid, gravel-like material with a faint odor and variable color; it consists of yellow, orange, red tears or drops, and it is somewhat less hard and brittle than olibanum which it resembles to a certain degree. This type of galbanum is known as **Persian Galbanum.**

Soft Galbanum or **Levant Galbanum** is collected in very large quantities, and tens of tons are used by the perfume industry, in contradiction to various statements that "galbanum is used to a limited extent in certain perfume types". It is true that its application is limited to a comparatively small number of perfume types, but some of these types are very common in use. The **Soft Galbanum** also serves as a starting material for the distillation of **Galbanum Oil** (see monograph) which is abundantly present in this type of galbanum.

Being an exudation of a physiological (naturally formed) product, **Galbanum** does not require much work beyond its actual collection. It is conceivable that the perfumery type of galbanum is mainly derived from those species of **Ferula** in which the exudation appears at the umbel itself. This exudation contains more essential oil, and is softer than the exudations from stalks, etc. from other species of **Ferula.**

See monographs on **Galbanum Oil** and **Galbanum Resinoid.**

Galbanum Oil.

Galbanum oil is steam distilled or steam-and-water distilled from **Galbanum** (see previous monograph). The "soft" or "Levant" type of galbanum is preferred since it contains far more essential oil. The yield of **Galbanum Oil** by steam/water distillation is usually in excess of 15%, often around 22%, calculated upon the weight of the crude botanical material. The author has obtained yields of 26% of galbanum oil from good qualities of galbanum. Distillation is undertaken far away from the origin of **Galbanum**; usually the oil is distilled in France, Germany, England or in the U.S.A., and it is quite customary for perfume houses to distil their own galbanum oil. As a rule, certain fractions of the distillate are eliminated prior to bulking of the essential oil. Sulfide odors in the light fractions (heads) and strong painty-terpeney notes in the tail fractions (and in the medium-light fractions), particularly those rich in alpha- and beta-pinene, are usually left out. A partially deterpenized (monoterpene-free) oil is known as **Galbanol.** There is no actual standard as to the composition of galbanum oil or galbanol, and the selection of fractions is primarily a matter of esthetics.

Galbanum Oil is a colorless to pale yellow or pale olive-yellow, mobile liquid which possesses an intensely green, fresh-leafy odor with a dry-woody undertone of balsamic, barklike character. A very striking description often heard is "like green peppers or tossed green salad". The oil has a pine-like topnote which is less pronounced in the odor of the resinoid. The latter, in turn, has a more woody-balsamic, conifer-resinous character. The pine-like topnote can be removed by fractional distillation of the oil. The woody-balsamic, soft-green and tenacious undertone can be isolated in the high-boiling fractions. **Galbanol** is a trade name for the latter type of galbanum oil fractions.

Galbanum oil finds extensive use, although always in very modest concentrations, in compositions of chypre, fougère, pine, forest, moss, etc., and it will introduce interesting notes in many florals where its leafy character is necessary in the completion of a true naturalness: hyacinth, violet, narcissus, lavender, gardenia, etc. It blends well with cinnamic alcohol, coumarin, cumin-aldehyde, dimethyl benzyl carbinol, geraniol, geranium oil, cyclamal, isoeugenol, linalool, oak-moss products, pine needle oils, fir needle absolute, methyl phenyl carbinyl propionate, styrax resinoid or styrax oil, etc., and it can actually find use in countless perfume types and bases.

The annual production of galbanum oil fluctuates to quite a degree, but it is steadily increasing, possibly exceeding 10 metric tons. Adulteration is not uncommon, usually by means of simple dilution with pinene, foreruns from "galbanol" (see above), camphene, etc. These additions will easily be detected by the experienced perfumer during an olfactory examination of the oil.

Galbanum Resinoid.

Galbanum resinoid is prepared from the crude galbanum (see monograph). Years ago, when galbanum was a hard, grainy mass or lumps, the resinoid was prepared in the conventional way, i.e. by extraction with a hydrocarbon solvent and subsequent removal of the solvent after filtration. Because of the significant water content in the lower grades of galbanum, it was necessary to use solvents which are not miscible with water. Acetone and ethyl alcohol could not be used.

During the 1950's, it became more and more "conventional" to prepare resinoids in such a way, that they would be pourable, regardless of the starting material from which they were derived. This was done by the simple addition of a solvent to the evaporation residue (which is the pure, "100%" resinoid). The customer had the advantage of getting a more handy material; weighing and mixing was easier, etc. This dilution idea was further developed into more practical extraction methods: an odorless, colorless, high-boiling solvent (or "plasticizer") was added during the evaporation, and it was left in the finished product which was just pourable at room temperature. Various botanical raw materials called for different amounts of solvent to be added according to the viscosity of the "100%" (i.e. solvent-free) resinoid. The content of essential oil in the resinoid determines the viscosity of the solvent-free resinoid. In exceptional cases, where the content of essential oil is so high that the botanical material is almost liquid (a so-called "balsam"), the above method can be revised to a simple addition of a non-distillable solvent to the crude botanical material. This mixture can be filtered or strained and the "resinoid" is ready for use.

Crude **Galbanum** can be mixed with a certain amount of diethyl phthalate, isopropylmyristate, isopropylpalmitate, diethyl sebacate or similar solvent under gentle heating. Water and dirt will rise to the surface, respectively fall to the bottom of the mixture. After filtration or straining, the dregs, etc. are usually extracted with a volatile solvent. The extract is filtered and evaporated. The residue is added to the above prepared solution of galbanum in an odorless solvent. Benzyl benzoate was used some years ago, but it contributes to the odor in an unwanted way. The plasticized resinoid is left aside for several weeks or months during which period a certain amount of precipitate will settle. Small amounts of water may also separate. The finished product is now soluble in all types of perfume materials, but not clearly soluble in diluted alcohol, propylene glycol or similar hydrophilic solvent types. The product should be labelled with clear information on the amount of solvent added, e.g.: **"Galbanum Resinoid 67%, in D.E.P."** or the like.

However, the "prepared" resinoids are usually sold under various trade names or they may often be used exclusively by the producer. The method obviously carries a certain hazard: The customer can no longer rely upon the viscosity of the material to evaluate the approximate content of essential oil. The oil can be partially removed— and it is so in many cases—or it can be replaced by other materials. The solvent acts as an odor-depressant, and it is difficult to evaluate the above "galbanum-solution" in comparison to a true resinoid (solvent-free), even if the supplier is willing to mention the exact percentage of resinoid and solvent in his product.

Solvent-free galbanum resinoid is a semi-liquid, dark amber or brownish-golden material, almost pourable at room temperature. The odor is intensely rich-green, woody-balsamic, yet with a dry undertone, and it has the typical "green peppers" foliage-like note which is so pronounced in the essential oil (see monograph). The resinous, conifer-balsamic notes are very pronounced in the resinoid and in the prepared solutions. The resinoid is usually not clearly soluble in alcohol. Extracts of galbanum, prepared with ethyl alcohol as a solvent, are available. These "resin absolutes" are almost clearly soluble in alcohol. They are more or less "terpeneless" products of entirely different odor type: less green-sharp, more soft-balsamic, rich, woody and very tenacious in odor.

Galbanum Resinoid is an extremely interesting fixative with an odor of its own. It is useful in lavender, fougère, Oriental bases, chypres, pine fragrances, woody bases, moss odors, and in certain floral types. Its use in hyacinth is almost classic. Galbanum resinoid has the definite advantage over many synthetic "green-odor" materials in the fact that it mellows in almost immediately: it is possible to evaluate the result

and the effect during the creation of the fragrance. Synthetic materials in this odor group often "grow" or "fade" in the perfume with a perceptible change in the odor of the perfume within a few weeks.

The annual world production of **Galbanum Resinoid** is adjusted to the demand which has increased enormously during the past decade (1950's). So far, there has been no shortage of this material.

Gardenia.

The gardenia shrub, **Gardenia Grandiflora** (and other gardenias), is quite common as an ornamental plant in subtropical and warm-temperate zones of the world. The flowers of this plant have been known and admired for their outstanding fragrance for thousands of years. However, these flowers are rarely submitted to extraction for the isolation of essential oil, concrète or absolute. One reason is the very small yield (about 1 kilo of absolute from 5000 kilos of flowers). Another reason is the limited use of the gardenia type of fragrance in perfumery. Finally, this type of fragrance has been comparatively easy to copy, although a good artificial gardenia base is more rare than for example a good artificial muguet base (lily-of-the-valley). Incidentally, a close resemblance to the natural product is not synonymous with unexcelled performance in a perfume.

A concrète of **Gardenia** flowers was produced many years ago in the Indian Ocean island of **La Réunion** when the French extraction expert, Charles Garnier established himself with his world-famous equipment on that island. Production in La Réunion has been abandoned long ago. Various sorts of **Gardenia Absolutes** are occasionally offered on the market today. Some of these may actually derive from Grasse factories, but quite recently, Chinese and Formosan producers have offered **Gardenia Concrète** in Europe and India.

The Chinese gardenia concrète is presumably derived from the flowers of **Gardenia Florida** which is a native of southeastern China. **Gardenia Grandiflora** is grown in China for its fruits which yield **Wong-Shi**, a yellow colorant. Other varieties grow in Japan, in the Philippines, Indonesia, India, the West Indies, etc., but they are rarely utilized for perfume extraction.

It serves no purpose to describe here outdated

samples of true gardenia absolute when this material is no more in regular production. Samples of Chinese and Formosan gardenia concrète submitted to the author were of comparatively weak perfume effect. They were pale orange or amber colored, waxy masses of fatty-floral, somewhat fresh-green odor with a tuberose-like, sweet undertone, faintly reminiscent of the fragrance of the gardenia flower, but with heavy emphasis on the leafy-green notes.

Gardenia Absolute was used for its intense and rich, floral effect and its peculiar sweet-green note. However, artificial gardenia perfume bases have now replaced the true and very expensive absolute from the flowers.

Garlic Oil.

If the users of this oil were aware of the sort of sufferings the operators in the still-room undergo when Garlic Oil is produced, the flavorists would probably appreciate the oil even more, and not complain about its high price.

Garlic Oil is produced by steam distillation of the crushed garlic, the bulbs of Allium Sativum which is grown all over the world in temperate areas. The oil is distilled in Bulgaria, China, Egypt, France, Germany, and Japan. Egypt has been a major producer during the past two decades. Fresh bulbs are preferred for distillation.

Garlic Oil is a colorless to pale yellow mobile liquid, and it has an extremely intense obnoxious odor, to a certain degree reminiscent of garlic, but with a predominant mercaptane-like note which masks the delicate, although strong and highly diffusive garlic odor. It is not lachrymatory, but simply so obnoxious that it scares even garlic-enthousiasts.

An amino-acid called Alliin is found in certain cells of the bulb. Alliin is nearly odorless; however, in separate cells in the undamaged bulb, we find an enzyme which can convert the Alliin to the sulfide Allicin, a substance which has the typical garlic odor. However, during the steam distillation, the latter material is further converted into other sulfides which we smell in garlic oil, although not in crushed garlic. Thus, garlic oil is *not* representative of the flavor effect of fresh crushed garlic. The oil is, however, used to a great extent as a replacement for garlic in the same way that spice oils replace botanical spices. Dehydrated garlic is now available as a fine

powder. It yields a more true-to-nature aroma than does the essential oil. The aroma of the powder appears immediately upon contact with the slightest amount of moisture. The odor principles of garlic and of garlic oil have been produced synthetically.

Garlic Oil has obtained great popularity during the past 20 years, not only in terms of the increasing popularity of garlic itself, but also because of its therapeutic value in pharmaceutical preparations. The annual production of garlic oil is limited to a few hundred kilos, mainly because of the very low yield by distillation. The oil is occasionally distilled from dry bulbs in countries other than those who cultivate the garlic.

See also Onion Oil and Onion Oleoresin.

Geranium (summary).

Before going into the description of the individual types of geranium and geranium products, it would serve a practical purpose to list briefly the types which are available today:

Geranium Absolute and Geranium Concrète:

The main producer of geranium concrète is Morocco. No concrète is produced in Réunion, Algeria or the Congo. Certain quantities of geranium concrète are processed in France to Geranium Absolute. Small quantities of geranium concrète and geranium absolute are produced in Italy from locally cultivated plants.

Geranium Oils:

1) The original oil, French Geranium Oil, whose production is at an all-time low, and is still decreasing.

2) The most important of today: Réunion Geranium Oil, amounting to more than 50% of the total world production of geranium oils.

3) The very popular but scarce oil, Algerian Geranium Oil, earlier known as African Geranium, and once the largest of all geranium oils. The production reached its peak in the late 1920's and early 1930's with annual outputs of about 150 metric tons of oil. Figures for the late 1950's fluctuate between 6 and 15 tons.

4) The recent and increasingly popular Moroccan Geranium Oil, produced in modern installations and in sizeable quantities.

5) The Congo Geranium Oil, produced in the

Belgian Congo, Kenya, Tanganyika, Angola, etc. in small, but increasing quantities.

6) Central American geranium, produced in El Salvador on French financing. The oil has successfully passed the experimental stage.

7) Various geranium oils, produced in annual lots of one to two metric tons, and often used locally: Haiti, Corsica, Italy, Lebanon, India, Japan.

8) **Russian Geranium Oil**, produced in large quantities in the Crimean area and Caucasus, but entirely for domestic use. The present annual production (1959) is estimated at 50 to 55 metric tons.

9) **Mawah Oil**—see this heading.

10) **Zdravetz Oil**, see this monograph.

Geranium Absolute.

This comparatively recent addition to the perfumer's shelf is produced from **Geranium Concrète** (see monograph) by the conventional method (see **Absolutes**, Part One of this work). By far, the largest part of all concrète comes from Morocco where part of the production is also processed further into **Geranium Absolute** in very modern installations, particularly in the region around Khemisset, Mâaziz and Tiflet in northwestern Morocco, inland from the Atlantic coast near Rabat.

Geranium Absolute can vary considerably in appearance and odor type depending on the type of solvent used in the extraction of the plant material. It seems that the petroleum ether concrète is becoming more popular, and it yields an absolute of lighter color than do most other concrètes. Geranium absolute is usually a green or dark green liquid with an intense and very powerful, somewhat leafy-earthy, but soft and pleasant odor. The leafy-green notes are quite pronounced, but the rich, rosy-minty undertone remains on a blotter throughout the evaporation of the oil. The odor of the absolute is less sharp and more tenacious than that of the essential oil.

Since the yield of absolute from geranium is slightly higher than the yield of essential oil from the same plant material (in Morocco), there is reason to believe that Moroccan geranium absolute will be of increasing interest in perfumery.

Geranium Water Absolute is produced by benzene- or petroleum ether extraction of the distillation waters from geranium *oil* production.

This "water absolute" is rich in "rhodinol" but poor in terpenes, esters and ketones. Thus, it is a comparatively weak perfume material but nevertheless quite valuable for its rhodinol content. Geranium water absolute is produced in Morocco only.

Since the geranium oil from Réunion ("geranium Bourbon") seems to decide the price of all other geranium oils, these products, including the absolute, are frequently adulterated. Only an olfactory examination in connection with an experienced instrumental analysis (vapor phase chromatography, infra-red, etc.), can establish a clever adulteration since all the main components and many of the trace constituents of geranium oil and geranium absolute are well known and synthetically produced.

Geranium Absolute is used in perfumery, particularly in high-class rose bases, chypres, fantasy perfumes, etc. The concrète (see following monograph) offers certain advantages over the absolute in soap perfumes.

Geranium Concrète.

Geranium concrète is produced from the same plant material, i.e. leaves and branchlets of **Pelargonium Graveolens,** from which the essential oil is distilled. Extraction is carried out in Morocco, Italy, and France, Morocco being the most important producer by far. Various solvents have been used: first benzene which, however, is difficult to remove entirely from the evaporation residue (= the concrète); later on, petroleum ether became more popular as a solvent. It produces a concrète of less green color although the yield is slightly smaller than the yield from benzene-extraction. In both cases, the yields are slightly higher than the yield of essential oil by steam distillation.

Geranium Concrète is a dark green or brownish-green, waxy mass; it has an intensely earthy-herbaceous, somewhat sharp-rosy, foliage-green odor and great tenacity. It is soluble in perfume oils to a modest degree, and can thus be used with advantage in soap perfumes where its effect is quite inimitable. It lends a beautiful rich body to rose perfumes, and blends well with the conventional woody or spicy additives in rose soap perfumes, Oriental rose bases, chypre soap perfumes, etc. A great part of the Moroccan geranium concrète is further treated to yield geranium absolute (see previous monograph).

Geranium Concrète is occasionally offered as a mobile liquid of green or olive-green color. Such products are not always true concrètes. However, extraction of geranium leaves with selective solvents which exhaust the plant material of odorous principles, but which do not extract waxes, coloring matter, etc., may lead to "liquid concrètes".

Decolorized Geranium Concrète is produced from the plant material directly with selective solvents or by treatment of the dark concrète with other solvents, occasionally followed by treatment with activated carbon and filtration. The finished product is often dark olive-green or brownish, but white concrètes have also been offered. The latter type are presumably artificial concrètes made from myristic acid, or waxes with the addition of true or artificial geranium oil and various synthetic additives.

Geranium Concrète is produced in increasing amounts and is available from Morocco with no difficulty. The annual production may soon exceed 5 metric tons.

Geranium Oil.

One of the most important and irreplaceable essential oils in perfumery is **Geranium Oil**. It does not range among the first 20 oils in quantity annually produced if we include all types of essential oils (industrial oils, flavor oils, perfume oils). But considering its value, we will find **Geranium Oils** very high on the list of all the perfumery oils, if not at the very top of the list. The annual world production of all types of geranium oils can be estimated at not less than 200 metric tons, and the value at approximately six to ten million U.S. dollars.

About half the world production comes from the small island of **La Réunion,** 500 miles east of Madagascar in the Indian Ocean. Next (in quantity produced) comes the U.S.S.R., Morocco. Algeria (once the world's leading producer), Colombia, El Salvador, East Africa (including the Belgian Congo) while West Africa, Japan, Italy, Spain, France and various other areas each produce less than two metric tons annually.

Geranium Oil is steam distilled from the leaves and branches of **Pelargonium Graveolens** and other species of **Pelargonium.** This comparatively small plant is a hybrid from other pelargonium species, all of which originally came from South Africa. The funny part of the geranium story is that practically all perfumery geraniums have taken the same trip: to Europe first, and then back to some overseas region where they have been cultivated for the purpose of producing essential oil. The author knows of only one pelargonium that did not take the trouble of emigrating from South Africa to Europe and back again: the **Kenya Pelargonium Radula Oil** (see monograph on **Mawah Oil**) has been brought to the east African mountains directly from South Africa, probably as pelargonium graveolens, and then the plant has hybridized in Kenya.

All geranium oils are distilled from cultivated plants. The yield is very small, usually from 0.1 to 0.3 percent (of the plant material), averaging less than 0.2%. In most areas, there are two crops per year, but climatic conditions in the most important areas play a decisive role in the annual output of oil.

Geranium Oils are used very extensively in perfumery. Significant quantities of geranium oil are used in the production of "rhodinol ex geranium" or "terpeneless geranium oil", etc., see **Geranium Oil, terpeneless.** Very small amounts of geranium oil are still used in certain types of flavors.

The individual types of geranium oil will be briefly discussed in the following monographs:

Geranium Oil, "African".

Only a few decades ago, the term "African geranium" was synonymous with **"Algerian Geranium".** Once the world's most overwhelming producer of geranium oil, Algeria barely achieves the rank of a small number three or four now. Several factors have contributed to the decline of Algeria as the leading producer of geranium oil: first, the increasing interest in the cultivation of vegetables and grapes in the beautiful, but rather limited "sun valley" of Algeria, the Mitidja plain; later, the gruesome and destructive years of insurrection, rebellion, strikes, riots, guerillas and warfare, terrorist actions, etc. These have reduced the size of the geranium fields, and the production of geranium oil has fallen off to less than 10 metric tons annually in recent years. As it is less exposed to climatic destruction, the Algerian geranium can grow peacefully in respect to weather conditions, and healthily, and the material is distilled in large and modern stills, producing a uniform oil of very attractive appearance: a pale yellow or pale olive-yellow liquid, usually crystal-clear, free from dirt and water; the odor is somewhat different from that of the Réunion geranium oil: it is lighter, more rosy-leafy, less minty, and usually free from the sulfide topnote. The herbaceous and powerful tone is subdued in the Algerian oil, and the rich, sweet-rosy dryout undertone is more pronounced. There are no traces of earthy or "potato"-like notes. Incidentally, a mixture of Algerian and Réunion geranium oil produces a very interesting combination odor.

Algerian Geranium Oil is scarce and usually follows the Réunion oil in price fluctuations. It is equally subject to adulterations, but it is also available airfreighted directly from the bulkers in Algeria when the oil is bought in 50-kilo lots or larger quantities.

Moroccan Geranium:

Of rapidly increasing importance is the geranium oil distilled in Morocco from plants that are cultivated in the northwestern parts of that country, a short distance inland from Rabat at the Atlantic coast. Harvest and distillation is highly rationalized and very modern, carried out on a large scale, partly thanks to clever political attitude of the larger producers toward the future government of Morocco. The production has thus not suffered significantly during the years of terrorism in Morocco in the first part of the 1950's or later.

Adulteration "on the spot" is rare, but there is a possibility of local adulteration with Moroccan pennyroyal oil and with the absolute from the distillation waters in the production of the essential oil. The latter manipulation could be considered a "sophistication" rather than an adulteration of the oil.

Moroccan Geranium Oil, now often called **African Geranium**, is a yellowish or dark yellow, rarely greenish-yellow liquid of sweet and powerful rosy-leafy, slightly herbaceous odor, combining some of the qualities of the Algerian oil with those of the Réunion type of geranium oil. The odor of the Moroccan oil is usually less fresh-leafy, but more earthy than that of Algerian oils, but there are commercial lots of Moroccan oils which are almost indistinguishable from the very best Algerian oils. Moroccan geranium oil was not very popular when it first appeared on the market, but consumers have become accustomed to this type now, and it seems to have a safe future as a regular perfume raw material. The huge stills ensure a uniform quality, and the locality offers a great advantage for the users in comparison to the faraway Réunion supplies. Thus, the Moroccan geranium oil now follows the Réunion and the Algerian oils closely in price fluctuations, taking advantage of occasional cyclones in Réunion and the possibility of a further drop in the Algerian production.

Belgian Congo Geranium:

In the Belgian Congo, particularly in the eastern provinces of Kivu and in the Urundi region, geranium has been cultivated for more than 20 years. Production has been as high as 15 tons of oil per year, but the enormous interest in coffee, particularly after World War II, tempted many settlers to leave the growing of geranium and change to coffee-growing which demands much less attention. An important uptrend occurred in 1958, however, when, after the World's fair in Brussels, one of the settlers succeeded in buying large amounts of stainless steel for stills and in having the steel shipped to the Congo at a low cost. Stills were constructed with all necessary gear, and a standard size, 800 U.S. gallon (3000 litres) still could be bought and erected on the plantation for as little as 600 U.S. dollars. Already in 1959, results are visible: increased production, reasonable cost, uniform quality (bulked oil) and regular availability. Thus, we have another **"African Geranium Oil"** as a regular perfumery raw material.

The oil is yellow and usually clear, free from water and dirt, has no sulfide topnote, but also less diffusive power than the Réunion and Algerian oils. The Congo oil is considerably sweeter and less herbaceous-minty, less earthy than these oils. It is, no doubt, generally an excellent starting material for the isolation of a natural "rhodinol". Lower in rough and terpenic notes, it also becomes a good item in combination with the other two oils. Congo oil is usually somewhat lower in cost than the Algerian or Réunion oils, but it may not be available "on the spot" all year round. As a rule, the oil is airfreighted from Goma or Bukavu airports in the eastern Belgian Congo, directly from the producing region to the buyer. Adulteration is thus practically out of the question.

Smaller quantities of geranium oils are produced in various other parts of Africa:

East African Geranium Oil:

In Kenya and Tanganyika, pelargonium grave-olens is cultivated and locally distilled. However, in Kenya, the **Mawah Oil** (see monograph) is more important. The mawah oil can not substitute the true geranium oil in perfume formulas. The Kenya geranium oil is generally of good quality, high in rhodinol, but comparatively poor in diffusive power. It is inferior to Algerian and Réunion oils in respect to performance in soap (perfumes). In Tanganyika, a few tons of a similar geranium oil are annually produced and shipped, mainly to Europe. The East African oils are generally low in monoterpenes and ketones, comparatively high in alcohols.

West African Geranium Oil:

In Angola, Portuguese West Africa, a German settler and world famous perfumer-author has cultivated and distilled geranium experimentally. The annual production is very small and there seems to be little interest in this oil.

Egyptian Geranium Oil:

Production of geranium oil has been discontinued. Geranium fields were abandoned in 1955 (prior to the author's last visit there), and cultivation has not been recommenced. Nevertheless, commercial lots labelled "Egyptian geranium oil" are offered from time to time. It is presumable that such oils are either rejected lots from other sources, or that they are compositions of true and artificial geranium oils.

It is still customary to use the term **"African Geranium"** in perfume formulas for true Algerian geranium oil. The above described African oils are substantially different in perfume type from Algerian oil.

Geranium Oil, Réunion.

Also called **Geranium Bourbon** from the old name of the island of La Réunion (Ile de Bourbon), **Geranium Oil, Réunion** is the most important of all the geranium oils. It is produced in hundreds of small, mainly primitive stills which treat often less than one metric ton of plant material per charge. The daily output of oil from one still may be only a few kilos after many hours of work at two or more distillations, not to speak of scores of hours of back-breaking work in the field, ploughing, weeding, cleaning, fertilizing and cut-

ting on steep hills where not even wheel-carts can go. The small lots of oil are sold to middlemen, who in turn sell larger lots to the brokers. The latter are usually French exporters or wholesale brokers. They bulk the oil lots, and this stepwise bulking of very small lots explains why the various drum lots of **Geranium Bourbon Oil** are fairly consistent and uniform in odor, but it also explains why the appearance of the oil is often poor: water, mud, precipitate and other worthless impurities may amount to several percent of the oil, and this can cause a sizeable loss for the buyer who wants to clean, filter or strain the oil. It is certainly no fun to buy water and dirt at the price of U.S. $ 55.– per kilo. It should be kept in mind, however, that certain exporters do filter the oil and remove the water before the oil is shipped overseas. The average temperature in Réunion island is about 25°C. At this temperature, the oil will dissolve more than one percent of water. Most of this water will "fall out" of the oil when the drums are shipped (particularly when airfreighted!) to the buyer. The latter will find a significant amount of water at the bottom of his drum with the expensive oil. But in most cases, this water separation cannot be blamed upon the bulker or exporter in Réunion. The water must be accepted as a calculated risk. It can only be satisfactorily and finally removed after arrival at its destination.

Freshly distilled **Geranium Bourbon Oil** has a very peculiar, rather obnoxious topnote which is partly due to dimethyl sulfide. The latter is probably not present as such in the leaves, but is produced during the rapid decaying of the plant material immediately prior to the field distillation. The unpleasant topnote will disappear after proper aeration or ageing of the oil, or when the oil is filtered or decanted. The color of the oil is then greenish-olive to almost brownish green. Later on, the green color fades, and the oil becomes more yellow when old. Its odor is very powerful: green, leafy-rosy, with a pronounced fruity-minty undertone and a rich, long-lasting, sweet-rosy dryout. As for the flavor of geranium oil, although the oil is very rarely used in flavors at all, it is worthwhile mentioning that it has a bitter taste, rather herbaceous and not at all pleasant as such. It is used sparingly in combination with rich and sweet flavor materials, e.g. in the classic "sen-sen" type of flavors: with ionones, artificial musks, vanillin, bergamot oil, patchouli oil, clove oil, heliotropine, etc. Old-fashioned toothpaste flavors still contain small amounts of geranium oil.

In perfumery, this oil is used so commonly that it is hardly possible to point out its particular application. For certain purposes, it is preferable to use a so-called **Terpeneless Geranium Oil** (see monograph: **Geranium Oil, terpeneless**) which may be produced from geranium oil "Bourbon" or from any of the other geranium oils with various results. Most often, the deterpenation is merely a removal of the light fractions in a vacuum distillation, and perhaps a few percent of the tail fractions and residue.

Geranium Oil "Bourbon" is frequently adulterated, although never directly on the island of La Réunion. Unfortunately, very few consumers receive their geranium oil in the original containers directly from the source of production, but the long transport and possible delay seems to scare many buyers. However, many lots of geranium oil are now airfreighted not only to France, but also to more distant customers. The fluctuations in availability and cost of Réunion geranium oil has encouraged certain supply houses to cut or plainly adulterate the oil, and only a thorough olfactory examination, combined with a solid knowledge of the true oil, can protect the customer from these frauds. Instrumental analysis has been a great help in detecting plain adulterations, dilutions, cutting, etc. and there is probably no other essential oil which has been so thoroughly investigated, or upon which so much time and money has been spent in order to detect and identify "key" odor constituents, as the geranium oil. This highly sensitive type of analysis has, unfortunately, also developed the unethical "art of sophistication" (or plain adulteration) to a point where the evaluation of a geranium oil is a challenge to the buyer, to his perfumers' noses, and to the analytical instruments at his disposal.

Geranium Oils, Various.

France:
Very little, if any, geranium oil is produced from the plants cultivated in the south of France today. Occasionally imported lots of oil are distilled over roses to yield the so-called "**Geranium sur Roses —de Grasse**". This product, which is not an essential oil according to our definitions, serves certain perfumery purposes. It offers a rich and very sweet-rosy base for rose perfumes, muguet bases, carnation modifications, etc., but the user of this material is limited in his choice of suppliers in order to obtain the same proportion of rose and geranium in this co-distilled oil. Similar co-distillations are common with: Sandalwood-rose, benzyl acetate—jasmin, petitgrain oil—orange flowers, etc. and e.g. the Indian "attars".

Corsica: Insignificant amounts of geranium oil are produced here.

Italy: The production mainly serves the local market which is far from saturated by the local production.

Spain: Similar to Italy.

Japan: The production in 1958 was 3 metric tons which is far from sufficient for the local comsumption. Recent import figures show an annual import of 15 to 20 metric tons to Japan.

El Salvador: A French perfume house has established a firm interest among local farmers in the cultivation of geranium, and they expect to produce from 20 to 50 metric tons of geranium oil annually. The oil has *not* yet been marketed as **Salvador Geranium Oil.**

Haiti: The production is insignificant. Political disturbances have greatly impaired the interest in perfume oil production.

U.S.S.R.: According to the author's knowledge, geranium oil is not exported from the U.S.S.R., although it is estimated that the annual production is far in excess of 20 metric tons, perhaps over 50 tons.

India: This country produces small quantities of geranium oil for local consumption. The production does not cover more than a fraction of the needs of the Indian soap and perfume industry.

Geranium Oil, Terpeneless.

Although the actual amount of hydrocarbons in geranium oil is comparatively small, the partial or total removal of "light" fractions of geranium oil (during a vacuum distillation) produces quite interesting perfume materials, distinctly different from the parent oil. From a chemical point of view, this treatment is not strictly a deterpenization (compare, e.g. wormwood oil, dethujonized) since the foreruns of a vacuum-distilled geranium oil will contain not only small amounts of pinene and other monoterpenes, but also certain amounts of aliphatic and olefinic alcohols of the C_6 to C_{10}-series, perhaps even higher members. Traces of aldehydes, ketones and low-boiling esters are also present in these "head" fractions. The "heart" fraction will consist mainly of the so-called "Rhodinol ex Geranium", a mixture of terpene alcohols, laevo-citronellol and geraniol presumably being the main components. In the "tail" fractions, there will again be certain components whose fragrance the perfumers do not appreciate to the same extent as for the rhodinol fractions.

Thus, a "Terpeneless Geranium Oil" may be a bulking of selected fractions of a vacuum-distilled geranium oil. The fractions are selected esthetically by perfumers who are specifically experienced in this art. Consequently, this product varies significantly according to the origin and the supplier (producer). It is generally assumed that Réunion geranium oil yields the best rhodinol, but apart from the indisputable fact that this oil usually gives the highest yield of terpene alcohol fractions, it is also the most expensive of all the geranium oils. The yield will usually be well over 50%, in rare cases as high as 70%, depending upon the content of ketones (laevo-isomenthone and other ketones), etc. in the oil. These will distil immediately prior to the "rhodinol" and they may impart a "minty" note which is harmful to the delicacy of a good rhodinol.

The terpeneless geranium oil or "rhodinol ex geranium" (two different perfume materials) are colorless or very pale yellow liquids. The odor of the "rhodinol" is delightfully sweet, yet fresh and rosy, very uniform and tenacious. The odor of the "terpeneless" geranium oil varies according to the individual supplier (producer) of the oil.

"Rhodinol ex Geranium" is used very extensively in perfumery as a base for rose, muguet, carnation, appleblossom and many other perfume types. Its floral sweetness, delightful freshness and delicate warm-rosy tonalities blend well with the odors of hydroxycitronellal, linalool, geraniol, dimethyl benzyl carbinol, cinnamic alcohol, cyclamen aldehyde, phenyl ethyl alcohol, geranyl esters, linalyl esters, etc. etc.

Rhodinol ex geranium is frequently adulterated with "synthetic" rhodinol, laevo-citronellol, dextro-citronellol, geraniol, nerol, fractions of palmarosa oil, citronella oil, phenyl ethyl alcohol, etc. In the evaluation of "rhodinol ex geranium", the instrumental analysis is a most valuable method to produce a proof in cases of suspicion as a result of the olfactory analysis. The fact that the large consumers are still willing to pay over 100 U.S. dollars per kilo for a good "rhodinol ex geranium" should be sufficient proof that there is no competitive substitute for this excellent perfume material.

Ginger Absolute.

Ginger Absolute is produced by extraction of the ginger rhizome (see Ginger Oil) with hydrocarbon solvents. After evaporation of the solvent, the residual extract is extracted with alcohol. After chilling and filtration of the alcohol extract, this extract is evaporated under gentle vacuum until the alcohol is removed. The residue is Ginger Absolute. However, since the absolute is not a commercially available item, it is customary for the interested party that he produce his own absolute. As a starting material, the commercially available Ginger Oleoresin (see monograph) is frequently used, unless the user of ginger absolute does not prefer to start all the way from ginger rhizomes, specifically selected for this purpose.

Bataflor Ginger is a specially prepared extract of ginger (see Ginger Oleoresin).

According to the method of production and partly to the type of ginger rhizomes used, the ginger absolute may vary considerably in appearance and flavor. Usually, it is a viscous orange-brown or dark, yellow-brown liquid, just pourable at room temperature. Its odor is best described as being a very true reproduction of that of ginger rhizome, concentrated many times. The sweetness is emphasized, the rich, warm spiciness is predominant, and the tenacity is only modest. The typical lemon-orange-like topnotes (particularly well known from the Cochin and the Jamaica gingers) are accentuated by the fresh, slightly camphoraceous-warm and later sweet-woody body-notes of this absolute.

The flavor is equally warm, but also pungent-spicy, truly representative of the candied rhizome ("Chinese stem ginger").

Ginger Absolute is used by certain flavor houses in compositions where alcohol-solubility is of paramount importance, and a true-to-nature flavor must be maintained. The absolute thus represents the aroma *and* the pungency of ginger, and it replaces the old ginger tincture in flavor work. The application of ginger absolute is similar to that of ginger oleoresin (see **Ginger Oleoresin**). In perfumes, **Ginger Absolute** may introduce the most interesting and surprising notes in high-class lotion perfumes, etc., or in the so-called "men's fragrances" in the spicy series, after-shaves, etc. It blends excellently with animal notes (castoreum, civet, costus, labdanum) and with woody notes (sandalwood, vetiver, patchouli, linalool, olibanum, etc.), with floral notes (very interesting effect in gardenia, etc.) and in many types of modern fantasy fragrances.

Gingergrass Oil.

A twin brother of the palmarosagrass, the gingergrass has very little importance in perfumery. The oil is distilled from the East Indian grass, **Cymbopogon Martini**, varietas **Sofia**, a physiological variety of the palmarosagrass (see monograph **Palmarosa Oil**). Cultivation of the two grasses interlace in the regions to the northeast of Bombay, in the states of Madras, Bengal, and Punjab. The grass is distilled when in full inflorescence, and usually the entire overground parts of the plant are cut for distillation. The stills are generally of a very primitive type.

Gingergrass Oil is an oily liquid of yellow to dark yellow, amber-brown or almost brown color. It has a peculiar fatty-sweet, oily odor, leaving a slightly woody and rosy dryout note. The grassy notes, and particularly the rather fresh-spicy topnotes are entirely different from those found in palmarosa oil. This peculiar odor is sometimes referred to as an "ensilage"-odor. The main constituent of gingergrass oil, **Geraniol**, is not even perceptible until the oil dries out on a perfume blotter. The odor of geraniol is masked in this oil by the grassy and rather unpleasantly smelling trace components, one of which, however, is quite interesting: **Perilla Alcohol,** also known as dihydro cuminyl alcohol. This alcohol possesses an extremely diffusive and strong, oily-grassy, fatty-herbaceous odor. It is present in a number of other essential oils (see monograph on **Perilla Oil**). For the effect of this alcohol, **Gingergrass Oil** finds some use in the construction of certain artificial essential oils, e.g. bergamot oil, jasmin absolute,

cumin oil, "tea"-notes, etc. The content of **Perilla Alcohol** in gingergrass oil is, however, not high enough to encourage a production (by isolation) of this interesting perfume intermediate from the oil.

Gingergrass Oil once was a popular perfumery raw material for rose compounds, particularly for soap perfumes, etc. Frequent and crude adulteration, often at the place of production, ruined the good reputation of this oil. The annual production has now dropped far below 50 metric tons, and the oil is mainly absorbed by the huge Indian market in soaps and detergents.

Gingergrass Oil is hardly a regular item on the European and American market reports, and it may slowly disappear from the perfumery field except in its country of origin.

Ginger Oil.

Ginger Oil is produced by steam distillation, occasionally by water-and-steam distillation of the dried, unpeeled, freshly ground rhizomes of **Zingiber Officinale,** a plant which is native to the tropical coastal regions of India. The rhizomes, sun-dried and unpeeled, have been known as a spice for several thousand years, and the plant was among the early introductions to the West Indies when the Spanish seafarers roamed the Caribbean Sea shortly after A.D. 1500.

The ginger plant is now cultivated in most tropical and subtropical regions, e.g. Jamaica, Indochina, Southwest India, Ceylon, West Africa (particularly Sierra Leone and Nigeria), south China, south Japan and Central America. Smaller crops are grown in Madagascar (Nossi-Bé), Indonesia, Zanzibar, northwest Australia, Haiti, The Dominican Republic, Cuba and other areas of the West Indies. For the production of essential oil, the Nigerian and the Jamaican gingers are the most important. It is worthwhile noting that the term "African ginger" refers to Nigerian ginger when we speak of **Ginger Oil**, while it generally means Sierra Leone ginger when the *spice* itself is discussed.

Sierra Leone ginger is usually sold as a spice for grinding, while Nigerian ginger—which is always unpeeled—is mainly used for the distillation of essential oil and for extraction of **Ginger Oleoresin** (see following monograph). Jamaican ginger is partially peeled and, accordingly, is lighter in color. Since the essential oil is located in cells immediately under the epidermis, peeling of the rhizome will inevitably result in a loss of essential oil, either by accidental removal of oil cells, or by resinification or evaporation of oil caused by exposure of the oilcells to the air. Jamaican ginger accordingly yields considerably less oil than does the Nigerian ginger, and there is a distinct difference in the olfactory characteristics of the two oils. The odor of Nigerian ginger oil is heavier, more grassy-fatty, oily and woody than that of the Jamaican oil. An individual odor description is given below.

There is no production of ginger oil in Nigeria, while the oil is produced on a small scale in Jamaica, Zanzibar (experimental stage), India, China and Japan. The largest proportion of all the ginger oil of commerce, however, is produced in Europe and the U.S.A. from rhizomes imported from Nigeria, Jamaica and the Far East. In Japan, an oil is distilled from locally grown ginger, but this oil has a different aroma, and is only of local interest. The author had an opportunity to follow the development of experimental ginger production in the Gold Coast in 1954 to 1956 (now Ghana), and he had fresh rhizomes shipped from that country to Denmark. The water content in the fresh rhizomes was found to be from 68 percent to 73 percent. The water content in commercial grades of dried ginger rhizomes varies from 12 to 20 percent. This is mentioned to emphasize the importance of drying ginger rhizomes (and other botanicals) prior to shipment (costly freight of unnecessary water, deterioration of the spice, hydrolysis of oil constituents, etc.).

Ginger Oil is a pale yellow to light amber-colored mobile liquid. Its viscosity increases upon ageing or exposure to air (resinification). The odor is warm, but fresh-woody, spicy and with a peculiar resemblance to orange, lemon, lemongrass, coriander weed oil, etc. in the initial, fresh topnotes. The sweet and heavy undertone is tenacious, sweet and rich, almost balsamic-floral. African ginger oil is generally darker in color and presents a more fatty sweetness. The freshness is not pronounced nor is it very characteristic of that type ginger oil. It is, however, extremely rich and tenacious. Jamaican ginger oil is usually very pale in color, mobile like a pine needle oil, and with a pronounced odor-freshness of lemon-orange-coriander-like character. The body is sweet but not balsamic, the tenacity is only moderate.

The initial notes of freshly distilled **Ginger Oil** from Jamaican rhizomes often have a peculiar "rubber"-like type, similar to that of freshly distilled nutmeg oil (myrcene-like notes?). This note is hardly ever perceptible in African ginger oil.

There is no pungency in the flavor of any of the ginger oils. The flavor is warm and spicy, slightly bitter at high concentration, but pleasant-aromatic at ordinary use level. The suggested use level for an average good grade of Jamaican ginger oil is 0.30 to 1.50 mg%, and the **Minimum Perceptible** is 0.02 to 0.05 mg%. See also **Ginger Oleoresin** which is generally preferred as a flavor material, representing all the characteristics of the ginger rhizome itself.

Ginger Oil is used in perfumery to introduce warmth and certain nuances of spicy sweetness which are often wanted in heavy Oriental bases and in a few floral fragrances, too. The interest in the oil for perfumery use has increased considerably during the recent years of the growing "spice-trend" in men's fragrances and in lotion perfumes in general. The oil blends well with bois de rose oil, cedarwood, coriander, coumarin, benzyl acetate, citrus oils, eugenol, ionones, nitromusks, rose de mai absolute, nonanolide, nerol, etc. The Jamaican oil lends more freshness and topnote, while the Nigerian oil will give a solid body note, a warmth which is quite unique and typical of this oil.

In flavors, traces of **Ginger Oil** have an interesting effect in strawberry, pineapple, peppermint (modifier), but the most important field by far is that of baked goods: cookies, powder cakes, spice cakes, where pungency is not particularly called for. (Ginger nuts are flavored with **Ginger Oleoresin**). In alcoholic beverages, the oil gives interesting twists to the herbaceous types of liqueurs (benedictine, etc.), while the non-alcoholic beverages, e.g. the carbonated ginger ale is usually flavored with ginger oleoresin, or with a mixture of ginger oleoresin, ginger oil, capsicum oleoresin and sweet orange oil. Ginger oil blends well with sweet orange oil, lime oil, bergamot oil, etc. in flavor compositions.

The oil is produced according to demand, and there is ample supply of the spice available. Deliberate adulteration can be made with galanga oil (China and Japan), but usually the differences in the quality of the oils can be traced back to lack of experience in distillation technique at the producer's place, or poor selection of botanical material for distillation.

The annual world crop of ginger is in the order of magnitude of 100 million lbs. of fresh, undried rhizomes. This quantity corresponds to about 10,000 to 15,000 metric tons of commercial grade, dried ginger rhizomes. A very large proportion of this quantity is absorbed in households in the Far East, particularly in India.

Ginger Oleoresin.

Ginger Oleoresin is a prepared oleoresin. It is produced by extraction of the dried and unpeeled rhizome of Zingiber Officinale, ground to a moderately coarse powder. The solvent is ethylether, acetone, ethyl alcohol, occasionally chlorinated hydrocarbons, but rarely benzene which is highly toxic. The removal of the last few percents of solvent is a problem which has yet to be solved satisfactorily. Certain solvents can be removed almost quantitatively through the use of small amounts of ethylalcohol as a "chaser" during the last stages of evaporation. Ginger Oleoresin is extracted from various types of ginger (see Ginger Oil), but the majority of all ginger oleoresins are derived from Nigerian and Jamaican ginger, the former being the most inexpensive material, the latter having the most refined aroma. From the southwest coast of India comes a highly appreciated quality of ginger which is preferred for the production of oleoresin for use in carbonated beverages (Ginger Ale, etc.).

Ginger oleoresin is a dark brown or very dark amber colored, viscous liquid which usually deposits a grainy mass at the bottom of the container. The contents of a container should be thoroughly stirred before the material is weighed for compounding or sale. The odor of ginger oleoresin is warm-spicy, sweet and very aromatic-rich. The flavor is equally warm, but pungent-biting, leaving a peculiar cooling aftertaste almost as a reaction to the pungency. It gives an immediate feeling of heat and produces perspiration from the facial glands. The reader, who may have tasted Chinese candied ginger or a good ginger-nut (cookie) along with a cup of hot tea, will certainly agree that this combination can produce a breathtaking heat-shock.

Ginger oleoresin is used in numerous sorts of baked goods, spice blends, meat sauces, chutneys, candies, throat lozenges and, more recently, in carbonated soft drinks (Ginger Ale, etc.). The latter application has become one of the major outlets for ginger oleoresin during the past decade or two. For this purpose, ginger oleoresin is frequently adulterated with capsicum oleoresin (see Capsicum), whose pungent effect is many times greater than that of ginger. The pungency of ginger oleoresin preparations disappears after treatment with hot alkali, while the pungency of capsicum is resistant to this test. Capsicum additions to ginger preparations may be detected in this way. Ginger oleoresin can replace the powdered ginger rhizome in Indian curry powder, but it is still customary to prepare this spice blend exclusively from powdered botanical drugs.

Capsicum oleoresin does not contain any essential oil, while Ginger Oleoresin contains from 15 to 30% of essential oil (ginger oil). Oleoresins from Nigerian ginger may contain as much as 25 to 35% of essential oil, while the oleoresins from Jamaican or south Indian ginger usually have a lower oil content but a considerably higher content of the resinous matter in which we find the pungent principles. The ketone, Zingerone, which has been named as "a principal constituent of ginger" has been produced synthetically from vanillin and acetone by condensation followed by hydrogenation. However, the author has been unable to detect any pungency in the flavor of synthetic zingerone at the concentration of 0.50 to 1.00 mg%. This concentration is higher than the concentration of natural zingerone in any finished product on the market. It seems more likely, that this ketone is the decomposition product which is formed when the pungent principle (or principles) in ginger is treated with hot alkali (see the above test for adulteration of ginger oleoresin with capsicum oleoresin). The pungent principles in ginger thus seem to be condensation products of zingerone with aliphatic aldehydes (hexanal and heptanal in particular). These facts should be kept in mind when ginger oleoresin is used in finished goods where alkali is present. Potassium carbonate is used to improve the crunchy texture of certain spice cookies. This type of alkali is liable to ruin the pungency of ginger in the baked goods. Certain types of ginger cookies are flavored with a ginger-lemon combination which enables the manufacturer to use a small amount of citric acid along with the flavor. In the latter case, the pungency of the ginger oleoresin (or ginger powder) is maintained.

Ginger Oleoresin is rarely used in perfumes, partly because of its poor solubility in alcohol (except when it happens to be an "alcohol-extracted oleoresin"), partly because of its color and incompatibility with a number of perfume chemicals. A few manufacturers of perfume raw materials and flavor concentrates have produced various interesting **"Ginger Absolutes"** or specialties like the **Ginger Butaflor**. This product probably represents the highest concentration of the odor and flavor principles in ginger rhizome (see also **Ginger Absolute**). Odorless or tasteless ballast resins and similar extractive matter with no individual odor or flavor have been eliminated in a selective solvent extraction. A highly true-to-nature, viscous, dark amber colored extract is the result. Such materials are useful in perfumery where a richer, warmer gingernote or undertone is wanted. It should be mentioned that these special extracts are five to ten times more expensive than ordinary oleoresins.

Goldenrod Oil, Texas.

Well known over most parts of the world, The Americas, Asia and Europe, a multitude of varieties of **Goldenrod** grow wild or are cultivated, usually for decorative purposes. Similar to its relative, the chrysanthemum, it is a very rugged and strong, healthy plant, a fact which may explain the wide distribution of **Goldenrod**. To the author's knowledge, only one goldenrod has ever obtained any significant interest among the perfumers and flavorists: the so-called **Texas Goldenrod**, botanically known as **Solidago Odora**. By steam distillation of the flowering herb, an essential oil is produced in Texas, U.S.A.

Oil of sweet goldenrod is a colorless, rather mobile liquid of sweet-spicy, aromatic-herbaceous odor, reminiscent of estragon (Tarragon). The odor is inferior to that of estragon in respect to sweetness, tenacity and delicate, green-foliage notes. The rather simple or homogeneous odor of goldenrod oil is probably the main reason why the oil has never become a "big item" on the perfumer's shelf. It does not present any significant advantage over estragon oil or over the main constituent, methyl chavicol (estragole), and it has no fresh-green topnote, such as we find it in sweet basil oil. The author never saw a genuine sweet goldenrod oil while he worked in Europe.

Sweet goldenrod oil would be of interest mainly for flavorists who could possibly use it as a modifier for anise, basil, estragon, etc. in candy and licorice flavors, "root-beer" flavors for soft drinks, etc. Suggested use level is 0.40 to 0.80 mg%, and the **Minimum Perceptible** is 0.08 to 0.15 mg%. The oil could find some use in perfumes of fougère type, chypre, l'origan, moss, etc., or in trace amounts in lilac, muguet, etc.

The annual production of Texas sweet goldenrod oil is very fluctuating, and the oil is presently available only upon request with due notice. It is very likely that the oil will entirely disappear from the market.

Grapefruit Oil.

This oil, which is not strictly an essential oil according to our definitions, is produced by cold expression of the peel of the fruits from a **Citrus** species which presumably evolved from the West Indian "shaddock" fruit. Although not a hybrid, the grapefruit did not exist 400 years ago, and it was still a rarity around the beginning of the twentieth century. Highly developed cultivation and refining of the fruits (better juice, meat, fewer seed, etc.) has, as so often in nature, caused some changes elsewhere in the fruits: the oil from the peel has become milder and sweeter of odor than it was only a few decades ago.

Grapefruit Oil is produced mainly in Florida, U.S.A., and to a lesser degree in Texas and California. Outside the U.S.A., the West Indies (Dominica island, the Dominican Republic, Jamaica and Trinidad), Brazil, Israel and Nigeria are also producers. All production in the U.S.A. is mechanized; this is also true in Israel. Hand pressing is still carried out in the West Indies.

Grapefruit Oil is a mobile, yellowish to greenish-yellow or pale orange-yellow oil, possessing a fresh-citrusy, rather sweet odor and a similar taste. As mentioned above, the bitterness particularly known from European and Middle-Eastern fruits and peels, is no longer found in today's American grapefruit oil. The odor resembles that of sweet orange oil to a certain degree, but also has notes in common with bitter orange oil. Thus, grapefruit oil is quite useful in bergamot compositions and for all modifications of citrus notes in perfumery. The main use, however, is in flavors, particularly in soft drink flavors. A partially deterpenized grapefruit oil is often preferred for

24: Two 20,000-litre stills (one is hidden behind a huge condenser) for **Geranium** at Tiddas, Morocco. The still to the left in the photo is redistilling the condense-waters from the main stills in order to recover water-soluble oil.

(*Fot. S. Arctander, 1960*)

25: An abundance of flowers decorate the wild-growing **Honeysuckle** near Seillans, Var (France).
(Fot. S. Arctander, 1960)

26: The **Honeysuckle** flower, particularly fragrant at night and in northern countries. Seillans, Var (France).
(Fot. S. Arctander, 1960)

this purpose. More than 90% of the grapefruit oil is made up of monoterpenes, mainly d-limonene which has only a minor influence upon the characteristic flavor of the oil. Like all other citrus oils, grapefruit oil is not very stable and deteriorizes easily upon exposure to moisture, air and daylight. Antioxidants and oxygen-free storage conditions can prolong the shelf-life of these oils. Certain combinations of antioxidants are effective in concentrations of 0.002% which is far below the threshold of flavor or odor perception. Terpenes are particularly disadvantageous in soft drink flavors since they tend to create a "ring" of opaque emulsion inside the bottleneck at the surface—or on the side of the bottle if it is stored lying down. However, a certain amount of terpenes is necessary to produce the natural freshness of citrus oils. Thus, "concentrated" grapefruit oils are often used for the above flavors. Fifty percent or more of the monoterpenes are removed by careful vacuum distillation at less than 30°C. "Cold processed" deterpenized oils are produced by alcohol washing (see **Terpeneless Oils**, Part One of this book).

Due to the tremendous growth of the grapefruit industry, the oil is no longer the rarity or scarce item it was only 15 or 20 years ago. Indeed, the grapefruit juice processors are faced with a problem of disposing of all the oil they can produce. Not only is there the machine-pressed oil, but also the **Distilled Grapefruit Oil**, produced by steam distillation of the crushed peels and residues from the juice extraction. Smaller quantities of oil is obtained during the evaporation of juice which inevitably contains some oil. **Distilled Grapefruit Oil** is a poor flavor material. It may have a comparatively high content of aldehydes, but the content of other oxygenated compounds in the distilled oil is negligible. The distilled oil finds its way into low cost perfumes, industrial fragrances, etc., often mixed with other distilled citrus oils and marketed under the name of **Citrus Oil**. Even the seeds from the grapefruit are now used for production of a fatty (vegetable) oil.

Grapefruit Oil (cold pressed) is rarely adulterated. There are different qualities of the oil and it is important to get a freshly produced or carefully stored oil. However, the **Distilled Grapefruit Oil** can be used as a diluent for the expressed oil. This fraud will show up not only in the decrease of evaporation residue (very small in distilled oils), but also in the lack of flavor richness of the adulterated oil in an organoleptic test.

Guaiacwood Oil.

Erroneously called guaiacwood concrète, this oil is steam distilled, occasionally steam-and-water distilled from the wood of **Bulnesia Sarmienti**, a wild-growing tree from the jungles of Paraguay and Argentina. It should not be confused with the **Guaiac** of the drug store where a resinous substance, produced from another tree, **Guaiacum Officinale** (the "lignum vitae" of the Bahama islands) is occasionally used. "Guaiac resin" is an entirely different product and only very rarely used in perfumery. A tincture is prepared from the resin. This tincture has a pleasant balsamic-vanilla-like odor with a somewhat smoky undertone. It was this tincture which was used by Sherlock Holmes when he identified bloodstains on a murderscene.

Guaiacwood Oil is now distilled locally, although some quantities of wood (known as "Palo Santo") are exported for distillation in Europe or the U.S.A. The wood is hard and its comminution before distillation presents quite a problem. It is a much-used wood for ornamental work (hand carved bowls, ashtrays, etc.).

Guaiacwood Oil is a soft or semi-solid mass, yellowish to greenish yellow or pale amber in color. When melted, it may stay supercooled and liquid for a long time. Once again, we meet a product which quite frequently presents odor types not reported in literature: apart from its delicately sweet, rosy-woody odor which is often referred to as "tearose-like", the oil may have a "smoked ham" odor which is definitely unwanted, but not uncommon. It is conceivable that this odor, which was never reported prior to World War II, occurs in oils which have been "forced" during the distillation through the addition of mineral acid (sulfuric, etc.) to the chopped, wet wood in the still. This increases the yield of oil, but it also creates a hazard of spot-burning of the woodchips. Similar to amyris, the age of the wood prior to distillation also has some influence upon the odor of the oil.

The main constituent of guaiac wood oil is called **Guaiol** ("gaiol") This sesquiterpene alcohol can be acetylated to the so-called **Guaiyl Acetate**. "Guaiac wood acetate" is the acetylated oil, often merely neutralized, not redistilled. Unfortunately, the "smoked ham" odor is carried over in the latter product which is frequently offered under the label **Guaiyl Acetate** (incorrect).

Guaiacyl Acetate (1-acetyl-2-methoxy-benzene) is the acetate of a phenol which is present in guaiac resin (see above). It has nothing to do with guaiac wood oil or its constituents.

Guaiacwood Oil is produced in large quantities and is readily available, the annual output being close to 100 metric tons. The oil is a low-cost fixative and modifier, an excellent blender in woody-floral perfumes, in soap compounds as well as high-class perfumes. It blends well with linalool, nerol, geraniol, terpineol, oakmoss, ionones, orris products, spice oils, etc. It is occasionally adulterated with copaiba balsam. Guaiac wood oil is, in turn, sometimes found as an adulterant in rose de mai absolute, amyris oil, sandalwood oil, costus oil, oakmoss concrète, etc.

Guarana Paste.

Although cocoa is not included in the monographs on natural flavor materials in this book (the author considers it primarily a nutriment), a few brief notes will be spent on a similar but less known and quite interesting material: **Guarana Paste.**

Guarana paste is made from the pulverized, roasted seed of **Paullinia Cupana** (paullinia sorbilis), a Brazilian tree. The seed looks almost like a chestnut when it is fresh. The roasted seed is pulverized and triturated with a small amount of water to form a dough which is then shaped into bars or balls and left to dry in the sun or on a grill over open fire.

The product which is known as **Guarana Paste** serves locally as a substitute for chocolate. It is distinguished by its combination of a chocolate-like flavor and a cola-like effect. It contains more caffeine than any other known natural product and it is accordingly a powerful stimulant. The caffeine content can amount to 5% while the content of tannin is about 25%.

Mixed with manioc flour or other starch material, the **Guarana Paste** can be baked to a bread; diluted with water, the paste can serve as a refreshing tonic. Sweetened with sugar (like cocoa paste) the guarana paste forms the so-called "Brazilian chocolate".

Guarana Extracts are commercially available. A "standard" liquid extract is prepared with diluted alcohol and it is adjusted to a content of 4% caffeine. One part by weight of the liquid extract is equivalent to one part by weight of an average quality of guarana paste.

Guarana Paste produces interesting **Aroma-distillates** (see Part One of this book) with sherry wines, cognac or rum. These distillates can be useful as flavor bases for the development of liqueur flavors, cordial flavors, pudding or soufflé flavors and other food flavors.

Gurjun Balsam.

Gurjun Balsam, also called **Gurjum Balsam** is a natural oleoresin, *not* a balsam according to the definitions outlined in Part One of this work. It is exuded from trees of the **Dipterocarpus** species, growing in the Far East, particularly in India. The oleoresin is a pathological product, formed only after incisions or other damage to the trunk of these tall trees.

Locally used in the varnish and lacquer industry, **Gurjun Balsam** finds some use in perfumery in other countries. It serves similar purposes as does copaiba balsam: it is a low-cost, comparatively mild-smelling natural fixative for woody, balsamic or pine-type fragrances. It is an odor-depressant and "stretcher" of general application. The natural oleoresin "gurjun balsam" contains from 60 to 80 percent of a viscous essential oil which is also used occasionally in perfumery (see **Gurjun Balsam Oil).**

Gurjun balsam, also called **Wood Oil** or **Gurjum Oil** (erroneously and misleading), is a viscous, ambercolored or greenish-olive to grayish liquid, occasionally opaque or slightly fluorescent. Its odor is faintly sweet, woody, pinelike, reminiscent of copaiba balsam and amyris oil, however, with a crude undertone similar to that of a steam distilled pine oil (American).

Although the production of **Gurjun Balsam** is still quite sizeable, its application in perfumery has declined significantly during the past decades. The product has always carried a reputation of being a material for adulteration "par excellence" of certain essential oils, e.g. palmarosa oil and other East Indian oils. See also **Gurjun Balsam Oil, Illurin Balsam, Copaiba Balsam.**

The physical properties (optical rotation, etc.) of gurjun balsam have been utilized to adjust the physical data of artificial essential oils, etc.

Gurjun Balsam Oil.

From the so-called **Gurjun Balsam** (see previous monograph) an essential oil can be steam distilled in a very high yield. Although of little value in perfumery as such, the oil should be mentioned since it occurs as an adulterant in several essential oils, or as a constituent of certain artificial essential oils. **Gurjun Balsam Oil** is usually produced in Europe or the U.S.A. from gurjun balsam imported from the Far East (India, Burma, etc.).

The oil is a pale yellow to pale amber colored, viscous liquid of a mild-woody, somewhat balsamic-sweet odor and great tenacity. The oil would find application as a fixative, modifier and odor-depressant material in woody or Oriental fragrances, e.g. in soap compounds where its great tenacity and mild, uniform odor is an advantage. It has very little "odor value", but it blends perfectly with a multitude of common perfume materials.

On account of its extraordinarily high laevo-rotatory power, gurjun balsam oil has served as a "correcting agent" in artificial essential oils which had to meet certain physical specifications or Pharmacopoeia demands. It is not infrequently found as a diluent in ylang-ylang oil, patchouli oil, sandalwood oil, vetiver oil, cubeb oil, etc.

Gurjun (Balsam) Oil is not a common commercial article any more, but it is still available since the parent "balsam" is regularly produced in large quantities in the Far East.

H

Hamamelis.

The north American shrublike tree, **Hamamelis Virginiana**, also known as **Witch Hazel**, has enjoyed a tremendous and over-exaggerated reputation for its virtues with respect to the hemostatic and astringent effects of its leaves and bark. Extracts and distillates of the leaves are still used, and these are quite popular ingredients in skin-lotions, after-shaves, creams, etc. The leaves do contain tannin which is astringent, and they do contain a small amount of an essential oil which has a hemostatic effect. The latter claim is based upon the fact that the **Hamamelis Leaf Distillate** has a hemostatic effect, and that tannin is not

distillable with steam or with hydro-alcoholic vapors; thus, tannin is absent in the leaf distillate.

Under the name of **Hamamelis Water**, another product is marketed and used as a popular embrocation. It is prepared from twigs of the witch hazel which are collected just before the buds open. This material is comminuted after partial drying; it is macerated with water, and the mixture is distilled after 24 hours. To the distillate is added alcohol sufficient to preserve the distillate from mold or fungus growth (about 15 percent ethyl alcohol). This product has a peculiar tea-leaf-like odor due to micro-percentages of essential oil. It is inconceivable that this **Hamamelis Water** can have any therapeutic value.

However, the dry extract of the leaves and the standard extract (= fluidextract) are commercially available products, and both are currently used in pharmaceutical preparations. They have occasional application in perfumery when this peculiar note of dry tea-leaves, a herbaceous-foliage type, is required.

Our much more common and popular **Hazelnut** shrub, **Corylus Avellana**, a cousin of hamamelis, could probably yield quite similar products from its leaves and bark. But it is probably spared because of the delicious nuts, a valuable and highly appreciated crop.

Hamanasu Concrète.

This perfumery material is derived from the flowers of **Rosa Rugosa**, a plant which is cultivated in Japan. The annual production (1958) is about 100 kilos, all of which is absorbed in Japan for finer perfumery products.

Hamanasu concrète is not regularly available outside of its country of origin. The author has no personal experience with the use of this material. Samples so far received have been olive-green to dark orange brown of color, and the odor has been woody-floral, sweet, somewhat honeylike. It is most likely that considerable variations in odor and appearance may occur in such a small scale production.

Hay Absolute.

The term "Hay" in this place refers to the type "new mown hay", also called "foin coupé". This type of fragrance has been desirable for perfume base creations for many decades, and it is quite surprising that a "natural" new mown hay product was not developed long before it did appear on the market.

There are various kinds of **Hay Absolute** available, and it is hard to give exact data on starting materials, processing or yields. The botanical material is extracted with petroleum ether to produce a concrète. The absolute is prepared by alcohol washing of the concrète.

Generally, the commercially available **Hay Absolutes** are viscous liquids, dark amber, dark green or brownish green in color, occasionally they are soft masses of olive-brown color. The odor is powerful and extremely sweet, quite diffusive, coumarin-like and faintly herbaceous, very uniform and tenacious. The undertone is almost jam-like sweet, reminiscent of figs or preserved prunes in odor type. There is a distinct difference among the hay absolutes extracted from hay without flowers, with flowers, or with seed. See also monograph on **Flouve Absolute.**

An absolute is also prepared from "Alpine grass", **Hierochlea Alpina,** by a Grasse perfume house.

Hay Absolute is used in perfumery not only in "new mown hay" bases, or in combination with flouve, melilotus, tonka, woodruff, deertongue, etc., but also as an individual note to be introduced whenever a truly herbaceous-sweet undertone is required: in lavender, fougère, chypre, colognes, tea-notes, "tabac"-notes, forest-notes and various bouquets. Interesting effects are obtained with hay absolute in jasmin bases, orange flower bases, etc. Hay absolute could be used in flavors, but the coumarin-ban is, at least ethically, extended to such natural products which contain significant amounts of coumarin. Flouve absolute (which *may* contain coumarin!) is slightly superior to hay absolute in respect to versatility in flavor use.

Hay Absolute is produced in France only, and in very limited quantities. However, the demand is weak, and an increased production is quite possible since the botanical material is present. The absolute may be adulterated with deertongue extract, flouve (no economical gain), melilotus extract, tonka extract, woodruff extract, synthetic coumarin or various methyl coumarins, etc.

Occasionally, plain compositions of natural and synthetic materials are offered under the label "hay absolute". True **Hay Absolutes** do exist, however.

See also **Hay Oil, Flouve Absolute, Flouve Oil.**

Hay Oil.

A comparatively new item which is not yet regularly found in the price lists is the essential oil of hay. The few producers do not specify from which grass (hay) the oil is distilled, or whether it is actually an extracted oil or a distilled one. It is most likely that one or several of the common ensilage grasses are collected during the period of inflorescence, properly dried, extracted with petroleum ether, and then finally distilled at very low pressure (molecular distillation of the extract with or without a co-distilling, neutral liquid).

Hay Oil is usually a pale amber or pale yellow liquid with a delightfully sweet-herbaceous, tea-like fragrance, reminiscent of the odor of sage clary, wet tea leaves and hay. The undertone and the dryout are almost floral-woody, but remain sweet and very uniform. Certain types of hay oil show no coumarin-like odors at all. It is most likely that such oils are true distillates and not extracts or molecular distillates of extracts. In the latter cases, coumarin would certainly be perceptible in the product.

Hay Oil is extremely interesting and useful in modern perfume types: citrus colognes, lavender-fougères, fantasy compositions, jasmin modifications, orange flower bases, as a "nuanceur" for spicy fragrances or "men's perfumes", carnation modifier, etc.

Unfortunately, the price of this material (it is about one-fifth of the price of jasmin absolute) prohibits its general use, e. g. for carrying notes in a "new mown hay" perfume base. **Hay Oil** blends extremely well with sage clary, champaca, mimosa, cassie, magnolia leaf oil, flouve oil, chamomile oils, helichrysum oil, tobacco leaf absolute, maté extracts, tea leaf absolute, phenylethyl alcohol, linalool, bergamot oil, lemon oil, ylang-ylang, bitter orange oil, deertongue, melilotus, coumarin, etc.

In flavors, the oil may be used as a modifier in the citrus-blends for cordials and liqueurs and as a modifier for peppermint oil, spearmint oil, etc. in candy or chewing gum. However, here again its poor availability prevents extensive use of this magnificent material.

See also **Flouve Oil, Hay Absolute, Magnolia.**

Helichrysum Kilimandjarum.

Among the numerous essential oils belonging to the so-called "herbaceous chamomile group", we can also place the oil of **Helichrysum Kilimand-jarum.**

The oil is steam distilled from the flowers of the above plant which grows abundantly in East Africa, and is produced in Tanganyika by a few of the local essential oil distillers. Botanically related to **Everlasting** (see **Everlasting Absolute** and **Helichrysum Oil**), the oil of helichrysum kilimandjarum is an orange-colored or reddish-brown liquid which has a sweet-floral, somewhat fruity-herbaceous odor. The oil is only very rarely offered in the market, but since the botanical raw material is abundantly available, it could be made available in sizeable quantities if reasonable notice is given.

The oil does not, however, possess any significant or outstanding asset in the shape of interesting perfumery notes. For this reason, it may never gain any great popularity among perfumers. It should be kept in mind that a large scale production may turn out an improved oil which could have odor qualities similar to those of **Helichrysum Oil**, European (see following monograph).

Helichrysum Oil.

See also **Everlasting Absolute.**

Helichrysum Oil is steam distilled from the flowering tops of the small plant, **Helichrysum Angustifolium** and other species of **Helichrysum.** The plant grows wild and is cultivated in the south of France, Italy, Yugoslavia and several other Mediterranean countries. The yield of essential oil from helichrysum angustifolium is very poor, but certain closely related species of helichrysum, e.g. **Helichrysum Orientale**, are usually co-distilled and increase the yield without impairing the odor qualities of the oil.

Helichrysum Oil is a pale yellow, oily liquid of powerful and diffusive, but pleasant and rich, natural odor. The topnote has certain features in common with those of the extracted material (everlasting absolute), and these topnotes are not exactly attractive at high concentration. The sweetness is so rich and overwhelming, honeylike and deep, that it takes more than the average of imagination to appreciate the odor of this oil. However, the sweet-fruity and tea-like, delicate undertone is unique, and the tenacity is quite outstanding.

The oil finds augmenting application in perfumery where it blends well with boronia, cham-omile, citrus oils, geraniol, ionones, labdanum, lavender, nerol, mimosa, oakmoss, orris products, sage clary, etc. It gives interesting effects in ambre, chypre, lily, muguet, rose and other bases. The main constituent of helichrysum oil is **Neryl Acetate** which is only rarely found in high percentage in essential oils. The oil is an excellent modifier for certain types of fruit flavors where its rich and deep-sweet notes are well utilized in raspberry, plum, fig, etc. It blends well with alpha-irone, phenyl ethyl alcohol, menthyl acetate, alpha ionone methyl glycidate, amyl esters, nerol, terpeneless and sesquiterpeneless lemon oil or lime oil, lemon petitgrain oil, etc., in fruit flavors for carbonated beverages, candy, etc. **Helichrysum Oil** is now produced on an increasing scale in Yugoslavia, and its cost is no longer prohibitive for its extensive use (1959-price was about engl. sh. 225/- to 275/- per kilo). It is conceivable that the oil will find a permanent place on the perfumer's shelf—and at his balance—in the near future, if it is not already one of his favorite items.

Heliotrope Absolute.

Originated in Peru and introduced in Europe more than 200 years ago, the **Heliotropium Peruvianum** is now cultivated commonly in the south of Europe. Knowing it from Danish greenhouses as a tender and tiny, unimpressive ornamental plant, the author was quite astonished to find a shrublike plant, the size of a sunflower, when he first met the heliotrope in the south of France in the 1930's. The name **Heliotrope** actually means the same as "sunflower" (for which the French name is "tournesol"). They both "follow the sun".

Heliotropium Peruvianum (also known as **Heliotropium Arborescens**) has a small clusters of grayish-purple or violet-colored flowers which emit a very sweet odor reminiscent of bitter almond oil, yet more heavy floral and with a distinct fruity undertone. The plant is known in the U.S.A. as "cherry-pie blossom". To the chemist, the odor of the flower may remind of heliotropine, but this note is not too obvious. The perfumer will find this note well concealed in heavy-sweet notes of the lilac-, hawthorne-, or carnation type.

Absolute of Heliotrope has never become a common perfume material, nor an inexpensive one, probably on account of heliotropine being available as a low-cost synthetic chemical. The absolute is occasionally produced in the south of France from the flowering tops of the plant by hot extraction with a fixed oil (digestion method). Heliotrope absolute is a semi-solid greenish-brown or dark brown mass of strongly herbaceous, but also intensely sweet odor. Only upon dilution to about 1% or weaker, the odor seems to resemble that of heliotrope flowers. The absolute blends well into violet, mimosa, cassie and other florals, but it does not offer any significant advantages over other natural or synthetic products in the same odor group. It is very likely, therefore, that **Heliotrope Absolute** will completely disappear from the perfume market within the next decade or two.

Henna.

Although not famous as a perfume or flavor material, the leaves and flowers of **Henna** are so abundantly available that a brief description will be given here in case its peculiar fragrance should sometime become of interest to an increasing number of perfumers. The leaves of the shrub or bush, **Lawsonia Inermis,** were used in Egyptian cosmetics probably thousands of years ago. There are still millions of women all over the world today, who dye their hair with **Henna** leaves, using various intensifying or dye-controlling additives such as mild alkali, mild acid, etc. They use water and powdered leaves made into a paste which is applied to the hair for a certain number of minutes or hours.

The main suppliers of henna leaves are Sudan, Egypt, Arabia, Iran, India, Ceylon, etc., and henna is also cultivated in China, Indonesia, the West Indies ("Jamaican mignonette"), etc. The dried leaves have a very pleasant tealike, herbaceous odor. The roots and leaves are used locally for the dyeing of the palms of the hands, the toes, nails and hair of Moslem women.

However, the flowers have such an attractive fragrance that an essential oil has been prepared from them on an experimental scale. The author has no personal experience with the use of a genuine (straight and authentic) henna flower oil, but he can confirm that the flowers smell extremely sweet, delicately floral and tealike, reminiscent of boronia and chloranthus spicatus oils. "No wonder!" the chemist would probably say, because

he has identified beta-ionone and alpha-ionone in the essential oil from henna flowers.

In India, the so-called "attars" are prepared from flowers which do not readily yield essential oils by steam distillation. From **Henna** flowers is prepared the "Hina" attar or "mendee attar". This product is a dark orange colored or dark brownish-yellow to reddish-brown, viscous liquid. Its odor is somewhat medicinal, phenolic or bitter, but with a tenacious leafy undertone. The odor characteristics varies from one source to another.

An **Absolute of Henna Flowers** has also been prepared although not on a commercial scale. The literature seems to disagree about the odor of **Henna Flower Oil,** and the author of this book will refrain from using any quotations, and only verify that the flower "in natura" smells in accordance with the above description (visits to Sudan and Egypt, 1956).

On account of the extremely small yield of essential oil by steam distillation of **Henna** flowers, it is inconceivable that this oil can become a common perfume material, even considering the abundance of the botanical material.

See **Boronia Absolute** and **Chloranthus Spicatus.**

Ho Leaf Oil.

This oil is steam distilled from the so-called **Ho-Sho** variety of the tree, **Cinnamomum Camphora** which is widely cultivated in Formosa, Japan, and, to a minor extent on the Chinese mainland. The leaves of the above tree can be stripped off once or twice a year without damaging the tree. The leaves of felled trees (for camphor oil production) can also be utilized. Thus, there is ample and inexpensive botanical material ready for the production of **Ho Leaf Oil.** Accordingly, the leaf oil is offered at a lower price than the **Wood Oil** (see Ho Wood Oil), and has become a potential competitor to the Brazilian bois de rose oil. Furthermore, Ho Leaf Oil, rectified or of a high grade, contains practically no camphor-like notes, and it presents such a clean linalool fragrance that no other essential oil comes closer to the pure linalool odor than a rectified **Ho Leaf Oil.**

The oil is practically colorless, and possesses a clean, sweet, floral-woody and delicate odor. There is little or no change in the odor during the evaporation on a perfume blotter, and the tenacity is only moderate.

Ho Leaf Oil can be used in high percentages in a multitude of perfume types: as a modifier, blender, sweetener, floralizer, or individual odor. It blends perfectly with phenyl ethyl alcohol, cinnamic alcohol, amyl salicylate, citronellol, geraniol, ionones, hydroxycitronellal, cyclamen aldehyde, lavandin oil, etc., and its very low cost broadens the fields for its use beyond measure. For the isolation of Linalool, for the production of linalyl esters, it is superior to any other natural starting material—and cheaper than any except lavandin oil. It performs excellently in soaps where it may very well replace linalool (from bois de rose oil). "Acetylated" Ho Leaf Oil is available in commercial quantities, and this product may replace linalyl acetate in soap perfumes, low-cost detergent fragrances, etc.

The annual production of Ho Leaf Oil has surpassed the 100-ton-mark, and this oil may one day find its place among the "upper ten" essential oils with respect to quantity produced.

Homalomena Rubescens.

An oil which has hardly yet reached the shelves in European and American perfume laboratories, has been known and used for quite some time in the Far East: the essential oil of Homalomena Rubescens which is steam distilled from the comminuted roots of this plant. The plant is related to calamus. It grows wild and commonly in India, Indonesia, the Malaccan peninsula and Borneo. It is experimentally cultivated in India for the production of larger quantities of essential oil.

Oil of Homalomena Rubescens is a pale yellow or amber-colored liquid of a sweet-woody, somewhat floral, but also harsh-pinelike odor. The odor is reminiscent of that of low grade Ho Wood Oils or of certain fractions of bois de rose oil. It serves in its homeland as a soap perfume ingredient, as a source of Linalool (the main constituent of the oil), and for the production of linalyl esters.

The rhizome of the plant is used locally for the flavoring of tobacco. To the author's knowledge, the rhizomes have not yet been exported or distilled outside their country of origin beyond the experimental scale. The oil does not offer any sensational or new notes in perfumery when Ho Oils, Bois de Rose Oil, Lavandin Oil, etc. are freely available.

The annual production of Homalomena Rubes-

cens Oil is still in the order of magnitude of a few metric tons. The entire production is consumed locally.

Honeysuckle Absolute.

This material is better known under the name from its producing country: "absolu de chevre-feuille". It is produced by extraction of the flowers of Lonicera Caprifolium and other Lonicera species. The plant is a climbing vine and is well known all over the world as far north as Scandinavia and south to South Africa, mainly in the temperate zones.

The flowers are extracted with petroleum ether to yield a concrète which, in turn, is further processed into an absolute by the conventional alcohol-washing method.

Honeysuckle Absolute is an orange-green to dark green or brownish, viscous liquid. Its odor is intensely sweet, fatty-floral, somewhat reminiscent of jasmin absolute from châssis and of orange flower absolute. The sweetness is not unlike the nauseating sweetness of tuberose. However, the various absolutes which are available on the market, do not truly represent the fragrance of the flower. It appears that the present extraction methods are imperfect, and it is very likely that the available honeysuckle absolutes are "compounded" from natural and synthetic perfume materials. The absolute has very little significance for the creative perfumer, but the honeysuckle type of floral fragrance is frequently used or requested by customers to the perfume houses. Small amounts of authentic Honeysuckle Absolute may be available upon demand. Flowers are available in France and England from cultivated and wild plants.

Artificial honeysuckle (perfume bases) can be created from available perfume materials, e. g. allyl ionone and other ionones, benzyl isobutyl carbinol, cyclamal, cassione, hydroxycitronellal-methylanthranilate, isobutyl phenylacetate, helichrysum oil, lily-bases, narcissus bases, orange flower bases, tuberose bases, tolyl acetate, rhodinol, cinnamyl acetate, floranol, phenylethyl-phenylacetate, phenyl propionaldehyde, etc.

Hop Absolute.

Used for flavoring purposes for more than 2500 years, Hops have also entered perfumery. In addition, they supply the flavor industry with some very interesting materials. **Hops** are the female flowercatkins from the climbing vine, **Humulus Lupulus.** This plant is cultivated all over Central Europe and in the U.S.A., particularly in California, Washington state and Oregon (not far from the peppermint fields). In the eastern U.S.A., Virginia and New York state produce the balance of the American demand for hops to the beer breweries.

The following perfume- and flavor materials are derived from hops:

1) **Hop Concrète** and **Hop Absolute,** extraction products from hops.
2) **Hop Oil,** steam distilled from the hops (see **Hop Oil).**
3) **Lupulin** and **Lupulin Distillate,** from the glandular hairs on the hops, known as **Lupulin** (see monograph).

The hops will yield **Hop Concrète** by extraction with ether gasoline or benzene. Petroleum ether is rarely used. The concrète is solid and dark green, waxy-resinous, and is only an intermediate in the production of *absolute from concrete of hops.*

Hop Absolute is produced by alcohol-extraction of the concrète and subsequent recovery of the alcohol in vacuum. The evaporation residue is **Hop Absolute.** The absolute is a semi-solid, dark green mass of intensely deep-herbaceous, rich and green-spicy odor with a peculiar and characteristic "bitter"-leafy undertone, distinct and tenacious. A valerian-like topnote develops in older oils, but it can be removed by careful washing of the absolute.

Used with caution and discretion in flavors, hop absolute introduces a most interesting naturalness to apple flavors, pineapple, etc., and it also lends a rich body to various types of spice- or seasoning compounds. The normal use level would be about 0.30 mg% to 1.00 mg%, and the **Minimum Perceptible** is 0.05 to 0.10 mg%. In perfumery, it offers a bitter-green note which is interesting in pine, fougère, hyacinth, citrus (lime in particular), and even in aldehydic perfume bases.

Hop Absolute is produced in France on a very limited scale only. The botanical material is, obviously, abundantly present. More recently, ultrasonic vibration has been introduced as a means of extracting botanicals, etc. **Ultrasonic Hop Extract** is commercially available, and, according to the type of menstruum used, the product will be soluble in water, alcohol or hydrocarbons.

Most commonly, a mixture of water and ethyl alcohol is used, thus producing an extract which is soluble in low-proof alcohol. The yield of extracted, aromatic matter is considerably improved by this method, over the yield attained by conventional extraction. A few French houses specialize in ultrasonic extraction. Ultrasonic extracts are generally very dark. See **Ultrasonic Extracts** in Part One of this book.

See also **Lupulin.**

Hop Oil.

An essential oil is steam distilled or steam-and-water distilled from the **Hops** (see **Hop Absolute).** The oil has odor and flavor characteristics quite different from those of the absolute or the concrète from the same botanical material. **Hop Oil** is produced in Germany, France, and occasionally in other countries in Central Europe, in England, etc. The best oils obviously come from the areas where the hops are grown, since the volatile constituents of the hops are very sensitive to air exposure and oxidation. Resinification and the formation of free acids in particular will ruin the odor and flavor of hop oils, e.g. oils which have been distilled from old or dried material, or by improper storage of the hops or the oil.

Hop Oil is a pale yellow (when fresh) to reddish-amber colored liquid, mobile when fresh, viscous when old. The odor of a *fresh* hop oil is very rich, spicy-aromatic, sweet and heavy, but overall pleasant. Due to ageing or improper storage, the valeric, isovaleric and caprylic acids are formed and liberated, heavily influencing the odor and flavor to the disadvantage of the oil. Oils of sour, butyric-valeric or sweat-like odor should not be used at all. Cold stored in filled, well stoppered bottles, protected from daylight—or stored in solution, hop oil is fairly stable over a period of a year or more.

Adulteration of hop oil is not uncommon. Nutmeg oil, copaiba oil, various terpenes and fractions from other essential oils, etc. have been identified in commercial lots of hop oil.

The oil is used in flavor work for its rich, bitter-aromatic and somewhat spicy aroma. In spice blends, tablesauces, tobacco flavors, and in flavors for alcoholic beverages, the oil may be used in combination with angelica root oil, cascarilla oil, and similar aromatic botanicals with which it introduces characteristic notes. The use of hop oil in the beer industry is comprehensively discussed in works dealing with beer brewing. The use level of hop oil in flavors is so strongly dependent upon the presence and concentration of other aromatic materials, that it serves no purpose to give approximate figures. The **Minimum Perceptible** of hop oil in neutral medium is about 0.03 to 0.06 mg% (fresh oil). In perfumes, **Hop Oil** lends a warm, rich and piquant, spicy note, useful in colognes, chypres, Oriental bases, fougères, etc. The true annual production of **Hop Oil** may be quite substantial, but the amount of oil available for the perfume industry is very limited. A few Hungarian and German distillers add sodium chloride to the distillation waters in order to produce a better separation of oil from the water. Furthermore, they may extract the water phase with benzene or other hydrocarbon solvents in order to collect certain water-soluble parts of the essential oil which are necessary to reproduce fully the volatile aroma of the hops. These "complete" **Hop Oils** are superior to ordinary hop oils in respect to flavor effect, but their keeping qualities are equally poor or even inferior to those of ordinary hop oils.

Horseradish Oil.

Of interest to the flavorist only is the essential oil and the various extraction products from the root of **Armoracia Lapathifolia,** a common plant in Europe, known as **Horseradish** ("raifort" in French). The root which is commonly sold on vegetable markets, can be classified as a pungent condiment, similar to mustard seed (see monograph on **Mustard Oil**); mustard seed is classified as a pungent aromatic seed. The most important of the constituents responsible for the pungency of horseradish, is identical to the main constituent of mustard seed oil from black mustard seed.

A very small yield of essential oil is obtained by water-and-steam distillation of the comminuted horseradish root, soaked in water. The essential oil is pale yellow or almost colorless, mobile, and of intensely sharp odor and lachrymatory effect, reminiscent of the virtues of mustard oil, but even more pungent or irritating than this oil. For flavor experiments, it is advisable to start with extremely high dilutions, e. g. p.1 mg% or even less in order to avoid irritation of the mucous membranes on tongue and palate. The oil finds some use in the canning- and ready-made salad industry, replacing

the fresh horseradish which may be inavailable for parts of the year.

Horseradish Oil is occasionally adulterated with black mustard oil, and it is a rough job to determine through organoleptic examination, whether or not you have a true oil.

A "concrète" or **Resinoid** of **Horseradish** (so-called) is produced by benzene extraction of the root. It is necessary to dry the root prior to this extraction. Fresh or semi-dried roots can be extracted with acetone or ethyl alcohol. The various extracts present a more true-to-nature aroma than does the oil. The "resinoid" is usually a dark amber colored, very viscous mass. It has a rich, but pungent and somewhat sharp odor with a peculiar warm and quite pleasant undertone. This product is very suitable for use in seasonings, etc. as a replacement for the root itself. However, the dried root is now available flaked or "grated" in airtight sealed packages for household or industrial use.

Horseradish Oil and **Horseradish "Resinoid"** are very rarely offered commercially. They may be produced upon demand, or they are produced by the individual consumers for their specific needs.

Ho Wood Oil.

From one of the many varieties of **Cinnamomum Camphora,** locally known as **Ho-Sho,** two essential oils are derived, both of which are quite important to the perfume industry:

A "camphor oil" (see monograph on **Camphor Oils**) is distilled from the wood which, upon fractionation, yields about 20% of the so-called **Ho-Oil** or **Shiu-Oil.** Formosa and Japan are the major producers, while minor quantities are produced in Red China. Japanese "**Ho Wood Oil**" is a fractionated ho oil, while the Chinese oil is usually "natural" and contains more camphor than linalool.

Before World War II, hundreds of tons of Ho Oil were produced annually, and most of it was exported to Europe where it was further processed into perfumery grade linalool, linalyl acetate and other perfume materials. It was not until quite recently that the essential oil from the leaves of the same tree became available in significant quantities. The latter oil has now greatly replaced the **Ho Wood Oil** as a source of **Linalool** (see monograph on **Ho Leaf Oil**).

Ho Wood Oil is a pale yellow or almost colorless oil with a sweet-camphoraceous, somewhat woody-floral odor. There have always been several grades of ho wood oil, the best ones being virtually free from camphoraceous notes. These oils were offered at a lower price than Brazilian bois de rose oil even in the years prior to 1955.

Only the better grades of Ho Wood Oil were used as such in perfumery, although the camphor-aceous types could be used in soap perfumes where lavandin, aspic, rosemary and similar materials were already present. As mentioned above, ho wood oil is now slowly but steadily being replaced by the leaf oil from the same tree. The wood oil still finds use in the producing areas as a soap perfume material and as a source of linalool.

Huon Pine Wood Oil.

A tree, Dacrydium Franklinii, which is probably a native of Tasmania, has been introduced in several other countries thousands of miles away from its homeland. With its very insect-resistant and useful lumber for furniture, ships and floorboards, etc., the tree is now cultivated in New Zealand, Borneo, Malaya, Indonesia, South America, etc.

Distillation takes place in Tasmania, but not regularly.

The wood sawdust, shavings, etc. are steam distilled to yield a pale yellow or reddish-brown liquid of a faintly sweet, woody-spicy and somewhat bitter odor, reminiscent of cedarwood, Texas. Huon pine wood oil was used during World War II as an insect repellant (it contains over 95% methyl eugenol), but the oil caused too many cases of skin irritation, and it was abandoned for this particular purpose. The oil may serve as a natural source of methyl eugenol, but with the abundance of clove leaf oil at floor level prices, a production of Huon Pine Wood Oil is not economically attractive.

The oil could be used as such as a modifier in woody perfume bases where the sharp, cedar-like note is not out of line, and where a rich, tea-like, herbaceous-woody undertone is wanted. For this type of perfume effects, the essential oil of Melaleuca Bracteata (see monograph) is preferable, and its odor is much more delicate. As a strange coincidence, the latter oil is a native of Australia; thus, we find the two strongest methyl eugenol-carrying essential oils originating in this area.

It is very likely, that Huon Pine Wood Oil will slowly disappear from the market on account of failing interest in this oil.

Hyacinth Absolute.

Probably originally from Asia Minor or the Balkans, the Hyacinthus Orientalis is now cultivated on a large scale in Holland, mainly for the production of bulbs which are exported to garden-owners all over the world. At a certain moment, there are substantial quantities of flowers available for extraction. In Holland, there is only one producer of importance, and this house probably produces 90 percent or more of all Hyacinth Absolute in the world. The annual world production in 1958 was estimated at 175 kilos. Extraction is performed either by the conventional two-step method via the concrète, or by the more recently developed adsorption method. The odorous principles are adsorbed on silicagel or prepared charcoal in a cylinder. The fragrance from the flowers is forced through this cylinder in an atmosphere of nitrogen or carbon dioxide. The gas acts as a carrier for the flower odor. In spite of the very limited production, Hyacinth Absolute is offered by a multitude of suppliers, and in a multitude of qualities, prices, etc. The appearance and odor varies too, and it is well-nigh impossible to give a description of a true, uncut absolute. Some perfumers even go so far as to state that, "if a product smells of hyacinths, it is definitely not a true hyacinth absolute!". Incidentally, very few flower oils will, undiluted and in a pure state, smell like the flower from which they are extracted. Dilutions down to 0.1 percent or even less will usually develop the true-to-nature odor.

Hyacinth Absolute is (usually) a reddish-brown or dark brown to greenish-brown, viscous liquid, and it has an intensely sweet, green-floral, but somewhat sharp and at first unpleasant odor; later in its tremendous tenacity, it tones down to a very hyacinth-like, floral and foliage-green fragrance.

The absolute could be used in a variety of floral fragrances, provided that it were available at a reasonable cost (it is offered at anything from $ 1000 to over $ 12,000 per kilo), and if it were readily available, uniform and reliable. The composing of an artificial hyacinth perfume base is still a favorite problem for many perfumers. Frequent adulteration of the commercial lots of

so-called hyacinth absolutes with narcissus absolute, violet leaf absolute, ylang-ylang, and a
wealth of synthetic materials, has only encouraged
perfumers to try composing their own hyacinth
base, rather than buy adulterated material.

Artificial hyacinth perfume bases may be composed from cinnamic alcohol, styrax products,
phenyl propyl alcohol, phenyl acetaldehyde,
phenyl ethyl alcohol, galbanum resinoid, ylang-
ylang oils, isoeugenol, floranol, tolyl acetate,
phenyl ethyl cinnamate, terpineol, hydroxycitronellal, methoxy phenyl butanone, amyl salicylate,
benzyl cyanide, benzyl formate, amyl cinnamic
aldehyde, indole, phenyl-ethyl dimethyl carbinol,
etc. etc.

To the author's opinion, the perfume industry
can do very well without a true (and unreasonably
expensive) **Hyacinth Absolute.**

Hyssop Oil.

Presumably originating in the Mediterranean area,
Hyssopus Officinalis has been known and cultivated as a culinary herb and for medicinal uses for
hundreds of years. The plant grows wild in the
coastal areas of the south of France, Italy,
Yugoslavia, U.S.S.R., etc., and is cultivated in
these countries and in Bulgaria, Hungary and
Holland for the purpose of distillation of its
essential oil. Hungary and France regularly produce small quantities of the oil by steam distillation of the overground parts of the plant, harvested
immediately prior to inflorescence.

Smaller quantities of oil are produced in Holland and Germany.

Hyssop Oil is a pale yellow or faintly greenish
yellow to almost colorless oil of a powerful,
somewhat sharp, but sweet-camphoraceous odor,
and with a warm-aromatic, spicy undertone. Its
flavor is warm and sweet, slightly burning or
biting, but rich aromatic and herbaceous-spicy.
The suggested use level is 0.10 to 0.40 mg%, and
the **Minimum Perceptible** is 0.03 to 0.05 mg%.

Hyssop Oil is used in flavor work, not only to
replace the herb in pickles, meat sauces and
seasonings, etc., but also to give bouquet to
alcoholic beverages, particularly the "chartreuse"
type of liqueur. In perfumery, the oil will induce
a rich body, warm and spicy-herbaceous notes and
personality or typical character to certain types
of fragrances, e.g. the citrus type colognes, fougères, ambres and light-aldehydic fragrances as

well as heavy, Oriental bases. Hyssop oil blends
well with citrus oils, lavender oil, rosemary,
myrtle, laurel leaf, sage and sage clary, amyl
salicylate, linalool, eugenol, geraniol, etc.

The oil is occasionally adulterated with cedarleaf oil, camphor oil or camphor oil fractions,
lavandin oil, myrtle oil, sage oil, etc. The annual
production of **Hyssop Oil** is very small, probably
less than one ton. It is not likely that production
will be increased as the herb has been known for
a very long time and still seems to lose in popularity almost continuously.

I

Illurin Balsam.

Synonyms: **Ilurin Balsam, Niger Balsam, "African
Copaiba".**

There are several products which are called
Illurin Balsam, although they are only occasionally offered on today's market. True "Illurin
balsam" is a natural oleoresin formed as a
physiological product in the trunk of certain
West African leguminosae, related to **Copaifera**
(see **Copaiba Balsam**). It is possible that **Daniella
Thurifera** is one of the parent trees to this "balsam".
The name **Illurin** is derived from the commercial
centre (**Ilorin**) of the southwestern corner of the
northern province of Nigeria. This big city is on
the Kano-Lagos road, but not on the river Niger
itself. The **Illurin Balsams** were usually shipped
to London from Lagos (on the "Niger coast").
Hence the name **Illurin** balsam or **Niger** balsam.

Another natural oleoresin, derived from a
related tree, is known as **Hardwickia Balsam,** and
occasionally sold as Niger balsam. The two
products are quite similar in appearance and odor.
See also **Gurjun Balsam.** A balsam (oleoresin) has
been obtained from the tree **Oxystigma Mannii**
years ago. This product served as a source of
beta-**Caryophyllene,** the main constituent of this
oleoresin.

Illurin Balsam is a dark amber colored to
brownish, viscous liquid, occasionally turbid or
opalescent. The odor is sweet-woody, balsamic,
very pleasant, uniform and tenacious. Certain lots
show more "burnt" or phenolic, tarlike odors than
others; however, as mentioned above, the product
is a physiological one, and it is not produced by

burning, boiling, heating, cutting or otherwise damaging the tree. The rough odor is probably due to a difference in origin. A number of related species of the tree grow in various parts of West Africa. Many of these trees are exploited for "balsam".

Illurin Balsam has become a scarce and rare item, but it could find use in perfumery as a blender for ionones and many other synthetic materials which may need a natural blender or "rounder-off". The oleoresin blends well with cedarwood, nitromusks, isobornylacetate, amyl salicylate, orris resin, vetiver oil, cinnamic alcohol, oakmoss products, lavandin oil, etc. etc. It could probably do well as an extender in low-cost perfumes for certain types of household products, insecticides, deodorants, industrial perfumes, etc.

Illurin balsam has served as an adulterant for **Copaiba Balsam,** but more recently, there have been cases where **Copaiba Balsam** has been sold as **Illurin Balsam.** This gives some indication about the scarcity of the African product.

The "balsam" contains a very high amount of essential oil which can be distilled from the "balsam" with steam. This oil is very rarely offered in a true and pure state. **Illurin Balsam Oil** is a pale amber or almost colorless liquid of a soft, mellow and pleasant, woody-sweet, later on somewhat dry odor of good tenacity. If available, the **Illurin Balsam Oil** would be interesting to use in the reconstruction of certain essential oils, e.g. spice oils, ylang-ylang, etc. The oil would be an excellent blender and extender in many bases where a high amount of synthetic components produce "sharp" notes or "rough" corners in the odor of the perfume base. However, with **Copaiba Balsam Oil** readily available at a very reasonable cost, there will probably never be a substantial demand for **Illurin Balsam Oil** although the latter has definite advantages in odor softness and tenacity over the former.

Inchigrass Oil.

From a species of the south Indian grass **Cymbopogon,** closely related to palmarosa- and gingergrass (see monographs), an essential oil is produced locally by primitive steam distillation.

Most of the local Hindi or Sanskritic names for the grass mean "gingergrass", referring to the fact that the fresh green grass produces a ginger-(root)-like odor when rubbed between the fingers.

It is interesting to note that the leaves of the gingerplant smell fresh, lemony, citronella-verbena-like when rubbed between the fingers. The two grasses are not botanically related. The yield of oil is fair, almost equal to the yield from Java-citronella grass. **Inchigrass Oil** is a pale yellow or pale amber colored liquid of fresh, sweet citronella-palmarosa-like odor with a tealeaf-like, rich-herbaceous undertone. The latter note is quite predominant, or even unpleasant, in certain lots of the oil. These types of inchigrass oil have some resemblance to perilla oil in respect to odor.

There are a number of varieties of the plant, all growing in the southern parts of India, and various types of **Inchigrass Oil** have been offered. The more camphoraceous-bitter smelling oils would certainly be less popular in the case that **Inchigrass Oil** should become commonly available on the European and American markets. Inchigrass oil is used locally for the scenting of soaps and detergents, household articles, etc. Only very occasionally it reaches the outside markets; accordingly, it has not found any place in American or European perfumery.

The oil might serve as a modifier along with palmarosa oil, citronella, lemongrass, eucalyptus staigeriana, eucalyptus citriodora, leptospermum citratum and other soap perfume materials of the "fresh-lemony" type.

See also **Cymbopogon Connatus.**

Iva Oil.

Practically unknown today, and probably never returning to perfume or flavor creation, is the essential oil which is steam distilled from the flowers of **Achillea Moschata.** The plant which is a Compositae member grows wild in central Europe, and it has been used in Switzerland and France for various local specialties of alcoholic beverages, particularly the "old" types of **Benedictine** and **Chartreuse** liqueurs (both of which are of French origin). Often more than forty different herbs, roots, spices, etc. go into the very complex "tincture" upon which the aromas of these liqueurs are based.

Iva Oil is, like many other essential oils from members of the Compositae family, blue or greenish-blue when freshly distilled, but it fades considerably on ageing. The odor too, varies significantly according to the age of the oil. Generally, the odor is warm-herbaceous, camphoraceous, with a similarity to hop oil and tansy oil, while it usually is difficult or impossible to perceive the "musky" notes which have given the name of **Musk Yarrow** to the plant. It is conceivable that the unpleasant, and to some people almost "animal" notes from an increasing amount of valeric acid in older oils can be responsible for the "musk" name. The related plant, **Achillea Millefolium**, the very common **Yarrow Herb**, is described in this work under **Milfoil**.

Oil of **Iva** could find use in perfumery to introduce rare and so-called "intriguing" notes in citrus colognes, fougères, herbaceous fragrances, etc.

With the present production at zero level, it is inconceivable that **Iva Oil** will find extensive use in future perfumery.

Ivy Leaf Absolute.

From the leaves of **Hedera Helix** and other species related to this climbing vine, a concrète is produced by hydrocarbon extraction. The concrète, in turn, is processed further to an absolute by the conventional method (see **Absolute**, Part One of this book). Ivy grows wild all over Europe: in the forests, and along the borderline of woods, and it is quite common in the United States too. Commercial extraction of the leaves for perfumery use is undertaken in France, and occasionally in Germany. The product is known in France under the name of **Absolu de Lierre**. The **Ivy** plant is an evergreen and it is the botanical symbol of constant affection.

Ivy Leaf Absolute is a dark green, semi-solid mass with an intensively herbaceous-green, or bark-green odor, and a rich, sweet-bitter foliage-extract undertone. These odor characteristics will immediately place the ivy leaf absolute among the most interesting "green" or "foliage"-like natural materials. It is used in a number of bases and compounds, particularly in those where a heavy, not expressly floral, green note is desired, e.g. as a modifier with violet leaf absolute, hop absolute, as a naturalizer for dibutyl sulfide, amyl heptine carbonate, beta-gamma hexenyl acetate, phenoxy acetaldehyde, cuminaldehyde, methyl phenyl carbinyl acetate, etc. It is also useful in forest blends, fougères, chypres, etc., or in the reproduction of certain natural materials, e.g. oakmoss extracts. **Ivy Leaf Absolute** blends well with oakmoss

products, mimosa absolute, linalool, nerol, galbanum resinoid, cyclamen aldehyde, amyl salicylate, etc. and it is particularly interesting in moss fragrances and pine needle fantasy bases.

This absolute is produced on a very limited scale only, but there are ample quantities of natural raw material present in nature. Since the plant is not cultivated beyond the indoor scale, collection of leaves involves quite a bit of handwork and, accordingly, the absolute has not yet become too common.

J

Jaborandi Oil.

Although very rarely found on the essential oil market, this oil deserves brief mention. The parent plant is very important in medicine since the alkaloid, **Pilocarpine**, is extracted from the leaves of **Pilocarpus Jaborandi**, a woody shrub native to Brazil. A number of varieties exist in other South American countries, e.g. Paraguay, and in Cuba, Martinique, and Guadeloupe in the West Indies, and in Central America.

Occasionally, an essential oil is steam distilled from the leaves prior to the extraction of the alcaloid. This oil is thus a by-product, and is not regularly produced. When the alcaloid is extracted from the pulverized leaves with ethyl alcohol (and no previous steaming of the leaves), some essential oil will separate when the extract is evaporated. The essential oil must be removed in order to facilitate further processing of the alcaloid.

Jaborandi Oil is a yellowish to orange-yellow liquid of a sweet-herbaceous, somewhat fruity, not exactly pleasant odor; the odor tones out later on in a tea-like, somewhat bitter, but quite pleasant undertone. The author declines from giving any comments on the flavor, although this usage has been mentioned and described in other works. The presence of **Methyl Nonyl Ketone** (see also **Rue Oil**), and the fact that the plant belongs to the family of rutaceae, places the oil among possible skin-irritants. Accordingly, the author would not recommend it for use in flavors. In perfumery, **Jaborandi Oil** could be used as a "piquant" additive in colognes, fougères, aldehydic bases, etc., if the amount of this oil is kept at a safe level. The very poor availability of the oil, however, prevents its extensive use.

Jasmin Absolute from Châssis.

See also monograph on **Absolute** in Part One of this work.

When the flowers are removed from the "châssis", and the fragrance-saturated fat (= the **Pommade**) is scraped off, to be extracted with alcohol, there still remains not only a certain amount of fragrant fat on the removed flowers, but some odorous matter is still contained in these flowers themselves. In order to isolate and concentrate this matter, the flowers are extracted with a hydrocarbon solvent, usually petroleum ether. The petroleum ether extract is evaporated (to an intermediate "concrète from châssis"), and the evaporation residue is extracted with alcohol. In turn the alcohol is removed from this extract, and what is left is called **Jasmin Absolute from Châssis**. This is actually a by-product of the enfleurage process, and the annual amount of available châssis-absolute is obviously very small. Furthermore, it is constantly decreasing with the lessening use of the enfleurage method.

Jasmin Absolute from Châssis is a viscous, very dark orange or chocolate-brown liquid; it has a peculiar odor, only faintly reminiscent of jasmin absolute from concrète or of the jasmin flower itself. It resembles somewhat the odor of orange flower absolute: warm, sweet, heavy, tenacious, fatty-floral, slightly herbaceous and deep-fruity, but less indolic-sharp than the odor of the jasmin flower itself.

In use, it cannot replace the absolute from concrète, but it does find application in floral bases where a non-indolic jasmin effect is called for. Its extremely rich and tenacious body lends a natural quality to perfume compositions where synthetic materials may tend to produce "rough" notes.

Jasmin Absolute from Concrète.

Of the two main types of **Jasmin Absolute**, the one made from concrète is the most important by far. It is produced by alcohol-extraction of jasmin concrète (see monograph). This extraction process is usually carried out in France who supplies most of the commercially available **Jasmin Absolute**. However, substantial quantities of absolute are produced by the larger consumers

who purchase jasmin concrète, sometimes from several different sources other than French in order to obtain a uniform quality which can be reproduced year after year. These consumers will themselves process the concrète into jasmin absolute according to their special needs. Minor quantities of jasmin absolute are produced in Italy, Morocco, Egypt, India, Formosa, and China. In India, the jasmin flowers are known as **Chameli** or **Chambeli**. The so-called **Chameli-Attar** is produced from jasmin flowers by extraction with hot fat.

Jasmin Absolute from Concrète is a dark orange (on ageing reddish-brown), somewhat viscous liquid, and it possesses an intensely floral, warm, rich and highly diffusive odor with a peculiar waxy-herbaceous, oily-fruity and tea-like undertone. The odor and the nuances in the undertone varies according to the origin, production, age and method of purification (from the concrète).

Jasmin absolute represents one of the most striking examples of nature's ability to round off and conceal—or unsurpassably utilize—the odor-effect of very simple odorants, e. g. benzyl acetate and linalool, the main constituents of jasmin absolute (in respect to quantity). Most perfumers have, at one time or another in their experience, tried to duplicate the jasmin fragrance by relying upon literature information as to the chemical composition of jasmin absolute (a very unartistic approach to a perfumery problem!). The perfumers will no doubt agree that the problem is not solved, nor is it hardly even approached in this way. The odor of a mixture of benzyl acetate, linalool, benzyl alcohol, methyl anthranilate, indole, etc. in the analyzed proportions is far from representative of the jasmin fragrance. More recently, a number of low-percentage components have been identified in the jasmin absolute, and these findings have greatly contributed to the improvement of artificial jasmin flower oil bases. A large number of synthetic materials, some of them chemically related to the jasmones, have been developed, and these are of great help to the creative perfumer in his attempts to reproduce the much wanted jasmin effect at a lower cost. A few natural perfume materials with no relationship whatever to jasmin (apart from the following) can be incorporated in artificial jasmin bases, and they lend striking true-to-nature effects: The deep-herbaceous tea-like notes from tealeaf or maté-extracts, the waxy or honeylike sweetness from beeswax extracts, the grassy fattiness from perilla oil or gingergrass oil, the warm tobacco-like and herbaceous notes from chamomile oils, the fatty-cresylic notes from high-boiling ethers of para-cresol (iso-butyrate, salicylate, caprylate, etc.), the tobacco-leaf-like notes from esters of nicotinic acid (methyl or propyl), are known examples from successful artificial jasmin bases.

Jasmin Absolute from Concrète is used in such a multitude and variety of perfumes that it is hardly possible to establish a rule for its use. "No perfume without jasmin" is an old saying, and this is not far from the fact. The jasmin-rose complex forms the more important part or "fond" of numerous "grands parfums" as well as quite ordinary perfumes and bases. The floral note, when required, is provided by the addition of jasmin absolute or any kind of a jasmin base in 8 out of 10 cases. And the practising perfume student will be surprised when he learns how little jasmin absolute he has to use in order to obtain just enough of a "floral" note. With that fact in consideration, even a true jasmin absolute is rarely too expensive to use.

The annual production of jasmin absolute from concrète can be roughly estimated from the known production of jasmin concrète which is in the order of magnitude of 10 metric tons. Only a minor portion of the concrète is used as such; the balance is processed into absolute, totalling about 4 metric tons per year, including private productions. The value of the total world production of extracted jasmin products can be estimated at about 5 million U.S. dollars.

Jasmin absolute is frequently adulterated. Its high cost seems to tempt certain suppliers and producers beyond their moral resistance. Additions of indole, amyl cinnamic aldehyde, ylang-ylang fractions, jasmin absolute from châssis (see monograph), artificial jasmin bases, various synthetic jasmones and homologues, etc. occur quite frequently in commercial lots of jasmin absolute from concrète. The quality of the various absolutes from French, Italian, Moroccan, Formosan, Corsican, Egyptian or other concrètes affects the quality of the corresponding absolutes. The method of processing concrètes into absolutes is an art and a science which demands experience, skill and general "know-how". Accordingly, the evaluation of jasmin absolutes prior to the purchase of this expensive and important raw material, is a very important part of the perfumer's job.

Jasmin Absolute from Pommade.

Also known as **Jasmin Absolute from Enfleurage**, this product is obtained by alcohol extraction of the fat from the trays in the enfleurage process (see **Pommade**, Part One of this book). The application of the **Enfleurage** process to the jasmin flowers is an old and well-known method of extraction, but it has become increasingly impractical or uneconomical due to the higher cost of labor. The method is employed almost exclusively in the Grasse region of France where the industry and its people have a century-old experience and inherited skill for flower treatment. It is estimated that less than 10 percent of the world's crop of jasmin flowers (from cultivations and regular fields) are treated by enfleurage, the balance being extracted with hydrocarbon solvents to yield jasmin concrète. Minor quantities of jasmin flowers are treated in India by liquid fat extraction (hot oil infusion) to yield the so-called "attars", local flower oil concentrates.

Jasmin Absolute from Pommade is a dark orange colored to dark reddish-brown, viscous liquid with a highly true-to-nature jasmin flower odor. By the nature of things, this perfume material has no odor of solvent, but upon ageing it may develop a slightly fatty off-note due to the extraction-fat. Modern anti-oxidants usually keep the fat from becoming rancid.

The jasmin pommade-absolute varies in odor according to the method of extraction, (and this process is a delicate one!), the quality of the flower material, the age after picking, the location of the field, etc. Generally, the indole note is more pronounced in the pommade-absolute than in the absolute from concrète.

The use of the pommade-absolute is similar to that of the latter product, but the poor availability of the pommade-absolute prevents general use. The very good yield in the enfleurage process is one of the main reasons for continued production of this fine concentrate of the fragrance of the jasmin flower. Jasmin absolute from pommade is likely to disappear slowly from the perfumery market because of the extremely elaborate process and huge amount of human hand-work involved in the production of this 200-year old natural perfume material.

Jasmin Concrète.

From the flowers of **Jasminum Officinale**, mainly

from the cultivated variety (var. **Grandiflorum**), is produced one of the most important, if not *the* most important natural perfume raw material. Jasmin concrète is prepared by petroleum ether extraction, occasionally by extraction with other hydrocarbon solvents, of the mature flowers.

The plant originated in the mountainous region of northwest India, and has been known for thousands of years in the East. Its fragrance is immensely popular in all parts of the world, but seems particularly attractive to the people in the countries where the jasmin plant grows wild or cultivated.

Jasmin concrète is produced in Morocco, Italy, France (and Corsica), Egypt, Guinea, Comoro islands, India, Syria (Lebanon), China, Formosa, Japan, etc. In respect to quantity, Morocco and Italy are the leading producers of jasmin concrète. The concrète must be produced very near the growing area, but the **Absolute** (see **Jasmin Absolute from Concrète**) can be prepared from the concrète anywhere and at a later time.

Thus, not all the growing areas produce jasmin absolute. In fact, very few do, partly because most large consumers will buy jasmin concrète and prepare their own jasmin absolute according to their needs and specifications.

The extraction with petroleum ether is carried out with the application of gentle heat, but certain processes (e.g. butane extraction) are carried out at room temperature. **Butaflor Jasmin** is an absolute-type, produced by butane extraction of the flowers and subsequent alcohol-washing of the concrète (see **Jasmin Absolute** in Part Two of this book, and **Absolute** in Part One of the book).

Jasmin Concrète is a solid, waxy, reddish-orange, dark orange, yellowish-orange or brownish mass. The odor varies according to type, origin, solvent used, etc., but is generally warm, intensely floral, somewhat indolic-sharp, but immensely rich and tenacious. There are various types of herbaceous-sweet, fatty green, tea-like or "bread"-like, almost "broth"-like odors found in various qualities and types of jasmin concrète. However, the odor is more correctly evaluated in the jasmin absolute which is free from the waxes and other alcohol-insoluble and practically odorless materials. The waxes act as powerful odor-depressors, and the characteristic radiation or diffusion of the odor of the absolute will not appear until the waxes are removed.

Jasmin Concrète contains approximately 50 per-

cent alcohol-soluble matter ($=$ **Jasmin Absolute**, see monograph), and part of the evaluation of a jasmin concrète should be devoted to the determination of the content of alcohol-soluble matter. For a quick evaluation of a concrète, it is often sufficient to make up a 10 percent solution of the concrète in a highly purified, fixed (vegetable) oil, and compare this solution to a 5 percent solution of an acceptable jasmin absolute in the same solvent. This test will give the perfumer a fair impression of the strength of the two materials. As was mentioned previously in this monograph, it is customary for large consumers and connoisseurs to purchase their own concrètes and process them into jasmin absolute.

Jasmin Concrète is also used in soap perfumes where its effect can be utilized at the most surprisingly low concentrations. This fact makes jasmin concrète useful even in the so-called medium-cost soap perfumes. Its effect is mainly that of "rounding-off" rough chemical notes, e.g. from benzyl acetate, tolyl acetate, amyl cinnamic aldehyde, methyl anthranilate, etc., lending body and naturalness and a warm, floral undertone. The concrète is particularly useful in soap perfumes where high amounts of these and other synthetic materials are present and would tend to produce a sharp, rough odor; jasmin concrète is an excellent modifier in chypre bases for soap, violet bases (where it blends well with mimosa concrète) and numerous floral bases.

Jasmin Concrète is not infrequently adulterated. The most common additive is the "spent wax" from the production of jasmin absolute. The odor of jasmin concrète is perceptibly impaired by comparatively small additions of these almost odorless waxes. A "special grade" of **Benzyl Acetate** is offered by a few perfume houses who distil benzyl acetate over a certain amount of "spent waxes" from the production of jasmin absolute. This benzyl acetate is particularly suitable for the creation of artificial jasmin bases. Obviously, it is necessary to start with a high-grade chlorine-free benzyl acetate in order to obtain a really soft and floral type of this ester.

Jonquil Absolute.

A very scarce and, partly for that reason, very rarely used perfume material is the flower absolute from the **Narcissus Jonquilla**. This very fragrant narcissus species probably originated in Asia

27: Hundreds of acres of **Geranium** plants ready for cutting at Khemisset, Morocco.

(Fot. S. Arctander, 1960)

28: The flowering **Geranium** plant at harvest time in north-western Morocco. *(Fot. S. Arctander, 1960)*

Minor, and it is cultivated in the Grasse region of southern France and in Morocco for the purpose of extracting perfume oil. The latter area seems likely to become the center of production very soon.

The flowers are extracted with petroleum ether to yield a concrète which in turn is processed to an absolute. Annual production has been as high as 100 kilos, but is presently only a fraction of this figure. In Morocco, the bulk of the flowers are processed into a concrète, while in France, the local flowers are either processed into concrète and absolute, or they are treated with hot oil (digestion) or with cold fat (enfleurage to produce a pommade). These products are further washed to yield alcohol-soluble products (see **Infusion** and **Pommade** in Part One of this book). The enfleurage yields a lighter-colored product, but it is worthwhile mentioning that the yield is poor as distinguished from jasmin and tuberose, where the flowers actually continue to produce perfume oil even while they are dying on the grease-plates (the "châssis"). Most of the jonquil absolutes available today are prepared by the simple and economical two-step extraction via the concrète.

Jonquil Absolute from Concrète is a viscous, dark brown or dark orange to olive-brown liquid of heavy, honeylike, deep-sweet floral odor with a strong green undertone and a somewhat bitter, very tenacious dryout note. The odor bears great similarity to the fragrance of longoza and tuberose, and a remote resemblance to hyacinth. Jonquil absolute blends excellently with jasmin, violet leaf absolute, orange flower absolute, longoza, ylang-ylang and other heavy florals, or with powerful green-floral absolutes. Hydroxycitronellal, iso-eugenol, cyclamal, linalyl acetate, cinnamic alcohol, rhodinol, methyl para-toluate, undecanolide, phenylethyl phenyl acetate, amyl phenyl acetate, n-propenyl methyl anthranilate, tolyl acetate, methyl benzoate, heliotropyl acetone, alpha ionone, etc., are examples of synthetic materials which are frequently used in artificial reproductions of the jonquil fragrance.

On account of its high cost and scarcity, **Jonquil Absolute** is frequently adulterated, e.g. with narcissus absolute, ylang-ylang absolute, benzoin Siam "resin absolute", longoza absolute, Peru balsam oil, everlasting absolute or helichrysum oil, vanilla absolute, etc. and various synthetic materials.

Juniperberry Oil.

Commercial **Juniper Berry Oil** is produced by two methods:

The best oil is steam distilled (or steam-and-water distilled) from the crushed, dried or partially dried, ripe berries (fruits). Occasionally water distillation is used. The greater part of all commercial juniperberry oil, however, is derived from the fermented fruits as a by-product of the central European juniper-brandy manufacturing. It should be noted that juniper berries (fruits) contain certain amounts of fixed oil, occasionally called "juniper oil" (see **Juniperberry "Resinoid"**).

The shrub, **Juniperus Communis**, grows wild all over central and southern Europe, southwest Asia, northern Asia, North Africa and North America. The best berries are collected in northern Italy, Austria, Czechoslovakia, Hungary, Yugoslavia, and France. Lower grades are collected in Germany, Poland, U.S.S.R., Portugal, Spain, Bulgaria, India, and Scandinavia.

The gin-distillers are also large consumers of juniper fruits. Some of them still make their own distillates from juniperberry tinctures rather than using a sesquiterpeneless juniperberry oil which never gives the same "body" of flavor to the beverage. The actual production of steam-distilled juniperberry oil is surprisingly small. Substantial quantities of so-called **Juniperberry Oil** are produced by another method:

The dextrose-containing juniper fruits are fermented in order to produce a popular beverage. An essential oil can be produced from the fermentation mass. This distillate, which is a mixture of flavored alcohol, water and essential oil (mainly monoterpenes and other fractions, insoluble in alcohol), is redistilled, and thus the flavored, low-proof alcohol (the beverage) is separated from the terpenic oil fraction. The latter constitutes commercial "**Juniperberry Oil**".

Juniperberry Oil (steam distilled from the fruits) is a water-white or very pale yellow, mobile oil, having a fresh, yet warm, rich-balsamic, woody-sweet and pine-needle-like odor. In fact, the oil of **Pinus Pumilio** (which grows in juniper-areas, too) resembles juniperberry oil very much in odor characteristics. The oil derived from the fermented fruits usually has a more turpentine-like, pinene-like odor and little or no balsamic sweetness. Its tenacity is inferior to that of the "true" oil. The fermentation oil is not suitable for flavor purposes. The flavor of steam distilled juniperberry oil is warm, slightly bitter-aromatic, balsamic and rich. The bitterness is quite persistent at all levels of dilution. It is quite typical of many perfume materials that they may present odors which give an impression of sweetness, while their flavor reveals an almost prohibitive bitterness. The suggested use level for a good juniperberry oil from selected fruit material is about 0.30 mg%. At this concentration, there is still a distinct and characteristic bitterness along with the aroma of the oil. The **Minimum Perceptible** is 0.05 to 0.08 mg%. The actual use level in alcoholic beverages is considerably higher than the above figure. High concentration of alcohol impairs the sense of taste.

Juniperberry Oil is used in perfumery for its fresh-balsamic notes, as a modifier for various pine needle oils (with which it blends very well), with citrus oils in room spray perfumes, in ambres, fougères, chypres, after-shave fragrances, spice compositions, colognes, etc. Labdanum absolute is an excellent fixative for juniperberry oil. Other fixatives and blenders are mastic, opopanax, fir needle absolute, oakmoss products, elemi resinoid, illurin balsam, cypress oil, sage clary, borneol, nopyl acetate, abitol, lavandin oil, lavandin concrète, lovage oil, benzoin resinoid, toluresinoid, etc.

In flavors, it is customary to use a sesquiterpeneless oil, produced from a high-grade true juniperberry oil (steam distilled from the fruits). The natural (total) juniperberry oil is poorly soluble in ethyl alcohol, and the oil has a pronounced bitter taste which is often translated as "turpentine-like" by the layman. Even better for flavors is a **Juniper Berry Distillate**, e.g. a distilled, concentrated tincture in low-proof alcohol which eliminates the terpenes. As a shortcut and poorer edition of the latter product, a **Juniper Berry Aroma Distillate** may be produced from juniper berry oil, alcohol and water. An aroma-distillate is obtained by subsequent distillation and rectification of the low-proof alcoholic distillate. In flavor quality, it is inferior to the distillate made from the berries (compare: production of gin).

Juniperberry Oil is very frequently adulterated. More justly, one could say that commercial juniperberry oil is rarely the true distillate from the berries. The most frequent additive (or substitute) is, obviously, the poor oil from the fermentation process. This oil is commercially offered under the label of juniperberry oil. Other adulterants are pinene, camphene, turpentine oil

fractions, juniper wood oil (see monograph), juniper twig oil, etc. Only a thorough organoleptic evaluation will reveal a poor or adulterated oil among samples of true oils, produced from the freshly crushed fruits by steam distillation.

An essential oil is distilled in Yugoslavia from fruits and twigs of **Juniperus Smreka**. The odor of this oil is somewhat lighter than that of true juniper berry oil, less ambra-sweet, less rich on a dryout. Oil of juniperus smreka is produced on a very limited scale and not yet widely known outside Yugoslavia.

Juniperberry Oil, terpeneless and sesquiterpeneless.

This oil is preferably produced from a high-grade true **Juniperberry Oil**, derived from juniper fruits by steam distillation (see **Juniperberry Oil**, previous monograph). The deterpenation may be either complete or partial; various methods of removing the monoterpenes and sesquiterpenes are described in Part One of this book (see **Terpeneless Oils**). The greater part of the monoterpenes may be removed by distillation in vacuum, but since some of the valuable flavor principles of the oil have boiling points only slightly in excess of 200°C. at 760 mm, it is advisable not to "push" the vacuum distillation too far. The monoterpenes distil at 160 to 185°C. (760 mm). At good vacuum (e.g. 1 mm Hg.-pressure or lower), the differences in boiling point are very small and the hazard of losing valuable flavor principles considerably increased.

Furthermore, the partially deterpenized oils have a pronounced tendency of resinifying within a comparatively short time, while the "absolute" (terpeneless) oils are more stable. Selective cold-extraction (liquid-liquid) of the oxygenated constituents from the partially deterpenized oil may lead to a totally deterpenized oil. Various patents cover the methods of removing the mono- and sesquiterpenes with the application of little or no heat, thus avoiding the detrimental effect of a prolonged fractional distillation of the oil. The yield of totally terpeneless, sesquiterpeneless oil from a good natural oil is usually less than five percent. The terpenes are almost worthless; consequently, the terpeneless oil is quite expensive. It presents the advantage of being soluble in low-proof alcohol, and it is stable against oxidation and resinification when kept cool, dark or in alcoholic solution. The oil is used in flavors for alcoholic beverages, particularly for gin and "Steinhäger" types, furthermore in the complex liqueurs, e.g. benedictine, D.O.M., etc. Interesting modifications of the juniperberry flavor are obtained with terpeneless lime oil, spice oils, angelica root oil, etc. The average use level would be about 0.10 to 0.30 mg%, while the **Minimum Perceptible** is 0.05 to 0.08 mg%. It appears from these figures that the actual flavor strength of the terpeneless, sesquiterpeneless juniperberry oil is only about twice the strength of a good natural juniperberry oil, although the material concentration may be as high as 30 times. The two flavors are, however, distinctly different and there is no doubt that the flavor or the deterpenized oil is superior to that of the natural oil, by far.

In perfumery, this oil is occasionally used to introduce a balsamic-sweet, almost ambra-like note, e.g. in modern aldehydic fantasy-perfumes, ambres, "powdery" fragrances, Oriental bases, high-class pine needle fragrances or forest blends, etc. It blends well with aliphatic aldehydes, cinnamic alcohol, cypress oil (tail fractions), cedrenol and its derivatives, fir needle absolute, labdanum products, ionones and methylionones (particularly the so-called "delta"-methylionone which is beta-iso-methyl-ionone), macrocyclic musks, nitromusks, oakmoss products, heliotropine, nerol, etc.

Terpeneless, Sesquiterpeneless Juniperberry Oil is usually a somewhat viscous, pale yellow or pale amber-colored liquid of intensely sweet, balsamic-resinous, yet fresh and somewhat fruity odor. The various methods of deterpenization produce oils of quite different appearance and organoleptic virtues. The oil is occasionally adulterated with deterpenized oils of pinus pumilio or of cypress. **Mastic Oil** (see monograph on **Mastic**) could be used, but it is too scarce and too expensive for this purpose.

Juniperberry "Resinoid".

A few European (mainly French) manufacturers of perfumery raw materials offer a product which is extracted from the dried, ripe fruit of **Juniperus Communis**, the juniper tree (see monograph on **Juniper Berry Oil**). One producer will label his material "**Juniper Berry Resinoid**", while another may call it "**Juniper Berry Concrète**", etc. According to our definitions (see Part One of the present book), an extraction of juniperberries with a hydrocarbon solvent will yield a concrète since the fruits contain a certain proportion of waxy or fatty matter (fixed oil) and only insignificant amounts of resins. The botanical material is a harvested, live material, not an exudation. Accordingly, the term "resinoid" is misleading. However, the commercial product is usually transformed into a resinous, viscous and sticky substance by the addition of natural or synthetic "resins". The viscous matter in commercial juniperberry "resinoid" may thus be an artificial replacement for the fixed oil which has been eliminated during the extraction. When juniperberries are extracted with a hydrocarbon solvent, the extract may contain 4 to 8 times as much resin as it contains of essential oil. To produce a pourable extract, the manufacturers add certain diluents, high-boiling odorless solvents, plasticizers, etc.

The perfumery effect of a good juniperberry oil, particularly that of a monoterpeneless oil, has inevitably tempted the manufacturers—or perfumers—to produce an extract from the fruits. The extracts are produced in France and Hungary. Reports on the Hungarian production and suggestions for the use of these extracts have been published in perfumery literature during 1959.

Juniperberry "Resinoid" (juniperberry **Concrète**) is a viscous syrupy substance or a semi-solid mass, hardly pourable at room temperature. It is clear and olive-green of color, homogeneous and attractive of appearance. Its odor will usually present a topnote of the solvent (benzene or petroleum ether) which can be "aired" out. The beautiful, rich, balsamic-sweet, delightfully ambre-like fragrance of the resinoid is, however, of a surprisingly poor tenacity.

Juniperberry concrète is an interesting material which can be used with advantage in chypres, Oriental bases, high-class pine needle fragrances or forest notes, ambres and aldehydic bases, etc. It blends extremely well with labdanum absolutes, benzoin, opopanax, sage clary, galbanum, cinnamates in general, oakmoss products, cedarwood derivatives, vetiver and sandalwood oils, methylionones, etc.

The present production of **Juniperberry Concrète** ("resinoid") is negligible.

Juniperus Macrocarpa.

The essential oil from the heartwood of **Juniperus Macrocarpa** is produced on a limited scale in Yugoslavia where it serves as a local cedarwood oil type for soap perfumes, detergents, disinfectants, etc. Small quantities of this oil are exported to other European countries and to the U.S.A. The oil has little or nothing to offer to the perfumer who already has two or more of the readily available cedarwood oils at his disposal.

Juniper Wood Oil.

Although this material is rarely found as a true essential oil, it deserves some attention. A number of oils are offered in Europe under the above name, but most likely none of them are true steam distillates from the wood and twigs of **Juniperus Communis**, the same tree which supply us with fruits (see **Juniperberry Oil**). From an olfactory point of view, the best "juniper wood oils" that the author has seen were very similar to good or fair commercial juniperberry oil. Most often, however, the so-called wood oils were merely berry oils which had been diluted with up to six or nine times the amount of turpentine oil, alpha pinene or mixtures containing cypress oil, etc.

According to private communication to the author, juniper wood oil is frequently produced by co-distillation of juniper berries, twigs and perhaps wood, with turpentine oil.

The commercially offered oils were all pale yellow or practically water-white, mobile liquids of sweet-balsamic, fresh-turpentine-like odor and of bitter, burning flavor. Juniper wood oil has little or no use in perfumes and flavors, but it is still used in veterinary medicine. The oil is usually offered by producers in Portugal, Hungary or France. In Yugoslavia, the wood from **Juniperus Oxycedrus** is distilled. The oil is colorless and of turpentine-like juniper odor. The fruits from this tree are occasionally distilled and the resulting oil offered as juniperberry oil. It is inferior to true juniperberry oil in respect to odor and flavor.

Juniper Tar is produced by destructive distillation of wood from **Juniperus Oxycedrus**. The product is described under its commercial name, **Cade Oil**.

K

Kaempferia Galanga.

In order to avoid confusion with true galanga oil (see monograph), the above essential oil is mentioned under its botanical name.

Kaempferia Galanga is a small tropical plant of the ginger family; it is cultivated quite commonly throughout India and Indonesia, partly for the production of essential oil from the rhizomes of the plant, partly for use as a local spice.

The rhizomes (underground stems) are steam distilled in India to yield a yellowish or pale amber-colored, somewhat viscous oil which deposits a substantial amount of crystals on standing. The crystals have been identified as **Ethyl para-Methoxy Cinnamate**. In this respect, the oil is quite similar to the east Indian **Ekangi Oil** from the rhizomes of **Hedychium Spicatum** (see monograph on **Sanna Oil**), a close relative to **Longoza**.

Judging from the odor of the comminuted rhizomes, it is conceivable that the steam distillation affects the volatile part of the material and that the above ester is not present as such in the botanical material itself. The author has not seen any type of extracted product from the rhizomes of **Kaempferia Galanga**, but it is most likely that such extracts would smell more like the rhizomes than does the oil.

Oil of **Kaempferia Galanga** has a sweet-woody, warm, balsamic, somewhat spicy odor of great tenacity. The flavor is less pleasant, camphoraceous, burning, yet very rich and aromatic.

The oil is not regularly produced, and it is rarely offered outside its country of origin. The rhizome is commercially available and is known in Indonesia under the name of "tjikoer" or "kentjoer". It is occasionally used as a replacement for curcuma, but it cannot introduce the same flavor (and color) effects in a curry powder as can the curcuma rhizome.

See also **Curcuma, Galanga, Longoza, Sanna** and **Zedoaria**.

Karna.

Various products, derived from the flowers of local **Citrus** varieties in Pakistan, are used as domestic perfume materials for cosmetic preparations. **Karna** products represent some of the most important perfume materials produced in Pakistan. They could be considered as equivalent to enfleurage products of orange flowers in Europe and Africa. The process of enfleurage is, however, not applied to orange flowers on a commercial scale in Europe or Africa.

Karna flowers are extracted with various oil-containing seeds, e.g. rape seed, sarson seed, sesame seed, etc. Kept under pressure, the flowers release their odorous substances to the fixed oil in a process resembling the "infusion" in oils.

Karna Flowers have been steam distilled experimentally to yield an essential oil. This oil is a pale green or olive-green, mobile liquid of fresh citrusy, somewhat bitter-leafy odor with a sweet and floral undertone. The odor resembles that of lemon petitgrain oil. Karna Oil is not yet available in commercial quantities outside of Pakistan and India.

If it were made readily available, Karna Oil could find some application in European and American perfumery for colognes, floral fragrances (interesting topnote for muguet), aldehydic bases, ambres, etc. It blends well with citrus oils, lavender, labdanum, linalyl acetate, citronellol, heliotropine, and numerous other natural and synthetic materials.

Karo-Karoundé.

The flowers of a small west-African shrub related to gardenia, have been used by the natives for a long time to perfume linen, hair oils, baths, etc. It is just one of many west African fragrant flowers, but this plant happens to grow in the region of Guinea where several essential oils have already been produced on a large, commercial scale by French companies.

The plant Leptactina Senegambica grows wild in the mountainous region called Fouta-Djalon in Guinea, southeast of the Senegambia. The shrub is found all the way up in Gambia, and south to the old Ivory Coast. The author also found the plant further south in Congo and other areas of the former A.E.F. However, only at Labé and Mamou in Guinea are there extraction installations capable of processing flowers into concrètes. Occasionally, the concrète is further processed to an absolute by the French people in Guinea, but most often the concrète is shipped to Grasse to be processed. Unfortunately, this is the first step toward the appearance of obviously "compounded" and "sophisticated" absolutes of such rare exotic materials, and it is regrettable that one must state that true karo-karoundé absolutes are offered very rarely from Grasse. The true absolute is, furthermore, very expensive, usually somewhat higher in price than jasmin absolute from concrète.

The plant is known by the natives under the name of "kaulathi" or "fara-koronte". The locally produced, petroleum ether extracted concrète is a solid, soft-waxy, dark orange-brown mass, while the absolute is a viscous liquid of chocolate-brown or dark orange-brown color. Its odor is intensely floral, deep-herbaceous and sweet, but somewhat nauseating. The undertone is slightly fruity, very tenacious, and it fades out in a delightful floral-woody, faintly green-herbaceous note. There is a certain similarity to orange flower water absolute, jonquil and jasmin pommade absolute with a peculiar bitter-almond-like undertone.

Karo-Karoundé Absolute blends excellently with the above materials and with ylang-ylang, narcissus, isoeugenol, cinnamic alcohol, styrax resinoid, galbanum resinoid, undecanolide, clove bud oil or clove bud absolute, phenylethyl alcohol, ar-methyl phenylethyl alcohol, methyl cinnamic alcohol, neryl acetate, heliotropine, mimosa and cassie absolutes, hexyl cinnamic aldehyde, tea leaf absolute, etc. The absolute of karo-karoundé gives very interesting effects in hyacinth, gardenia, stephanotis and tuberose bases and it can be used in a multitude of other heavy-floral or Oriental-floral perfumes. The absolute must be used with care because of its peculiar topnote which reminds of the odor of benzylformate or phenylethyl formate. This note is probably due to the presence of large amounts of phenylacetonitrile (benzyl cyanide) in the volatile part of the absolute.

The annual production of karo-karoundé absolute is estimated at less than 100 kilos. A high proportion of this quantity is swallowed up by a few French perfume houses who use this powerful material in some of their "grands parfums".

Kauri-Copal.

A number of conifers in Australia, New Zealand and the Pacific islands are exploited for their natural resins. The Kauri-Copal is a natural oleo-resin exuded from Agathis Australis, a conifer from New Zealand. Upon steam distillation of this oleo-resin, an essential oil is produced, known as **Kauri-Copal Oil.** A similar oil is produced by direct (dry) distillation of the natural oleo-resin. The two oils are pale yellow liquids of fresh, lemon-terpene-like odor. These oils are probably not used in perfumes or flavors at all, but they present by their mere presence a certain hazard of contamination and adulteration of other essential oils.

Another essential oil is produced by steam distillation of the leaves and twigs from the same tree **(Agathis Australis).** This oil is hardly used, if used at all, in perfumes or flavors.

Kuromoji Oil.

From a small tree in Japan, **Lindera Sericea,** is distilled various essential oils. The author finds that the oil from the leaves is still a commercially available item, and would like to submit the following comments from the studies of this oil:

Kuromoji Oil, also called **Lindera Leaf Oil,** is a pale yellow or almost colorless, mobile liquid possessing a very strong, fresh-aromatic odor, reminiscent of myrtle leaf oil, eucalyptus smithii, eucalyptus dives, elemi oil, cajuput oil, etc. The flavor is spicy-warm, aromatic, somewhat bitter and slightly biting, not unlike the flavor of a poor-grade ("weedy") natural spearmint oil.

Kuromoji Oil is steam distilled from the leaves of the bush, but even the twigs, bark and wood of this bush have been distilled experimentally. To the author's knowledge, and through direct communication with the producing areas, it appears that only the leaf oil is presently available. The oil has been produced in Formosa, too.

Kuromoji Oil could find use in perfumery for its fresh and aromatic-spicy fragrance. In fougères, fougère-colognes, chypres, after-shave lotion perfumes, spicy colognes, etc., the oil would no doubt lend interesting notes. It produces interesting topnotes in high-class perfumes of the Oriental type, ambres and aldehydic fantasy types. In this respect, the oil resembles **Evoulimba Oil** (see monograph). It is more complex than the mela-leuca oils or the eucalyptus oils, more powerful than myrtle oil, but its diffusive power and low-boiling constituents will place it as a "small" ingredient among the perfume materials which have to be adequately fixed and rounded off. Araucaria, cubeb oil, elemi resinoid, labdanum resinoid, opopanax resinoid, etc. are excellent fixative blenders for **Kuromoji Oil.**

Ar present, the production of this oil is irregular and small, but there is ample material available for distillation on a larger scale.

L

Labdanum.

Labdanum is a resinous exudation from **Cistus Ladaniferus,** a small, wild-growing shrub, probably originating in the mountainous coastal regions of the eastern mediterranean countries and the Middle East. The shrub is now found in all the countries which surround the Mediterranean Sea. Before going into a monographic description of the individual products derived from this plant, a brief summary is given below:

1) **Labdanum,** also called **Labdanum Gum,** which is the crude or strained botanical, consists of the natural (physiological) exudation from the plant, combined with the natural resinous matter, which can be forced out of leaves and twigs of the plant in boiling water.

2) **Labdanum Resinoid** is the hydrocarbon extract-ed matter from the above crude **Labdanum.**

3) **Labdanum "Resin Absolute"** is the alcohol-extracted matter from the crude botanical. This product is also called "purified labdan-um", "soluble labdanum", "labdanum con-centrate" etc.

4) **Labdanum Resin.** Products under this label can unfortunately be a number of things. Most often they are made up by the alcohol-insoluble portion of **Labdanum Resinoid.** Selective solvent extraction of crude labdanum with benzene, petroleum ether, alcohol, etc. will often produce a dry and hard residue. This by-product is either sold as **Labdanum Resin** or "reconditioned" with **Labdanum Resinoid** in order to produce cheaper labdanum extracts.

5) **Cistus Oil.** The name is misleading, since the commercial product is derived from crude **Labdanum,** not from the plant itself (see # 8). **Cistus Oil** is steam distilled from crude Span-ish labdanum or, in rare cases, steam distilled from the **Absolute from Concrète of Labdanum.** The latter type of cistus oil is considered a very fine perfume material. Since the crude lab-danum is often mistreated, the term "cistus"

has for many decades been used to designate either 1) a better quality of labdanum or, 2) a product, derived from the plant itself, particularly from the plants grown in the South of France (Esterel etc.).

6) **Labdanum Concrète** is the hydrocarbon extract from the leaves and twigs of the above labdanum plant. It is a true concrète in accordance with the definitions in this book.

7) **Labdanum Absolute from Concrète** is the alcohol-soluble part of the above labdanum concrète. Products #6 and 7 are thus derived from the entire plant.

8) **Labdanum Oil** (so-called). Under this name is sold various essential oils, produced by steam distillation of the plant material (leaves and twigs of **Cistus Ladaniferus**). Such oils could justly be called **Cistus Oils**. They are of a certain interest to the perfumer, since the true cistus oils represent the odorous characteristics of the entire plant and not exclusively those of the resinous exudation. The oil is described in this book under the monograph **Cistus Oil** (true).

Spain is by far the largest producer of labdanum. Thus, the products #1, 2, 3, 4 and 5 are directly dependant upon the Spanish crop of labdanum "gum". Extraction of the plant itself is carried out mainly in France, rarely in Spain. The products #6 and 7 are thus dependant upon the French crop of cistus ladaniferus plants. These latter products usually display a green or an olive-green color, while the first 5 products appear in various nuances of yellow, amber or brown color. "Gum" products are never green, and true concrètes are never amber colored unless they happen to be of the so-called "decolorized" type.

Out of the above 8 main types of products, the Nos. 1, 2, 3, 5, and 7 are the most common in the trade and the most important in perfumery.

The individual products derived from **Labdanum** ("gum") or from the plant **Cistus Ladaniferus** are described in the following monographs:

Labdanum (crude).

Labdanum, often called **Labdanum** "gum" is the resinous matter, which is derived from the plant **Cistus Ladaniferus** and other species of cistus by boiling the leaves and twigs of this plant in water. According to our definitions (see Part One of this

book) labdanum is a natural oleo-resin. It differs slightly from other oleoresins in the fact, that labdanum contains more waxes and less volatile oil than most of the other natural oleoresins.

The plant grows wild in most countries around the Mediterranean Sea, but the production of labdanum is concentrated in Spain. The "gum" is skimmed off the surface of the water and mixed with other resinous matter, which sinks to the bottom of the boiling water. Smaller quantities of the "gum" are produced in Portugal, Morocco, Yugoslavia, and Greece. The plant is also known under the name of "rock rose". It is a small shrub, the white flowers of which have only a very faint odor. The flowers as such are not exploited in perfumery.

Labdanum (crude) is a dark brown, more or less solid mass. It may contain up to 20% water, but this should be either squeezed off or cautiously dried off the gum. When fresh, **Labdanum** is plastic but not pourable. It becomes harder on ageing and may even become brittle. If it is brittle at room temperature, labdanum should be rejected as a starting material for the processing of labdanum derivatives (perfume materials). **Labdanum** should contain a minimum of dirt, sand, water, leaves, stalks, wood-splinters, insects, etc. A strained (i.e. melted and cleaned) labdanum is preferable.

The odor of **Labdanum** is sweet, herbaceous-balsamic, somewhat ambra-like and slightly animalic, rich and tenacious. For proper evaluation of this material, an alcoholic extract should be made up from the sample. This test will tell about yield and about the odor and color of the wax-free, resin-free material.

A so-called **Cistus Oil** (see this monograph) is prepared by steam distillation of the crude "gum". There is thus a possibility of adulteration of crude labdanum with exhausted "gum" from such distillations or with insoluble residues from the extraction of labdanum absolutes (see this).

Labdanum Absolute from Concrète.

By alcohol extraction of **Labdanum Concrète** (see this monograph) is obtained an absolute. This type of material is produced mainly in the South of France where the plant, **Cistus Ladaniferus** grows wild and abundantly. Insignificant amounts are produced in Italy, Spain and Morocco and there is an irregular production in the island of Cyprus. The labdanum absolute from Cyprus—when available—is of very high quality. It is derived from a benzene-concrète of the labdanum herb. Experimental production of a "one-step" alcohol extract of the plant material has yielded interesting results, but is not yet a common process.

Labdanum Absolute from Concrète is a semi-solid, soft, but very sticky and non-pourable mass of olive-green, green or amber-green color. The odor is deep, sweet-balsamic, faintly but persistently herbaceous with an ambra-like, rich undertone. The latter is characteristic and rarely found in other perfume materials. Certain fractions of cypress oil, juniperberry oil, pinus pumilio oil, Moroccan chamomile oil, sage (clary) oil can display similar notes of ambra-like character.

Labdanum absolute from concrète is used extensively in perfumery, partly as an excellent fixative, partly to introduce a rich, suave sweetness and natural undertone, which blends well with citrus-colognes, lavender-colognes, all kinds of Oriental bases, chypres, ambre bases, pine and "forest" blends, etc.

Labdanum Absolute from Concrète blends excellently with nitromusks, oakmoss products, sage (clary), bergamot, lavender, pinus pumilio, calamus, lavandin, and citrus oils, or with amyl-salicylate, ionones, coumarin, isobutylcinnamate, opopanax, etc.

Recent years have seen the interest in labdanum absolute from concrète decrease significantly and switch to the large variety of labdanum "gum" products from Spanish raw material. The former product has, however, its own fresher and more peculiar note, which is not found in any of the "gum" products, see e.g. **Labdanum "Resin Absolute"**.

Labdanum Absolute from Resinoid.

This product, although quite common in the trade, is rarely sold under the above proper name. It appears under a wealth of trade names, etc., and in an equally large variety of colors, qualities, viscosities, etc. The direct alcohol extract from labdanum "gum" surpasses the above product in popularity. See **Labdanum "Resin Absolute"**.

Labdanum Absolute from Resinoid is prepared from **Labdanum Resinoid** (see this monograph) by alcohol extraction. In this two-step extraction, the yield is inevitably somewhat smaller than in

the case of direct alcohol extraction of the "gum". On the other hand, the two-step extraction does a better job of eliminating the waxy and resinous, mostly non-odorous and alcohol-insoluble matter. Resinoids prepared by petroleum ether extraction yield very attractive and light amber-colored alcohol-extracts (absolutes). A number of such materials are commercially available, usually under all kinds of fancy names, rarely revealing the true nature of the composition of the product.

As a result of the two-step extraction, a hard, dark and almost odorless residue is left from the second extraction. This residue finds some use in the so-called **Labdanum Resins** (see that monograph). Resinoids prepared by benzene extraction yield absolutes which are darker and more solid. The odor of such products varies significantly according to the solvent used. It is hardly possible to give a satisfactory odor description other than to mention briefly that the labdanum absolutes carry the odor characteristics of the resinoids from which they are prepared.

From a perfumery point of view, the petroleum ether extracts yield absolutes of a "cistus oil" type of odor, more dry and ambra-like. The absolutes from benzene-resinoids have a sweeter ambre-like odor and often a somewhat "caramellic" or burnt note, probably due to the higher temperatures during the solvent recovery combined with the differences in extract composition (higher content of plant colors, non-odorous plant extract, etc.).

The general application of **Labdanum Absolute from Resinoid** is similar to that of the resinoid itself. The absolute has the advantage of being alcohol soluble, and it is better suited for lotion perfumes, colognes, aerosol perfumes, face powders, etc.

Labdanum Concrète.

Labdanum Concrète is produced by hydrocarbon solvent extraction of the leaves and twigs (= the herb) of **Cistus Ladaniferus** and other species of **Cistus**, see the general monograph on **Labdanum**. The extraction of the dried plant material is usually carried out after the inflorescence, but may take place earlier.

France, Italy, Cyprus, Greece, Corsica, Yugoslavia and Morocco all produce this concrète, but France (with Corsica) is the largest producer by far. Very little, if any, labdanum concrète is produced in Spain, the main supplier of crude labdanum "gum".

Labdanum Concrète is a sticky-waxy, green to olive-green or brownish-green mass of sweet and pleasant, balsamic ambra-like odor with a tenacious undertone of rich, herbaceous character. This is an odor which is quite familiar to anyone who has visited the Mediterranean countries or islands during the months of March to July.

Labdanum Concrète is used in soap perfumes where its alcohol-insoluble matter is no serious drawback. It may at times even be an advantage through the fixative effect of the waxes and resins.

The concrète represents the first of the two steps in the production of **Labdanum Absolute from Concrète** (see this monograph). The latter finds a more versatile use in perfumery.

Labdanum concrète from the island of Cyprus is very viscous, but can be poured at about 30–35°C. It is light colored, olive-green and will not color the perfume significantly in use. It is a benzene extract and often carries a faint note of this solvent. This is not unusual with concrètes and other extracts.

Labdanum concrète from other sources vary according to origin, solvent used, extraction method applied, etc. Apart from the above use in soap perfumes, etc., **Labdanum Concrète** serves mainly as an intermediate in the production of **Labdanum Absolute from Concrète**. It should be mentioned that the extracts from labdanum "gum" have become increasingly popular lately, and may take over many of the applications where earlier the concrète from the labdanum plant or the corresponding absolute were used. An **Ultrasonic** extract of labdanum herb is available. It is a pale olive-green, soft-waxy material of strongly herbaceous odor type.

Labdanum Resin.

In strict accordance with our definitions, **Labdanum Resin** is the resinous matter from crude labdanum, soluble in hydrocarbon solvents but insoluble in alcohol. It is a non-volatile and almost odorless matter. However, due to the method by which it is prepared, the resin usually carries some odor of the parent "gum". During the past few decades, labdanum has been subject to very thorough investigations in the sense that various attempts have been made to isolate the odorous matter and leave out the odorless portion.

Extraction by selective solvent methods is now quite common. More simple is the two-step extraction.

As an example, it can be mentioned that alcohol extraction, followed by petroleum ether extraction of the alcohol-soluble matter, yields one product, while petroleum ether extraction, followed by alcohol extraction of the petroleum ether soluble matter yields another product. Similar experiments have been carried out with benzene and other solvents. Obviously, it is preferable to perform the first extraction with a hydrophilic type of solvent (like alcohol) since the crude "gum" inevitably contains some moisture. Even a modest water content would act as an inhibitor on a hydrocarbon solvent extraction, and it can form emulsions which are difficult to break, etc.

When **Labdanum** ("gum") is extracted with benzene and the extract in turn is treated with alcohol, a resinous matter separates from the alcoholic solution. Similar precipitates are formed during petroleum ether/ethyl alcohol extraction of labdanum (this process yields a very light-colored absolute), or during other two-step extractions. In all these cases, a very dark, hard and resinous, almost brittle mass is separated. It has only a very faint odor and it particularly lacks the sweetness of the total labdanum. **Labdanum Resin** is used primarily to "cut" other labdanum extracts, e.g. for cost reduction. It also finds some use as a fixative in soap perfumes, detergent perfumes, industrial perfumes, etc. when its dark color and poor solubility do not prohibit its application.

Unfortunately, the term **"Labdanum Resin"** is also applied to other products from labdanum or to the residue from the steam distillation of **Cistus Oil** (see this monograph) from Spanish labdanum "gum". The latter type of "labdanum resin" is superior to the above mentioned resin in respect to odor.

An almost obsolete perfume material is the type of **"Labdanum Resin"** which is produced by destructive distillation (at atmospheric pressure) of crude labdanum.

Labdanum "Resin Absolute".

In order to distinguish between **Labdanum Absolute** (which is usually the absolute from concrète extract of the plant material) and **Labdanum**

"Gum" Absolute, the suppliers have resorted to using various odd names for their products. These products should have at least one thing in common: alcohol solubility.

Labdanum Resin Absolute is a fairly logical designation for the alcoholic extract of crude labdanum "gum". In other words, it is an alcohol-resinoid of labdanum, prepared in a one-step hot or cold extraction. This product is also the cheapest of all the available alcohol-soluble and generally applicable labdanum extracts.

For practical reasons, it is customary to add an inert solvent to the alcohol extract, preferably prior to the recovery of the alcohol in modest vacuum. The solvent can be diethylphthalate, diethylsebacate, isopropylpalmitate, or it may be a weak-smelling, high-boiling odorant like isobutylcinnamate or benzylbenzoate. Such diluents are often used to make the extract pourable at room temperature. The yield of alcohol-soluble extract from a waterfree, good-quality, cleaned crude labdanum "gum" is about 60 to 70%. In order to make this extract pourable, an addition of 20 to 35% of a solvent may be required.

Labdanum Resin Absolute is a viscous, dark brown liquid when solvent is added. It is a semisolid mass when solvent-free. Its odor is somewhat stronger and sweeter than that of the crude labdanum, and the "burnt" notes of the botanical raw material are subdued or eliminated in the odor of this extract.

Labdanum Resin Absolute is used extensively as a general fixative with a distinct sweetening effect and an ambra-type odor. It blends extremely well with nitromusks and other artificial musks, with ionones, linalool, linalylesters, pine needle oils, bornylacetate, cypress oil, clary sage oil, citrus oils (bergamot in particular), vanillin and coumarins, cedarwood oil and its derivatives, vetiver, sandalwood, etc. in countless types of perfumes and perfume bases. Its main use is in the creation of an Ambre note, in which bergamot oil, nitromusks, vanillin and ionones also play a significant role. The term Ambre refers to the Ambra (see this monograph) from the sperm whale. Ambrein is a name often given to a compounded perfume base of high fixative value. Various Ambreines of the trade consist of an extracted labdanum product with addition of nitromusks, bergamot oil, vanillin, vetiver oil, patchouli oil, olibanum resinoid, etc. In organic chemistry, the name Ambreine is applied to a

terpenoid compound derived from farnesol and related to squalene.

Since Labdanum Resin Absolute is obtained by direct—and usually hot—extraction from the crude botanical, it must be kept in mind that a separation of minor but very annoying amounts of a resinous matter may occur in dilute alcoholic compounds, e.g. colognes and lotions. To ensure crystal clear solutions and to safeguard completely against resinous deposits, Labdanum Absolute and Cistus Oil (see these monographs) are often preferred.

Anhydrol Labdanum is a pale yellow liquid, obtained as a molecular distillate or co-distillate of a labdanum extract. The extraction of the crude botanical is carried out with a high-boiling oil-soluble solvent, completely avoiding the presence of alcohol or water. Anhydrol Ethyl Labdanate is presumably prepared from a labdanum extract made under reflux with alcohol. The natural acids are esterified, and will appear in the final molecular distillate as part of the odorous complex. The latter product is thus not truly representative of the natural raw material, but it may be considered as a derivative of labdanum. See also the monograph on Anhydrols in Part One of this book.

Labdanum Resinoid.

This perfume material is prepared by extraction of the crude or cleaned labdanum (see this) with a hydrocarbon solvent. The method of extraction, particularly in respect to this product, has been greatly and successfully improved during the past decades. Selective solvent extraction has produced the most beautiful perfumery materials from this important natural.

The labdanum ("gum") which is used for extraction is most often the Spanish labdanum. When benzene is used as a solvent, the yield of resinoid is quite good, but the product is very dark brown, rather hard, and not pourable at room temperature. It almost invariably carries a noticeable odor of the solvent. Petroleum ether has been used more frequently during the past years since it yields a beautiful light-amber-colored, pourable resinoid which contains the most wanted odor principles in high concentration. The yield is lower than in the case of benzene extraction, but the improved odor of the petroleum ether extract more than compensates for the loss in yield.

Methanol, dichloromethylene, trichloroethylene

and other solvents have also been tried out in the experimental extraction of labdanum. Some of these solvents have yielded interesting, attractive, light-colored extracts of various odor types. Due to the abuse of the terms "resinoid" or "resin" in commercial labelling of certain extracted perfume raw materials, it is not possible to give a general odor- or appearance-description of **Labdanum Resinoid**. In general, they are dark brown, semi-solid resinous masses of a somewhat subdued labdanum odor (see labdanum absolute from resinoid).

Labdanum Resinoid is a very useful fixative, sweetener and blender in soap perfumes of the "ambre" type, in fougères, chypres, lavender perfumes, colognes, tabac bases or aldehydic bases, etc. Its dark color is its main drawback, but the trade offers lighter colored extracts for special use, e.g. in white soaps or where a high concentration of labdanum is wanted. For other applications, see also **Labdanum Resin Absolute** and **Labdanum Resin, Labdanum Concrète**.

Labdanum Resinoid is frequently marketed as a viscous pourable liquid. In such cases, the product contains a "plasticizing" solvent, e.g. 10 to 50% of Diethylphthalate. It would be ethical and correct if the suppliers label the diluted materials accordingly.

Larch Turpentine.

Larch Turpentine or **"Venetian Turpentine"** is a turpentine type of a natural oleoresin. It occurs as a physiological secretion in the larch tree, **Larix Decidua**, a conifer. The tree is quite common in Central and Southern Europe, Austria, Italy, Greece, Yugoslavia, etc. The production of this material is declining, and the small lots available to-day are mainly of German or Austrian (Tirolean) provenance; occasionally some is produced in France. The cultivation of larch trees is greatly inhibited by the stubborn growth of parasite fungi on the trunks of these trees.

Larch Turpentine is a very viscous liquid, just pourable at room temperature. It is of light amber or pale yellow color, and possesses a soft, balsamic-terpenic odor, reminiscent of fresh conifer resins and cones. The turpentine resinifies slowly on exposure to air and becomes increasingly viscous, almost hard. It will remain a slightly plastic lecquer upon drying, and, due to this ability, it has been used extensively in years past.

Larch Turpentine is used in Europe, when and where it is available, as a fixative for pine or fir needle fragrances, low-cost fougères, industrial perfumes, etc. It is an excellent fixative, but it has been replaced by methylabietate (e.g. **"Abalyn"**) or hydroabietic alcohols (e.g. **"Abitol"**) and other abietic acid derivatives in countries where **Larch Turpentine** is not available or where the demand is far in excess of the European production. However, the faint and pleasant fragrance of true Venetian turpentine favors the use of the natural product. If this effect is wanted, only **Oregon Balsam** or **Canada Balsam** (see these monographs) may replace larch turpentine outside Europe.

On the other hand, **Larch Turpentine** has been used to adulterate the more expensive **Canada Balsam** in Europe. American turpentine producers also prepare a substitute for larch turpentine for use in the United States. This substitute is acceptable only in industrial and "technical" preparations, not as a perfume material.

See also **Canada Balsam** and **Oregon Balsam**.

Laurel Berry Oil.

Almost obsolete, but undoubtedly still imprinted in the minds of older perfumers, is the essential oil which is steam distilled from the fruits of **Laurus Nobilis**. This small tree grows in most of the Mediterranean countries. Italy, Yugoslavia and Turkey are among the more important producers of the botanical raw material. The tree is cultivated mainly for its wood which is very suitable for fenceposts or supporters of wine plants. The leaves of the tree are described under **Laurel Leaf Oil** (see this monograph).

Laurel Berry Oil, when steam distilled, contains substantial amounts of fixed oil, consisting mainly of odorless lauric acid, myristic acid and related compounds. These acids are eliminated by washing the total oil with diluted alcohol or by freezing an alcoholic solution of the total oil, compare **Orris Oil**. Occasionally the fruits are extracted with petroleum ether, and the fatty acids are isolated from the concrète product. This yields a **Laurel Berry Absolute**, rarely offered commercially, but sometimes prepared by certain perfume manufacturers for their own use. Steam distilled, de-waxed and fatty-acid-free **Laurel Berry Oil** is a pale yellow, greenish yellow or olive-green, mobile liquid of warm camphoraceous and spicy odor, reminiscent of myrtle, juniperberry, hyssop, Comoro-basil, cajuput and similar oils. Its fresh-medicinal, but pleasantly spicy and warm flavor has also been appreciated, but in this respect the oil has been replaced by one or more of the above oils or compositions.

Laurel Berry Oil has been used as an insect repellant and as a spice oil (or more correctly, a culinary herb oil, see monograph on **Spices,** Part One of this book). In perfumery, the oil has found use as a modifier in chypre, colognes, luxury pine fragrances, ambre bases, etc.; in a multitude of perfume types, the oil can enter as a trace additive to give fresh-warm, camphoraceous-spicy effects in the topnote.

The oil itself is hardly available today, but the botanical raw material is abundantly available, see **Laurel Leaf Oil.**

Laurel Leaf Oil.

The laurel tree is a small unimpressive shrub or tree, originating in the eastern Mediterranean countries, or perhaps in Asia. It has been known for thousands of years, but the use of its leaves as a household culinary herb is a comparatively recent one. The tree, **Laurus Nobilis,** is cultivated in China, Israel, Lebanon, Turkey, Yugoslavia, U.S.S.R., Italy, Sardinia, France, etc. The production of **Laurel Leaf Oil** by steam distillation of the leaves and branchlets of the above tree is undertaken in China, Yugoslavia, Italy (Sardinia), France, and occasionally in Spain. Production of this oil in Algeria, Morocco and Cyprus Island has been abandoned. In Turkey, and to a certain degree in Italy, the laurel leaves serve as a packaging material for the world-famous bars of licorice extract (in Italy) or cubed blocks of the same (in Turkey). To prevent crusting of the hygroscopic extract, it is packed between layers of the sun-dried leaves of the nearby growing laurel tree. Since laurel leaves are a minor item on the import list of northern countries (e.g. Scandinavia), the entire import of laurel leaves for household use in those countries may be covered by this "packaging material". The licorice bars adopt a faint medicinal flavor of the cineole type which is perfectly compatible with the licorice flavor. The laurel leaves, on the other hand, will acquire a faint "sweet-extract" flavor which is quite acceptable for the purpose to which they are put (gravy, sauces, seasonings, etc.). However,

the housewives in these countries will not know the true flavor of laurel leaves unless they pick their own leaves from the miniature laurel trees which, in huge pots, decorate the sidewalk cafés in northern countries during summertime.

Laurel Leaf Oil is a pale yellow to very pale olive-green or almost colorless liquid of fresh, strong but sweet, aromatic-camphoraceous, somewhat spicy-medicinal odor. As a rule, the dryout notes of this oil are sweet, pleasant and slightly spicy, unlike those of eucalyptus, cajuput and, to a certain degree, myrtle oils. The two former oils are found occasionally as adulterants in commercial lots of laurel leaf oil. Chinese laurel leaf oil is distinguished by its very high content of eugenol (over 30%) which impairs the fresh notes of the oil significantly.

Laurel Leaf Oil is used as a flavor ingredient by the canning industry (in pickles, seasonings, sauces, etc.) since, in comparison to the leaves, the oil presents the advantages of greater accuracy, uniformity, lower shipping weight, etc. The author disagrees strongly with published statements that the flavor of this oil is bitter. On the contrary, it is surprisingly sweet and pleasant. The suggested use level is 1.00 to 2.50 mg%, while the **Minimum Perceptible** concentration is about 0.25 mg%. The flavor is fresh, almost orange-like, with a rich and delicately spicy undertone, warm and soft.

In perfumes, the fresh and warm-camphoraceous notes blend well with citrus oils, spice oils, bay leaf oil, pine needle oils, juniperberry oil, cypress, sage (clary), rosemary, etc. It produces interesting notes with olibanum, labdanum and lavender. The oil also finds use in aldehydic types of air fresheners, and as a modifier or "twist" note in men's colognes, after-shaves, etc. The odor characteristics of **Laurel Leaf Oil** are not very unique or immediately striking. This may be one of the reasons why this oil never has attained any significant importance in perfumery. It could be produced in substantial quantities from readily available raw material, but the oil remains a minor item offered by only a few European supply houses and very few actual producers.

Lavandin Absolute from Concrète.

A **Lavandin Concrète** (see this) is produced by extraction of the flowering **Lavandin** plant (see **Lavandin Oil**) with a hydrocarbon solvent, usually petroleum ether or benzene. The concrète is subsequently extracted with alcohol; the alcoholic extracts are chilled and filtered, then evaporated cautiously, applying vacuum towards the end of the distillation. The extract thus produced is known as **Lavandin Absolute from Concrète**. Production takes place in the south of France, right in the heart of the lavandin-growing areas. Very small quantities are produced in Italy, Yugoslavia, Hungary and—experimentally—in Spain and Argentina.

Lavandin absolute from concrète is a viscous, very dark green liquid of pronounced herbaceous odor, resembling that of the flowering herb closely. In comparison to the **Lavandin Oil**, the absolute from concrète has a deeper sweetness and body as well as a rich undertone. The camphoraceous-camphene-like topnotes of the oil are subdued, if present at all, in the **Absolute**.

Lavandin Absolute from Concrète is used in fougères, new-mown-hay types, herbaceous-floral fragrances, "forest"-notes, refreshing colognes, etc. It blends excellently with patchouli, clove oil, citrus oils (bergamot and lime in particular), amylsalicylate (whose "rough" corners it rounds off), ionones, etc.

Its intense green color may be a disadvantage in some cases, but partially decolorized products are available. However, the natural and unbleached extract gives the note of the flowering herb which is most true to nature. This absolute is available in quantities to meet any demand, and its price is so low that this cannot possibly be an obstacle to the use of **Lavandin Absolute from Concrète**.

See also: **Lavandin Absolute from Distillation Water**.

Lavandin Absolute from Concrète, decolorized.

Various methods (charcoal treatment, chlorophyll precipitation etc.) can be used to decolorize the dark green **Lavandin Absolute** partially without seriously affecting the odor of the perfume material.

Although it is not a very common item, **Decolorized Lavandin Absolute from Concrète** finds use in the cases where the intensely green color of the parent absolute would be a drawback (certain lavender-colognes, etc., which must not turn out in a green note). The decolorized material is an olive-brown to olive-yellow liquid, and its odor resembles that of the parent green absolute. The sweetness and rich body can be impaired by the decolorizing process, but when a skillful partial decolorization is carried out, the pale product should give about the same performance in a perfume as would the green absolute.

With the tremendous developments in extraction processes for perfumery materials that have taken place during the past two decades, it is likely that **Decolorized Lavandin Absolute from Concrète** may become quite a common item on the perfumer's shelf. Its very attractive price and popular odor should make it a generally applicable perfume material.

Lavandin Absolute from Distillation Water.

Since **Lavandin Oil** has become such an important article, produced in quantities of about 1000 metric tons per year, the steam distillation of this oil must obviously be carried out with due respect to yield, cost of production, loss, etc. And since **Lavandin Oil** is a comparatively recent shoot on the perfume tree (the oil was practically unknown 30 years ago), it is usually distilled in very modern stills. Some of these stills have a capacity of 20 tons of plant material. In such a large-scale operation, certain by-products often add up to significant quantities, and, if they are interesting, they may be recovered economically.

Lavandin Oil contains small amounts of water-soluble components, and in a 20-ton still the amount of odorous substance dissolved in the distillation waters is quite significant. Most **Lavandin** distillers also have extraction facilities (petroleum ether or benzene), and this is why we have seen **Lavandin Absolute from Distillation Water** appear on the perfumery market recently. The distillation waters are extracted with petroleum ether or benzene, and the extract, free from solvent, can subsequently be extracted with alcohol to produce an absolute. The alcohol-washing process is sometimes omitted. The latter extract is a pale green, mobile liquid (unlike lavandin absolute from concrète) of a peculiar woody, somewhat dry, non-floral lavender type of odor. Like other water-absolutes, it is distinguished by the complete absence of terpenes. Accordingly, its solubility in diluted ethyl alcohol is excellent.

Lavandin Absolute from Distillation Water is used in colognes, fougères, lavender "waters", and other non-floral fragrances. It blends well with clove and other spice oils, bergamot, oakmoss, sage clary, cypress, labdanum, amylsalicylate, coumarins, linalool, isobornylacetate, etc. The water-absolute can even replace or support the effect of high-grade **Lavender Oil** in certain perfume compositions. **Lavandin "Water Absolute"** is an interesting perfume material and it should have a solid future in creative perfumery as well as a possible application in the reproduction of other essential oils.

The production of **Lavandin "Water Absolute"** is limited, but can be adjusted to demand with due notice. In this connection it is worthwhile noting that **Lavandin Oil** is produced only once a year. If there is no "water-absolute" available in November, there will be no possibility of buying this material for another 8 months or so.

Lavandin Concrète.

Even newer than the essential oil of lavandin are the extracted **Concrète** and **Absolute** from Lavandin. The concrètes have found extensive use in soap perfumery, and range among the most inexpensive floral-herbaceous perfume extracts.

A **Concrète** of **Lavandin** is produced by solvent extraction (usually petroleum ether or benzene) of the flowering tops of the **Lavandin** shrub, see **Lavandin Oil**. The solvent is recovered under vacuum but it is not unusual that trace amounts of solvent are perceptible in the odor of the commercial concrète.

As the lavandin plant is cultivated almost exclusively in the south of France, the **Concrète** of **Lavandin** is produced in nearby extraction installations belonging to a number of perfume houses. Very small quantities of lavandin concrète are produced in Morocco, Spain, Hungary and Yugoslavia, mainly for local use.

Lavandin Concrète (from **Benzene**-extraction) is a solid, waxy, dark green mass of intensely herbaceous, rich but not very sweet odor. The petroleum ether-extract concrète is a viscous liquid, just pourable at room temperature. Its fragrance closely approaches that of the dry herb of lavandin, almost chokingly camphoraceous-woody, without being sharp. It is typical of a natural extract, well balanced in odor, reproducing the floral as well as the leaf-stem-herb notes. The latter are derived primarily from non-volatile components, and this may be the reason for the

naturalness in the odor of the concrète as compared to that of the essential oil.

As mentioned above, **Lavandin Concrète** finds extensive use in soap perfumery where its contents of waxes, etc. is an advantage, and where alcohol-insolubility is no drawback. Sweetened up with coumarin, heptalactone, hydroquinone dimethyl-ether, isoeugenol, etc. it forms an excellent base for a lavender soap compound. It is soluble in most essential oils and synthetic perfume materials, and it blends well with all lavender materials, amylsalicylate, oakmoss, artificial musks. pine needle oils or other pine odors, cedarwood products, cis-para-tertiary butyl cyclohexanylacetate, etc.

Lavandin Concrète is readily available in large quantities in the late fall when the autumn crops have been treated. The green concrète can also be partially decolorized or processed to an absolute, see **Lavandin Concrète, Decolorized** and **Lavandin Absolute from Concrète**.

Lavandin Concrète, decolorized.

The intensely green color of **Lavandin Concrète** (benzene or petroleum ether extract) can be of some disadvantage, e. g. when this material goes into a perfume for a white or cream-colored soap and the concentration of **Lavandin Concrète** in the perfume exceeds a few percent. Various methods of decolorization are utilized, but a total removal of all coloring matter without seriously affecting the odor is well-nigh impossible. The majority of the chlorophyll and related substances can be removed, but even this process affects the odor. Charcoal treatment and subsequent filtration of the hydrocarbon solution of the concrète yields an olive-green product, whose color is much less intense than that of the natural concrète. Extraction of the herb with petroleum ether gives a lighter colored concrète than in the case of extraction with benzene or gasoline.

There are several snow-white **Lavandin Concrètes** on the market, but their olfactory properties show a substantial difference from those of the green concrètes. In some cases, the white concrètes are merely compositions of lavandin oil, myristic acid, traces of coumarin, methyleugenol, etc., and they have a much thinner odor (less "body") and poorer performance on soap than have the green concrètes. A partially decolorized **Lavandin Concrète** is preferable. It offers a "happy medium" similar to that in the case of oakmoss: a fair reduction in color intensity, and still a good odor performance.

Colorless or Decolorized Lavandin Concrète has not attained the same importance as its green parent substance, and it will probably remain a small item on the market, used mainly by those who need a colorless perfume and still want a lavandin-concrète effect.

Lavandin Oil.

The story of Lavandin Oil is one of tremendous success. Unknown until the late 1920's, this essential oil today ranges among the world's 10 largest perfume oils from nature (in respect to volume). About 1000 metric tons was distilled in 1959, and half of this amount was either sold or contracted for even before it was distilled. From a 1954-price of almost U.S. $ 3.00 per lb., it has dropped to about $ 0.80 five years later. Even when we consider the very good yield, the very large and modern distillation units, the mechanization and rational centralization in the production, it is almost incredible than an essential oil can be distilled from a shrub, a once-a-year crop, and sold at this low price.

Lavandin is a hybrid plant, developed by crossing the true lavender plant (Lavandula Officinalis) with the aspic or "spike" lavender (Lavandula Latifolia). The resulting plant is called Lavandula Hybrida, and it exists in a great number of forms (varieties), a few of which are distinctly more interesting than the others. When visiting the lavender fields, aspic fields and the cultivated lavandin areas, one is often told that the blue color of the lavender and the grayish color of the aspic will show up in a nuance in the lavandin, revealing which one of the parent plants is predominant in the hybrid. However, it is not possible to predict the yield, the composition or the approximate odor type of the oil from the color of the flowers alone. A wild growing lavandin is found in the south of France where both parents also grow wild, although at different altitudes.

Lavandula Hybrida is cultivated on a large scale in the south of France, while small quantities are distilled in Spain, Hungary, Yugoslavia, Argentina, etc. The wild-growing lavandin plants are of insignificant importance for today's large-scale distillation of lavandin oil.

Lavandin Oil is a pale yellow to almost colorless liquid which can be somewhat turbid and brownish after shipment in galvanized drums. A filtration and separation of water may be necessary in order to produce an attractive looking oil. The odor is strongly herbaceous with a very fresh camphene-cineole-like topnote which should not be distinctly camphoraceous. The rich, woody-herbaceous notes of the body components will usually become predominant within the first 60 seconds on a perfume blotter. It is important to evaluate a lavandin oil on a freshly dipped blotter since the characteristic notes of lavandin and the typical notes of poor oils or adulterated ones will show up immediately. The odor of the oil is not very tenacious, and after a few hours on the blotter, it may be impossible to distinguish a good quality from a poor one.

Lavandin Oil is used for its fresh, refreshing notes, and is often used in very high concentration in the perfume formula. For detergent perfumes, liquid cleaners, dishwasher liquids, etc., this oil gives excellent results and does not need strong fixation. In soap perfumes, a good fixation of the lavandin oil is necessary, as well as in hair preparations, etc.

The oil consists mainly of linalool, linalylacetate (today about 30 to 32%, in some cases even more), cineole, camphene, pinene, traces of camphor, and a small, but very important percentage (one or two percent) of ethyl-n-amylketone. This last material has often been confused with methyl-hexyl-ketone, and the latter has even been named "lavender ketone" in various literatures. This ketone does not, to the author's knowledge, occur in nature. It does not give that "missing lavender touch" to a perfume based on synthetic materials. (The author is well aware, that this is a matter of opinion, not a matter of knowledge, but he feels convinced that he shares this opinion with the majority of other perfumers).

Lavandin Oil blends well with countless natural and synthetic perfume materials. More recently the old-fashioned "Rondeletia"-theme has found a renaissance in the combination of lavandin oil with clove oils, eugenol, bay leaf oil, cinnamon leaf oil, etc. Other blenders are aliphatic aldehydes (modifiers, topnotes), amyl salicylate, citronella oils, cypress oil, decyl alcohol, geranium oils, geranyl acetone, isobornyl acetate, pine needle oils, thyme or origanum oils, patchouli (also fixative), etc. Fixation is obtained with sesquiterpene fractions from various essential oils (good for soap perfumes), labdanum products, nitro-musks, coumarins, oakmoss, lavandin concrete, etc.

Lavandin Oil is also acetylized to yield a product containing about 75% of "natural" linalyl acetate. This product was a source of low-cost linalyl acetate in the 1946 to 1956 period, when linalyl acetate from bois de rose oil cost about U.S. $ 8.00 per lb.

10 to 15% of monoterpenes can be eliminated from the lavandin oil by careful vacuum distillation. The oil loses completely its characteristic odor and resembles certain grades of lavender oil. It is conceivable, that the vacuum distillation also causes a loss of cineole and camphor, whereby the typical notes of lavandin obviously disappear.

Lavandin Oil is available in almost unlimited quantities, but it seems to find wider application every year, and the increasing production is readily absorbed by the hungry soap perfume industry.

Lavender Absolute from Concrète.

Lavender Absolute is prepared by alcohol extraction of the lavender concrète, chilling of the alcoholic solution and filtration and subsequent removal of the solvent in vacuum. Lavender Absolute is produced almost exclusively in France. Smaller quantities are produced in Italy.

Lavender absolute is a dark green, viscous liquid of very rich, sweet-herbaceous, somewhat floral odor; in dilution, it bears a close resemblance to the odor of the flowering lavender shrubs. Its woody-herby undertone and coumarin-like sweetness duplicate the odor of the botanical material far better than does the essential oil. The absolute is sweeter but less floral than the essential oil, and the two materials can form a very pleasant combination. However, one cannot replace the other in compounding. Chemically, the difference between the essential oil and the absolute seems surprisingly small in percentage. The absolute contains almost an equal amount of linalool and linalylacetate (or other linalyl esters), these materials constituting about 90% of the oil. Typical notes in the absolute are probably derived from coumarin, umbelliferone and their derivatives, most of which are non-distillable with steam. Also linalyl esters of non-volatile acids. Although most of the umbelliferone-ethers are odorless,

they may play important roles as fixatives or stabilizers in the absolute.

Lavender Absolute is used in citrus-colognes, chypres, fougères, new-mown-hay bases, forest notes, etc. It blends well with labdanum, oakmoss, vetiver, patchouli, pine needle oils, coumarin, heptalactone, terpinyl propionate, geraniol and esters, sage clary, dodecanal, flouve, nitromusks, salicylates, etc.

A partially decolorized Lavender Absolute has been prepared directly from the green lavender concrète. These absolutes are available, but not very common items. They are olive-green or yellow in color, and the odor is somewhat different from that of the green absolute.

Lavender Absolute from Distillation Water is also available, but it is a comparatively rare item. Its odor is distinctly different from that of the absolute from concrète: it is more haylike, less sweet, less floral. It is usually a mobile liquid, pale yellow in color. It finds use as a "rounder-off" and modifier in certain new-nown-hay perfumes of the more modern type, in herbaceous bases, and in the duplication of certain flower absolutes and essential oils.

Lavender Concrète.

A Lavender Concrète is produced by extraction of the freshly cut flowering herb of true lavender, Lavandula Officinalis, with benzene, gasoline, petroleum ether or other hydrocarbon solvent followed by removal of the solvent in vacuum. This extraction is carried out in or close to the growing areas in the south of France. Insignificant quantities are produced in Italy and a few other countries.

According to the solvent used, Lavender Concrète varies in appearance from waxy solid to viscous liquid. Petroleum ether yields a more liquid concrète. The color is usually dark green, but it appears darker in the liquid products than in the waxy-solid ones, probably due to the microcrystallized myristic acid, etc. in the waxy concrètes. Apart from an inevitable note of the solvent, the odor is generally sweet-herbaceous, somewhat haylike, coumarin-like, but resembling the lavender flowers and stalks very closely.

Its poor solubility in alcohol is no drawback for Lavender Concrète when this material is used in soap perfumes. The concrète is soluble in most perfume materials, and the waxes, myristic acid,

29: Well-instructed Berbers collect **Labdanum** plants in the highlands of central Morocco.

(Fot. S. Arctander, 1960)

30: The odorless but eyecatching flower of **Labdanum** (Cistus ladaniferus). central Morocco.

(Fot. S. Arctander, 1960)

31: **Jasmin** flowers are picked by hand in the early morning hours on a plantation at Khemisset, Morocco.
(Fot. S. Arctander, 1960)

32: Installations for extraction of **Jasmin** flowers with purified petroleum ether near Rabat, Morocco.

(Fot. S. Arctander, 1960)

palmitic acid, etc. will only act as fixatives and blenders in such cases. The concrète is readily available at a comparatively low price; a fact, which makes it practical to apply **Lavender Concrète** in soap perfumes of the lavender type, fougères, new-mown-hays, chypres, forest-notes, pine needle fragrances, ambres, "tabac" perfumes and numerous other types. The concrète blends well with bergamot, citrus oils (of the "lighter" type, too), labdanum products, oakmoss products, patchouli, rosemary, sage clary, thyme oils, etc. and with coumarins, nitromusks, cedarwood derivatives, eugenol and isoeugenol, nopylacetate, etc.

Lavender Concrète is occasionally adulterated. The most common additive is **Lavandin Concrète**. Exhaust waxes from the production of **Lavender Absolute from Concrète** are also used for "cutting" the true lavender concrète. The latter fraud is simply a dilution. A partially **Decolorized Lavender Concrète** is commercially available, but the author has yet to see (and smell) a decolorized material whose odor has not been affected severely by this process. In the case of lavender, the loss of attractiveness and naturalness of odor is not compensated for by the fact that one has disposed of part of the color problem which exists in the green concrète.

The major part of all **Lavender Concrète** produced goes into further processing to the **Absolute. See Lavender Absolute.**

Lavender Oil.

Lavender Oil is steam distilled from the freshly cut flowering tops and stalks of **Lavandula Officinalis**, a wild growing or cultivated plant, native to the Mediterranean countries. Distillation takes place mainly in the south of France where the plants grow at medium altitudes of this mountainous region (from 600 to 1500 metres altitude). Distilleries located at high altitude produce oils of higher ester content, not only because of the theory that the high-altitude, wild-growing plants contain more esters, but also because of the fact that high-altitude distillation means lower-temperature-boiling. Consequently, the distilled oil is not exposed to 100°C. hot steam, but perhaps only to 92 or 93°C. Even this small decrease in temperature means that the hydrolysis of the natural linalylesters take place at a much slower rate. A rapid distillation at slightly reduced pressure (high altitude) may thus produce an oil with nearly all the natural linalylesters.

Lavandula Officinalis (in several varieties) grows wild in the south of France, in Italy, Corsica and Yugoslavia. It is cultivated widely all over the world, however not always successfully. Some of these areas are in Argentina, Brazil, Bulgaria, Cyprus, England, Greece, Hungary, Italy, Japan, U.S.S.R., Spain, Tanganyika, Tasmania, Turkey and Yugoslavia. There is some experimental cultivation and distillation in the farwestern state of Washington, U.S.A. English distilled lavender oil from English grown lavender plants deserves special mention (see below). Of the other countries mentioned, only Italy is exporting quantities of any significance. The production in Tasmania is mainly absorbed by Australia; Japan produces 2-3 metric tons per year which is far from sufficient for its own needs, and even the Russian production does not cover local consumption. The annual production in France varies from about 50 metric tons to almost 100 tons. It is difficult, however, to establish accurate figures for the production of this oil since it is subject to very extensive cutting, adulteration and other kinds of "handling", during which processes many other locally distilled oils and synthetic perfume materials are used in quantity.

English Lavender Oil is distilled from a different variety of the lavender plant. It yields an oil rich in linalool, but rather poor in linalylesters. However, it is not rough or harsh like the aspic or lavandin oils, but represents an individual type of lavender which is obviously appreciated in the country where it is a common garden plant, and where its fragrance is well-known and very popular. It should be emphasized, that **English Lavender Oil** is distilled from flower material with very few stalks or leaves (compare **Rosemary** "flower" oil).

Lavender Oil (French type) is a colorless or pale yellow liquid of sweet, floral-herbaceous refreshing odor with a pleasant, balsamic-woody undertone. An almost fruity-sweet topnote is of a very short life, and the entire oil is not distinguished by its tenacity in odor. It is used extensively in colognes (citrus-colognes or the well-known lavender-waters), in fougères, chypres, ambres and countless floral, semi-floral or particularly in non-floral perfume types. The oil blends well with bergamot and other citrus oils, clove oils (for "**Rondeletia**" type perfumes), flouve, liatris, oakmoss, patchouli, rosemary, sage clary, pine needle oils, etc. Also with amyl salicylate, coumarins, citronellol and geraniol and their esters, heptanolide, menthyl acetate, musk ambrette, moskene and ethylene brassylate, nopyl acetate, menthanyl acetate, isobornyl propionate, phenylacetaldehyde and its acetals in particular. Labdanum products are excellent fixatives and the oil of **Mentha Citrata** can be useful for modifications. **Lavender Oil** is subject to extensive adulteration, cutting, etc. Among the most common additives or "cutting" materials are: acetylized lavandin oil, synthetic linalool and linalyl acetate, fractions from the production of linalyl acetate from **Ho Leaf Oil** or **Bois de Rose Oil**, not to speak of the more crude additives such as terpinyl propionate, isobornyl acetate, terpineol, fractions of rosemary oil, aspic oil, lavandin oil, bois de rose oil, trace additions of ethyl-n-amyl ketone and its homologues, etc. **Lavandin Oil** is produced in quantities of about 10 times that of **Lavender Oil,** and at a fraction of the price of lavender. Strange as it may seem, this fact has indirectly caused a decrease in the adulteration and "cutting" of true lavender oil. Its price has come down to a more reasonable level again, and it is once more possible to obtain a true, genuine lavender oil. The latter oil will, however, remain a small item, and will probably eventually disappear from soap perfumery, being replaced by lavandin oil.

True **Lavender Oil** is still unequalled as a popular, fresh-sweet herbal-floral fragrance in lotions, colognes, or as an additive to modern perfume types, aldehydic bases, spice compounds, etc.

A **Terpeneless Lavender Oil** can be produced by careful vacuum-distillation of lavender oil. A "topping-off" of about 10 percent of the oil is usually sufficient to produce a virtually monoterpeneless oil. It is not necessary to continue distillation thereafter. The terpeneless oil is distinguished by an unequalled mellowness and softness in odor, a superior solubility in diluted alcohol and an improved stability. Its odor is somewhat similar to that of **Lavender Absolute from Distillation Water.**

Lawang Oil.

Among the comparatively few sources of eugenol from nature is an Indonesian tree, whose bark can be steam distilled to yield an essential oil rich in eugenol.

Lawang Oil is probably derived from more than one species of **Cinnamomum** tree (**Cinnamomum Culilawan** and others). The bark is collected in Indonesia, Malaya, China and New Guinea. Distillation from locally collected material takes place occasionally in Indonesia from New Guinea material, in Australia. The eugenol content varies according to the species of **Cinnamomum** used, and up to practically 100% of eugenol has been reported. Other oils have a distinct safrolenote behind the eugenol, changing the clove-like odor to a nutmeg-like fragrance.

Lawang Oil is a dark yellow-brownish oil of warm, rich, spicy odor, varying as described above. It is used quite regularly in the local areas as a spice, while the oil only occasionally reaches Europe or the U.S.A. Since it does not present any substantially unique or particular odor or flavor, the oil has not attained any importance through all its 70 or 80 years of existence on the market. It is conceivable that it will remain a partial substitute for—or additive to—clove, cinnamon and nutmeg in the local spice industry.

The author has not been able to estimate the annual production of this oil.

Leather.

The term "leather"-notes or "leather" perfume types occur quite frequently in the perfumer's language. There are even a number of different perfume types which fall under the category of "leather". Originally and truly, the odor should only derive from leather, more exactly from untanned leather. But the use of the term "leather" for an odor has slowly changed to become a description of the tanning and processing materials in respect to odor type. The curing and tanning of leather involves the use of a number of chemicals, and the process is well known for the obnoxious odor emitted by the wet leather in the tanning brine. Various phenols are used as preservatives, but natural tars have also been used as "masking" odors during the process. The leather will acquire an odor of such tars and retain that odor for a very long time. This odor has become synonymous with "leather" odor. As a final step away from the original meaning of the term, also the various chemicals used in the curing are known as having a "leather" odor.

A true **Leather Tincture** was produced in Germany years ago. Waste pieces of **"Juchtenleder"** or other cuttings of leather were chopped and extracted with alcohol by maceration. Such tinctures are not commercially available.

In France, the "leather" notes are generally known as "cuir" or "cuir de russie" (Russian leather), but none of the commercial products are based upon natural leather. **Birch Tar Oil** fractions, **Castoreum Tincture**, various phenols, cresols, creosol, isobutylquinoline, cananga oil, zingerone, anhydrol ethyl labdanate, maté, styrax, crude amber oil, cade oil, origanum oil, etc. are used in the artificial reproduction of the odor-type which is today generally known in perfumery circles as a **Leather** type.

Lemon Aroma.

Lemon Oil "aromas" or "aroma distillates" are various products used by flavor houses; these products are usually manufactured by the individual houses according to their specific needs.

In general, the "aroma" is a solution of an almost terpeneless, sesquiterpeneless lemon oil in diluted alcohol (about 50% up to 70% alcohol) or propylene glycol (80 or 90%). The terpenes are simply separated out of a lemon oil solution in the straight solvent by the addition of distilled water. It may not even be necessary to add water in the case of propylene glycol which is a poor solvent for terpenes. See general procedure under **Aroma** and **Aromadistillate** in Part One of this book.

The **Aromadistillates** of **Lemon** are based upon an alcoholic or hydro-alcoholic extraction of the lemon peel. The alcoholic or hydro-alcoholic extract is adjusted to about 30 or 40% alcohol strength with distilled water, and the terpenes are separated. The alcohol-layer is then distilled slowly over a short column (packed) at atmospheric pressure. An all-glass still is preferred by most flavor extract manufacturers. Two layers are formed in the receiver: terpenes in the upper layer, since some terpenes will distil with water and will be insoluble in the low concentration of alcohol in the receiver. When the temperature at the top of the column is 100°C., the distillation is carried on only until the alcohol percentage in the receiver (or in the total distillate) is 60%, 50%, 45% or whatever the manufacturer has

established as his standard prescription. The terpene layer is removed from the turbid hydro-alcoholic aroma-solution. If lemon oil has been used in place of lemon peels, the amount of terpenes will be quite significant. The terpenes are dried, filtered and sold as **Lemon Oil, washed.** This product is occasionally used in perfumery. The aromatic hydro-alcoholic solution is now redistilled slowly until the desired strength of alcohol is attained in the second distillate which is clear and water-white. The **Lemon Aroma-Distillate** contains the most delicate and light-aromatic parts of the fragrance and flavor of the lemon oil. Aromadistillates are particularly useful in the creation of flavors for carbonated beverages. The actual flavor strength of aroma-distillates is comparatively low (about 5.0 to 25.0 mg% is **Minimum Perceptible**), but they are unquestionably superior as background and body-notes in the respective flavor types. The low flavor concentration also leads to the advantage of crystal clear solubility in the carbonated drink.

Lemon Aroma and **Lemon Aroma-Distillate** are, when produced from the essential oil, all-year-round available materials. Aroma-distillates made from lemon peels (by far superior in flavor) are only available when fresh, ripe lemons are available. Aroma-distillates should be aged for at least one month at a uniform temperature of not more than 15°C. prior to use or sale. In this respect they are somewhat similar to the old-fashioned citrus-colognes, obtained by distillation of peel extracts.

Lemongrass Oil.

Lemongrass Oil is produced from two distinctly different botanical species of **Cymbopogon**. One is a native of East India (Travancore, etc.) where it grows wild, and is now cultivated over a comparatively limited area in the western parts of India. The plant is **Cymbopogon Flexuosus**, and only cultivated plants are used for distillation.

The other plant, **Cymbopogon Citratus**, is possibly a native of Ceylon and parts of East India, but it is now found only under cultivation. Unlike C. **Flexuosus**, the **Citratus** is widely distributed all over the world, and it has been given the somewhat confusing name "West Indian Lemongrass". The two oils will be described under one monograph, but there will be an individual odor description.

Lemongrass Oil is steam distilled from the fresh or partly dried leaves of the above grass; occasionally, it is water-and-steam distilled. Outside of India, the "west-Indian" grass is distilled in Africa (Kenya, Tanganyika, Belgian Congo, Angola, Equatorial Africa, Madagascar, Comoro islands, etc.), in Central America (Guatemala and Honduras), in the West Indies (Dominican Republic, Haiti, Jamaica, Puerto Rico), in South America (Argentina, Brazil, Suriname), and in Formosa, Indochina, Indonesia, Malaya, etc. It is one of the 10 largest essential oils in the world in respect to volume produced annually (about 1500 tons in 1958), although a good portion of this goes into the production of citral either for perfumery or flavor use, for the production of ionones, or for pharmaceutical use in the synthesis of vitamin A, etc. Lemongrass oil, as such, is not used very extensively in perfumes and not at all in flavors.

Lemongrass Oil is a yellow or amber-colored, somewhat viscous liquid with a very strong, fresh-grassy lemon-type, herbaceous or tea-like odor. The oil is often turbid when it arrives from the producers, but care should be taken that it be kept dry (free from water) since it is able to keep $2\frac{1}{2}$ or 3% of water clearly dissolved at room temperature. This water content is definitely harmful to the citral which decomposes rapidly in the presence of water, air and daylight. The water is conveniently chilled out under stirring of the oil and it separates as a bottom liquid layer. In the Belgian Congo, the largest producer (at Obokoté in the district of Stanleyville) redistils his lemongrass oil, and offers a water-free oil of 90–95% citral content. The foreruns from his redistillation consist of terpenes (myrcene, etc.) and methyl heptenone. They are used locally as low-cost detergent perfumes.

When crude and unrectified, West Indian lemongrass oil is usually of a slightly lower citral content and it contains significant amounts of myrcene. In respect to odor, it has an earthy undertone reminiscent of Ceylon citronella oil (terpineol or borneol?), while the "East Indian" lemongrass oil smells sweeter, more distinctly citral- and lemon-like, fresh and light. It contains little or no myrcene.

As mentioned before, **Lemongrass Oils** are mainly used as starting materials in the production of ionones, methylionones, vitamin A, or for the isolation of citral, which in turn is used either as

such in perfumes or flavors, or it is processed into other perfume materials (acetals, etc.).

Recently the Chinese oil of **Litsea Cubeba** (see this monograph) has presented a strong challenge to lemongrass oil with respect to citral production. The Chinese oil has been available in large quantities at about $ 0.77 per lb. but at the present moment (1960) it is not available at all in the U.S.A. and the quantities available in Europe are far from sufficient to cover the production of ionones, methylionones, etc. In recent years, the world production of ionones and in particular of the methylionones has exceeded 500 metric tons per year and may soon surpass 1000 metric tons. **Lemongrass Oil** contains about 70% citral which is the starting material for the production of ionones.

In many tropical regions, the production of lemongrass oil is a by-product of the cattle raising: cattle feed being scarce, the exhaust grass from the distillation offers a good nutritive when added to molasses residues, etc. from sugar cane, etc. This also logically explains why the settlers continue to plant lemongrass in spite of the fact that it exhausts the soil to a considerable degree. The plant takes out nourishment, but it is fed back to the cattle who will return the yield in nature's great circulation of organic matter. It is conceivable therefore, that **Lemongrass Oil** will continue to be one of the "big 10" of our essential oils. Adulteration is not easy since the oil is purchased against analysis of its citral content, almost the only component of interest to the buyer. And synthetic citral is still too expensive to be used as a "cutting" agent in this case!

Lemon Oil.

Next to sweet orange oil, the oil of lemon peel is the most important citrus oil. It is produced by expression (by hand or machine) of the ripe lemon peel after the juice has been removed from the fruit (machine pressing or sponge pressing of the peel), or it can be expressed prior to removal of the pulp and juice (ecuelle method of oil extraction). The various methods of expressing citrus oils have been discussed comprehensively in recent literature and will not be dealt with in this work.

Lemon Oil, Distilled is an unimportant item in respect to flavor and perfume creation. Even steam distillation of chopped lemon peel under partial vacuum does not lead to a useful lemon oil. Certain quantities of distilled lemon oil are regularly offered from the producers of concentrated lemon juice (compare distilled sweet orange oil).

The most modern and highly mechanized processing of lemons and other citrus fruits take place in California and Florida (U.S.A.) and on the island of Cyprus. **Lemon Oil, Expressed,** is produced in California, Cyprus, Italy, Guinea, Brazil, Tunisia, Israel, Mexico, Jamaica, India, Pakistan, Spain, China, Australia, Union of South Africa, and in several other countries where the tree, **Citrus Limomum,** is cultivated.

The lemon tree is probably a native of East India and Burma, and it arrived in Europe with the returning crusaders in the 12th century. It is also known that Columbus brought along lemon and orange seeds on his second voyage to Hispaniola in 1493, thus founding the world's largest lemon industry (California, late in the 19th century). California is the largest producer of machine-pressed lemon oil, followed by Cyprus Island. Italy probably exports more lemon oil than does the island of Cyprus, but the Italian oils are partly machine pressed, partly hand pressed; unfortunately, a large portion of the Italian oils are of such poor grade that a dilution or adulteration, cutting, etc. with terpenes, citral, etc. is obvious. The author has observed no such mistreatment of lemon oil from Cyprus. Guinea is the world's largest producer of hand-pressed lemon oil (by the spoon-ecuelle method) but this country cannot compete with the other producers in quantity. See also **Orange Oil, Sweet,** from Guinea. Most of the other countries produce lemon oil only for local consumption. The total annual production of expressed lemon oil exceeded 1000 metric tons in the 1950's and was estimated at 1200 to 1300 metric tons in 1959.

Expressed Lemon Oil is a yellow to greenish yellow or pale yellow mobile liquid of very light, fresh and sweet odor, truly reminiscent of the ripe peel. No turpentine-like, harsh-terpene notes should be detectable on a perfume blotter. Good oils retain their fresh lemon odor practically unchanged on a blotter until there is no odor left at all. The odor of lemon oil is not very lasting, but the tenacity varies considerably with the method of expression. See below notes on the evaporation residue. The oil should be clear, not hazy or turbid, and it should not show resinous deposits. It has become customary to treat lemon oil (and other citrus oils) with an antioxidant in order to retard the deterioration of the oil when the original container has been opened, and the oil has been exposed to air, daylight and—in particular—moisture or water. Old-fashioned stabilizers, such as absolute alcohol (5% addition) or olive oil, are not without effect, but modern antioxidants can be used with good effect at a much lower level (combination-antioxidants at about 0.005%). This treatment is preferable as it will not affect any later flavor or perfume work with the oil. Most antioxidants are without effect unless the oil is waterfree. When stored in a dark place at cool and constant temperature in a dry, ironfree container with little or no atmospheric air above the surface (carbon dioxide, nitrogen or other inert gas can be injected to replace the air in the container), lemon oil can be stored for years without losing its fresh and pleasant odor and flavor. The outstanding keeping qualities of Cyprus lemon oil could be due to the ultramodern processing by which the oil is very effectively freed not only of pulp and albedo particles, but also of water (in high-speed silver-lined centrifuges).

It is a known fact that the old-fashioned sponge method, now almost abandoned in Italy, yields oils with very low evaporation residue, while machines will produce oils with either high residue (Italian machine pressed oils) or low residue (Californian machine pressed oils). However, the content of non-volatile matter (= evaporation residue) is not a very good indication of the quality of the oil since lemon oil residues, sesquiterpenes, etc., are commercially available from the producers of sesquiterpeneless oils. A thorough olfactory and organoleptic examination of the oils is the only safe means of evaluation.

Expressed Lemon Oil is used in perfumes and flavors for its refreshing, sweet-fruity note. It is one of the more important ingredients in the old-fashioned citrus-type of colognes, in "Eau de Verveine" and other toilet waters, lotions, aerosol sprays, etc. It finds general application as a freshener and topnote ingredient in countless perfume types.

Lemon Oil blends well with other citrus oils, with lavender oil, lavandin, elemi, labdanum, petitgrain, neroli, etc. and among the most common fixatives for lemon oil are coumarin, vanillin, cinnamates, elemi resinoid, oakmoss products, araucaria oil, etc. Lemon oil is often accompanied by aliphatic aldehydes as modifiers for the lemon-topnote.

In flavors, **Concentrated Lemon Oils** or **Sesquiterpeneless Lemon Oils** (see these monographs) are preferred since a high terpene content will cause problems with regard to solubility, and will tend to produce harsh notes when the flavor is incorporated in moist or aqueous preparations (carbonated drinks, candy, sherbet ice, etc.). The masking effect of **Lemon Oil** is well known from everyday life: lemon quarters or halves are often served along with fish and other seafood. The fresh lemon-odor completely masks the amine-like odors of the seafood. This masking effect is due to the minute amounts of peel oil, which inevitably are squirted upon the food, when the lemon is squeezed. The juice plays a significant role in the masking job: citric acid from the juice neutralizes the amines in the seafood, thereby eliminating part of the obnoxious odor.

With vanillin and other synthetic flavor ingredients, lemon oil forms the base of the old-fashioned "custard" flavor, and certain types of hard candy are flavored exclusively with lemon oil in acid media. In view of the general acceptability and popularity of lemon as a flavor type, and considering the very wide variations in quality of various lemon oils, it is extremely difficult to give an approximate use level for lemon oil in flavors. The concentration would generally be from 1.50 mg% to 10.0 mg% in aqueous media with about 12% cane sugar and 0.05 to 0.08% citric acid or equivalent amount of other edible acid (tartaric acid, lactic acid, etc.). In a similar medium, the **Minimum Perceptible** is 0.50 mg% to 1.00 mg% for a good and fresh, commercial quality of lemon oil. Lemon oil in high dilution does not give a true impression of the peel of the lemon fruit unless it is accompanied by a certain amount of acid. The acid taste seems so inseparably bound up with the lemon flavor that we subconsciously expect acidity along with the odor and flavor of lemon. For further discussion of lemon oils in flavors, see **Lemon Oil, Concentrated** and **Lemon Oil, Sesquiterpeneless.**

Lemon Oil, Expressed, is frequently adulterated. Distilled lemon oil (see above in this monograph), lemon terpenes (from deterpenation), d-limonene (natural isolate or synthetic from pinene), synthetic dipentene, synthetic or isolated citral, and numerous other synthetic materials are used to "reconstitute" a poor lemon oil or a lemon oil with

a low citral content, etc. Unfortunately, these cutting materials are readily available in Italy, and heavy fluctuations in the lemon oil price (particularly outside of the U. S. A.) have caused occasional increases in the cutting and adulteration of this essential oil to a point where consumers have been tempted to judge all Italian lemon oils under one mutual designation. The consumers or factories who carry out deterpenation of lemon oils can judge each oil in this respect. There are still some outstandingly good Italian lemon oils to be found and used by those who really know good quality from poor. The "scientific" adulteration of lemon oil (addition of known and identified components, derived from synthetic materials and added in correct proportions) can be very hard to find. But such "sophistications" may occasionally improve the oil and, in such a case, there is no reason for a customer to be disappointed. It should be mentioned, however, that physico-chemical properties, absolutely correct in every detail, can be established in an entirely artificial lemon oil which contains no natural oil at all. **Lemon Oils** with the labelling "USP" or "BP" or other recognized authoritative works of standards (Pharmacopoeias, Codexes, etc.) are commercially available. Certain suppliers seem to specialize in "correct physico-chemical properties" of their essential oils without regard to the olfactory virtues of the oils.

Lemon Oil, concentrated.

Expressed **Lemon Oil** consists of more than 90% hydrocarbons (mainly d-limonene) which have but little flavor value, and whose insolubility in alcohol is a nuisance in flavor compounding, etc. By careful vacuumdistillation, most of the terpene fractions of **Lemon Oil** can be removed. This method of concentration leads to the so-called two-fold, five-fold, ten-fold, etc. **Lemon Oils.** However, these concentrates present certain drawbacks: The waxes and high-boiling sesquiterpenes have been concentrated with the remaining oil, and have made it dark and not clearly soluble in all proportions in alcohol. The terpenes have carried over some oxygenated compounds (important flavor and perfume principles of the oil) and a certain loss of aroma must be expected. A five-fold lemon oil does not yield 5 times the flavor of a natural oil. The residual concentrate has been exposed to considerable heat during the last part of the distillation (concentration process).

The delicate aldehydes in lemon oil may suffer during this kind of treatment.

A more advanced method of concentrating citrus oils is a combination of vacuum distillation and alcohol-washing. The principle is that an "absolute" lemon oil is prepared. This "absolute" is subsequently "cut back" with selected fractions from the vacuum distillation in order to produce a wax-free, sesquiterpeneless, partially monoterpeneless oil, possessing the freshness from the purified and selected monoterpenes and the solubility of other essential oils. It has, furthermore, an attractive, yellow color, not more intense than the color of the natural oil.

Example: 120 kilos of a selected Cyprus or Californian cold-expressed **Lemon Oil** is submitted to vacuumdistillation in an all-glass still at 0.1 to 0.3 mm Hg.-pressure. At this vacuum, either infra-red lamps or a hot-water glass coil heat exchanger will produce sufficient heat to start distillation. The temperature in the pot (distillation flask) will remain below 40°C. and, at the top of a four-foot column (6 inches diameter and packed with half-inch glass raschig rings), the distillation temperature will be 21 to 28°C. An acetone—CO_2—trap will secure the ballast-type vacuum pump with a freeze of minus 90°C. The first 10% of the distilling oil is "broken" into one-kilo fractions. 75% of the oil is distilled off, leaving 30 kilos in the pot and almost 90 kilos of distillate (lemon terpenes).

The 30 kilos are transferred to a smaller glass still, and 10 kilos (of monoterpenes) are distilled off under similar conditions although the pressure is now 0.05 to 0.15 mm. Hg. at the receiver. The remaining oil, about 20 kilos, is then extracted with a mixture of 70 parts by weight of ethyl alcohol and 30 parts by weight of distilled water. Three to four extractions, using respectively 40 kilos, 30 kilos, 20 kilos and 10 kilos of alcohol-water mixture at room temperature, will usually prove sufficient to exhaust all the oxygenated materials from the concentrated lemon oil. Some manufacturers use a 60% alcohol or even more diluted. More than four extractions are then required. Lemon oil contains little or no solid waxes, and the alcohol-insoluble part is a viscous, orange-yellow liquid. It can be vacuum distilled to yield certain useful fractions, but it is of little or no flavor value. When distilling lemon sesquiterpenes even at very reduced pressure, care should

be taken that the "skin temperature" (the inner surface temperature of the flask) does not exceed 110°C. Viscous liquids tend to "burn" during distillations at elevated temperature because of the slow circulation and heat exchange in the liquid.

The alcoholic solutions from the above mentioned extractions are mixed, and the alcohol is cautiously evaporated. Vacuum is applied during the last part of the evaporation. It will be necessary to interrupt the distillation when oil separates from the water or weak alcohol in the pot. The two layers are then distilled separately in order to avoid loss by water-distillation of the oxygenated compounds (azeotropic distillation of a binary/ternary mixture). The oil layer, freed from alcohol and water, is dried with anhydrous sodium sulfate and weighed. The "cutback operation" is then carried out with fractions from the first distillation according to the flavor needs of the company. It is possible to establish a standard prescription for this oil-concentration if the oil to be used is adequately flavor-checked prior to the above processing.

The sesquiterpene fraction, insoluble in 70% alcohol, is an excellent material for the compounding of artificial citrus oils. A faster but less delicate method involves no alcohol-extraction. The **Lemon Oil** is vacuum distilled all the way and may be transferred to a smaller still at the end of distillation (the last 20% of the oil). If the pot temperature (the maximum temperature to which the oil is exposed) can be kept below 80°C. through sufficient vacuum, cautious heating and careful distillation, the oxygenated components of the oil will not suffer severely. However, the high-boiling residue ($2\frac{1}{2}$ to $4\frac{1}{2}$ percent of the oil) will act as a strong "fixative", and will retain small but important amounts of flavor components.

It should be mentioned that trace amounts of very important flavor ingredients are found in the lowest boiling fractions; these components are thus hidden or lost in the first terpene fractions. Accordingly, these fractions should be comparatively small (one-half to one percent of the oil, each fraction). A skillful "cut-back" process may reproduce the natural aroma of the oil with a minimum amount of monoterpenes.

See also **Lemon Oil, Terpeneless** and **Sesquiterpeneless.**

Concentrated Lemon Oils are used extensively in flavor work where a high amount of unstable and insoluble terpenes may cause trouble: Carbonated beverages (terpenes tend to form an oil-ring in the neck of the bottle), sherbet ice flavors (terpene peroxide formation and rancidity), etc. The **Concentrated Lemon Oils** are particularly superior to the sesquiterpeneless-terpeneless oils when used in soft drinks since the former will have the fresh notes from the monoterpenes which are so characteristic of lemon peel. A six-fold, alcohol-washed, concentrated lemon oil is soluble in alcohol in the proportions usually needed. A plain 6-fold concentrated lemon oil is not.

Lemon Oil, terpeneless and sesquiterpeneless.

Expressed **Lemon Oil** can be deterpenized totally by the methods described in Part One of this work (see **Terpeneless Oils**). It should be remembered that the commercially available "terpeneless" oils frequently contain substantial amounts of terpenes. The author found 43% monoterpenes in a "terpeneless lemon oil" from a well known supplier. This amount is too high, and does not assure the customer of an alcohol-soluble product.

A totally terpeneless, sesquiterpeneless lemon oil is a yellow or pale yellow to almost colorless liquid with an intensely sweet, almost rosy-fruity odor, only faintly reminiscent of the odor of lemon peel. However, when used in flavors, it takes only a slight amount of added citric acid to convince the customer that this flavor is lemon. Many soft drinks are flavored this way (lemon sodas, etc.). Concentrated lemon oils (see the previous monograph) can be compounded to present suitable lemon flavor effects even without added citric acid. This is how ice cream is flavored with lemon (acid can not be included in emulsified milk products).

The flavor effect of a totally terpeneless and sesquiterpeneless lemon oil is somewhere between 15 and 25 times as strong as that of the natural oil. Theoretically, one would expect it to be about 40 times as strong since the yield of oxygenated components (non-hydrocarbon odor-flavor principles) is about 2.4% up to 3.2% by weight of a good quality expressed lemon oil. But there is a small loss in the terpene fraction, and the terpenes themselves do supply some fresh flavor effect.

In the figures given below the author has used a virtually terpeneless, sesquiterpeneless lemon oil.

This oil was produced by countercurrent (liquid-liquid) extraction with selective solvents. The loss of oxygenated components is negligible by this method.

The suggested use level was estimated at 0.10 to 0.50 mg% and the **Minimum Perceptible** was 0.01 to 0.02 mg%. It appears from these figures that the flavor effect *in actual use* is only 15 to 20 times stronger than that of a good, expressed lemon oil. However, the calculated increase in strength by the total deterpenation is clearly pictured in the minimum perceptible, which is 50 times smaller for the deterpenized oil than it is for the natural, expressed oil. One could say, that the power is maintained but that the loss is that of a decrease in "flavor body" or "flavor volume".

Terpeneless, Sesquiterpeneless Lemon Oil is very stable but it should not be kept in alcoholic solution. Dilutions for flavor experiments should be made fresh every time they are needed, or they should be kept in neutral oil solution (edible, odorless solvent of non-alcoholic type). The terpeneless, sesquiterpeneless lemon oil contains 60 to 72% aldehydes, mainly citral. Citral decomposes rapidly when dissolved in ethyl alcohol under the formation of acetaldehyde, etc. The progressive decomposition is distinctly perceptible in the odor of alcoholic citral-solutions through the appearance of "coffee-like", "breadcrust-like" off-odors.

Lemon Petitgrain Oil.

From the leaves and twigs and occasionally also from undeveloped small fruits of the lemon tree, **Citrus Limonum,** an essential oil is produced locally by steam distillation. Although it is grown all over the world, the lemon tree is usually cultivated for its fruits only, see **Lemon Oil.** However, in Guinea (West Africa), in Italy, Tunisia and occasionally in Algeria and Morocco, the **Lemon Petitgrain Oil** is produced.

The main producer is Guinea, from which country the very best and richest oil comes. Apparently the high altitude (1200 to 1600 metres) of the plantations *and* of the distilleries in Guinea have some influence upon the chemical composition of the oil (compare geranium, lavender, linaloe seed oil, etc.).

Lemon Petitgrain Oil is a pale yellow to greenish yellow or olive-amber colored liquid of very strong, fresh odor with a distinct bitter undertone, at times woody, in poorer oils grassy. The dryout should be very rich and sweet, slightly floral-fruity. The natural oil is not useful in flavors, see **Lemon Petitgrain Oil, terpeneless.**

Lemon Petitgrain Oil contains up to 50% citral, and thus it finds application in citrus-types of colognes, in chypres (for refreshing notes, topnotes, etc.), fougères, rose bases (can introduce very interesting topnotes), etc. But the particular bitter-fresh notes, the immensely rich and tenacious depth and undertone in the odor of this oil—these are due to minor constituents. The terpenes are partly responsible for the bitter-fresh notes since the terpeneless oil (see following monograph), does not present this particular effect.

Lemon Petitgrain Oil blends excellently with geranium, lavandin rosemary, sage clary, etc., as well as with a wealth of synthetic perfume materials to which it imparts roundness and naturalness even at very low percentages.

Lemon Petitgrain Oil is produced on a limited scale mainly due to lack of demand. Another reason is the remoteness of the producing areas in Guinea. When a customer asks a supplier for a sample of lemon petitgrain oil, he will in most cases receive an Italian oil. These are generally poor and the customer loses interest in lemon petitgrain oil.

Production could be increased to 100 metric tons per year, if a demand existed, but at present, only 2 to 5 tons are produced annually in Guinea, and far less in Italy. An Algerian oil, studied by the author, was quite similar in type to the Italian oils but also slightly superior in quality to the best Italian lemon petitgrain oils which are the most common as samples from European brokers. Adulteration takes place with lemongrass oil fractions, citral, lemon oil, petigrain oil Paraguay, eucalyptus staigeriana oil, and various fractions from other essential oils. The author has not yet seen a poor oil coming directly from Guinea. See also **Lemon Petitgrain Terpeneless,** following monograph.

Lemon Petitgrain, terpeneless.

For flavoring purposes and for certain perfumery purposes, there are definite advantages to the removal of all or most of the monoterpenes and sesquiterpenes from **Lemon Petitgrain Oil** (see previous monograph). The best starting material is the Guinea oil which is by far the richest in oxygenated constituents (important odor and flavor materials).

A very cautious fractionated distillation under vacuum, preferably lower than 1 mm. Hg.-pressure in an all-glass still, may produce a satisfactory oil. It is usually necessary to interrupt the distillation when 35 to 45% by weight of the oil has distilled at a maximum still-head temperature of 30°C. (and not more than 50°C. pot temperature). The residue in the pot is then "washed" (extracted) with 70% ethyl alcohol (in distilled water) whereby the oxygenated components of the concentrated oil are dissolved and the sesquiterpenes are left undissolved. There are no waxes. The alcoholic solution is evaporated, and care is taken to see that the water does not carry over some of the aromatic materials. When alcohol and water are removed, the residue is **Lemon Petitgrain, Terpeneless** (and **Sesquiterpeneless**).

This oil is an excellent flavor material, and does wonders when minute additions are made to a raspberry flavor. It has an unequalled freshness and an enormously rich sweetness; its power will surprise most "first-users". To introduce just that touch of freshness (without being perceptible per se) which is so often needed in artificial fruit flavors, this oil is an excellent material. The suggested use level is accordingly just a trifle above the **Minimum Perceptible** which is approximately 0.005 to 0.020 mg%.

In perfumes, the **Terpeneless Lemon Petitgrain Oil** will show its tenacity in high-class colognes, and it blends well with neroli oil, sage clary, bergamot, citronellol, cumin ketone, cyclamal, geraniol, heliotropine, hydroxycitronellal (eliminates the sickly-sweet chemical notes), linalool, linalyl acetate, etc. It gives fine topnote effects in muguet, rose, lilac, gardenia, etc.

Terpeneless Lemon Petitgrain Oil is not commercially available as such, but it is produced by the individual users who can calculate on an average yield of 45 to 55% based upon genuine Guinea oils.

Leptospermum Citratum.

Leptospermum Citratum Oil is obtained from a shrub belonging to the so-called "Ti-trees" (or "tea-trees"). See also the monographs on **Melaleuca Oils.** The shrub originated in Australia, and is now cultivated in Kenya, Belgian Congo and in the Union of South Africa.

The essential oil is steam distilled from the small leaves of this slowly growing shrub; the yield of oil is not very large. Consequently, the farmers are not overly enthusiastic in undertaking the cultivation of this bush which does not yield a reasonable amount of leaves until it is about 10 years old. The production of this essential oil is still at the "few-tons-per-year" level, with an estimated annual production of 15 metric tons. By far, the greatest amount comes from Eastern Belgian Congo and East Africa.

Leptospermum Citratum Oil is a yellowish to dark olive or brownish yellow liquid with a very strong, fresh, sweet, yet somewhat sharp or pungent odor, reminiscent of lemongrass, lemon petitgrain and Java citronella oils in a sweet, well-balanced mixture. About 80 to 88% of the oil is made up of citral and citronellal, the former being slightly larger in quantity. However, it is not at all possible to achieve anything like the odor effect of **Leptospermum Citratum Oil** by simply mixing these two aldehydes in the calculated proportions. The power and diffusiveness of this oil is simply striking. It is an excellent base for detergent or soap-flake perfumes of the citronella- or lemongrass-lemon type. In minute quantities, it will impart a sweet freshness to colognes, fougères, lavenders for soap, air fresheners, etc. The oil is quite stable in soap when correctly blended and fixed.

Leptospermum Citratum Oil is difficult to obtain in ton-lots, and it is therefore frequently adulterated. Very logically, lemongrass oil, citronella oils (Java or Formosa types), eucalyptus citriodora oil, etc. are commonly used as adulterants; all of these reduce the strength of the true oil.

It is interesting to observe that the "inevitable" methyl heptenone is present in this oil only in traces, judging from the odor. This makes the **Terpeneless Leptospermum Citratum Oil** a very pleasant smelling perfume material. By cautious "stripping" of the natural oil under good vacuum, 10 to 15% by weight is removed as top fractions. The distillation is discontinued. A little citral is lost, but the terpeneless oil turns out with a clean-sweet, intensely fresh odor, and even a pleasant taste. It apparently becomes more stable in respect to oxidation, and its area of application is greatly enlarged.

As mentioned above, even if there is a strong demand, an increase in the production of this oil is only possible after many years of plantation work and the use of valuable soil. On the other hand, if there weren't a certain demand, the oil would definitely disappear from the market and we would be one highly interesting perfume material poorer. Once this oil is used in a formula, it is hard to replace.

Licorice.

Although without interest for perfumery, this product is one of the most important of the non-fruity flavor materials from nature. One of the more practical reasons as to why licorice finds no use in perfumery is the physical reason that all licorice preparations are water-soluble; they are not alcohol- or oil-soluble.

Licorice or, more correctly, **Licorice Extract** is produced from the rhizomes and roots of **Glycyrrhiza Glabra,** a leguminous plant. There are two main varieties of this plant: the **Typica** which is known commercially as "Spanish licorice", and the **Glandulifera** which is generally called "Russian licorice". The former comes from Spain and Italy, the latter from Turkey, U.S.S.R. and the countries around Asia Minor towards India.

By extraction of the comminuted rhizomes and roots with boiling water, followed by evaporation of the aqueous extract, the well-known solid **Licorice Extract** is prepared. It is usually marketed in cylindrical bars (6 inches by ¾ inch.) from Italy (Calabria), or in large, crude blocks of about 10 kilos (from Turkey).

Licorice Extract is black and brittle, and has a sweet, mild odor somewhat different from that of the botanical starting material (the aqueous extract is often evaporated over an open fire and some caramellization of the extract may occur). Licorice extract has a very sweet taste, and a rich, "rootlike", slightly spicy-caramellic body of flavor. It leaves a faintly scratching feeling in the back of the mouth, and it is used in medicine for its mildly expectorant effect.

The sweetness of **Licorice** is due to an acid, **Glycyrrhizin,** which is about 50 times as sweet as saccharose (household sugar). Glycyrrhizin is present in the root combined to ammonia. Unfortunately, the commercially available qualities of glycyrrhizin will color any aqueous solution in which they are used, strongly brown.

Except for this drawback, **Glycyrrhizin** could be an interesting sweetener of negligible calorie value.

Outside of medicine, licorice extract finds its major application in the candy industry, as a masking agent for bitter flavors and, to a minor extent, in the breweries where certain kinds of beer (porter, bass, etc.) are colored and at the same time flavored with licorice extract. The bitter herb extracts in the beer are masked by the licorice sweetness and flavor. Another effect enjoyed by the breweries is that **Licorice Extract** produces a very stable foam in carbonated beverages. (For this effect, licorice extract is also used in fire extinguishers). The tobacco industry uses tremendous amounts of licorice, particularly for pipe and chewing tobacco.

It is worthwhile remembering that licorice extracts can *not* be used for flavoring in acid media. The **Glycyrrhizin** is inactivated as a sweetener by acids. This is a serious drawback since the masking of a bitter flavor is usually obtained by introducing a sour (acid) taste. The acid taste sensation is intensified in the presence of bitter tasting substances. The actual result is that the sour (acid) taste sensation arrives faster to the brain than does the bitter taste. This brief interval or delay is then utilized by the introduction of flavor materials such as sweeteners, etc.

As mentioned above, only aqueous extracts come into consideration. If licorice root or rhizomes are extracted with ethyl alcohol, the resulting extract will have an acrid taste due to an oleoresin which is insoluble in water but partly soluble in alcohol. It seems to be customary in flavor literature to describe the odor of anise, fennel, etc. as "licorice-like". This is another typical example of association of two flavors: licorice is very often flavored (in candy, cough-syrup, etc.) with anise oil, anethole, etc., and the anisic flavor has become almost synonymous with that of the name: **Licorice**. (Compare the similar error of: chocolate-vanillin, see also **Odor Description** in Part One of this work). Licorice does not smell of anise, nor does anise smell of licorice. They have a certain sweetness in common. Anyone who has ever tasted or smelled "Baracco" licorice extract bars from Calabria in Italy or chewed the rough, cubed blocks from Turkey will agree.

The annual world production of **Licorice Extract** can be estimated only very roughly at many thousands of tons.

Lilac.

Next to rose and jasmin, the **Lilac** fragrance is probably the perfume which is most frequently "created" by the perfumer from synthetic and natural raw materials. Up to now, the essential oil-producing houses have been unable to offer a true, natural oil, derived from lilac flowers and representing these flowers satisfactorily in odor effect. Only a few houses in Grasse, France offer materials which are said to be derived exclusively from lilac flowers. But the author has still to meet one product which strikes him immediately as a true-to-nature, rich and powerful lilac absolute or lilac oil. The so-called **Butaflor Lilas** is one of the closest approaches and even that material is inferior to certain entirely artificial bases.

The lilac **Syringa Vulgaris** and other species of **Syringa**, is a shrub or a bushy tree, originating in Iran (Persia) and probably in other countries of the Middle East. The lilac was introduced in Europe in the Middle Ages, and is now one of the most common ornamental shrubs in gardens all over Europe: from Italy to Norway, from Greece to Scotland. It is characteristic of many plants that they yield their best fruits, flowers, growth, etc. when they are growing under the "borderline" of cold climate. It is as though nature gave these plants extra strength. In Denmark, the author has seen lilac bushes 60 years old, and over 10 meters high, and other lilacs whose petals measured an inch across, growing in Canada. Both places can boast of lilac flowers with exceptionally delightful and rich fragrance. England, too, is famous for her beautiful and very fragrant lilacs. The flowers bloom in several colors: from snow-white and creamy through all shades of "lilac color", red-blue, to the deepest purple lilac. There is a certain variation in the fragrance of lilac flowers of different color.

An absolute has been prepared from the flowers of lilac by hydrocarbon solvent extraction and subsequent alcohol extraction of the produced concrète. According to all reports so far, the results have been very discouraging. A few products labelled **Lilac** are available today under the brand name of the special process used by the producer (**Butaflor Lilac**, etc.). As mentioned above, none of the existing lilac absolutes, etc. have anything exceptional to offer with respect to odor effect or power. These virtues can be obtained from an artificial lilac base. As in the case of **Muguet** (see **Lily of the Valley**), most perfumers think—and justly—that a good creation of an artificial lilac or muguet is far superior to the so-called natural extracts.

An artificial lilac may be based upon synthetic materials to the extent of more than 90% by weight, and may still yield a more true-to-nature odor than any "absolute of lilac" does.

Among the most common materials used in the construction of an artificial lilac fragrance are:

Amylcinnamic aldehyde methylanthranilate, anisalcohol, anisaldehyde, cassione, cyclamen aldehyde, dimethyl benzyl carbinol, dimethyl benzyl carbinyl acetate, dimethyl phenylethyl carbinylisobutyrate, heliotropine, hexyl cinnamic aldehyde, hydroxy-citronellal, alpha ionone, indole, lilial, linalool, linalylcinnamate, iso cyclocitral, para methoxy phenylacetaldehyde, methyl hexyl acetaldehyde, para methyl phenylacetaldehyde, phenylacetaldehyde dimethylacetal, phenylethyl alcohol, ar-methyl phenylethyl alcohol, phenylpropyl alcohol, beta methylcinnamic alcohol, alpha terpineol, etc. etc. Useful natural materials are: Jasmin absolute, rose de mai absolute, mimosa absolute (or concrète for soap perfumes), civet, sage clary concrète or absolute, ylang-ylang oil extra (or ylang-ylang concrète for soap perfumes), etc.

In view of the above, it is inconceivable that natural extracts of lilac flowers will find any importance in perfumery unless extraction methods can be improved to the point where they will yield a superior product.

See also **Syringa.**

Lilium Candidum.

The popular and very beautiful madonna lily or "White Lily", **Lilium Candidum** originated in the Middle East, and is now grown for its flowers in Europe, particularly in the south of France. Bulgaria also grows substantial amounts, and experimental batches of perfume oil have been produced there.

Only rarely are surplus flowers treated in Grasse, France, to yield an **Absolute** of **Lily** (absolue de lys). According to private communications to the author, the maximum annual production of **Lily Absolute** in France has been about 2 kilos. These products were of dark orange-yellow color or pale amber color and very viscous liquids. The odor is usually delicately floral with a pronounced oily-waxy topnote. The

balsamic-sweet body is reminiscent of narcissus and boronia, also faintly of karo-karoundé. It is less green in odor than these but more fatty-balsamic or cinnamic. There are notes which distinctly recall beta ionone, and the undertone is almost "jam"-like sweet, reminiscent of figs or plums. The odor is extremely tenacious and uniform, never pungent. It would offer interesting twists to jasmin or neroli fragrances, and it blends excellently with violet bases, cassie, mimosa, etc. The flowers of the madonna lily (erroneously called "Easter Lily") have a very sweet, heavy-floral, honeylike fragrance with a short cresylic, ylang-ylang-like topnote and, at other times of the day, a suave, balsamic-sweet fragrance.

A true **Lilium Candidum Absolute** would undoubtedly find application in high-class perfumes as an interesting modifier and "bouquetting" material for floral or aldehydic bases, perhaps even in the heavier perfume types. Small quantities of true absolute of lilium candidum can always be made available upon reasonable notice. The material is not regularly produced in France.

A local variety of the lily is grown in Bermuda and other sunny west-Atlantic islands, and the flowers are treated by the enfleurage method in a perfume factory. Because a very large amount of synthetic perfume materials is imported to these islands, the author prefers not to describe Bermudan Lily "pommade"-absolute as a natural perfume material.

Lily of the Valley.

Laymen or people outside the perfumery profession are often very surprised when they are told that lily of the valley is not one of the important raw materials. In fact, it is hardly commercially available as a natural perfume oil. There are various reasons for this:

The cultivated **Convallaria Majalis** is considerably less fragrant than its wild growing relatives. The small, decorative plant grows wild in nearly all parts of Europe, and is found plentiful even in England and Scandinavia. However, the collection of individual flowers (which are very small), would demand a tremendous volume of hand labor which is not available at low cost in Europe. The yield of absolute by the conventional two-step extraction is not exactly low, but the product does not present to the perfumer either any strikingly unique notes, or a true-to-nature fragrance. As a matter of fact, in most cases, he can create an artificial lily-of-the-valley perfume base which is technically superior to the natural absolute, i.e. it performs better in a product than does the natural oil.

Incidentally, next to rose, jasmin and lilac, the creation of a lily-of-the-valley perfume type is one of the first problems presented to the advanced apprentice-perfumer. The author admits, with much regret, that he may never have been faced with a true, uncut absolute of the lily-of-the-valley flower. The odors of the samples and products with which the author has had an opportunity to work were all very far from the natural flower odor. At their best, these absolutes were very pleasantly fragrant, with a delicate floral quality and a distinct touch of greenness, surrounded by a fresh, rosy-lemony body note. **Butaflor Muguet** is one such commercially available product. The above described notes are all quite natural, and probably belong in the absolute, but the entire "picture" of this bouquet was far from that of the live flower and far inferior. It seems to be common practise in France to extract the entire inflorescence of the lily-of-the-valley and not only the individual flowers. The absolute will inevitably show a high percentage of "greenstalk" extract which affects the odor perceptibly. If improved extraction techniques cannot present the perfumers with an absolute of "muguet" or "lily-of-the-valley" which is powerful, rich and superior to the artificial muguet bases, there is little or no future for **Muguet Absolute**.

Among a great number of fashionable perfumes which are based mainly or entirely upon the "muguet" theme as a floral bodynote, are "Diorissimo", "Muguet des Bois", etc. The former is one of the most expensive perfumes on the market.

Lime Oil.

Commercially, we may define two types of **Lime Oil**:

1) Expressed lime oil, which can be prepared in the same way that lemon oil, orange oil, etc. are prepared from their fruits (by hand or by machine).

2) Distilled lime oil, which was the by-product (now often the main product) of the juice industry, similar to distilled sweet orange oil, but not obtained in quite the same way.

There are two main types of lime and several sub-varieties, but only one lime has any importance in lime oil industry: the so-called *sour lime*, also known as **Mexican Lime** or **West Indian Lime**, obtained from the small tree now called **Citrus Aurantifolia, Type** (earlier known as **Citrus Medica,** var. acida). The sweeter type of lime, another variety of **Citrus Aurantifolia,** is used only rarely for the production of essential oil. Yet another variety of the lime tree, **Citrus Limetta,** grows in Italy, and small lots of oil from the peel of its fruit occasionally enter the European market under the name of **Limette Oil.**

The origin of the lime tree is not definitely known, but it is believed that the tree came from the Far East, probably from the East Indian archipelago where it is found on almost all the islands to South America's Pacific coast and the jungles inland. The tree was also brought in the opposite direction to East Africa, Arabia, Iran (hence the name "Persian lime"), Egypt and southern Europe. It is most likely, that the West Indian and Florida limes are descendants of lime seeds brought to the West Indies shortly after the discovery of America. The lime trees now grow abundantly in all these tropical and semi-tropical regions, wild, semi-wild and in a cultivated stage.

Lime Oils are produced from unripe (green) fruits together with variable amounts of semi-ripe or fully ripe (yellow) limes (distilled lime oil), or exclusively from green limes (expressed lime oil). See the individual monographs on:

Lime Oil, distilled,
Lime Oil, expressed and
Lime Oil, terpeneless and sesquiterpeneless.

Lime Oil, distilled.

Out of an annual world production of more than 400 metric tons of **Lime Oils**, the major part by far is **Distilled Lime Oil.** There are two ways of producing a distilled lime oil:

1) By steam distillation of the crushed or comminuted peels,

2) By distillation of the acid juice from the lime fruit presses.

This juice will separate into three layers during a 2–4-week storage period in wooden tanks. The middle layer is lime juice and will usually be concentrated and canned. The upper layer is good juice, pulp and lime oil. The lower layer also contains some partly dissolved lime oil. This mixture is steam distilled cautiously, and the oil in the receiver is separated.

During the evaporation of the good lime juice, significant amounts of lime oil are separated, and this oil is mixed with the steam distilled oil. Obviously, the treatment in boiling water of high acidity has a pronounced effect upon the flavor of the delicate essential oil, but, surprisingly enough, most people prefer the distilled lime oil over the (hand or machine) expressed one because of its "greater similarity to natural lime flavor". Thus, the distilled lime oil is by far the most important of the lime oils.

Distilled Lime Oil is a pale yellow or almost water-white mobile liquid of sharp, fresh, terpene-like, somewhat perfumey-fruity citrus-type odor. The oil is very volatile (poor tenacity), but shows increasing sweetness on drying out, the notes becoming more orange-like, less lemon-like. As pointed out above, the general impression is that the odor of this oil is very reminiscent of the odor of fresh limes when they are halved and squeezed. In the author's opinion, however, the odor of distilled lime oil is considerably more "paint-can-like" or harsh-terpeney than that of the scratched peel of a green lime fruit. But when a halved lime fruit is squeezed in the preparation of limeade, the very acid juice is flavored with squirts from the peel; this mixture of acid juice and peel oil has a flavor very different from that of the oil alone.

The most modern method developed so far for the production of distilled lime oil uses super-heated steam and vacuum simultaneously; thus it is possible to distil halved, juice-exhausted fruits directly without adding water and at a comparatively low temperature. However, the conventional method of distilling the expressed juice from the whole fruit is still the most economical method: it requires less complicated equipment, and the operation itself requires less skill or technical knowhow.

A general description of **Distilled Lime Oil** would be rather superficial since there are numerous types and qualities on the market. For flavor use, a thorough evaluation of the flavor in the end product is recommended. There is a distinct difference between the oils distilled from the acid juice and those distilled from the juiceless, chipped peels.

The flavor quality of lime oil is dependant upon the content of so-called oxygenated constituents (as distinguished from the hydrocarbons = terpenes which form the bulk of the oil). Citral and some of the aliphatic aldehydes (C-8 to C-10), linalool, geraniol, terpineol, borneol and their esters supply the characteristic notes. The freshness, however, is undoubtedly due partly to the terpenes, among which limonene and natural dipentene actually have pleasant odors. Needless to say that if the oil is not fresh and if the terpenes are perceptibly decomposed or oxidized, the oil is worthless no matter how good the oxygenated components are. It seems that methyl anthranilate is found in expressed lime oil only (see the following monograph).

Distilled Lime Oil is used as a flavoring agent in soft drinks, candy and many kinds of food products. Terpeneless and sesquiterpeneless lime oil (see this monograph) is preferred for soft drinks for its superior solubility and stability. The **Cola**-type of carbonated beverages probably absorb the majority of all lime oils. The suggested use level of **Distilled Lime Oil** is 1.00 to 8.00 mg%, and the **Minimum Perceptible** is about 0.30 to 0.60 mg%.

In perfumes, the **Expressed Lime Oil** is often preferred since the terpeney note of the distilled oil is a note rarely wanted in perfumery. The peculiar freshness of the expressed oil has a unique effect in certain types of colognes, chypres, etc.

See monographs of **Lime Oil, Expressed** and **Lime Oil, Terpeneless** and **Sesquiterpeneless.**

Lime Oil, expressed.

A much smaller item than the distilled lime oil is the oil that is expressed by hand or machine from the peel of unripe, green limes. Only a very limited amount of this type of lime oil is produced, and the production is mainly carried out in the West Indies where Grenada, Montserrat and other islands specialize in expressed lime oil.

The uneven and very small size of lime fruits make machine expression of the oil a difficult operation. As a sort of a "happy medium" between hand pressing and distilling, the Mexican lime oil is often produced by centrifuging the liquid (pulp and oil) from the entire fruit in modern, high-speed centrifuges, the oil thus being separated quickly from the acid juice. This oil is obviously distinctly different from hand-pressed "ecuelled" oil since it has been in contact with large amounts of an acid liquid. These two types of cold-processing of lime oil give lower yields of oil than does the distillation process. Accordingly, expressed lime oils are more expensive than distilled lime oils.

Hand- or machine-pressed lime oil is a yellowish green, olive-green or dark green mobile liquid of intensely fresh, rich and sweet, peel-like odor, perhaps more lemon-like than the odor of distilled lime oil, but also mellower and somewhat "per-fumey". Thus, it does not reproduce the odor of the lime juice, and this may be the reason why many people think that the distilled oil bears a closer resemblance to the odor of lime than does the cold-processed, expressed oils.

In perfumes, where the cost is of minor importance since the concentration of lime oil always will be very low, the expressed oil is generally preferred. It gives interesting modifications to neroli in cologne bases, chypre bases, etc. and it lends a delightful topnote to modern aldehydic perfumes, etc. The author finds it particularly interesting in combination with cyclamal, lilial or similar floral aldehydes. It blends well not only with all other citrus oils, but also with citronella oil and its derivatives, lavender, lavandin, rosemary, sage clary, etc. In general, it is a fine topnote ingredient for "over-sweet" perfume types. In ambre bases, it produces quite intriguing notes which, in spite of their remoteness from the ambre type, lend a pleasant effect. The tenacity of the fragrance of expressed lime oil is quite outstanding. It exceeds by far that of the distilled lime oil and it is even superior to that of terpeneless, sesquiterpeneless lime oil. The natural fixatives in the oil are derivatives of coumarin, and their spicy-herbaceous and sweet-balsamic odor is distinctly perceptible in the dryout of expressed lime oil even after several days on a perfume blotter.

The **Expressed Lime Oil** is rarely used in flavors, although it has the typical peel flavor. It has also excellent masking effect on protein- or garlic-like food odors. Anyone who has enjoyed "Paw-Paw with lime" in British colonies, or the Islam specialty "samoussa" along with a quarter-section of an unpeeled green lime fruit, will admit that the peel flavor in combination with the acid juice has a tremendous masking effect in food where either bland taste (the paw-paw, also called papaya) or unpleasant flavor notes from cooked, chopped meat with garlic and spices (the "sam-oussa") profit from the refreshing addition of

lime peel-and-juice flavor. The effect is similar to that of **Lemon Oil** with its acid juice being used as a masking flavor for off-flavors in seafood (see **Lemon Oil**).

Expressed Lime Oil blends particularly well with **Lemon Oil** in flavor compositions. The combination of the two flavors has become one of the most popular flavors in carbonated beverages and sherbet ice, hard candy, etc. In general, lime oil is a good modifier for lemon oil and vice versa. This use of a related flavor as a modifier resembles the use of spearmint oil in peppermint flavors (and vice versa).

The author suggests a use level of 0.60 to 2.50 mg% for **Expressed Lime Oil**. The **Minimum Perceptible** is about 0.10 to 0.20 mg%. These figures show, that the oil is not a very powerful flavor material and that the superior perfume effect of **Expressed Lime Oil** as compared to terpeneless and sesquiterpeneless lime oil is not reflected in the flavor effect of expressed lime oil. Expressed lime oil is rarely processed into a terpeneless oil, although it would seem reasonable to do so in view of the much lower content of "residue" in expressed oil as compared to distilled oil. But the annual production of expressed oil remains very low, perhaps only a few tons.

Expressed lime oil may be adulterated with additions of distilled lime oil, lemon oil, terpenes from lime oil or other citrus oils and, rarely, with turpentine, pine oil fractions, dipentene, etc. The small amounts of anthranilates in expressed lime oils give these oils a comparatively high specific gravity which is easily lowered by the addition of monoterpenes. Unfortunately, modern instrumental analysis has made it possible to perform an even more skilful adulteration of lime oil, but a thorough organoleptic evaluation will usually tell the buyer when he has a good and natural oil.

The numerous varieties of lime fruits on the market indicate that wide variations must be expected in the types of lime oils offered. Lime oil is now the main product (economically); previously, it was only a by-product. Consequently, more attention is paid to the quality of lime oil, and it is beyond doubt that the quality has improved significantly during the past decades. Production of lime juice offers many problems, and the waste is enormous due to the fermentation of the sugar-and-acid-containing juice in the tropical climates.

Expressed Lime Oil represents a comparatively

rare example of natural occurrence of anthranilates and aldehydes in the same oil. This combination is often avoided in perfumery because of the color-intensification and odor-change by the formation of the so-called "Schiff's bases".

Lime Oil, terpeneless and sesquiterpeneless.

Terpeneless, sesquiterpeneless lime oil is prepared from distilled lime oil, rarely from expressed lime oil, by the conventional methods of deterpenation. See **Terpeneless Oils**, Part One of this work and **Lemon Oil, Terpeneless** and **Sesquiterpeneless**, Part Two of this work. The author would certainly prefer to work with a terpeneless, sesquiterpeneless lime oil from **Expressed Lime Oil**. The virtually deterpenated lime oil is a pale yellow or almost colorless liquid of a powerful, sweet-fruity, grape-like, somewhat perfumey odor, reminiscent of neroli or terpeneless petitgrain oil on the dryout.

The terpeneless fraction constitutes only a very small part of the lime oil, and the terpeneless oil thus becomes quite expensive. The separated terpene fractions find little use in perfumery. They are often mixed with other terpenes under the name of "citrus terpenes", but they also find their way back to lime oil as an adulterant (diluent). The flavor value of lime terpenes is negligible.

Terpeneless, Sesquiterpeneless Lime Oil is used extensively in flavors, particularly in carbonated beverages where its superior stability, good solubility and richness of body is greatly appreciated. Trace amounts of cyclamal can give very interesting twists to a lime flavor based upon terpeneless lime oil. For hard candy, etc., the natural, distilled lime oil is often preferred for its lower cost and for its greater similarity to the lime-juice + lime-peel flavor picture. In the popular lemon-lime flavor combination for soft drinks, however, a comparatively large proportion of terpeneless, sesquiterpeneless lime oil is needed to produce a pleasant balance, sufficiently different from straight lemon flavor. Recent statistics show that lemon-lime flavor is second in popularity next to cola flavor in the U.S.A. and several other markets. In the cola-type of flavor which is the most popular all over the world, lime is combined with cinnamon, orange and other natural flowers. Terpeneless, sesquiterpeneless lime oil blends excellently with bitter orange oil and it produces

interesting modifications in grape, gooseberry, red currant, mandarin, "tutti-frutti" and many other types of fruit flavor. The suggested use level is 0.05 to 0.10 mg% and the **Minimum Perceptible** is as low as 0.005 to 0.010 mg%. These figures reveal a great flavor power, but they do not tell about the lack of flavor body at this high silution. In this respect, the **Expressed Lime Oil** is superior.

Linaloe Seed Oil.

From the "seeds" (these fruits are berries) and husks of the **Linaloe** tree (see monograph on **Linaloe Wood Oil**), an essential oil can be steam distilled, often producing a very attractive yield. While the linaloe tree grows wild in Mexico and probably originates from that area, the seeds are not distilled in Mexico in any great amounts. When trees are felled so that the wood may be distilled, it is not a good policy also to distil the seed with which new trees may be produced after 20 to 30 years of growing.

Shortly after 1900, English settlers in India brought linaloe seeds along with seeds of many other interesting Central- and South American plants to their Fareastern estates. In the fertile Mysore province, great plantings were laid out, and not many years later, the first experimental distillations of **Linaloe Seed Oil** were undertaken in India. Thus, the trees continue to grow, and the harvesting of seeds can even take place earlier than the cutting of wood for distillation.

Furthermore, in India, the **Husks** from the linaloe fruits are distilled, and they yield oil in abundance. **Linaloe Seed-and-Husk Oil** is quite similar in odor type to **Linaloe Wood Oil**, but it is somewhat harsher, with a slightly bitter topnote. The more husks included in the distillation, the higher content of **Linalyl-Acetate** in the oil will be. It is even claimed that **Linaloe Husk Oil**, if steam distilled under reduced pressure, e.g. 250 mm. Hg. (a recent and interesting development in distillation technique), consists almost entirely of linalyl acetate, an ester which apparently is hydrolyzed in the ordinary steam distillation; compare steam distillation of lavender at high altitude (low atmospheric pressure!).

A linaloe leaf-and-twig oil is also distilled in India. This oil consists almost entirely of linalool (about 50%) and linalyl acetate (about 40%). Oils of this composition have very little if anything at all, to offer to the perfume industry in countries

33: Rotary extractor for **Lavandin** at Tiddas, Morocco. Similar extractors are at hand for the production of **Geranium, Labdanum** and **Oakmoss** concrètes in that area. *(Fot. S. Arctander, 1960)*

34: Flower, leaves and a tiny, unripe fruit of the **Lemon** tree in Cyprus island. The leaves yield **Lemon Petitgrain** oil upon steam distillation. *(Fot. S. Arctander, 1956)*

35: The gigantic **Lemons** of sunny Cyprus island yield an excellent juice and a very high grade **Lemon Oil** in the modern citrus fruit processing plant of Lanitis, Limassol.　　　　　*(Fot. S. Arctander, 1956)*

where linalool-bearing oils are freely available at low cost, or where synthetic linalool is produced at competitive price. Consequently, these Indian oils are rarely exported. It serves no purpose to describe individual samples of these oils since they vary substantially according to the ratio of seed, husks or twigs used in the distillation. The oils are almost colorless and present typical linalool-linalyl acetate odors with more or less pronounced terpene-like topnote. The topnote is generally lighter, less "rubberlike", less myrcene-like than the topnote of Brazilian or Peruvian bois de rose oils.

Linaloe Seed Oil is used locally in India in the same way as bois de rose oil is used elsewhere, while the **Linaloe Husk Oil** is a local (Indian) source of natural isolated linalyl acetate. The annual production of these oils is steadily increasing and is presently estimated to be in excess of 10 metric tons.

Linaloe Wood Oil.

Linaloe wood oil, also called **Mexican Linaloe Oil**, is steam distilled from the wood of old and deliberately damaged trees of **Bursera** species, particularly **Bursera Delpechiana**. It is a common practice to include the fruits of the tree in the distillation since this increases the yield of oil considerably (see **Linaloe Seed Oil**, previous monograph).

Distillation of linaloe wood oil takes place in the central and western parts of southern Mexico where the trees grow wild or replanted, partly self-propagated. The essential oil can be considered partly a pathological product since the oil content in undamaged trees is too low for an economical exploitation. Occasionally, wood from damaged (incised, lacerated, etc.) trees is shipped to the U.S.A. or Europe to be distilled. Experiments have shown that the oil yield in a modern still is far better than that from local stills.

Linaloe Wood Oil is a pale yellow or almost colorless liquid, occasionally turbid or dirty; its color may be pale orange when it is kept in poor containers (iron, rust, dirt, moisture). The odor of this oil is sweet-woody and floral, with a more or less green and oily topnote according to the quality of the oil. Very good oils are rare, and they show little or no pungent notes in the top, but have a sweet, delicate floralness which remains fairly constant and uniform throughout all stages

of evaporation. In perfumery, therefore, good grades of linaloe wood oil can be used as blenders or even bases in floral perfumes, e.g. muguet, lilac, appleblossom, freesia, rose, sweet pea, etc., while the oil can find general application as a modifier for numerous floral and floral-woody perfume types.

Linaloe Wood Oil has been exposed to persistent adulteration in the years when the oil reached its greatest popularity, i.e. before the intense competition offered by Brazilian and Peruvian **Bois de Rose Oil** and Formosan **Ho Leaf Oil** (see these monographs). With the abundance of these linalool-bearing oils, and with the appearance of low-cost synthetic **Linalool** in rapidly increasing quantities on the market, **Mexican Linaloe Wood Oil** has little or no hope of a bright future. The yields from the primitive Mexican stills are poor, and the necessity of felling entire old trees to produce an essential oil is certainly less practical than that of distilling leaves which can be stripped from live trees year after year.

Seeds from Mexican linaloe trees were brought to India early in the twentieth century. See monograph on **Linaloe Seed Oil**.

Linseed Oil Absolute.

Among a wealth of unusual products which are often produced only upon demand, we must include the alcohol-extraction product of raw **Linseed Oil**. This kind of perfumery material represents the results of various perfumers' study of natural flowers and their fragrance. In their intense search for notes with which they can duplicate certain of nature's fragrances, the perfumers often have to use materials other than the conventional flower extracts or straight synthetic chemicals. If a perfumer feels that there is a garlic-like note in a rose-base which he must duplicate, he will not hesitate to study the garlic-type odors available in his laboratory or from a well-furnished supply-house: for example, absolute of asafoetida.

Linseed Oil Absolute is obviously an example of just such a situation. When perfumers tried to duplicate the finer shades of lily, lilac, orange-flower, jasmin, tuberose, gardenia, etc., they found that the conventional amyl cinnamic aldehyde was not satisfactory. Modifications with hexyl cinnamic aldehyde, undecanolide, etc. did not solve the problem. Rancid castor oil has notes similar to the unwanted notes in amyl cinnamic aldehyde (poor grade ACA, heptanal-odor, amyl nonenal-odor, etc.). Beeswax absolute (see monograph) does not lend the natural fatty-greasy odor of the flower petals. But Linseed Oil (raw, but not rancid!) definitely has notes like those of the flower waxes, notes which are particularly distinguishable in the "enfleurage"-type absolutes.

Linseed Oil is hydraulically expressed from the seeds of Linum Usitatissimum. This small plant originated in western Asia and is widely cultivated all over the world. Argentina, Canada, India, U.S.A. and U.S.S.R. are main producers of linseed. The raw (crude) linseed oil is a yellow, oily liquid of faint odor. It oxidizes easily upon exposure to air. The oil consists mainly of the glyceryl esters of oleic, stearic, myristic, palmitic, linoleic and linolenic acids. Linseed oil is slightly soluble in cold ethyl alcohol.

Only raw (i.e. unboiled and unoxidized) linseed oil can be used for preparation of absolute. Poppyseed Oil has a similar odor, but is not nearly as freely available as linseed oil.

Linseed Oil Absolute is a yellowish to light amber colored, oily liquid of mild, fatty-oily odor, reminiscent of the odor of freshly expressed linseed oil (after proper ageing). The odor is also reminiscent of the slightly fishy-animal-like odor of fresh cod liver oil and of a refined oleic acid.

The absolute is not commercially available, but it is prepared upon request. Some consumers prefer to produce their own linseed oil absolute. The use of this material is limited to the above flower oil duplications and similar perfumery problems.

Lippia Carviodora.

English botanists have been busy in East Africa where the flora of Kenya, Uganda, Tanganyika and Somaliland has been thoroughly investigated. The author found the labiate Lippia Carviodora growing wild in Kenya, but the plant is also cultivated experimentally to facilitate harvesting and distillation of the essential oil.

Oil of Lippia Carviodora is steam distilled from the flowering tops of the plant, but if increased production becomes important, the leaves undoubtedly will also be distilled since their oil is almost identical to that obtained from the flowers.

The oil is pale yellow to brownish-yellow, rather mobile, and possessing an odor which can hardly be described without the use of the term Caraway.

Except for dill seed oil, no other essential oil is so strikingly similar to caraway as the oil from Lippia Carviodora. It is an obvious source of a caraway-spearmint type of flavor oil for African countries (chewing gum, toothpaste, etc.), and may also find some application in perfumery since this oil is surprisingly stable in soaps. It has great odor-power, and equals caraway oil in this respect. Its flavor is less refined, but through rectification, the author believes this drawback could be removed.

Production of lippia carviodora oil is still on an experimental scale, but the oil should have a solid future in Africa's huge, local markets. The oil is not offered as a regular item by European or American essential oil houses. It has nothing in particular to offer in countries where spearmint, caraway and synthetic carvone is freely available.

See also Lippia Daunensis.

Lippia Daunensis.

For many decades, Italian scientists and botanists have investigated the flora of East Africa, particularly that of Abyssinia (Ethiopia) and Somaliland. They found the labiate Lippia Daunensis among the more interesting perfume plants. A comprehensive report on the findings and the results of the analytical work with respect to this and other East African plants can be found in the Italian periodical: Rivista Italiane Essenze, Profumi, Vol. 38, 1956, page 506.

The author has no personal experience with the essential oil of Lippia Daunensis, but finds it interesting enough to warrant mention since various other Lippia species have attained a degree fame:

Lippia Citriodora—see: Verbena Oil, and
Lippia Daunensis (East African carvone source). The two oils are described in this book.

Lippia daunensis oil is steam distilled from the flowering tops of the plant which grows wild and very abundantly in Somaliland. The oil is yellow and its odor reminded the author of the above Italian periodical of tagette ("marigold") and wormwood, later, also of tobacco. It apparently has a dark-foliage type of Compositae-fragrance. Other authors may have confused this oil with the Kenya oil of Lippia Carviodora (see monograph).

Oil of Lippia Daunensis may very well find a future in the African perfume industry, but the oil does apparently not present odor characteristics of sufficient interest to the European and American perfume houses.

Litsea Cubeba.

The Chinese "May Chang" tree of the laurel family has been known for its fragrant flowers, fruits and leaves for a long time. But it was not until the early 1950's that the essential oil steam-distilled from the small, pepperlike fruits (for which the name Cubeba probably was attached to the botanical name) became more widely known, although it is still not available in all countries of the world.

The small tree, Litsea Cubeba, grows in Eastern Asia, former Indochina, and is cultivated to a minor extent in Formosa and Japan. Today, China produces substantial quantities of this oil, the annual output probably exceeding 50 metric tons, and still increasing. Only a small part of the production is exported. The oil is irregularly available in Europe, Africa, Asia and Australia, and it offers strong competition to lemongrass oil, even in the cost.

Oil of Litsea Cubeba is a pale yellow, mobile oil of intensely lemon-like, fresh and sweet odor, with a soft and sweet-fruity, uniform dryout. There are few or no "fatty-grassy" methyl heptenone notes detectable. This is where the oil of litsea cubeba has a definite advantage over lemongrass oil. The citral contents of the two oils are almost equal. However, lemongrass oil has a superior odor-tenacity due to its "heavy" sesquiterpene-part, with a tone-out of sweet and moderately pleasant notes. Furthermore, the oil of Litsea Cubeba has also a pleasant taste, and a rectified oil could be used in flavor work as a modifier for lemon and lime flavors, and as a general freshener in fruit flavors. For use in perfumes, litsea cubeba oil could replace lemongrass oil to a certain degree, but the Chinese oil would probably find better use in artificial verbena type bases, colognes, household sprays, air fresheners, etc. It blends well with all the citrus oils, petitgrain oils, rosemary oil, lavandin, camphor-sassafras oils, ocotea pretiosa oil, bois de rose oil, decyl alcohol, geraniol, citronellol, nerol and countless other natural and synthetic perfume materials. The oil has very little fixative power and needs clever blending and fixation for successful use in soap perfumes.

Oil of Litsea Cubeba serves as a source of Citral in China. A related tree, Litsea Citrata, is planted as a windbreaker in Chinese tea-groves. The leaves of this tree yield an essential oil upon distillation. This oil contains certain amounts of citral, but not enough for economic isolation of this material. The literature often confuses the two oils or the two trees which are considered distinctly different species according to authoritative botanical works. It is very likely, however, that the Chinese name "May-Chang" was originally applied to the Litsea Citrata.

Longoza Absolute from Concrète.

Probably originating in Malaya and East India, the decorative plant of the Zingiberaceae (ginger family), Hedychium Flavum, was brought to Madagascar and the surrounding islands by early immigrants. The flowers, known under the English name of Garland or Butterfly Lilies, were used for decorations and perfuming. These names are still used by the English in India. It has been claimed that the "False Cardamom", Aframomum Angustifolium, was also the source of longoza flowers. The author was unable to find aframomum angustifolium in Madagascar, Nossi-Bé or Réunion, but he found hedychium flavum profusely growing partly wild in all the three of these areas (1955/1956). The fruits are a delicacy of the native children.

In Nossi-Bé, the tiny perfume island off the northwest coast of Madagascar, longoza flowers are treated with petroleum ether to yield a concrète which is shipped to France to be processed to an absolute. The annual production of Longoza Concrète in Nossi-Bé is about 30 to 50 kilos. Production in Réunion and on the Madagascan mainland had been abandoned at the time of the author's last visit (1955/1956). Little is known about production in India, but according to private communications received by the author, there is no regular production of a pure Longoza extract in India today. A production was commenced in 1958 in Formosa where the concrète and the absolute are produced locally. Small quantities of Formosan concrète and absolute of longoza have been offered in Europe and the U.S.A. since 1959.

Longoza Concrète is a chocolate-brown, waxy, almost solid mass. It yields about 50% of an alcohol-soluble absolute.

Longoza Absolute from Concrète is a dark

brown or orange-brown, very viscous liquid; at times, it can hardly be poured at room temperature. The odor is extremely rich, sweet-floral, deep-fruity-honey-like, with a peculiar spicy and vanilla-tuberose-like undertone. Its tenacity and penetrating power in perfume compositions is often underestimated. Fractions of one percent in a perfume base may change the entire performance and overall characteristics of the fragrance. The green-floral, lily-like note in the odor of longoza absolute is often enhanced unexpectedly when the absolute is used in mixed floral compositions. It blends well with orange flower absolute, jasmin, tuberose(!?), narcissus (for pronounced green-floral notes), ylang-ylang, benzyl acetate, isojasmones, cassione, isoeugenol, undecanolide, phenylethyl phenylacetate, Peru balsam oil, phenylethyl cinnamate, amyl cinnamate, veratraldehyde, linalyl cinnamate and numerous other sweet-floral, balsamic or honeylike perfume materials. Longoza Absolute is one of the best natural tools in the hand of the experienced perfumer who wants to duplicate the tuberose fragrance. It is amusing, however, to find in the perfumery literature certain formulas where tuberose absolute is recommended as a substitute for longoza! The present cost of longoza absolute is only a few percent of the cost of tuberose absolute (if and when this is available). In other words, longoza absolute is a relatively inexpensive flower oil (1959: about $ 85.– to $ 100.– per lb.).

Longoza Absolute from Concrète can be used in flavors with a quite interesting effect and very good results. It will lend a certain naturalness and rich undertone to artificial vanilla flavors, particularly those intended for chocolate. The absolute blends excellently with vanillin, "ethyl"-vanillin, anisyl alcohol, castoreum tincture, methyl anisate, etc., materials often used in artificial vanilla flavors. Its enormous power compensates for its cost and poor availability, but although "a little goes a long way" the material is far too scarce to become a current item in the "large" ice cream flavor formulas. The average use level is about 0.10 to 0.30 mg% and the Minimum Perceptible is 0.03 to 0.05 mg%.

Unfortunately, Longoza Absolute is very often adulterated, and since only a few French houses supply this material, the true absolute suffers due to the poor impression left with customers, whose first experience with this material may be unpleasant due to their receiving a heavily adulterated longoza absolute. The oddest materials are used in this fraud: cyclamenaldehyde, amyl phenylacetate, vanillin, methyl benzoate, Peru balsam, vanilla extracts, St. John's bread extracts, etc. etc. Only an organoleptic examination of the material will screen the true longoza from the adulterated ones. This is a case where buying the concrète as directly from the source as possible may be the only solution for a would-be consumer of this rare material.

On the other hand, longoza absolute is an excellent material for adulterating other, more expensive flower absolutes, e.g. tuberose and gardenia. But here again, its poor availability puts a certain limit to large scale adulteration.

Longoza Absolute has no substitute, and it will probably remain on the list of only a few suppliers. It would be interesting, however, to see this material become more readily available and to study the endless field of application of this outstanding perfume and flavor material.

Louro Brasileiro.

Among a wealth of trees belonging to the family of Lauraceae in South America, Louro Brasileiro and Louro Nhamuy (see following monograph) may possibly have some future in the perfumery field. Louro Brasileiro is a tree whose wood is steam distilled to yield an essential oil of some local interest to the Brazilian soap perfumery market. The oil is rarely, if ever, offered outside Brazil. Production could easily be increased to meet almost any demand, but it seems inconceivable that this oil will ever attain much interest in large scale perfumery outside its country of origin.

Oil of Louro Brasileiro is a pale yellow or almost colorless, somewhat viscous liquid. Its odor is dry and woody with a brief, oily-green, almost cuminic topnote. The dryout of this tenacious odor is faintly cedar-cubeb-like. It can be used as a blender in general, and it contributes very little odor to the perfumes in which it is incorporated. In view of its rather uninteresting odor, it is not likely that this oil will find many enthusiasts outside of Brazil. The annual production is at present less than 5 metric tons.

Louro Nhamuy.

This oil, also known as Louro Inhamuy, has in

itself probably little or no interest for the practising perfumer. But investigations made a decade ago (see Yves-René Naves' bulletin from the Givaudan Research Laboratories in Geneva, Oct. 5, 1951, bulletin No. 245) show that the distillation of Brazilian bois de rose oil used to be carried out with little consideration given to the correct botanical species. Other trees growing nearby were felled and occasionally admixed with the "bois de rose" (see monograph) in the native stills at Manaus, Brazil. Among the trees suspected in connection with this contamination was **Louro Nhamuy**, whose botanical name is **Nectandra Elaiophora** (or **Aniba Elaiophora**). Oil of louro nhamuy has been distilled in that area for more than 30 years.

The oil is a pale yellow, mobile liquid of fresh and strongly terpene-like, sweet odor. There is little or no resemblance to the odor of true bois de rose oil, but the author finds that the odor of louro nhamuy oil has much in common with the odor of petitgrain monoterpenes and foreruns (from the production of terpeneless petitgrain oil). The sweet, bitter-leafy undertone and the fresh-terpenic bodynote is pleasantly rounded off by distinct notes of linalyl acetate type.

Oil of **Louro Nhamuy** is a possible source of contamination of the Peruvian bois de rose oil, too. This oil is shipped from Iquitos almost 2,400 miles on the Amazon river before it reaches the Atlantic Ocean. It is interesting to note that Brazilian bois de rose oil is shipped 900 miles on the same river. The Peruvian oil passes right by the Brazilian distilleries after 1,500 miles of river transportation. Yet, the Peruvian oil is usually slightly lower in cost!

Louro Nhamuy Oil is still produced for local consumption in Brazil. It is not likely that the oil will find a market in the American or European perfume industry.

Lovage Herb Oil.

Probably the most powerful natural flavor material that the author has ever encountered in his studies is the essential oil of **Lovage Herb**. See monograph on **Lovage Root Oil** for details about the botanical origin, etc.

Lovage Herb Oil is steam distilled from the freshly harvested overground parts of the lovage plant at full maturity. The oil is not produced on a commercial scale, but smaller lots are available from Yugoslavia, Hungary and Belgium.

The oil is a colorless or very pale yellow to greenish-yellow, mobile liquid of extremely diffusive odor. The initial notes of its odor resemble those of lovage root oil, celery seed oil and mentha citrata oil. The undertone and dryout notes are extremely sweet-aromatic, sweet-floral, reminiscent of cardamom oil and bergamot oil. The celery-lovage note is quite persistent throughout the stages of evaporation, and the tenacity is good. The flavor is even more interesting to study since it reveals all the virtues—and many of the components—of the oil at various stages of dilution. Although the author would recommend an average use level of 0.01 to 0.06 mg% in neutral media, it is difficult to give exact figures in the case of an oil with a very peculiar flavor type. Its use is strictly limited to such flavor compositions where a lovage-celery-cardamom flavor will be accepted. The **Minimum Perceptible** of this oil is approximately 0.0001 to 0.0002 mg%. In other words, the flavor or this oil can be identified as lovage (lovage-type) flavor in the dilution of one part in more than 500 million parts of a 9% sugar water at 10°C. In a previous publication, the author has pointed out the use of the flavor "power-factor" (Soap, Perfumery & Cosmetics, April 1959, page 389-393). With a "power-factor" of over 100 (the minimum perceptible is at least 100 times lower than the "pleasant average" use level), the oil of **Lovage Herb** is unique as a most penetrating flavor.

The oil can find use in numerous types of food flavor, meat sauces, seasonings, pickle flavors, etc. The author has used the oil experimentally in an artificial cardamom oil, and it is very likely that the oil can find a wider field of application. Its use in perfumery would be very limited, and it would take more than the average of experience and skill to incorporate this oil successfully in a perfume for cosmetic purposes.

See also **Lovage Root Oil**.

Lovage Oleoresin.

See also **Lovage Oil**. Quite frequently, lovage extracts are sold under the label, "**Lovage Oil**". The yield is higher, and the product is superior as a flavor material when lovage roots are extracted rather than steam distilled. There seems to be a tendency towards general acceptance of lovage extracts as "lovage oil". In all cases, unless otherwise stated, the **Root** is the botanical starting material. By extraction of the roots with petroleum ether, ethyl alcohol, rectified gasoline, benzene or acetone, various extracts are produced. Petroleum ether yields less extract, but a lighter colored one. Benzene must be removed completely from the extract prior to its being used in food.

Lovage Oleoresin is usually a very viscous, dark brown or dark amber colored liquid of intensely sweet, rich and spicy-aromatic, warm odor, reminiscent of celery, angelica, tonka, etc., with a slightly musky-woody undertone. Although quite similar to the essential oil in odor characteristics, the extract is much "heavier" in type, presenting little or no "lift" or topnote, yet, it has comparatively good diffusive power. (Compare angelica root oil and angelica root absolute). The flavor of lovage oleoresin is more pungent than that of the oil and, here again, the reduced topnote effect influences the overall flavor effect.

In perfumery, **Lovage Root Oleoresin** or **Lovage Root Absolute** is used sparingly in heavy, Oriental bases, fougères, spice blends, new mown hay bases, etc.

In flavors, it may replace the root or the abandoned tincture in the flavoring of meat sauces, seasonings, pickles, salts, etc. The suggested use level is about 0.03 to 0.10 mg%, and the **Minimum Perceptible** is close to 0.008 mg%. These figures vary considerably according to the type of oleoresin, type of solvent used, etc. The power of this material is easily underestimated, and great experience is needed to enjoy fully the effects of this extremely tenacious odor and powerful flavor in perfume and flavor creation.

Lovage Oleoresin and **Lovage Absolute** are occasionally adulterated with the materials mentioned under **Lovage Oil** (see following monograph). The annual production is very limited, but it has been steadily increasing beyond the 100-kilo mark.

Lovage Root Oil.

Previously known as **Lovage Oil**, this very interesting and extremely potent material is produced by steam distillation of the comminuted roots of **Levisticum Officinale**, a man-size herb related to angelica and pimpinella. The herb grows wild in central and southern Europe and is cultivated in numerous countries: Belgium, Czechoslovakia, France, Germany, Holland, Hungary, Yugoslavia, etc. It belongs to the group of medicinal plants commonly cultivated by the monks in medieval times all over Europe. At this point, it should be stated that the product which is commercially labelled **Lovage Oil** often is an extracted product (compare: chamomile, myrrh, costus, etc.). The extracted product has been described in the previous monograph (see **Lovage Oleoresin**).

Lovage Oil is an amber to olive-brown colored liquid of very powerful and rich, spicy-warm, fresh-aromatic, intensely sweet and "root-like" odor, suggestive of celery, angelica, licorice extract, deertongue oleoresin, etc. The flavor is slightly pungent, but only in high concentrations. The warm-spicy and "soup-like" celery note is predominant; the intensity is striking. **Lovage Oil** is used in perfumes in minute amounts to produce "special effects", or to lend warm background notes in spicy or Oriental bases. It gives interesting effects with rose bases and in carnation compositions, it blends excellently with costus, galbanum, macrocyclic musks, opopanax, coumarin derivatives, oakmoss products, bay leaf oil, lavandin absolute, isoeugenol, cinnamic aldehyde and cinnamic alcohol, flouve oil (particularly in flavor compositions), etc. In flavors, it gives rich body to essences for alcoholic beverages (liqueurs of the D.O.M. and similar types), and it is an excellent additive in spicy compounds for seasonings, pickles, meat sauces, etc. It gives interesting combinations with flouve oil, deertongue and bergamot oil for tobacco flavoring. The suggested use level (food flavors) is about 0.02 to 0.08 mg%, and the **Minimum Perceptible** is approximately 0.0005 to 0.0010 mg%. In respect to penetrative odor, this oil ranks among the most powerful of all natural materials.

Lovage Root Oil is occasionally adulterated with the essential oil from lovage seed or herb (see **Lovage Herb Oil**), or it can be "bouquetted" with synthetic additives such as **Cyclotene** (hydroxymethyl-cyclopentenone), **Maraniol** (4-methyl-7-ethoxy coumarin), or with **n-butyl phthalide** and **n-butylidene phthalide**, synthetically prepared constituents of the natural lovage root oil. These synthetic materials are commercially available.

The annual world production of **Lovage Root Oil** is less than one metric ton.

Lupulin.

See also monographs on **Hop Absolute** and **Hop Oil.**

Lupulin is the glandular trichomes from the strobiles of the **Hops.** It constitutes the most important part of hops with respect to flavor. Various flavoring materials are prepared from lupulin. The intensely yellow, dustlike, yet sticky substance, **Lupulin,** is extracted with volatile solvents to produce an oleoresin, or, in the case of alcohol-extraction, a tincture. The **Lupulin Oleoresin** is particularly rich in the typical bitter flavor materials for which beer is so well known. However, these bitter substances are hardly at all distillable, and are not present in distilled flavor concentrates.

The very large and comprehensively described every-day flavors (beer, cocoa, coffee, fruits, tea, etc.) will not be discussed in this work; but hops and lupulin can be used in a multitude of flavors other than beer. When lupulin is extracted with ethyl alcohol, and subsequently washed with weak alcohol and, finally, with water, a cloudy tincture is produced. This tincture can be distilled to produce a 45%, 50% or 60% alcoholic, clear tincture known as **Lupulin Aromadistillate** (see **Aromadistillate,** Part One of this work). This product is an extremely interesting flavor material. It lends a rich, natural body to many fruit flavors, particularly apple, and it blends well with the spicy flavors, e.g. as a modifier in ginger ale flavors, or in the complex flavors where sweet or bitter orange are among the carriers.

Lupulin Oleoresin is very rarely used as such, but it might find application in flavors or perfumes, e.g. in combination with **Armoise, Wormwood Absolute,** etc. **Lupulin** is commercially available in many grades, and it takes considerable experience to select good from poor quality. The quality of **Lupulin** is heavily impaired by ageing or poor storage conditions.

M

Mace Extract.

Because of the considerable amount of odorless alcohol-soluble matter (ballast materials) contained in nutmegs (see **Nutmeg Extract**), mace (the dried arillodes) has been suggested as a starting material for the production of aromatic extracts. Mace does not contain significant amounts of fixed oil or other odorless matter, soluble in hot alcohol. On the other hand, it should be kept in mind that for every ton of dried nutmegs harvested, there are only 50 or 60 kilos of dried mace. But the demand is rather small for perfumery use, and the perfume industry can afford to be particular in such cases.

The dried comminuted mace is extracted with alcohol. After removal of the solvent under gentle vacuum, a viscous, orange-red or brownish-amber colored liquid is produced in a yield of 12 to 14 percent of the dry arillode. Since this is a product of hot extraction, it is not a true absolute, but it is generally called **Mace Extract.** It is soluble in almost any perfume or flavor material. The odor is fresh and spicy with a warm, rich and almost balsamic undertone. There are no sharp or pungent terpene-like notes or "rubber-like" topnote such as can be experienced with nutmeg oil. Its flavor is warm, slightly pungent at higher concentrations, sweet and aromatic-spicy with an excellent masking effect. The power seems immediately rather moderate since there is no "lift" from monoterpenes in this product. Suggested use level is 2 to 4 mg%, and the **Minimum Perceptible** is 0.30 to 0.80 mg%.

In flavor work, it gives a very close reproduction of the natural spice; it may even be classified as an improved edition of the natural spice with respect to organoleptic performance and overall attractiveness. It is furthermore one of the most concentrated forms of the nutmeg/mace flavor. It has the great advantage over the essential oils of nutmeg and mace in that it contains less terpenes, and accordingly is more stable in aqueous and acid flavor media, a condition under which nutmeg and mace are frequently used (pickles, sauces, seasonings, etc.). With lime oil, cinnamon bark oil, bitter orange oil, cardamom oil, ginger oil, etc., it produces the most delightfully rich aromatic-spicy flavor blends, and its excellent masking effect is known and utilized in the food industry (cabbage odors, etc.).

In perfumery, mace extract finds some use along with other spicy and warm-aromatic materials for "men's colognes", after-shaves, fougères, chypres, in modern fantasy lotion perfumes, etc. It blends well with geraniol, nerol, lavandin absolute, oakmoss products, linalool, coriander oil, sage clary oil, terpineol, petitgrain oil, lime oil, mandarin oil, rosemary oil, etc.

Mace Extract is also available as an **Ultrasonic Extract,** and this material, too, seems to have a good future in the perfume and flavor industries. Due to the special method of production, however, the ultrasonic extract is generally more suitable for flavors than for perfumes.

See also **Nutmeg Extract** and **Nutmeg Oil.**

Machilus Oil.

Machilus oil is distilled from the wood of **Machilus Kusanoi,** a Formosan tree of the genus Lauraceae. The oil is produced in Japan, occasionally in Formosa.

The main constituent of this oil is **Eudesmol** (see also **Cryptomeria Japonica, Atractylis Concrète, Araucaria Oil,** etc.). The wood oil of machilus is amber-colored or pale olive-green, viscous or almost solid. The odor is slightly spicy-woody, tobacco-like or cigarbox-like, somewhat earthy, mild, but tenacious. There is some resemblance to the odor of araucaria, guaiacwood, atractylis, etc.; it is, however, milder and less peppery than the latter.

Machilus Wood Oil could find use as a fixative in perfumes for soap, or to sepak generally, where a woody fixative is called for. The oil blends well with oakmoss, ionones, linalool, cedarwood oils and cedarwood derivatives, sandalwood oil, citrus oils, clove oils, pine needle oils, coumarin, cinnamic alcohol, etc. Its limited availability may restrict its use to that of a local soap perfume fixative.

An essential oil distilled from the leaves of the same tree and labelled **Hayata Oil** was submitted to the author. This oil was almost colorless, and its odor was strongly reminiscent of that of camphor oil (sassafras type), pine oil and pine needle oil. If available in larger quantities, the **Hayata Oil** or **Machilus Leaf Oil** could find use in soap perfumery, or as a source of **Safrole,** etc. **Hayata Oil** is produced in Formosa (irregularly) and on the Chinese mainland. The oil resembles **Hinoki Leaf Oil** in respect to odor (see **Chamaecyparis Obtusa** forma formosana) and the two oils are often confused in markets outside their countries of origin.

Magnolia.

To the best of the author's knowledge, there are no true, natural **Magnolia** flower products commercially available for perfumery use. But since various products under the label **Magnolia Absolute** or the like are occasionally offered by a few perfume material suppliers, a few lines will discuss **Magnolia.**

Out of a wealth of magnolia species, only a few come into consideration as possible perfume plants: **Magnolia Grandiflora** is a tree indigenous to the southeastern states of the U.S.A., but cultivated quite commonly in southern Europe for its beautiful flowers. Experimental batches of magnolia oil and **Magnolia Absolute** have been prepared in Italy. The flowers of this magnolia have an extremely delicate, sweet fragrance, reminiscent of rose, violet and orangeflowers or, in the opinion of others, like rosa canina, the common hedgerose (dogrose, hiprose). In Japan and China, various magnolias are cultivated as ornamental trees and shrubs. To the author's knowledge, these magnolias are not exploited for perfume oil production.

The northeast-American **Tulip Tree,** the beautiful **Liriodendron Tulipifera,** best known for its wood ("whitewood"), produces a wealth of characteristic cup-shaped, yellow flowers of a faint, but very pleasant odor. The tree is occasionally called **Magnolia** when offered for sale in European tree nurseries. It does belong to the same family, but it is not a magnolia species, and it is not used as a perfume plant. Other perfume plants of the genus Magnoliaceae are **Champaca** and **Star Anise** (see monographs).

An essential oil has been distilled from the leaves of **Magnolia Grandiflora** in China and experimentally in Italy. The **Michelia Leaf Oil,** see **Champaca,** is produced from the leaves of a related tree in China.

Mandarin Oil.

Unless otherwise specified, this name refers to the essential oil expressed from the peel of the true mandarin, which we will call the "European type" of mandarin in this monograph. See also **Tangerine.** The two trees are both botanically **Citrus Reticulata** varieties, originating in south China and other Fareastern areas. The mandarin arrived in Europe in 1805, and in the U.S.A. about 40 years later. In Europe, the fruit developed into the small, ellipsoidic **Mandarin** while in the U.S.A., the fruit remained quite similar to the Chinese original; however, it was re-named **Tangerine** in the United States.

Mandarin Peel Oil is produced in Italy, Spain, Algeria and Cyprus, and in smaller quantities in Greece and the Middle East. The Brazilian mandarins are slightly different, and yield a different oil. The Brazilian production was 2 metric tons in 1958. This oil is rarely exported.

The mandarin peels are expressed either by hand or by machine in Europe. **Mandarin Peel Oil** is an orange-brown to dark yellowish-brown or olive-brown, occasionally lemon yellow (certain types of handpressed oil), mobile liquid of intensely sweet, not very fresh odor, occasionally with an amine-like, "fishy" topnote and usually with a rich neroli-like, floral undertone. Upon extreme dilution e.g. in ethyl alcohol, the oil shows a beautiful bluish fluorescence which fades significantly when the solution has aged. This effect, and the peculiar "perfume-like" odor type, is explained by the presence of about one percent of methyl-N-methyl-anthranilate in the oil. This material is erroneously called dimethyl anthranilate and is a common perfumery chemical, produced synthetically on a large scale. The "fishy" or amine-like topnote in the mandarin peel oil could be due to the anthranilate which, in acid media, occasionally produces this type of odor in essential oils.

Mandarin peel oil is used mainly in flavors where it gives interesting modifications with sweet and bitter orange oils, grapefruit oil, lime oil, etc. in flavor compositions for soft drinks, candy, etc. The terpeneless or sesquiterpeneless mandarin peel oil is preferred as the main flavor material in certain types of liqueur (see below). Mandarin peel oil is an excellent blender-intensifier for sweet orange oil in flavors where its rich body compensates for drawbacks in certain types of sweet orange oil. The average use level for "straight" mandarin peel oil (the effect is considerably intensified in combination-flavors with other citrus oils) is about 3.00 to 10.0 mg%, and the **Minimum Perceptible** is 0.30 to 0.60 mg%.

In perfumery, mandarin peel oil is used sparingly in colognes as a modifier for other citrus oils, in neroli bases, in fantasy "moss" notes, or as particular note for "special" effects. In this respect, however, the mandarin-petitgrain oil (see monograph) is superior by far.

Mandarin peel oil is also offered as a "five-fold" oil. This oil is usually produced by simple concentration in vacuum. The concentrated oil is, accordingly, very dark and its solubility in alcohol only slightly improved. Its flavor is about three (note: 3) times as strong as the flavor of the natural mandarin peel oil.

Terpeneless and **Sesquiterpeneless Mandarin Peel Oil** is produced as described in Part One of this book (**Terpeneless Oils**). These oils are usually prepared by the consumer; they are rarely offered commercially by the raw material supply houses. The total removal of the terpenes from the mandarin oil changes its odor and flavor characteristics beyond recognition. The flavor of the terpeneless, sesquiterpeneless oil is extremely "perfume-like" and its odor type approaches that of orange flowers.

Mandarin Aroma (see **Aromas** in Part One of this book) is prepared as described, and is used for liqueurs or soft drinks since it gives a more true-to-nature flavor than do the evaporated (concentrated) oils, and since it presents a good solution to the problem of insoluble terpenes in the natural oil.

Mandarin Peel Oil is produced in steady amounts of 20 to 50 metric tons per year, but it can still be difficult to buy large quantities of the oil immediately prior to the European harvest (late fall).

Mandarin-Petitgrain Oil.

A very interesting essential oil is steam distilled from the leaves, twigs and occasionally from the small, undeveloped fruits of the mandarin tree, "European type" (see **Mandarin Oil**). Only Italy, Spain and, at times, Algeria produce small quantities of this oil. Spain supplies the best and richest oil, by far; Italy supplies perhaps a larger quantity. The Guinea (West African) mandarin-petitgrain oil is derived from a tree which closely resembles the American tangerine.

Mandarin Petitgrain Oil is a dark olive-green liquid of intensely sweet, rich, deep-fruity, grape-like, floral odor in which a distinct mustiness is characteristic, and a plum-grape-like fruity undertone lends a peculiar and very powerful, perfumery sweetness. Like the peel oil, the petitgrain oil of mandarin also produces fluorescence in alcoholic dilution. Methyl-N-methylanthranilate makes up more than 50% of a good Spanish mandarin petitgrain oil.

Oils that are distilled exclusively from the leaves with no unripe fruits admixed contain fewer terpenes, and are more valuable flavor and perfume materials.

Mandarin petitgrain oil is used in small quantities as a modifier in various citrus flavors, grape flavors, and occasionally in gooseberry, apple, "tutti-frutti", etc. A deterpenized oil is sometimes preferred, but this oil lends practically no freshness and must be backed up by sweet orange, lemon or grapefruit so that some terpenes may be re-introduced in the flavor. For perfumes, the mandarin petitgrain oil is equally interesting, e. g. in fougères, Oriental bases, chypres and in modern aldehydic perfume types. It lends excellent body and undertone in neroli bases, and it is worthwhile noting that methyl-N-methylanthranilate does *not* discolor or form condensation products in the presence of aldehydes (compare: Schiff's bases with methyl anthranilate). In pine fragrances, the mandarin petitgrain oil produces a most attractive effect of natural forest sweetness with oakmoss, pine needle oils, fir needle absolute, coumarin derivatives, aldehydes, etc. Unfortunately, the oil is not available in very large quantities. The annual production is limited to about 2 metric tons. Spain produced 300 kilos in 1957.

Manevoro Oil.

Not widely known, and rarely offered in more than 10-kilo lots, **Manevoro Oil** is an essential oil, produced by steam distillation of a Madagascan herb of the genus Labiatae. **Manevoro** is a term which is native for "crocodile herb". The plant grows wild in the shady forests of northwestern Madagascar and the off-shore island of Nossi-Bé. The plant is not cultivated, and the author knows of no other place where this plant is to be found.

The leaves of the wild growing plant are steam distilled in Nossi-Bé, and the distillation waters are extracted with petroleum ether in order to avoid the loss of the oil. The specific gravity of manevoro oil is close to 1.00, and the oil easily forms emulsion with water. The combined oil phases are washed with alcohol to remove resins and waxes, and, after filtration and evaporation of the alcohol in vacuum, the **Manevoro** oil is obtained. It is a pale amber to dark amber or brownish-colored, somewhat viscous liquid of sweet-woody, very rich and somewhat herbaceous odor, reminiscent of patchouli, orris, costus, Atlas cedar and sage clary concrète. The dryout on a blotter shows an increasing sweetness and a rich, "tobacco-like", herbaceous undertone with a tremendous tenacity and great diffusive power.

Manevoro Oil can find application in high-class perfumes of the "powdery" type, in aldehydic bases, ambre-colognes, etc. It blends excellently with the above mentioned materials and with labdanum products, styrax, cinnamic alcohol, nitromusks, heliotropine, methylionones, cedarwood derivatives, vetiver, citrus oils, helichrysum oil, cypress oil, juniperberry oil, cardamom, ginger, black pepper oil, etc. The usual concentration of manevoro oil in a perfume base may be around 0.2 to 0.5 percent, and overdosage is very easily reached.

Less than twice the price of geranium oil and about six to eight times the price of patchouli oil, the manevoro oil cannot be classified as an expensive oil when its strength is taken into consideration. At present, the annual production of **Manevoro Oil** is only about 50 to 100 kilos.

Maple.

Although it is a rather local specialty and not very widely applicable as a flavor material, **Maple Syrup** deserves some attention for its truly unique flavor character.

Only the two species (**Acer Saccharum** and **Acer Nigrum**) from among hundreds of maples known are of commercial interest to syrup production. In springtime they produce a sap which contains up to 6 percent sugar. The balance is water, apart from minute traces of certain organic compounds which lend a typical flavor to the evaporated syrup. The sap is boiled down to a point—learned by experience—where it will stay liquid after cooling and yet not grow mold.

Until a few years ago, little was known about the apparently powerful materials which were the flavor principles of maple syrup. Synthetic flavor chemicals like **Cyclotene** (hydroxy-methylcyclopentenone), **Maraniol** (4-methyl-7-ethoxycoumarin), various butylidene phthalides, or natural materials such as fenugreek, flouve, celery seed, lovage, etc. had been used both in- and outside America to imitate the flavor. Maple syrup is derived from a mere 2½ million trees in upstate New York, Vermont, Maine and parts of southeastern Canada, and it is hardly known outside the United States. There is only one crop per year, and a true maple syrup is hardly available in the months immediately prior to the new tapping (March-April).

para-**Coniferaldehyde** (= 4-hydroxy-3-methoxy cinnamic aldehyde), also known as "**Maple Aldehyde**", is apparently a natural oxidation product from coniferyl alcohol, which is gamma-hydroxyisoeugenol. This alcohol is widely prevalent in nature, e.g. in the form of a glycoside (abietin), a parent substance of the so-called lignin-vanillin. Coniferyl benzoate and coniferyl cinnamate are the main constituents of Siam benzoin and Sumatra benzoin, respectively. para-**Coniferaldehyde** may be one of the "key" materials by which reproduction of maple flavor may be effected. Unfortunately, this chemical has not yet been successfully synthesized.

Maple Syrup is used extensively in the U.S.A. with pancakes, wafers, for confectionery, tobacco and on ice cream, etc. The consumption in the U.S.A. alone goes far beyond the production of natural maple syrup, and perhaps five or ten tons of artificial maple syrup is sold for each ton of natural syrup produced. The artificial syrup is base upon sugar syrup with the addition of the above mentioned natural and synthetic flavor materials.

Marigold Absolute.

Also called **Calendula** absolute, **Marigold Absolute** is extracted from the ligulate florets of **Calendula Officinalis**, known as "**Marigold**", "**Marybud**" or "**Hollygold**" in the United States of America. There is, however, some confusion with respect to the term "marigold" since it has been applied to various other plants of the Compositae family, e.g. **Tagetes**, etc. Tagetes will be described under its proper name.

The calendula absolute from the true calendula officinalis is probably produced only in France, but it is sold in English speaking countries under the name of **Marigold**.

The absolute is a very dark greenish-brown, very viscous liquid of an intensely bitter-herbaceous odor. Little is known about its constituents, but as a perfumery material, it has certain interesting and unique notes. Since the plant grows commonly all over Europe, cultivated in the northern part, an increased production could easily be effected.

Its very peculiar note and intense color, however, limits the use of "marigold" to fancy perfume types, modern aldehydic-herbaceous types where the green "crushed-stalk" note may be called for. **Marigold Absolute** introduces certain natural notes in chrysanthemum fragrances, and it gives interesting effects with oakmoss, maté extract, tea leaf extract, cypriol, iso cyclo citral, etc. Traces of the absolute can be useful in hyacinth, lilac, gardenia, reseda, moss-bases, etc.

See also **Tagetes**, under which **Tagetes Glandulifera** is discussed, and **Tagetes Patula** under which heading the Indian "genda" is mentioned.

Marjoram Oil, sweet.

The poultry seasoner, the dried herb of **Origanum Majorana**, also called **Majorana Hortensis** when cultivated is well known to housewives all over the world. The plant is probably originated in the eastern Mediterranean countries, and is now cultivated in central and southern Europe (Bulgaria, etc.) as well as in North Africa. The plant grown in the United States is used as a culinary herb and not for the production of essential oil. It should be mentioned at this point that the outstanding majority of all so-called marjoram *oil* used in the U.S.A. and elsewhere is **Spanish Wild Marjoram** (see the following monograph), derived from a completely different plant.

Sweet Marjoram Oil is steam distilled from the dried leaves and flowering tops of the plant (origanum majorana). Distillation takes place in France, Tunisia, Morocco, Italy, Hungary, Bulgaria, Poland, Germany and experimentally in Turkey. French and Tunisian oils are considered among the best.

Sweet marjoram oil is a pale yellow or pale amber colored, rather mobile liquid of a warmspicy, aromatic-camphoraceous and woody odor, reminiscent of nutmeg and cardamom. The flavor is spicy-warm, aromatic and somewhat bitter. It serves little or no purpose to mention an average use level or a **Minimum Perceptible** since the author has experienced huge differences in flavor strength among the various qualities of oils commercially offered. For those who are familiar with the odor of **Melaleuca Alternifolia** (see monograph), it is interesting to note the similarity in odor between this oil and sweet marjoram oil.

Sweet marjoram oil is used in spice compounds for the flavoring of meat-sauces, canned foods, vinegars, etc., and occasionally in perfumery to introduce a fresh, slightly medicinal-aromatic, warm note in fougères, colognes, Oriental bases, etc. As mentioned above, the annual production of sweet marjoram oil is very limited, and there is no strong demand for this oil. Adulteration takes place, usually with terpineol and fractions from the production of turpentine-terpineol, or with the oil of melaleuca alternifolia. Plain mislabelling is also common in the sense that Spanish, wild marjoram oil, or mixtures of this oil and the sweet marjoram oil, origanum oil, etc. are labelled "oil of marjoram, sweet".

Marjoram Oil, wild (Spanish).

One of the most confused areas of botanical perfumery nomenclature is that of **Calamintha – Marjoram – Origanum – Thyme – Verbena.** For many decades, outstanding authors and authorities have done their best to straighten out this confusion, but some suppliers continue to mislabel their materials, overlooking all the efforts made to establish correct names. We meet this sad fact with respect to resinoids also.

The *so-called* **"Wild" Marjoram** is the common garden herb, **Origanum Vulgare,** *cultivated* all over the world. An essential oil is distilled from this plant in southern U.S.S.R., Bulgaria and Italy.

See also **Origanum** and **Thyme.**

Spanish Wild Marjoram Oil is water-and-steam distilled from the flowering herb of **Thymus Masticina** and other **Thymus** species with similar odor. The plant grows wild in Spain and is distilled locally. The production of this oil is quite significant, and fluctuates between 5 and 20 metric tons per year.

Spanish (wild) marjoram oil is an orange-amber to pale orange-yellow colored, mobile liquid of strong, fresh, slightly sweet-spicy, aromatic, but predominantly eucalyptus-like, camphoraceous odor. Its flavor is warm, slightly burning, bitter-sweet, occasionally with a cool, aromatic-medicinal aftertaste. Huge variations in the qualities of different lots of this oil make it meaningless to report any suggested use level concentration. The oil is used extensively as a flavoring agent in meat sauces, mixed spices for soups, etc., but has, in the author's opinion, little or nothing in common

with **Sweet Marjoram Oil** (see previous monograph). Frankly, the author cannot see how in the world the former can be used as a substitute for the latter. But this is just another case of a "matter of opinion" which is everyday fare for perfumers and flavorists.

Spanish Wild Marjoram Oil can hardly expect to find much application in perfumery. Its effects and constitution do not offer any particular value to recommend it to the perfumer.

Mastic.

Mastic or **Mastix** is a natural oleo-resin, produced in the very small tree, **Pistacia Lentiscus,** as a physiological (voluntary) material. In order to obtain the oleoresin, however, it is necessary to make incisions in the trunk. The exuded oleoresin soon solidifies (resinifies), and becomes hard and brittle.

Mastic is produced in various Mediterranean countries, but most of the world production comes from the small Greek island of Chios, just offshore from Izmir in Turkey. Smaller quantities are collected in Algeria, Morocco and the Canary islands.

The dry mastic, as we know it, has only a faint, balsamic-turpentine-like odor, but it does contain a small amount of essential oil which can be obtained by steam distillation of the oleoresin.

Mastic Oil is a pale yellow, mobile liquid or turpentine-like, fresh-balsamic odor. The oil is scarce and comparatively expensive. It is occasionally used in citrus colognes, lavender-fougères, etc. as a topnote ingredient, lending a certain naturalness and bitter-balsamic tonality to these perfume types. The oil is also used in certain types of liqueur flavor.

By extraction of the **Mastic** with alcohol or a hydrocarbon solvent, various types of **Mastic Resinoid** are produced. These are merely soluble versions of the mastic itself. Hydrocarbons will dissolve up to 98% of natural mastic, while ethyl alcohol dissolves about 85%. The latter solvent produces a resinoid which is safer for use in perfumes where a separation could cause trouble later on.

Mastic Resinoid (known in France as "résinoide lentisque") is a pale amber colored, hard and brittle mass with an odor quite similar to that of natural mastic. It is an interesting perfume material and a good fixative, e.g. for mimosa compounds where it introduces a certain "twig-odor" effect. It can also be used in straight floral bases to produce a bitter-woody, natural undertone and a good fixation.

Mastic Resinoid and **Mastic Oil** are scarce materials, but they are available in sufficient quantities to meet present demands. The natural mastic is used extensively in pharmaceutical and technical preparations, varnishes for dentists, etc.

Maté.

Known to the natives for hundreds, perhaps thousands, of years, and to the greater part of the present population of South America, **Maté** is an everyday tonic. It is prepared from the leaves of **Ilex Paraguayensis** and other **Ilex** species. These trees grow wild and cultivated in Argentina, Brazil, Paraguay and other Latin-American countries. The cultivated trees are usually pruned to bush-size to facilitate picking of the leaves. The forests where the trees grow are known as "yerbales", and the leaves are called "yerba maté". The leaves are dried, usually over a smoldering fire of certain woods. The smoke from the fire enhances the dry-smoky flavor which derives from phenolic and tannic materials in the leaves. The dry leaves are either cut or ground to a coarse powder which are the commercial forms of **Maté**. The pot from which the infusion is usually taken (through a special straw) is called **Maté** (the original, local name), hence the name of the leaves.

Only recently, the perfumers became interested in maté. Tinctures, then extracts, resinoids or absolutes were produced although such preparations are not regularly offered commercially. An essential oil has been produced, but the yield is very small and the odor of the oil is less interesting than that of the extracted products. **Maté Absolute** is prepared by extraction of the dry leaves with petroleum ether. The resulting concrète is subsequently extracted with alcohol. A completely solvent-free **Maté Absolute** is a semi-solid, sticky, very dark green mass. It is customary to leave sufficient alcohol or other (occasionally non-volatile) solvent in the extract as to make it pourable at room temperature. Other producers or consumers will make a strong tincture of maté leaves (20% of the weight of the alcohol).

Maté Absolute has a very peculiar, rich-herbaceous, dry-leafy, woody-foliage like and somewhat phenolic or smoky, medicinal odor, resembling that of the leaves. A decolorized extract of maté is commercially available, but only part of the color is actually removed. **Anhydrol Maté** and **Resinoine Incolore Maté** are distilled extracts of maté. These products are pale of color and yet present the most characteristic notes of the odor of maté extracts. Maté extracts are used in perfumery to introduce a pronounced greenness in floral bouquets. The green notes of maté are free from the sharpness which usually accompanies the "green" odor materials (beta-gamma-hexenol, nonadienal, amyl heptin carbonate, methyl phenyl carbinyl acetate, etc.). Maté absolute or tincture blends well with orange flower bases, jasmin, oakmoss, coumarin and its derivatives, lavender absolute, narcissus, arnica absolute, tea leaf extracts, de-thujonized wormwood oil, chamomile, manevoro oil, cananga oil, castoreum products, spice oils, etc.—quite a varied field of application. In the reproduction of natural fragrances or substitutes of natural perfume materials, maté absolute can often add the missing notes to the match (duplication). In fougères, new mown hay, hay or meadowsweet fragrances, it lends a rich body and herbal undertone of unique tenacity.

Since the leaves are so abundant and low in price, there is no problem of availability of **Maté** perfume products. It may, however, still be necessary for the consumer to prepare them from the botanical material since the finished extracts are rarely offered.

A west-American plant, **Eriodictyon Californicum**, also called **Mountain Balm**, is sometimes sold under the name of **Yerba Santa**. It has no relationship to the Latin American **Yerba Maté**. The Californian plant has been used for some time in the pharmaceutical industry since an extract from its leaves has the ability of masking effectively the bitter taste of quinine in pharmaceutical preparations, etc.

Matico Oil.

The leaves of **Piper Matico** and a number of other **Matico** species of the genus Piperaceae have been used in medicine for a long time, and still appear in a number of Pharmacopoeias and Codex'es.

The trees grow wild in many parts of South America, particularly in Brazil and Peru. Distillation, if it takes place at all, is not performed in the countries of origin. Brazil has no commercial production of **Matico Oil,** and the matico leaves collected in South America come from a number of species of matico trees, often without designation.

The almost universal feature of the odor of matico leaves, regardless of their origin, is a strong, camphoraceous, pepperlike or minty odor with a pronounced woody undertone. The oil, when it was available, never attained any significant importance in perfumery or flavor work.

The **Matico Oils** occasionally offered in the market today, are usually dark green, olive-green, dark amber or brownish colored, somewhat viscous liquids. The oils turn darker on ageing or upon exposure to daylight, air or iron.

Matico oil can be produced upon request. The botanical material is at hand, but it is not always easy to determine the exact species of **Matico** used. Thus, it may be difficult to get a uniform quality of oil. **Matico Oil** has little or no application in flavor work.

Mawah Oil.

See monographs on **Geranium African.**

Like many other "geranium" plants, the **Pelargonium Graveolens** has a tendency towards hybridizing into local vaieties. This has happened to most of the pelargoniums introduced (or, more correctly, re-introduced) in Africa.

Late in the 19th century, the ancestor of the **Mawah** plant, a variety of **Pelargonium Radula,** came to Kenya, East Africa, but it has been only during the past few decades that the settlers have bothered with distillation of this decorative plant. It is now cultivated or grows semiwild in the highlands of the Masai people, between Nairobi and Lake Victoria, toward the border of Tanganyika. About 5 to 8 metric tons of essential oil is steam distilled annually from cultivated plants in this area.

Mawah Oil is greenish-yellow to dark olive or pale brownish of color. Its odor is somewhat bitter-harsh, leafy-woody, slightly earthy, but later toning out in a much more pleasant rosy, "geranium" type of odor. The dryout note is, however, more similar to that of palmarosa than to ordinary African geranium oil.

Mawah Oil is not a substitute for geranium oil. It can only be used for what it is: a powerful, but coarse, woody-leafy, floral-rosy and quite stable perfume oil. It is useful in soap perfumes if the typical and highly diffusive topnote of true geranium oil is not needed. The oil blends excellently with all the usual perfume materials as needed in rose compounds for soap, etc.

Mawah Oil is available in Europe, and occasionally also in the U.S.A., but production originates exclusively in Kenya as described above, and is very limited. The oil may be adulterated with palmarosa oil, fractions from geraniol and citronellol production, geranium terpenes, etc. and **Mawah Oil** itself has been used in the adulteration of various African geranium oils. The latter fraud is rare, and quite easily detected.

Melaleuca Alternifolia.

Melaleuca Alternifolia is one of the smaller "tea-trees" from southeastern Australia. Its leaves are collected and water- or steam distilled locally. Until now, the oil has not been produced outside Australia, although the tree, a native of Australia, can easily be cultivated elsewhere, propagated from seed. The annual production of the oil is only between 10 and 30 tons, but this amount seems to be sufficient at present. The true figure for the annual production may be considerably lower since the above figures may very well refer to the total annual production of all so-called tea-tree oils.

Oil of **Melaleuca Alternifolia** is a pale yellowish-green or almost water-white mobile liquid of a warm-spicy, aromatic-terpenic odor, reminiscent of nutmeg, cardamom and sweet marjoram, but with a strong emphasis on the terpinene- and terpinenol-notes (odor of the foreruns from rectification of synthetic terpineol). The flavor is warm-aromatic, somewhat burning, spicy and yet fresh, faintly camphoraceous, slightly bitter.

The oil has served as an antiseptic for many decades, but only recently has it been proven scientifically, that the oil really possesses an outstanding germ-killing effect and high penetration power. The oil is sold locally and abroad under trade names, such as **"Ti-Trol"** or **"Melasol",** etc. as a germicide, gargle, skin-disinfectant, spray, etc.

In perfumery, however, the oil has been gathering increasing interest for its warm-spicy, aromatic and fresh character, a type of fragrance, which has become particularly popular since the introduction of spicy colognes and after-shaves for men, etc. The oil is non-toxic and does not irritate the skin. Nutmeg oil cannot claim the same advantages or virtues.

Oil of **Melaleuca Alternifolia** blends well with lavandin oil, lavender, isobornylacetate, clove oils, rosemary oil, oakmoss products, cananga oil, amylsalicylate, coumarin, geraniol and nerol, etc. The oil has been used as an adulterant for nutmeg oil and for sweet marjoram oil. If this oil were made regularly available in ton-lots, it would no doubt catch the interest of the larger perfume houses and perhaps become a favorite perfume material for the introduction of "new" notes in certain lines of perfumery.

Melaleuca Bracteata.

Belonging to the group of so-called "tea-trees", the Australian tree, **Melaleuca Bracteata** has leaves and twigs which are distilled in Australia, and recently also in East Africa (Kenya). By steam distillation a yellowish to pale amber or pale olive-green oil is obtained. The odor is very delicate, sweet-woody, herbaceous, recalling the odor of dry tea-leaves. The "tea" note has nothing to do with the "tea-tree" name of these plants, but this fragrance is quite characteristic of this particular oil. The main constituent of the oil is **Mathyl Eugenol**. However, the synthetic or isolated methyl eugenol does not present the same peculiar odor of tea leaves as the one we find in melaleuca bracteata oil. It seems quite possible that small amounts of cinnamates in combination with methyl eugenol are responsible for the delicate and very pleasant odor of melaleuca bracteata oil.

When this oil is available at all, it finds use in perfumery for the note described above, and the oil blends excellently with amyl salicylate, hydroxy-citronellal, dimethyl phenylethyl carbinol, linalool, beta-gamma-hexenol (traces for "tea" notes), phenylethylalcohol, ionones and methylionones, mimosa absolute, sage clary oil or absolute, pine needle oil, juniperberry oil, ylang-ylang (best in minute traces), etc. Melaleuca bracteata oil will round off the sharp notes of synthetic ingredients, and produce an improved fixation and naturalness in the perfume.

Like many other Australian trees, the melaleuca trees exist in several "physiological" forms which yield different essential oils. This fact affects the production of the individual melaleuca oils.

Consequently, the oil of **Melaleuca Bracteata** is produced on a limited scale only, the total annual production being about two to five metric tons. With an increased interest and stronger demand, the production in Australia and East Africa could easily be intensified. This oil certainly deserves more attention in perfumery.

Melaleuca Linariifolia.

The oil of **Melaleuca Linariifolia** is of comparatively limited importance in perfumery. The tree is another Australian "tea-tree", very similar in appearance to melaleuca alternifolia (see monograph), but larger than this tree.

Distillation takes place on the spot, i.e. in southeast Australia, where the leaves are water- or steam distilled. The tree is not cultivated on a commercial scale outside this area.

Melaleuca linariifolia oil is a pale yellowish oil of strong camphoraceous-eucalyptus-like odor, with a warm-terpenic undertone. Somewhat similar to the oil of melaleuca alternifolia, the oil of melaleuca linariifolia is much more eucalyptus-like in odor and flavor, and it does not recall the odor of nutmeg. One could say that the odor type is a less aromatic one.

At this point, however, it should be noted that various samples of oils, labelled **Melaleuca Linariifolia** may turn out quite differently on an odor evaluation. The author has seen samples which presented little or no eucalyptus note (cineole-like note) as well as other samples which were strong in this note. This non-uniformity of various lots of the oil may be partly responsible for the lack of interest in melaleuca linariifolia oil.

Generally, the oil could find application in air-fresheners, household-sprays, room-deodorants, lavender-perfumes, soap- and detergent perfumes, mouthwashes and gargles, etc.

The oil is produced on a very limited scale, and is not regularly available in sizeable lots. It is very likely that the oil will slowly vanish from the perfumery market.

Melaleuca Viridiflora, Variety "A".

Years ago, before the sesquiterpene alcohol **Nerolidol** was prepared synthetically, considerable time and energy was spent in the search for natural sources of this fine perfume material. Apart from cabreuva oil (see this monograph) only one essential oil yielded sufficient nerolidol to make isolation profitable: the oil of **Melaleuca Viridiflora,** variety "A". The ordinary melaleuca viridiflora tree yields **Niaouli Oil** (see this monograph).

The fact that the two trees are physiological forms of the same botanical specimen means that the selection of the correct form requires expert botanical assistance. This explains the failure in the production of the above oil.

Melaleuca Viridiflora, variety "A" grows in southeastern Australia among many other melaleuca species. Distillation of the leaves of this particular tree gives an oil consisting of about one-third linalool and two-thirds of **Nerolidol.** The latter can be separated in a fairly pure state by fractional distillation. In New Caledonia, the melaleuca viridiflora tree seems to grow only as the "type" which yields **Niaouli Oil.** Accordingly, the niaouli oil is not produced in Australia, but only in New Caledonia.

The oil of melaleuca viridiflora, variety "A" is a pale yellow or almost water-white, somewhat oily liquid of soft, sweet-balsamic, woody and slightly floral odor. On drying out, it shows not only great tenacity, but also a very pleasant, floral-woody body, although of very faint odor.

This oil is only occasionally available upon request with due notice to the Australian producers.

With the appearance of low-cost synthetic nerolidol (1960-price is about $ 14.– per lb.) it seems conceivable that the oil of melaleuca viridiflora, variety "A" may disappear from the perfume market. The oil has little value and no particularly interesting notes to offer as such in perfumery.
. See also the monograph on: **Cabreuva Oil, Niaouli Oil** and **Oleo Vermelho.**

Melilotus.

Closely related to the clover are several species of **Melilotus,** among which **Melilotus Officinalis** and **Melilotus Arvensis** have particularly attracted the interest of the perfume- and flavor industries. The plants grow wild in most parts of Europe and Asia Minor; other species are found in the United States, Asia and Africa. The above two species are used for the extraction of a so-called **Oleoresin Melilotin,** a petroleum ether or benzene extraction product of the dry flowers. Chlorinated aliphatic and olefinic hydrocarbons have also been used, e.g. methylene dichloride. Extraction

takes place in England, France, Germany, and the U.S.S.R.

The above plants have very little odor or flavor when fresh, but upon drying, various chemical reactions (decomposition of glycosides) take place, and coumarin, coumarin derivatives and other odorous materials are set free. This drying or curing is quite frequently met, e.g. bitter almond, tonka, vanilla, liatris, wintergreen, woodruff, etc.

The extract is theoretically a concrète (according to the definitions in Part One of this book), but it is usually called a "resinoid" or "oleoresin" perhaps on account of the fact that the manufacturers present the extract in a more or less liquid form.

Melilot Extract (so-called **Oleoresin)** is a viscous, dark green liquid of a very sweet, herbaceous-root-like and rich odor. Although this odor is often described as "tobacco-like", the author of this book disagrees since the odor of melilot extract is an odor type which is artificially introduced in cured tobacco for the purpose of flavoring the tobacco with this sweet note. Coumarin, liatris, methylcoumarin, prune juice, flouve oil, etc. are all used in the flavoring of tobacco when the root-like coumarin notes are wanted. Unflavored tobacco leaves have no sweet odor, but rather a distinct amine-like, dry-herb odor. However, the coumarin-type odor has become more or less synonymous for tobacco odor for many people.

Melilotus "Oleoresin" is used extensively in the flavoring of tobacco in countries where the use of coumarin-containing preparations is permitted in tobacco flavoring. It was used in the flavoring of cheese at one time, but substitutes have now replaced melilotus for this purpose.

In perfumery, the "melillotin" is most useful in the new mown hay, fougère, lavender, pine and forest type fragrances where it is an excellent blender to "round off" the effects of sharp smelling synthetic materials. Melilotus extracts blend well with maté extracts, oakmoss, dimethyl benzyl carbinylacetate, amyl salicylate, labdanum products, fir needle absolute, lavandin and lavender oils, bois de rose oil, nerol, nitromusks and cinnamic alcohol (for "powdery" notes!), etc.

An **Absolute** of Melilotus has been prepared, and it offers the advantage of producing no resinous or insoluble separations in alcoholic perfumes, etc. In connection with the above statements with respect to "tobacco odor", the

36: Semi-wild **Lily-of-the-Valley** in New Jersey, U.S.A. The plant grows wild all over Europe. Cultivated flowers usually have poorer fragrance. *(Fot. S. Arctander, 1960)*

37: Fruit-bearing **Néflier** tree on the French Côte d'Azur. The flowers yield **Néflier Concrète** upon extraction with volatile solvents. Fruits are edible and delicious. *(Fot. S. Arctander, 1960)*

38: **Lime Oil** distillery at Port Malindi, Zanzibar. These modern installations belong to the Clove Growers' Association, the worlds largest producers of clove buds and the only producers of clove stem oil. *(Fot. S. Arctander, 1955)*

reader may be interested in studying Georges Igolen's contribution to the problem in "Les Parfums de France", 1936, vol. 14, page 225. Obviously, the coumarin concentration in the **Absolute** of **Melilotus** is beyond the saturation point (compare absolute of tonka, etc.), but a high concentration of coumarin will remain in the liquid phase of the absolute which contributes distinctly to the so-called "tobacco-odor".

The annual production of **Melilotus** extracts (all types) is declining, not because of any shortage of the abundant wild growing herb, but mainly because of the coumarin-ban in the most important fields of application for these materials. In perfumery, they continue to attract the interest of many perfumers, and only the intense deep-green color is a distinct disadvantage in perfumery application. This problem should be rather easily solved since many commercial lots of melilotus extract are colored artificially with chlorophyll in order to look more "natural".

Lavandin concrète, synthetic coumarin, various methylcoumarins, etc. are known to be used as adulterants of melilotus extracts at the present time.

Melissa Oil.

Melissa oil or **Oil of Balm** enjoys the reputation of being probably one of the most frequently adulterated essential oils of the perfumery trade. **Melissa Oil,** cedrat oil, verbena oil, wintergreen oil, etc.,—these oils are almost never genuine distillates of the botanical. It might be appropriate to quote from the definition of essential oils adopted by the Geneva Congress for the suppression of frauds: "Essential oils are the exclusive product of the extraction of the aromatic principles contained in the substances of vegetable origin of which they bear the name".

See also **Essential Oil** in Part One of this book.

Melissa Officinalis is a small plant of the genus labiatae, and it has been known for hundreds, probably thousands of years in central and southern Europe. The local name for the plant in many countries is "heart's delight", and infusions of the dried herb were supposed to cure heart diseases, melancolia, etc. Perfumers will no doubt recall a French perfume of the late 1930's, put out by Nina Ricci and named "Cœur-Joie", which means "heart's delight". This perfume certainly

had a melissa-like, fresh topnote and lightness of floral fragrance.

The herb is distilled in the south of France, Germany, and in Italy and Spain only rarely. However, the total production of genuine melissa oil is only a small fraction of the quantity commercially offered. The herb may be distilled with lemon oil, Spanish so-called verbena oil, lemongrass oil, citronella oil, and various mixtures or fractions thereof. This process leads to commercial qualities of **Melissa Oil,** e. g. the **"Lemon-Melissa",** etc. It seems quite certain, however, that the extremely small yield of oil obtained by steam distillation of melissa herb is another and more acceptable reason (?) for—or explanation to— the conventional adulteration.

The author has seen numerous melissa oils during the past 25 years, but he prefers to refrain from any further comments on the pure oil since he has no personal experience with the use of a guaranteed pure and genuine **Melissa Oil.** The plant itself has a very pleasant citral-citronellal type of fresh and sweet-herbaceous odor.

Mentha Arvensis Oil.

The essential oil, steam distilled from the dried herb of **Mentha Arvensis** immediately prior to the inflorescence of the plant, is known in the U.S.A. as **"Mint Oil"** or **Cornmint Oil",** while it is quite commonly called "peppermint oil" in other parts of the world. The latter term is definitely wrong and misleading. Only the plant mentha piperita (see monograph on **Peppermint Oil)** yields true peppermint oil. On the other hand, only in the U.S.A. is the control of production or import of **Mentha Arvensis Oil** sufficiently strict so that adulteration of true peppermint oil with "mint" oil is well-nigh impossible. This adulteration is extremely widespread in other parts of the world.

There are several varieties of **Mentha Arvensis,** but the one which has attained greatest distribution is the variety **Piperascens.** The plant is found growing wild in China and parts of Japan, but is now cultivated on an enormous scale in Japan, Brazil, Formosa, less on the Chinese mainland, and on a smaller scale in Argentina, India, western Australia, the Union of South Africa, Angola, etc. Japan, Brazil and Formosa are the main producers. The annual world production of **Mentha Arvensis Oil** (i.e. total oil, before dementholization) is about 3,000 metric tons (1959, and has been increasing in spite of the very successful synthesis of **Menthol** from cheaper raw materials (piperitone, citronellal, and even pinene).

The natural oil of mentha arvensis (forma piperascens) contains so much menthol that it will solidify at room temperature. By freezing the total oil, about 40% menthol is recovered, leaving the so-called "dementholized" oil which is liquid and still contains about 55% menthol. Part of this menthol, and most of the menthone in the dementholized oil can be further exploited by chemical treatment which converts the bitter-tasting menthone, a ketone, into various isomers of menthol. True l-menthol can be isolated from the mixture, and the remainder can be sold as "liquid menthol". Thus, the oil of mentha arvensis is mainly a starting material in the production of menthol, one of the most important of all flavoring agents.

A wealth of information on the subject of cultivation of the plant, distillation of oil, isolation of menthol, etc. has been published during the past decades, and the author sees no need to repeat such information here. It should be noted, however, that there is a distinct difference in the chemical composition of the mentha arvensis oils of different origin:

The Chinese oil contains about 2 percent esters, calculated as menthylacetate, the Brazilian contains from 5 to 30 percent (in exceptional cases) of esters, and the Japanese mentha arvensis oil contains from 10 to 12 percent esters.

The oil of **Mentha Arvensis** (dementholized) is a very common article exported from Japan, Formosa or Brazil. It is a pale yellow or almost colorless liquid of strong, fresh and somewhat bitter-sweet odor, to a certain degree reminiscent of the odor of peppermint oil. The undertone is somewhat harsh-woody and the dryout is bitter-herbaceous. It produces a cool feeling on the mucous membranes in the nose and mouth cavities or upon direct contact with the skin. The flavor is cool, minty, somewhat rough and slightly bitter-green or sharp, less balsamic-herbaceous or sweet than the flavor of true peppermint. There is considerable difference in the organoleptic properties of the various types of mentha arvensis oil. It is hardly of any use, therefore, to mention a certain suggested use level or **Minimum Perceptible**. The oil is usually "bouquetted" prior to its use in flavors, see below.

Various tests have been suggested to distinguish analytically between mentha arvensis oil and true peppermint oil (even the expert nose is not acknowledged in a court if it comes to a juridical discussion!). One of the best known tests is based upon a color reaction due to the presence of **Menthofuran** in true peppermint oil; this cumaron-derivative is not present in mentha arvensis oil. Unfortunately, these analytical findings are not always used to the benefit of the product; they might even be used against the chemist analyst in attempts to fool him:

A mixture of 15% true peppermint oil and 85% mentha arvensis oil will produce almost the same color reaction (with a slight difference in time and color shades) as would the pure peppermint oil. Even worse: this color reaction can be "introduced" in the mentha arvensis oil by the addition of foreruns from the rectification of true peppermint oil. Menthofuran is present in the fractions between the monoterpenes and the menthol, and peppermint oil is frequently submitted to fractional distillation in order to produce certain sweet types of peppermint oil for flavors, etc. The above mixture of peppermint oil (or fractions) and mentha arvensis oil will usually be revealed in an organoleptic test of the oil (sample) against a known and good peppermint oil. Modern instrumental analysis will, in most cases, also reveal such fraud. Mixtures of peppermint oil fractions with mentha arvensis oil are sold in Europe, Africa and Asia as "peppermint oil" with the further indication of standard quality such as "B.P.", or "D.A.B. VI", etc. or other Pharmacopoeias. "Quality", at this point, refers to physico-chemical standards, not to odor or flavor. In brief, peppermint oil is one of the most adulterated essential oils in the trade outside the United States (see monograph on **Peppermint Oil**).

Mentha Arvensis Oil finds extensive use in the flavoring of candy, e.g. chewing gum, hard candy, chocolate fillings, etc. and in all kinds of toothpastes, mouth washes, gargles, etc.

Although more than 1,000 metric tons of menthol is isolated from crude "total" mentha arvensis oil per year (the crude oil is rarely sold commercially), the oil is still larger in quantity than the oil of true peppermint. Through skillful compounding (bouquetting) of selected fractions or of rectified mentha arvensis oil, the flavorist can create quite attractive artificial "peppermint" oils. As mentioned above, such oils will find use only outside the U.S.A. But the lower cost of dementholized mentha piperita oils will constantly tempt the suppliers to use this oil as a basis of their "special" peppermint oil (so-called). In 1946, when the Brazilian production and war-time left-over stocks of mentha arvensis oil hit an all-time high (over 1,000 metric tons), the price fell to about U.S. $ 0.70 per lb. (almost like citronella oil). Since the price of menthol (synthetic or isolated) at no time fell below about $ 5.00 per lb., it is quite understandable that the Brazilian producers abandoned plantations and distillations for many years thereafter. It could never be profit-able to sell an oil with 55% menthol (the de-mentholized oil) at such low prices.

It has become customary to use mentha arvensis oil as "peppermint oil" all over the world except in the U.S.A. In chewing gum, one of the main outlets of "peppermint oil", the gum is often flavored with about one percent oil of mentha arvensis, while the sugar coating is flavored with 0.7 to 1.0 percent of a true peppermint oil. After a few "chews", the customer is unable to identify the arvensis oil inside the gum because of the pleasant cooling and paralyzing effect of the good peppermint oil in the outer coating.

See also **Peppermint Oil.**

Mentha Citrata.

Like most other "mints", the so-called **"Bergamot Mint"**, the plant **Mentha Citrata**, originated in central and southern Europe. However, the only present-day cultivation of the plant and distilla-tion of oil of commercial importance is carried out in the farwestern United States, particularly in the states of Oregon and Washington (Pacific Coast, inland).

The fully grown plant is steam distilled locally, the annual production fluctuating between 2 and 15 metric tons. The present decline in the price of lavender oil, the abundance of lavandin oil, and the keen competition in the linalool/linalylacetate-field has limited interest in the oil of **Mentha Citrata**. Its main constituent is linalyl acetate. Produced similarly to peppermint oil, it is priced almost equal to that oil.

Mentha citrata oil is a pale yellow or pale olive colored to almost water-white liquid of a sweet-herbaceous, somewhat fruity-fresh odor type; it resembles bergamot, but is distinctly more harsh in its terpenic topnotes, less rich in body, and

without the oily-sweet, candy-like undertone of good bergamot oils. On the other hand, mentha citrata oil presents a certain bergamot note without the citrus notes. This makes the oil more interest-ing in the lavender-fougère field. Its dryout has some resemblance to sage clary, but lacks the richness of that oil.

The flavor of mentha citrata oil is sweet-fruity at low concentrations, but bitter-perfumey at higher levels. It is necessary to remove the mono-terpenes from mentha citrata oil prior to its use in flavors. But since this operation yields an oil at about the same price level as bergamot oil, it is reasonable that the oil of mentha citrata has failed to catch the interest of the flavor industry. The oil itself is definitely not a flavor-body, but it could find use as a modifier in bergamot-candy flavors, etc.

Mentha Citrata Oil could also find some use as an adulterant of sage clary and bergamot oils, lavender oil, petitgrain bigarade oil, etc., but the limited quantity available and the comparatively high cost of the oil does not invite large-scale operations of this kind. Besides, lavandin oil is fractionated commercially on a large scale. After acetylation of the selected fractions a very inter-esting perfume material is obtained. This material is an excellent "stretcher" for the above mentioned oils, and it is used more or less artistically by many supply houses in the industry.

It is conceivable in view of the above that oil of **Mentha Citrata** may slowly disappear from the market unless it can be produced at a much lower cost, e.g. in another country.

Mikan Oil.

Mikan oil is a citrus oil, prepared by expression of the peel from the fruit of **Citrus Unshiu**, a local Japanese species of citrus. The oil can be charact-erized as a mandarin-tangerine oil according to its odor and flavor. The annual production is between 5 and 10 metric tons, and the entire quantity is used in the Japanese perfume and flavor industry. The oil is mentioned here for the sake of completeness and for its local importance. It is usually not available outside of Japan, and the author has no personal experience with its use in perfumes or flavors.

Milfoil.

Another very well known botanical, used in

popular medicinal infusions for hundreds of years, is **Milfoil**, also known as **Yarrow**. Its use in perfumery is of minor extent.

The herb, **Achillea Millefolium**, grows wild all over Europe, western Asia, and the United States, and is probably not cultivated on an extensive scale anywhere in the world. Germany, Belgium, Hungary and Yugoslavia are main suppliers to the drug houses in Europe. Steam distillation of the dried herb takes place occasionally in Germany, France, Hungary and Yugoslavia.

Milfoil Oil is a dark blue or greenish blue to dark olive colored liquid with a sharp, somewhat camphoraceous odor, drying out in a sweeter, faint and pleasant note. The overall odor may recall the odors of cedarleaf and tansy, Texas cedarwood (faintly) and valerian (but without any acid notes). The bluish color is due to the presence of azulenes (see chamomile oil), but the author has been unable to find any other similarity between milfoil oil and the so-called "german" chamomile oil. Literature sources claim that milfoil oil has been used in the adulteration of chamomile oil. It is indeed possible that the two herbs could have been co-distilled, but the resulting product would hardly fool any connoisseur of true chamomile oil. **Milfoil Oil** itself has been adulterated with cedarleaf oil, Siberian pine needle oil, or with synthetic materials such as isobornyl acetate, camphene, etc. The oil could find some use in perfumery for its unique fresh-herbaceous note. The production of the oil is sporadic, however, and users may have to perform their own distillations in order to obtain even small quantities of the oil.

See also **Iva Oil**.

Mimosa Absolute from Concrète.

Like many other perfume plants, **Acacia Decurrens**, a native of Australia, was brought to Europe as an ornamental plant in the early part of the 19th century. The tree is known in Australia under the name of **Sidney Black Wattle** and is used as a tanning material. Other mimosa species were introduced at about the same time, but these have found more application in the florists' business.

Mimosa Concrète is produced from the flowers and the twig-ends of the above species by extraction with petroleum ether. It is worth noting that material other than just the flowers is used, but at the same time it must be emphasized that extracts obtained from flowers exclusively are available also. They obviously command a higher price, but they also yield a richer, more floral-sweet, true-to-the-flower odor. Ultrasonic extracts of mimosa flowers and twigs are available. Extractions are made almost exclusively in the south of France where the trees grow most abundantly. Small quantities are treated in Italy. The harvest takes place in the very early spring, and the entire production is often sold out before the end of the year. The heavy frost in January-February 1956 killed all the mimosa trees in certain areas of southern France, and mimosa absolute was practically unavailable for a year or two.

Mimosa Concrète is a hard and wax-like, pale yellow or whitish yellow-opaque material of a sweet-woody, fatty and deep-floral odor. The author does not agree with the recent statements of authors who claim that the odor of mimosa concrète "is in no way reminiscent of that of the flower". This is, of course, a matter of opinion, but the author of the present work finds that good and true mimosa concrètes, produced exclusively from flowers, do smell suggestively of the flowers of mimosa (acacia decurrens). It is agreed that the concrète has a pronounced waxy-sweet, almost honeylike undertone, but its sweetness is certainly of a true-to-nature floral character. The author is inclined to believe that the statement quoted above is based upon studies of so-called mimosa-replacements which were flourishing in the perfume industry during 1956 and 1957.

Mimosa Concrète, as such, finds application in perfumery primarily in soap perfumes where its outstanding fixative value accompanies its delicate, woody-floral, slightly green notes. For lilac, muguet, new mown hay, violet and similar floral and herbaceous-coumarinic types, a small addition of mimosa concrète can do wonders. In amounts of 0.5 percent up to 2.0 percent in a soap perfume, this material can make all the difference between a flat, common or nondescript odor, and a radiant, natural, deep-rich and intriguingly interesting fragrance of unusual tenacity and stability in soap.

Mimosa Absolute is prepared from the concrète as described in Part One of this book. The absolute is a very viscous, ambercolored or yellowish liquid, similar in appearance to fresh honey. Its odor is very rich, floral-woody, slightly green and resembling cassie absolute to a certain degree.

It is sweeter and more natural flower-like, but less spicy-complex than cassie. Mimose absolute blends perfectly with ionones, methylionones, isoeugenol, cassione (!), heliotropine, anisyl alcohol and esters, alpha terpineol, phenylethyl alcohol, dimethyl benzyl carbinol, dimethyl phenylethyl carbinol, michelia leaf oil, terpeneless lavandin oil, amyl salicylate, ylang-ylang oil or absolute, trimethyl undecylic aldehyde (traces), hydroxy-citronellal, anisyl acetone, cinnamic alcohol or styrax products (styrene-free), linalool, bucinal (para-tertiary butyl alpha methyl hydrocinnamic aldehyde), methyl para-toluate, benzyl acetate, indole (traces for lilac), etc. The absolute is used in numerous lilac bases, violet, muguet, high-class new mown hay, colognes, ambres, etc. Actually. mimosa absolute will generally act to round off the "rough notes" from synthetic materials, and "lift" the natural materials in a perfume composition. The radiance deriving from the mimosa absolute alone is amazing, and taking this fact into consideration, the material is very economical. Its normal price level is slightly above that of true cardamom oil.

The annual production of **Mimosa Concrète** fluctuates (according to demand and to frosts!) between 200 kilos and about 1½ ton. The amount of absolute produced is in the neighborhood of 100 to 300 kilos. The author has seen thousands of **Acacia Decurrens'** and other **Acacias** useful for perfume extraction growing wild or semi-wild in all parts of northern, northeastern and central-eastern Africa. Unfortunately, these trees are often located far from inhabited areas. The botanical material for an increased production of **Mimosa Concrète** and **Mimosa Absolute** is abundantly available.

Mimusops Elengi.
The flowers of this tree are known in India as **"Bakul"** or **"Vakul"**, and they present the starting material for the preparation of **Attar of Vakul** (attar of bakul, or attar vakula), a perfume oil. The large tree grows wild in northern and northwestern India as well as in south India, particularly in the northern province of U.P.

The flowers are steam distilled locally and yield a very small amount of essential oil. An attar is also produced, usually on sandalwood as a base.

The essential oil of **Mimusops Elengi** is a pale yellow, mobile liquid of very delicate, sweet and

extremely tenacious floral odor, somewhat reminiscent of orange flower and tuberose, or the more well-known stephanotis floribunda (gardenia undertone). A honeylike, heavy-sweet undertone is quite persistent, and this essential oil could, if it were made regularly available, certainly find use as a modifier of countless floral fragrances.

Oil of **Mimusops Elengi** is not a commercial item yet, but it has been produced and shown to the outside world with the intention of increasing demand and production of this exquisite perfume oil. The **"Attar Vakula"** is regularly produced and finds application in the local Indian perfumes.

Mistletoe Absolute.
A very rare perfume material which is only occasionally available is the **Absolute** of **Mistletoe,** known in France as **Absolue de Gui.** It is prepared by the usual two-step extraction from the leaves and twigs of **Viscum Album,** a parasitic plant, quite common in central and southern Europe. It grows on various trees, particularly on apple trees, poplars, willows, etc., but almost never on oak trees. The French eastern highways are often bordered with poplars, and in the springtime one can see all these "bird's nest"-like plants in the poplars before the leaves of the poplar appear.

Infusions of the leaves and twigs of mistletoe have been used in popular medicine and teas for a long time.

Mistletoe Absolute is a dark green, very viscous liquid of a bitter-herbaceous, foliage-green, or rather green-bark type of odor. The dryout is sweeter and more pleasant.

Small quantities of this material are produced in France, probably only upon demand. The material is used in perfumes of the "forest" type, chypres, moss-bases, fougères, "men's fragrances", etc. to introduce a non-perfumey masculine note, or a bitter cortex-type of natural "fond" in certain perfume bases. Mistletoe absolute blends well with oakmoss absolute, dimethyl benzyl carbinyl acetate, cedrela odorata, cypriol, amyl salicylate, cedarwood deruvatives, lavandin concrète, isobornyl propionate, etc. The use of this material, if it is to achieve its full effect, is dependent upon great skill and experience from the creative perfumer.

There is ample material available for extraction,

but is not at all likely, that **Mistletoe Absolute** will ever acquire any great interest for perfumery.

Muhuhu Oil.

In the group of sandalwood-amyris-cedarwood type of essential oils, we find numerous wood oils which are either produced on an experimental scale only, or produced for local consumption in a limited area. A few of these oils have reached the "outside" world of perfumery, accidentally, or justified by their particular and outstanding effects.

From an East African Compositae, **Brachyleana Hutchinsii,** comes an oil which is steam distilled from the wood of this tree. The tree is known locally in Kenya and Uganda as **Muhugwe** tree, and the oil is commercially known as **Muhuhu Oil.** The oil has been known for about 30 years outside East Africa.

Muhuhu Oil is a viscous, amber-colored or brownish-yellow liquid of a soft, balsamic-woody, somewhat sweet and faintly floral odor, reminiscent of vetiver, sandalwood and tail-fractions of Atlas cedarwood oil. Fresh oils show a strong topnote of styrene-cadinene type and a dry, somewhat harsh caryophyllene-like bodynote.

Unfortunately, the odor characteristics of this oil vary considerably since distillation of the oil demands extensive experience in order to achieve a uniform product. A significant amount of the oil consists of partly water-soluble sesquiterpene alcohols or related materials, and the presence and percentage of sesquiterpenes, etc. is largely dependent upon the length of distillation, steam pressure, etc. The wood, which is an excellent but very hard furniture lumber, has been distilled experimentally in modern stills in Europe.

Taking all this into consideration, **Muhuhu Oil** will have some difficulty in attaining any great importance as a perfumery material, but the delicate fragrance, the low cost, and the excellent fixative effect of better grades of the oil (or of the high-boiling fractions thereof) may still attract the interest of many perfumers who work with "precious wood"-notes, Oriental bases, tenacious powdery and aldehydic fragrances, vetiver bases, sandalwood variations, etc.

Muhuhu Oil is produced in very limited quantities and is not available at all times. It is very likely that it would be available if the producers were allowed to charge a reasonable price for the troublesome work of producing this oil.

See also **Osyris Tenuifolia.**

Murraya Paniculata.

A great number of trees, shrubs and plants are cultivated in the Far East for the purpose of producing flowers or leaves with which the Indian and Chinese sorts of tea are scented.

Murraya Paniculata is a small tree which carries a wealth of fragrant flowers almost all year round. The tree originates in India and Indochina where its flowers are occasionally admixed to the cured tea leaves in order to add a special fragrance. An essential oil and a petroleum ether extracted concrète have been produced in China from these flowers. These products could be classified as orange-flower-like or jasmin-like in odor, but none of these perfume materials have been offered in commercial lots outside China yet. The concrète is used in Chinese perfumery. The author has no personal experience with the essential oil or with the concrète of **Murraya Paniculata,** but it is possible that the concrète will be available in Europe in the years to come.

Musk.

For some reason, it seems that whenever perfume materials are the subject of popular discussion, the few animal products ambergris, castoreum, civet and musk attract much more attention than do the material of vegetable origin. It must be admitted that the circumstances in which these animal perfume materials are obtained do contain quite exciting, romantic or surprising details.

Musk is obtained from the male musk deer, **Moschus Moschiferus,** and possibly other **Moschus** species, animals that live in the inaccessible mountains of Himalaya-Altai, in Tibet, southern China and northern India. The musk is a secretion contained in an internal pouch on the abdomen of the male deer. It is still common practice to kill the animal in order to remove the pouch. More than 70,000 male musk deers die annually and unnecessarily for the sake of producing somewhere between $\frac{1}{2}$ and $1\frac{1}{2}$ ton of **Musk.** It has been proven that the pouches can be removed without killing the animal. The killings continue recklessly, however, and the animal faces extinction.

The musk pod is shipped whole and dried; it is rarely cut open. Inside is the active and valuable ingredient called **Musk Grains** which form the starting material for preparation of **Musk Tincture** or various extracts. The musk pod is slightly ovoid or pear-shaped, two to five cms. by five to eight cms., and hairy on one side, with silky appressed hairs radiating from the small orifice in the follicle. The color of the pod is grayish-brown. When dry, the pods exhale the characteristic animal-type, slightly amine-like, sweet and very persistent odor. From 60% to 75% of the weight of the pod should consist of "grains".

Musk Tincture is prepared as described under **Tinctures** in Part One of the present work, or it may be prepared to suit special demands by the user himself. Resinoids have been prepared by benzene extraction, but ethyl alcohol extraction is generally preferred. This produces an alcohol-resinoid ("resin-absolute"), free from most of the fatty insoluble matter of the crude musk. **Musk Tincture** is pale brown or dark amber colored and will, after proper ageing, present the typical odor of musk.

Musk Absolute is produced by alcohol extraction of a petroleum ether "resinoid" from musk grains. This absolute is a dark brown very viscous liquid of intense, yet typical musk odor. It is one of the most expensive of all perfume materials. One gram will cost from 50 up to 80 shillings (engl.). It offers the advantage of occupying very little space in the perfume laboratory (if it is not kept in the safe!). Most perfumers still prefer to use the old-fashioned tincture with which the risk of overdosage is negligible.

Musk Tincture and other **Musk** preparations are used quite extensively in perfumery, not only for the fixative effect of the **Musk** (this can hardly be classified as a strictly physical effect of lowering the vapor pressure in the perfume composition by the minute addition of musk), but mainly for the characteristic effect of the musk tincture. It gives a distinct "lift" or "life" to almost any well balanced perfume base when used in the proper concentration, i.e. just above the level of perception, or at the level where the effect is a perfect "rounding-off and levelling-out" of the perfume. The "animal note" should, in most cases, not be distinctly perceptible.

With such precautions kept in mind, one can apply musk tincture to a great variety of perfume types: Oriental and heavy-floral types, aldehydic bases, muguet, rose, clover, violet, etc., etc.

In flavor work, it is possible to take advantage of the "rounding-off" effect of musk tincture e.g. in tobacco flavors, in nut or caramel flavors, and even in certain fruit flavors. However, in this respect, synthetics of similar effect (Exaltone, Exaltolide, etc.) have frequently been used as substitutes for the natural product.

Musk Pods are frequently adulterated, e.g. by removing the grains and substituting invaluable matter for the removed grains. Partly extracted pods, or emptied pods can be admixed, but this fraud is detected more easily. Adulteration will practically always take place *before* the musk pods are shipped from the final shipping port.

Mustard Oil.

The trade usually speaks of two kinds of mustard seed:

Black Mustard and **White Mustard.** Only the **Black Mustard** yields an essential oil. Consequently, **Mustard Oil** is always the essential oil from the seeds of **Brassica Nigra.** There is another variety of mustard, called **"Sarepta"** or **"Russian Mustard",** produced from **Brassica Juncea,** whose seed also yield an essential oil on distillation.

Brassica Nigra originated in southeastern Europe, the eastern Mediterranean countries, Asia Minor, etc., and it is cultivated in the coastal area of northeastern Abyssinia (formerly Erithrea). The Russian variety originated in southern Russia, India and northern Iran.

Table mustard made with "Russian" mustard is considerably more pungent than that from ordinary black mustard seed. In India, a local variety is used, **Brassica Integrifolia,** and in China and the Far East, still another, **Brassica Cernua.** These have little or no importance on the American or European markets.

Mustard Oil is produced by steam-and-water distillation of the enzymatically hydrolyzed suspension of comminuted press-cakes of black mustard seed in warm water. The essential oil is not present as such in the seed (compare to bitter almond oil, etc.). A glycoside, located in certain cells, is decomposed by hydrolysis under the influence of an enzyme which is present in othe cells in the seed. Comminuted and triturated in warm water, the seeds will release glycoside and enzyme, and form the essential oil which is steam-distillable.

Mustard Oil consists almost entirely of **Allyl Isothiocyanate** which is also produced synthetically on a commercial scale. This material is often offered under the name of "artificial" or "synthetic" mustard oil, occasionally called "allyl mustard oil". As a matter of fact, the largest part by far of all **Mustard Oil** sold today is synthetic allyl isothiocyanate.

Black Mustard is cultivated in Holland, Denmark and southern Europe. The two varieties of black mustard will both yield an odorous mixture when triturated with water at room temperature. The odor is sharp, acrylic, lachrymatory. **White Mustard** will not produce an odorous triturate with water (see **Mustard, White** in the following monograph).

Mustard Oil is a water-white to pale yellow, mobile liquid of extremely sharp, acrylic, irritating odor, and of lachrymatory effect. It is a powerful skin-irritant and it is used in medicine for this effect (as a so-called rubefacient). The oil finds extensive use in the pickle and canning industries, in household seasonings, table sauces, etc. The oil is definitely not recommended for use in perfumery, although traces can have quite interesting effects in the most unusual perfume bases, e.g. violet, geranium, hyacinth, etc.

When crushed seed of **Black Mustard** is triturated with vinegar, salt and water, the preparation is called **German Prepared Mustard**, the flavor effect being different, richer than that of a plain water-trituration.

The seeds of **Black Mustard** contain 30 to 35% vegetable, non-volatile ("fixed") oil, which can be used as a household cooking oil. In this respect, however, the fixed oil from **White Mustard** is more important.

Oil of **Black Mustard** is freely available, but, as mentioned above, usually as a synthetic chemical.

See also: **Mustard, White** and **Horseradish.**

Mustard, White.

For the sake of completeness, the seeds of **Brassica Alba**, known in Europe as **"Yellow Mustard"**, elsewhere as **"White Mustard"**, shall be mentioned briefly. The seeds do not contain any volatile oil, and they do not produce any volatile substances even when treated as described under **Black**

Mustard (enzymatic hydrolysis). However, an enzymatic hydrolysis of white mustard seed will produce a very pungent material: **Acrinyl Isothiocyanate**, also known as para-hydroxybenzyl isothiocyanate. This material is practically non-volatile with steam. Consequently, **White Mustard**
1) is a poorer rubefacient in household medicine,
2) produces an almost odorless, non-aromatic triturate with water—and
3) is not lachrymatory when treated with water.

The mixture of crushed white mustard, vinegar and salt in water is known as **English Prepared Mustard.** This mixture, as well as other triturates of white mustard, is strongly pungent and also skin-irritating, although less so than are the black mustard preparations.

White Mustard is used for its pungency when triturated as described above. It is often mixed with crushed black mustard in order to produce a powerful, aromatic-rich mustard-seasoning.

White Mustard is cultivated in many European countries in order to produce the fatty ("fixed") oil from the seeds by hydraulic expressing. The yield of fixed oil is about 20 to 25%. This oil must be purified from any trace of the above pungent material prior to use as a cooking oil. In addition, the white mustard plant acts as a soil-conditioner. The plant is grown as an in-between-crop, and then is plowed down into the soil where its abundant foliage re-conditions the soil.

Myoporum Crassifolium.

Under the name of **Anyme Oil,** an essential oil is occasionally distilled from this Australian tree. The wood oil is a pale yellow, somewhat oily liquid of terpenic fresh topnote and a pleasant woody-balsamic undertone, reminiscent of cedarwood and balsam fir needle oil. The oil may still have some local importance, but it is no longer a commercial item outside Australia. It has found a little use in soap perfumes and as a fixative in pine fragrances.

Myrrh.

Myrrh is a natural oleo-gum-resin, and is indeed a typical one. It contains a significant amount of essential oil, the balance being made up of about two-thirds of water-soluble gum, and one-third of alcohol-soluble (or hydrocarbon-soluble) resins. As a perfumery material, the crude **Myrrh** is one of the oldest known, and it is mentioned as far back as 3700 years ago in ancient history.

Myrrh is formed as a physiological, viscous oleo-gum-resin, and thus occurs naturally in the trunks of the small trees of various Commiphora species. The trees, often mere shrubs, grow in various parts of eastern Africa, north of the Equator, and in southern Arabia opposite the East African coast. It is collected in Arabia, Ethiopia (now including Erithrea), Somaliland and parts of Sudan. The main shipping ports are Djibouti, Aden, Massaua and Port Sudan.

To increase yield and production, the native collectors make incisions in the bark. Some lumps of resinified oleo-gum-resin fall to the ground and become contaminated with sand, gravel, etc. Other lumps are peeled off the trunk, and these usually make a better grade of myrrh. However, myrrh cannot be evaluated justly by its appearance only. Lumps of high odor value may have a poor appearance because they have fallen to the ground; they will give a poorer yield, quantitatively.

Myrrh consists of rounded or irregular tears, or agglutinated masses of smaller and larger tears of a moderate yellow to dark or reddish brown color. The lumps are usually covered with a lighter-colored or yellowish dust. The odor is warm-balsamic, sweet and somewhat spicy-aromatic; it is also somewhat sharp or pungent when fresh, but it is never terebinthinate.

From crude myrrh, Myrrh Absolute, Myrrh Tincture, Myrrh Oil and Myrrh Resinoid are prepared, see the following monographs.

Myrrh Absolute.

A true Absolute of Myrrh should be prepared from myrrh resinoid (see monograph) by alcohol extraction and subsequent evaporation of the chilled and filtered extract. However, the usual method of producing an alcohol-soluble extract of myrrh, is the direct alcohol-extraction of the crude botanical. The resulting product which in pharmaceutical terms would be an extract, is commercially known as a "resin-absolute". There are various types of resin-absolute according to the method of extraction. The comminuted crude Myrrh is treated with cold or lukewarm ethyl alcohol, the extracts are mixed, filtered and chilled after a precipitation period. The extract is then produced by evaporation under reduced pressure. The so-called "hot-extraction" yields a

different "resin-absolute". Its advantage is in the reduced extraction time, its disadvantage in the fact that certain components of the crude myrrh are dissolved which at a later moment will not dissolve readily in cold alcohol. The natural resin-acids form small amounts of odorous esters with the alcohol, thereby influencing the overall odor of the extract. Accordingly, cold-extracted "resin-absolutes" are preferred for their true-to-nature odor and good solubility. They may show a superior odor strength in many cases since they contain less of the odorless resinous components than do the hot-extracted products. Besides, cold-extracted resin-absolutes are generally lighter in color.

A solvent-free resin-absolute of myrrh is not pourable at room temperature. This is a drawback in perfume compounding and handling of the material. It is customary to adjust the amount of liquid phase in the extract in the following manner:

Towards the end of the evaporation, a high-boiling, odorless solvent is added which acts not only protectively against "burning" of the residual extract in the evaporator, but also as a plasticizer so that the Myrrh Absolute becomes pourable at room temperature and more handy in compounding operations. In this case, it is correct to label clearly how much solvent has been added, e.g. "Myrrh Absolute, 75%, with 25% Diethyl Phthalate", or the like. It is not correct to omit all mention of diluent. If the alcoholic extracts are prepared "cold" (i.e. room temperature), and the mixed extracts are not evaporated, one may obtain a concentrated Tincture of Myrrh. Starting with 20 parts of crude myrrh, and ending up with 100 parts of alcoholic extract, it is customary to label the product "Myrrh Tincture, 20%". The content of extractive matter (i.e. essential oil + resin) in this tincture will be about 6 to 8 percent since the alcohol-insoluble gum is disposed of. Myrrh tinctures are used in pharmaceutical and dental preparations, rarely in perfumery.

Myrrh Absolute is a very dark reddish-brown or orange-colored, viscous mass, only slightly more plastic than the resinoid. The absolute, if free from solvents or plasticizers, is not pourable, but it should be soft and sticky at room temperature. Its content of essential oil may be as high as 18 to 20%, in rare cases, higher.

Stronger tinctures of myrrh can be prepared either directly from the crude Myrrh, or by dissolving myrrh absolute in the required amount of alcohol. The latter solution is even more easily achieved when the alcoholic extracts of myrrh, during the preparation of cold-extracted **Myrrh Absolute,** are evaporated to a previously calculated weight. This processing requires accurate knowledge of the yield of alcohol-soluble matter in the myrrh in order to prepare a uniform concentrated **Myrrh Tincture.**

Example: 1000 grams of **Myrrh** is extracted with alcohol until the last menstruum (i.e. fresh alcohol) does not dissolve any more of the myrrh. In this part of the process there is a distinct difference between "hot" extraction and "cold" extraction. The hot process is usually carried out as a boiling of the myrrh and alcohol under reflux. The temperature in this mixture will be considerably in excess of 80°C. Cold extraction is carried out under vigorous stirring of the comminuted myrrh with alcohol at room temperature. A few manufacturers may use percolation of a mixture of washed sand and comminuted myrrh with alcohol. The sand prevents "clogging" of the myrrh with the saturated resin-solution during the beginning of the extraction.

The mixed extracts are filtered and weighed. The weight is 4300 grams (example). A preliminary, small-scale extraction of the same **Myrrh** has shown that it contains 30% alcohol-soluble matter. Our alcoholic extract is then evaporated under suitable vacuum until the pot residue is 600 grams. The finished product is a viscous, dark-orange or reddish liquid which represents a 50% solution of **Myrrh Absolute.** It can also be called **Myrrh Extract 6 = 10,** which means that 6 parts of our extract contains the soluble ingredients from 10 grams of **Myrrh.**

A true and purified **Absolute** of **Myrrh** can be produced by hot extraction (reflux) of the comminuted myrrh with a hydrocarbon solvent. A resinoid is prepared by evaporation of this extract. If the hydrocarbon extract is washed free from resin-acids with weak aqueous alkali prior to evaporation, a neutral resinoid is produced. This may subsequently be extracted with hot alcohol to produce a "purified" absolute. The yield is significantly smaller than the yield by ordinary and total extraction, but the product is superior in respect to odor and performance in soaps, etc. The purified absolutes are generally lighter of color.

Myrrh Absolute or concentrated **Myrrh Extracts** are used in perfumery in circumstances similar to those described under **Myrrh Resinoid.** They have a lower acid index and slightly higher essential oil content than the resinoids, and they are soluble in all perfumery materials. **Myrrh Extracts** which contain alcohol are not clearly soluble in vegetable oils or mineral oil and they may cause slight turbidity with certain other solvents occasionally used in perfumery. The extract mentioned in the above example can be made oil-soluble if a calculated amount of diethyl phthalate is introduced prior to the evaporation of the alcoholic extract. The alcohol may then be recovered quantitatively, leaving the high-boiling solvent in the extract.

Myrrh Oil.

By steam distillation of crude myrrh, an essential oil is obtained, appropriately called **Myrrh Oil.** It is worth mentioning that materials based mainly upon **Myrrh Extracts,** perhaps washed and neutralized, partly decolorized, are frequently offered as **Myrrh Oil** even by well-known essential oil suppliers. Similar mislabellings are observed with costus oil, lovage oil, elecampane oil, etc. These extracts are not true essential oils although they may contain all—or part of—the essential oil available in the botanical raw material. In the extracts, the essential oils are accompanied by non-volatile matter which often has little or no odor value or which may act as odor-depressants.

Steam distilled **Myrrh Oil** is produced in Europe and in the U.S.A. by more or less experienced essential oil houses. A select raw material and a profound "know-how" of distillation technique is indeed "essential" in order to obtain good oils from oleo-gum-resins, spices, herbs, etc.

Myrrh Oil is a pale yellow to pale orange or amber-colored, oily, but not very viscous liquid. Its odor is warm-spicy, often showing a very peculiar, sharp-balsamic, slightly medicinal topnote with a delightful "lift", free from any terebinthinate notes. The sweetness increases to a deep, warm-spicy and aromatic dryout which is quite unique and difficult to duplicate. The tenacity is not very outstanding (unless the oil contains extracted matter!). The flavor of myrrh oil is warm, somewhat pungent, but very rich and pleasantly aromatic.

Myrrh Oil is used in small amounts in perfumes of the heavy-floral type, heavy-Oriental type, woody-balsamic bases, etc. and it is excellent in high-class forest notes, moss notes, etc. modified with cypress oil, juniperberry oil, mandarin petit-grain oil, etc. The oil is occasionally used in oral preparations, dentifrice flavors, etc.

The annual production of **Myrrh Oil** is heavily fluctuating according to demand which is generally very weak. It is estimated that less than 1 metric ton is produced annually.

Myrrh Resinoid.

For the preparation of **Myrrh Resinoid** and other perfumery materials, it is essential that the starting material, the crude botanical (in this case, the **Myrrh**), be selected for the purpose, i.e. it must be of the highest olfactory value. Not only must it be the so-called "heerabol"-myrrh, but it should be free from odorless, foreign resins, etc. Commercial myrrh contains various amounts of "bisabol"-myrrh which today is called **Opopanax** (see this monograph), but since the latter is considered more valuable, the "bisabol"-myrrh is usually distinguished from the true myrrh. The two raw materials have distinctly different odor characteristics.

Myrrh Resinoid is produced from selected myrrh which is extracted with benzene, petroleum ether or ethyl alcohol. The product from the latter solvent is described under **Myrrh Tincture** and **Myrrh Absolute.**

Myrrh Resinoid is a very dark, reddish-orange-brown, viscous mass, hardly pourable at ordinary room temperature. It is soft and sticky, however, unless essential oil has been removed from the myrrh prior to the extraction. This is one way of producing a low-grade myrrh resinoid.

The odor is intensely warm, deep-spicy, balsamic-aromatic and very rich. The resinoid is distinguished by its bitter taste as opposed to the flavor of **Opopanax** extracts. In spite of its intense color which is a drawback, **Myrrh Resinoid** finds use in perfumery as an excellent fixative and sweetener in Oriental-spicy bases, chypres, woody bases, forest notes, pine fragrances, etc. It blends excellently with cinnamic alcohol, geranium oil, linalool, nitromusks, patchouli oil, spice oils, etc., and with the heavier, floral perfume bases. In flavors, the biting-burning, somewhat acrid-aromatic taste blends favorably in mouth-washes, toothpastes, etc. with clove oil, thyme oil, spearmint and pepper-mint oils, methyl salicylate, etc. Its actual medicinal value is disputable, but it does impart a pleasant-aromatic body to gargles, mouthsprays, etc.

Myrtle Oil.

Among the numerous perfume plants originating in the Mediterranean countries, is **Myrtus Communis,** a bush or a small tree that grows wild in Algeria, Corsica, France, Italy, Morocco, Portugal, Sardinia, Spain, Tunisia, Turkey, Yugoslavia, etc. The plant is also found abundantly on the island of Cyprus, but production of **Myrtle Oil** was abandoned in 1955, prior to the author's last visit to Cyprus.

The essential oil is produced by steam distillation of the leaves and twigs; in some places, the flowers, which are highly fragrant, are also included. This explains partly the significant difference between the myrtle oils from various producing areas. Distillation takes place in France, (insignificant quantities), Corsica, Spain, Italy, Morocco, Tunisia and Yugoslavia.

Myrtle Oil is a pale yellow to orange-yellow or pale amber-colored mobile liquid of strongly camphoraceous-spicy, but also sweet-herbaceous and fresh body-notes. The better oils, e.g. Tunisian and Corsican myrtle oils, are very fresh and strong in topnotes, and yet display an almost floral sweetness and little or no residue note. Myrtle oil belongs unquestionably to the "top-note" materials and not to the fixative oils. It blends excellently with bergamot, lavandin, lavender, rosemary, sage clary, hyssop, artemisia oils, lime oil, bay leaf oil, etc., and is thus an interesting item for colognes, also those of aldehydic type.

Furthermore, **Myrtle Oil** is used in flavors where it has found some popularity in meat sauces, seasonings, etc. in combination with spice oils and herb oils. In this respect, it blends well with clove bud oil, laurel leaf oil, cinnamon oils, cardamom oil, etc., giving freshness and lift to the heavy spices. It enhances the effect of ginger and it modifies nutmeg oil in a pleasant way. By itself, it is somewhat bitter and sharp, but when well blended, it acts favorably as a fresh and appetizing agent in many spice blends.

The annual production of **Myrtle Oil** ranges between 3 and 15 tons. Adulteration is not infrequent, and cineole, camphene and fractions from the production of lynalylacetate have been used for this purpose.

N

Narcissus Absolute from Concrète.

Narcissus Absolute is prepared from Narcissus Concrète which is extracted by petroleum ether or benzene from the flowers of Narcissus Poeticus, also known as *"Pinkster Lily"* or *"Pheasant's Eye"* (the latter name, however, often refers to adonis, a different flower).

Presumably originating in the Middle East or the eastern Mediterranean countries, the narcissus now grows wild in the south of France and sporadically in other areas. It is cultivated in the Grasse region of France, in Holland, and in numerous other countries for its flowers, but only the two former countries produce extracts from Narcissus Poeticus flowers.

Narcissus Concrète is very rarely offered since the narcissus fragrance is used almost exclusively in high-class perfumes for lotions where alcohol solubility is a necessity. A few, larger users of Narcissus Absolute may purchase the concrète and undertake the final alcohol washings themselves.

Narcissus Absolute is a dark green or dark orange, occasionally dark olive-colored, viscous liquid, at times somewhat grainy due to a separation of waxes which have not been eliminated quantitatively during the alcohol washings. The odor of narcissus absolute is strongly foliage-green, very sweet-herbaceous over a faint, but quite persistent floral undertone. The tenacity is very good. There is a distinct difference between the two French types of narcissus absolute: "des plaines" which is orange-colored, very viscous, and has a floral-sweet, mild and rich, but not very powerful odor. This type is mainly derived from the Grasse area. The other type, "des montagnes", is a greenish-brown, viscous liquid of powerful, sharp, somewhat violet-leaf-like odor of green and somewhat earthy type. The undertone is sweet and balsamic-spicy, reminiscent of carnation and hyacinth, but still carrying a strong, green foliage note. This type is derived mainly from the Estérel area in the south of France. The terms "des plaines" and "des montagnes" actually refer to the cultivated and the wild growing plants. The Dutch production is derived exclusively from cultivated plants (corresponding to "des plaines"). The annual production of narcissus absolute is estimated at less than 100 kilos.

Accordingly, the use of this fine flower absolute is rather limited. It demands great skill and experience to exploit fully the effects of this material. Well blended with synthetic materials such as para-cresyl caprylate (= octoate), various high-boiling phenylacetates, tolyl acetate, hexyl cinnamic aldehyde, bucinal, heliotropyl acetone, methoxy phenyl butanone, phenyl dimethyl carbinol, isoeugenol, etc. or with natural materials such as clove bud absolute, carnation absolute, jasmin absolute, orange-flower absolute, ylang-ylang absolute, rose de mai absolute, mimosa absolute, etc., the best effects of Narcissus Absolute may show off to the fullest extent.

Although not always adulterated, narcissus absolute is often sold in a more or less "compounded" or "bouquetted" form, with additions of violet leaf absolute, mimosa absolute, methyl tuberate, indole, etc. which give an impression of power.

Néflier Concrète.

The small evergreen tree, Eriobotrya Japonica is originating in China and Japan, and better known for its refreshing fruit, the Japanese medlar, also known as the loquat. The tree, which belongs to the family of Rosaceae, was introduced in the Mediterranean countries more than a century ago. It is also cultivated as an ornamental plant and for its fruits in southern California, Texas and Florida, U.S.A. Furthermore, it is cultivated in Brazil for the fruits which are very popular there. Ships from the Far East brought back shoots of this shrub or small tree to Europe in the middle of the 19th century, and the trees were later introduced in the U.S.A. Only very recently, a few perfume houses became interested in the fragrant flowers and leaves of the "néflier" as it is called in the south of France. Experiments with perfume oil production were carried out in Spain and France.

A Concrète of Néflier (flowers and leaves) was prepared by cold extraction, but the yield was very small. The concrète is a dark-green or dark olive-green colored, soft paste of extremely rich, delicately floral odor, reminiscent of lilac or hyacinth, however, more suave-balsamic than the odor of these flowers.

If it were made available in reasonable amounts, Néflier Concrète would undoubtedly prove of wide interest in floral perfume bases such as appleblossom, sweet pea, freesia, lilac, muguet, etc. Since the concrète is soluble in 95% alcohol, it is generally not necessary to produce an Absolute of Néflier. The odor yield from the concrète is very encouraging, but a regular production of Néflier Concrète is not yet effective.

Neroli Oil.

Neroli Oil is the essential oil water distilled from the flowers of the cultivated bitter orange tree, Citrus Aurantium, subspecies amara, which also is important for the production of petitgrain oil ("bigarade"-type) and bitter orange peel oil (see these monographs). The flowers from the sweet orange tree are not used for the distillation of one particular essential oil, but occasional admixture, contamination, etc. of the bitter orange flowers with sweet orange flowers is possible.

Neroli oil, also called Neroli Bigarade Oil (néroli bigarade pétales) or Orange Flower Oil is produced in the south of France, Italy, Tunisia, Morocco, Haiti, Guinea, Comoro Islands, Algeria, Lebanon and, in small quantities, in China, Spain, Egypt, Cyprus, etc. France, Italy and Tunisia hold first places in quantity. France and Tunisia lead in quality. The Haitan oil is quite different. It is produced by *steam* distillation of a mixture of bitter orange flowers and the flowers from the "shaddock" grapefruit tree. The flowers suffer under poor transportation conditions prior to the distillation. The Haitian oil offers interesting notes as a modifier or as an individual perfume material, rather than as a replacement for the French or Tunisian oils.

Since Neroli Oil is sold at about half the price of jasmin absolute, and is produced in annual quantities of several tons (provided there have been no severe frosts), the oil has substantial economical importance for the countries in which it is produced. Added to the production of orange flower extracts (see Orange Flower Absolute and Concrète), the total production of orange flower perfume materials can be valued at somewhere between 3 and 5 million U.S. dollars annually.

The orange flowers must be distilled immediate-ly after being picked in order to avoid decay and unpleasant off-notes due to decay processes. After having processed the flowers, the distillers usually carry on with distillation of leaves (petitgrain bigarade oil) since the trees are trimmed anyway. Thus, production of petitgrain bigarade oil follows shortly after that of neroli oil from the same plantation. It is of interest to note at this point that a good, terpeneless petitgrain bigarade oil is one of the most suitable adulterants for neroli oil.

Neroli Bigarade Oil is a pale yellow, mobile oil which becomes darker and more viscous on ageing. The odor is very powerful, light and refreshing, floral with a peculiar sweet-terpeney topnote, but its tenacity is rather poor. This oil is primarily a "top-note" material in perfumery. The keeping qualities of neroli oil are very poor, and its odor loses its freshness after a few months if the oil is not kept cool, dark and well sealed.

Neroli Oil is one of the "classic" materials in eaux de cologne of the "Maria Farina" type, "4711", etc. It blends excellently with all the citrus oils, with numerous floral absolutes and countless synthetic materials. Next to rose, jasmin and ylang-ylang, it is probably one of the most frequently used "florals" in perfume compounding. Most perfumers have a number of "neroli bases" on their shelf to be used when a cost problem or availability problem prevents the perfumer from using the natural neroli oil. Artificial neroli oils may be composed of terpeneless petitgrain oil, bitter orange oil, indole, linalylacetate, linalool, methyl-beta-naphthyl ketone, decanal, nonanal, decanol, nonanol, nerol, nerolidol, isojasmone, hydroxycitronellal-methyl-anthranilate (Schiff's base), phenylethyl alcohol, menthanyl ketone, nopyl acetate, lime oil expressed or terpeneless, tolu balsam, beta naphthyl ethyl ether, skatole, terpeneless lavandin oil, decyl propionate, propenyl-N-methylanthranilate, geraniol, various aliphatic aldehydes, aldehydic bases, specialties, etc.

When Neroli Oil is dissolved in alcohol, the solution shows a beautiful blue fluorescence which fades away on ageing of the solution in daylight. Old neroli oils do not always show this fluorescence in solution. Incidentally, this phenomenon is not at all appreciated by the perfumers in general, and great efforts are made to avoid this visible sign of the presence of anthranilates. It is conceivable that the anthranilates in the neroli oil

266

slowly add their molecules to the aldehydes in the oil, thereby producing a more intense yellow (darker) color, while the fluorescence disappears.

Neroli oil is not quite insoluble in water, and, during the distillation of the flowers, significant amounts of oil remain dissolved in the condensed distillation water. This solution is known as "Orange Flower Water", and was once a very popular cosmetic ingredient, household flavor for baked goods, etc. This water does not keep well; it loses its fresh floral aroma and bouquet, and it is subject to fungus growth. Today, there is insufficient demand for this water, and the producers instead extract the water with a hydrocarbon solvent. This leads to the so-called "Orange Flower Water Absolute" (see monograph). Every three tons of distillation water yield about one kilo of orange flower water absolute; this is another interesting perfume material, entirely different from neroli oil in composition and odor type. Other "water absolutes" are produced from distillation of leaves and twigs of the bitter orange tree (see monograph: Orange Flower and Petitgrain Water Absolute).

Neroli Oil has only limited use in flavors, but it can produce interesting effects as a modifier in fruit flavors for candy (e.g. with bergamot oil), in flavors for liqueurs, soft drinks, etc. The average use level is strongly dependent upon the type of other flavor materials present. In general, the most useful concentration of neroli oil in flavors should be slightly in excess of the Minimum Perceptible which is about 0.03 to 0.06 mg%. Maximum use level is estimated at 0.50 mg%.

The production of Neroli Oil is heavily influenced by the weather conditions, and there are years of very small crops where the oil is scarce or unavailable. The quality of the oil varies from one area of production to another. These circumstances, together with the comparatively high price level of neroli oil, have to a certain degree encouraged adulteration of the oil.

Niaouli Oil.

Among the more well-known "tea-tree" oils (see monographs on Melaleuca Oils), is Niaouli Oil which is steam distilled in New Caledonia (French Pacific islands) from the leaves of Melaleuca Viridiflora. The tree grows wild and in such abundance that cultivation is not at all necessary. Production of the oil has been as high as 60 metric

tons in one year, but the interest in the genuine oil has declined significantly. Production in 1959 was about 10 metric tons.

The New Caledonian tree is a native of Australia and it exists in several physiological forms. The Melaleuca Viridiflora which yields Niaouli Oil is usually considered as a "typical" form of the tree, while the varieties which still grow in Australia yield oils of entirely different composition. The best known of these Australian oils is the Melaleuca Viridiflora, variety "A" (see monograph). The essential oil from this tree contains significant amounts of Nerolidol, and the oil has at one time been considered as a possible source for isolation of this interesting sesquiterpene alcohol.

Niaouli Oil, also called Gomenol in French speaking countries is a pale yellow to greenish-yellow or almost colorless liquid of strong, fresh, sweet-camphoraceous, but cooling odor, reminiscent of eucalyptus oil and cardamom oil, however, less spicy than the latter. The flavor is warm, only slightly biting, aromatic, somewhat sweet and fresh eucalyptuslike. The sweetness in odor and flavor is quite characteristic, different from eucalyptus oil, cajuput oil, etc.

Niaouli Oil is used in medicinal or pharmaceutical preparations, in flavors for cough drops, more or less as an active ingredient in vaporizer liquids, mouth sprays, gargles, toothpaste flavors, etc. The oil is frequently adulterated in countries where it is not readily available (far from the source of supply). Eucalyptus oil, to which is added trace amounts of terpinyl esters, aldehydes, terpineol, terpinolene, benzaldehyde, borneol, etc. is often sold as niaouli oil. The fact that the larger part by far of the entire production of niaouli oil is shipped indirectly from New Caledonia to the consumers, is a major cause of the frequent adulteration. Large amounts of Niaouli Oil are used locally for all kinds of ailments.

Nigella Damascena.

Originating in the Middle East and growing wild in that area, in Turkey and in southern Europe, is the small plant Nigella Damascena. On account of its beauty it is also cultivated in many European countries as far north as Scandinavia. It is known as a garden plant under the name of "Virgin in the Green" (in Eerope) or the no less romantic "Love-in-a-Mist" (in the United States). Erroneously called "Black Caraway" it is often confused with **Nigella Sativa** which has no perfumery value and only limited use in flavors (see next monograph).

The seeds of **Nigella Damascena** are occasionally steam distilled to yield an essential oil of quite unique and interesting aromatic characteristics. Distillation takes place almost exclusively upon demand from a customer, or the customer will buy the seeds and undertake the distillation according to his specific needs. The oil is very rarely offered commercially.

Oil of nigella damascena is a yellowish liquid of a peculiar and intensely sweet-fruity, nauseating and somewhat unpleasant odor when freshly distilled. After proper ageing—or after drying out on the perfume blotter—the oil shows its great tenacity, a very pleasant dryout of a peculiar winy or "brandy-like" character, reminiscent of ambrette seed oil, cognac oil, decyl propionate and certain higher esters of anthranilic acid or N-methyl anthranilic acid. The peachy or grape-like, fruity note has often been compared to that of strawberries, and the author agrees that there is a certain similarity to the odor of *wild-growing* strawberries, but not to the cultivated garden varieties.

The flavor of the oil is sweet and distinctly fruity, but also "perfumey" unless the oil is diluted to a point only slightly above the **Minimum Perceptible** which is 0.02 to 0.06 mg%.

The oil shows, particularly when diluted, a magnificent blue fluorescence due to a nitrogen compound, called **Damascenine**. Damascenine is present in the oil to the extent of about 8 or 10%. It is an alkaloid of comparatively simple structure (methyl-2-methylamino-3-methoxy benzoate). This material has been produced synthetically, but the synthetic damascenine cannot replace the essential oil of nigella damascena in perfumes and flavors. The damascenine is also held responsible for the blue fluorescence of the essential oil in solution. The material itself has a somewhat fruity, grape-like flavor, but it lacks the rich and sweet body which is found in the essential oil. Damascenine and the essential oil of nigella damascena suffer from a severe drawback as flavor materials in the fact that the most characteristic part of the flavor is lost in acid media. Grape and peach flavors are usually presented to the customers in acid media and, accordingly, there is little sense in using the oil or the alkaloid for such flavors.

Nigella Damascena Oil can be used in perfumery, not only for lipstick perfumes where it produces interesting modifications of the conventional strawberry-peach-pineapple type of fruity perfumes, but also in many floral bases, e. g. gardenia, honeysuckle, jasmin, lilac, neroli, etc. The oil blends well with linalool, phenyl ethyl alcohol, hydroxycitronellal, benzylacetate, terpeneless petit-grain oil, ylang-ylang oil, bergamot oil, nerol, undecanolide, nonanolide, gamma-valerolactone, palatone, etc. It is a comparatively powerful and penetrating perfume material which can be used effectively at concentrations below one percent. In combinations with palatone, oxanone, etc., it may lose some effect due to the alkaline reaction of damascenine upon the very sensitive materials (palatone, oxanone, etc.).

Nigella Sativa.

Known in Europe as **"Black Caraway"** or **"Black Cumin"** is a small plant, originating in the Middle East like so many other spice plants, culinary herbs, etc. **Nigella Sativa** is cultivated in France and Germany, and it is found abundantly growing wild in Egypt, Asiatic Turkey and the Balkan States.

The seeds of this plant are used locally and in many European countries in household spices, usually blended in combination spices where the nigella sativa seeds lend a faint pepperiness, and a flavor which reminds slightly of cubeb. An essential oil is produced by steam distillation, but the oil has, to the author's knowledge, never been commercially available.

The essential oil of **Nigella Sativa** is mentioned at this place because of possible confusion with the much more interesting oil of **Nigella Damascena** (see previous monograph).

Oil of **Nigella Sativa** is a yellowish to dark amber-colored liquid. It does not show fluorescence, not even when diluted with alcohol. A fixed oil (fatty, vegetable oil) is produced by hydraulic expression of the seeds of nigella sativa.

Nindi Oil.

An extensive research on perfume plants was undertaken in the late 1930's and continued some years after World War II. English and French scientists were busy in Africa and other areas, and their reports included often several hundred species of common—but outside the place of origin—unknown, odorous plants, trees, etc.

The French botanist R.-L. Joly, the English H.T. Islip, the Australian A.R. Penfold, and many other local and travelling botanist-explorers and scientists have given the perfumers all over the world dozens of highly interesting "new" perfume oils.

Nindi Oil is derived from the African Aeolanthus Graveolens and probably other species of aeolanthus. This small plant grows wild in many parts of western Africa, but the essential oil is produced only in East Africa, particularly in Rhodesia and Tanganyika. The entire overground parts of the plant, occasionally including the underground parts, are steam distilled.

Nindi Oil is a pale yellow liquid of powerful and fresh-rosy, lemony odor with an almost muguet-like, delicate topnote and a sweet, pleasant, rosy dryout note.

To the author's knowledge, Nindi Oil is produced on a limited scale only. It finds local application in soap and cosmetic perfumes. The oil is not regularly offered outside East Africa, and it is doubtful whether the oil will ever become a potential competitor of citronella and palmarosa oils.

Nindi Oil has some scientific interest since it is one of the comparatively few geraniol-nerol type essential oils which is produced from a plant of the family Labiatae.

Nutmeg Extract.

Nutmeg and mace have—like most other spices—been extracted to yield products with a richer, more true-to-nature flavor than the one reproduced by the essential oil. A few flavor houses specialize in Nutmeg Extract, but many consumers will produce their own extract from selected nutmeg or mace. For flavor purposes, a hydrocarbon extract is preferable since it has greater tenacity and stability to heat in a later processing of food, etc. For perfumes, the "Absolute of Nutmeg" or the evaporated alcoholic extracts are more suitable. They are soluble in alcohol and in most perfume materials, and they will not deposit any resinous substance later on in bottles, aerosol containers, etc.

Nutmeg Extract is prepared from the dried, ripe seed of the fruit from Myristica Fragrans, a tree originating in the East Indian archipelago

(see Nutmeg Oil). The nutmeg tree is now cultivated widely all over the tropical zones. Indonesia is the main supplier of "East Indian nutmeg" while the Federation of the West Indies are main suppliers of "West Indian nutmeg". Ceylon produces "East Indian nutmeg".

West Indian nutmegs yield slightly more monoterpenes by distillation than do the East Indian nutmegs. Consequently, the latter are preferred in flavor work. If the nutmegs are extracted with a hydrocarbon solvent, it will be necessary to remove from the extract the significant amount of odorless and flavorless matter, which is solid and consists mainly of glycerol myristate. This ester is the main constituent of the so-called nutmeg butter (hydraulically expressed, fixed nutmeg oil, a solid, waxy mass). Glyceryl myristate is almost insoluble in cold alcohol, and the hydrocarbon extract of nutmeg is consequently washed with alcohol to yield an "absolute". Most often, the comminuted nutmegs are extracted directly with ethyl alcohol, and the extract is chilled, filtered and evaporated cautiously under slight vacuum.

Nutmeg Extract is usually a dark orange colored, somewhat grainy, viscous mass of very warm, suave, spicy-balsamic and strongly aromatic odor. The flavor is slightly burning, warm and spicy, truly reminiscent of nutmeg. The extract finds now and then use in old-fashioned types of Oriental perfume where it procudes delightful effects in combination with e.g. sandalwood, vetiver, cypriol, sage clary, oakmoss, lavender absolute, tonka absolute, labdanum extracts, bergamot oil, patchouli oil, geranium oil, etc. Minute additions of nutmeg extract can have very interesting effects in rose bases, etc.

Ultrasonic Nutmeg Extract is produced in France. The product is semi-solid and rather dark, but it is applicable in flavors and perfumes with a strikingly natural effect.

See monograph on Nutmeg Oil (including Mace Oil).

See also monograph on Mace Extract.

Nutmeg Oil.

Nutmeg Oil is produced by steam distillation or steam-and-water distillation of freshly comminuted, dried nutmegs (see Nutmeg Extract). The nutmegs should preferably be free from most of their fixed oil (e.g. by hydraulic expression) prior to distillation. The fixed oil can be alcohol-

39: The huge flower of an ornamental **Magnolia** tree on the French Côte d'Azur. The **Magnolia** fragrance is frequently copied by the perfumer, rarely extracted from the flower.

(Fot. S. Arctander, 1960)

40: Experimental **Peppermint** field (first year, "row-mint") at Menthe, Michigan, U.S.A.

(Fot. S. Arctander, 1958)

41: **Peppermint** plants immediately prior to harvesting in Michigan, U.S.A. The plant is cut during or shortly before the inflorescence. *(Fot. S. Arctander, 1958)*

extracted to yield a small amount of essential oil which has been dissolved in the fixed oil during the expression. As a curiosity, it should be mentioned that nutmegs are favorite dishes of certain worms who eat away the fixed oil, but who leave the essential-oil-bearing tissue (which is probably poisonous to the worms!). Wormeaten nutmegs are thus easier to distil, but they may—by their poor appearance—indirectly tell the buyer that they could be old and poorly stored nutmegs.

The fixed oil is odorless and tasteless (mainly glyceryl myristate), and it may retain small amounts and significant fractions of the essential oil in solution or emulsion when the nutmegs are hydraulically expressed (see above). The production of nutmeg oil is thus not without problems for the distiller. Only recently, the nutmeg planters began to distil oil locally (West Indies, and now also Indonesia). However, considerable amounts of nutmeg oil are still produced in the U.S.A. and in Europe by specialists in the field who select the raw material for distillation, and who have generations of experience in the distillation of "troublesome" spices. The so-called "Padang" nutmegs from Indonesia are generally preferred for distillation in Europe.

Dried nutmeg as a spice is a well-known commercial article, and distilling essential oil from the unattractive nutmegs (wormeaten, broken, odd shapes and sizes, etc.) is obviously an advantage for the importer of all grades of nutmegs (provided the nutmegs are not downgraded in other ways).

The dried finger-like, husk-like arillode which surrounds the nutmeg (seed) inside the shell of the fruit is known commercially as **Mace.** Perfumers no longer discriminate between the essential oil from mace and that from nutmeg. Dried, pulverized mace is another well-known household spice. With its better keeping qualities (absence of fixed oil which may become rancid in the comminuted nutmeg) it is more popular than the nutmeg. The masking power of the flavor of nutmeg or mace is excellently demonstrated in its use with cooked cabbage, whose odor is one of the most obnoxious household odors, and is actually used in tests for household sprays, etc. Mace or nutmeg sprinkled upon cooked cabbage completely masks the sulfide odor (compare lemon oil on fish or other seafood, lime oil on garlic and protein-foods, etc.). Perfumers do distinguish, however, between the nutmeg oil

from East Indian nutmeg and that from West Indian nutmeg. The former is generally preferred for its higher aromatic value, better solubility in ethyl alcohol and for its richer body. When they are freshly distilled the two oils have a peculiar "rubberlike" topnote due to certain low-boiling terpenes. This odor settles down and vanishes after a few months of ageing or after proper, thorough airing of the oils.

Nutmeg Oil is a pale yellow or almost water-white mobile oil of a light, fresh, warm-spicy and aromatic odor, a distinctly terpeney topnote and a rich, sweet-spicy, warm bodynote. The undertone and dryout is somewhat woody, but remains warm and sweet in good oils. There is some similarity to the odor of sweet marjoram oil.

The oil has found increasing use in perfumery lately for the modern "spicy" perfumes and for "men's fragrances" in after-shaves and other lotions. Small additions in fantasy bouquets or aldehydic perfumes, florals, chypres, etc., can have very interesting effects. Nutmeg oil blends well with amyl salicylate, oakmoss, bay leaf oil, linalool, lavandin oil, coumarin or deertongue extract, methyl cinnamic aldehyde, Peru balsam oil, etc.

For flavor work, a terpeneless oil is generally preferred, although the best grades of natural oils have superior diffusive power and masking effect. The oil is used in food preparations in combination with other spices for meat sauces, etc. It is one of the major spice additives in the conventional type of tomato ketchup. The **Terpeneless Nutmeg Oil** is usually prepared by countercurrent solvent extraction (see chapter on **Terpeneless Oils** in Part One of this book) since the monoterpenes in nutmeg oil are extremely sensitive to heat and tend to polymerize or produce ill-smelling compounds when they are exposed to dry distillation. The terpeneless oil is used in certain types of soft drink flavor, in spice blends for canned food, meat sauces, seasonings, etc.

Nutmeg Oil (natural) is not a very powerful flavor material. The suggested use level is 1.50 to 3.00 mg% and the **Minimum Perceptible** is 0.50 to 1.00 mg% for the very best grades of East Indian nutmeg oil, European distilled. The figures for the terpeneless oil are slightly lower. This may be due to the water-insolubility of the terpenes (strong flavor effect) and the solubility of the oxygenated compounds in water to a certain extent (this fact is pictured in the lowering of the flavor strength).

Nutmeg Oil is produced in substantial quantities and there is ample supply of botanical material available for a further increase in production. In 1959, an estimated 60 metric tons of nutmeg and mace oils were produced with a value of far beyond U.S. $ 1 million. This quantity, however, represents only a small fraction of the total world production of nutmeg and mace, both being used extensively as powdered spices. The production of nutmeg (whole, dry spice) in 1959 was estimated at 10,000 metric tons. The mace production was less than 800 tons.

Adulteration of **Nutmeg Oil** is performed with monoterpenes, e.g. myrcene, camphene, terpinolene, dipentene, pinene, etc., and with oil of melaleuca alternifolia, terpenes from the deterpenization of nutmeg oil, or with certain rare oils which contain a high amount of myristicin (Peruvian clavel moena leaf oil, etc.). Myristicin (= 1,2-methylenedioxy-6-methoxy-4-allylbenzene) is considered toxic, yet it is generally considered an important flavor ingredient. Myristicin is chemically related to safrole which possibly is present in nutmeg oil in traces. Safrole has been in the "limelight" of the health authorities in various countries, and it is very likely that safrole will be banned from use in flavors in the future.

Nyctanthes Arbortristis.

Known and used for many decades, perhaps hundreds of years, is the medium-sized East Indian and south Chinese shrub, **Nyctanthes Arbortristis.** Its white flowers are known in India under the name of **Parijata** flowers, and they have been used since long in the flavoring of tea in the Far East.

Recently, the Forest Research Institute at Dehra Dun, India, became interested in a further exploitation of these fragrant flowers. Their perfume is somewhat similar to that of orange flowers and jasmin.

An essential oil is water-distilled (compare neroli and ylang-ylang) from the large white or creamy-white flowers which open only by night and wither the following day. The receptacle next to the still should contain benzene or petroleum ether in order to prevent loss of the very small yield of oil which is partly water-soluble. A direct extraction of the flowers yield a concrète, but the yield in this operation is equally poor. Oil of **Nyctanthes Arbortristis** is a pale yellow to orange-yellow colored liquid of fresh and strong gardenia-jasmin type odor.

Absolute of **Nyctanthes Arbortristis** is a dark orange to brownish-colored, viscous liquid of intensely floral odor of jasmine-orangeflower type, somewhat indolic and sharper than the odor of orangeflower.

Oil or absolute of nyctanthes arbortristis are produced on a very limited scale only and they are not regularly available. But since the flower is a commercial article and is regularly harvested from the cultivated shrub, a production of these perfume oils is actually possible. The so-called "attars" of nyctanthes arbortristis are produced in India by co-distillation of the flowers with sandalwood oil, or by extraction of the flowers with fixed oils. The author has only little experience with the use of these materials in perfumery.

O

Oakmoss (summary).

The so-called **Oakmoss** belongs to one of the lowest ranking botanical specimens among all the perfumery raw materials. The various extracts of oakmoss belong to some of the finest perfumery materials at our disposal, and there are few high-class French fashion-perfumes which do not have at least a touch of an oakmoss product in their formulae.

The trade distinguishes between various types of oakmoss, and the perfume material suppliers offer an endless line of different extracts of these botanical specimens. It should be pointed out at this place in our oakmoss discussion that very, very few commercially available oakmoss extracts are "true and genuine" in the same terms as those applied to the essential oils: "– – derived by a physical process from odorous plant material of a single botanical form and species, with which it agrees in name and odor". The author would like to repeat that he fully agrees with the viewpoints of those suppliers who place odor quality and product performance above all other considerations in the processing of natural raw materials for perfumes and flavors. If it is in any way possible to improve the odor quality of a processed natural raw material by the use of several botanical specimens instead of one, or by the addition of small amounts of other natural or synthetic perfume materials, then we cannot speak of "adulteration" or "cutting" or "falsification"— not even of "sophistication" since the product is really not *less* than what it pretends to be. On the other hand, there is hardly any other perfume material that is so frequently "doctored up", "compounded", "bouquetted", etc., etc. as are the oakmoss extracts. A certain group of consumers or perfumers in the consuming part of the industry may be of the opinion that if an oakmoss product (or any other perfume raw material) *must* be compounded, bouquetted or the like in order to yield maximum performance, the perfumer might as well do this bouquetting himself and not pay the supplier to do it for him. The question is not as simple as that. The perfumer may have to spend years of daily experiments in order to arrive at anything like an improvement over the original odor and performance of his "pure and natural" oakmoss extract. The supply industry has this experience—generations of it—and it may be less expensive to buy this experience for a slight overprice per kilo of oakmoss product. Unfortunately, there are countless poor or worthless oakmoss products in the trade, and it takes time to evaluate just a fraction of the number of all available oakmoss products. However, for the consumer who may use as much as 500 or 1,000 kilos of oakmoss extract per year, there is definitely an economical advantage in buying the "straight" extract of one botanical material. A few central European manufacturers specialize in such extracts.

True **Oakmoss** is the lichen, **Evernia Prunastri,** which grows primarily on oak trees. It is collected all over central and southern Europe, particularly in Yugoslavia and France, and also in Morocco and Algeria. Smaller amounts are collected in Hungary, Czechoslovakia, Greece, etc. It is considered the finest raw material for production of perfume extracts ("true" oakmoss extracts).

The **Evernia Furfuracea** and **Usnea Barbata,** two related lichens, yield the so-called **"Tree Moss"** or **"Fir Moss"** (see monograph on **"Tree Moss"**). These lichens grow on spruces and pines in the humid forests of central and southern Europe. The tree- and firmosses produce a much darker extract, the odor of which is much less refined than that of true oakmoss extract.

Various lichens from peach, apple, almond, mimosa and many acacia trees are collected in France, Spain, Italy, Corsica, Yugoslavia, etc., and these yield extracts of various quality. A good, light-colored and aromatic moss usually comes from mimosas and acacias. Numerous other lichens and even algae are employed in the manufacture of so-called oakmoss products. (See also monograph on **Seaweed Absolute** about extracts from carragheen and other seaweeds).

Extracts are produced from the above botanical materials which can be classified briefly as follows:

1) **Concrètes**—by extraction with hydrocarbon solvents.
2) **Absolutes**—by alcohol extraction of concrètes.
3) **Absolute Co-Distillates**—by co-distillation of the absolute with a high-boiling, odorless solvent, usually by applying molecular distillation conditions.
4) **Absolute Oils**—by vacuumdistillation of the absolute.
5) **Resins**—so-called, are generally produced from the washed residues which are insoluble in alcohol during the production of oakmoss absolute (see #2). The waxy residue is "touched up" by the addition of various natural and synthetic perfume materials and solvents.
6) **Resinoids**—so-called, are produced by hot alcohol extraction of the botanical material. The residue (= the extract) is usually "touched up" with other perfume materials. The terms **Resin** and **Resinoid** are used erroneously and indiscriminately for various "compounded" extracts of oakmoss (and other mosses) with hot alcohol. The resulting extract is apparently subject to no standardization at all from the suppliers' side.

All of the above products (except #3 and 4) are also prepared in a more or less decolorized form. The above groups of materials appear in the market in countless varieties.

Oakmoss. (Uses of oakmoss products).

Oakmoss products are used extensively in perfumery. They form important parts of the notes in all fougère, chypre or "moss" perfumes, and they are common ingredients in colognes, crêpe de Chines, forest notes, new mown hay, pine fragrances, lavender bouquets, Oriental bases, fancy or modern bases, etc. They can lend body and naturalness, rich pleasant undertones and high fixative value in numerous types of floral fragrances as well.

Oakmoss products blend well with so many groups of perfume materials that it is hard to confine its use to certain mixtures. The oakmoss product never amounts to many percent of the total weight of a perfume formula (except in very rare cases), but it very often plays a decisive role in the overall performance of the perfume, even when the oakmoss product amounts to a few percent or less by weight.

1) The **Concrètes** are usually restricted in use in colored soaps, unless the oakmoss concrète is used in very low concentration in the soap perfume. Partially decolorized oakmoss concrètes can offer some advantages at this point, but they rarely produce the same odor type as do the corresponding green extracts. It is interesting to note that, although oakmoss owes its odor to aldehydes and phenolic and acidic types of components, it can still produce a unique and inimitable effect in a soap which is an alkaline medium and in the presence of moisture.

2) The **Absolutes** are the most versatile in perfumery use. Their solubility and great power make them the most popular forms of oakmoss extract. The absolute from benzene extraction is very dark green, viscous or semi-solid, while the absolute from petroleum ether extracted concrète is liquid and brownish-green, less intense in color. Furthermore, most oakmoss products are, in reality, mixtures of oakmoss and treemoss products, the latter being less green in color, but also different in odor and less aromatic than true oakmoss (see monograph on **Oakmoss,** summary).

3) **Absolute Co-Distillates** represent the absolute in a more or less diluted form and in various odor types according to the starting material. **Anhydrol Oakmoss** is a specialty of this type. It is produced by high-vacuum co-distillation of oakmoss extract with a high-boiling, odorless solvent which is miscible with perfume materials. Molecular distillation is usually applied, and the finished product contains a certain amount of the solvent. These products are almost colorless and they represent certain volatile fractions of the oakmoss fragrance. Their fixative value is inferior to that of oakmoss absolute by far. Oakmoss absolute co-distillates are used where good solubility, no color and no typical moss effects is wanted. They are versatile in use and reasonable in

cost, but not very typical of oakmoss in odor type.

4) **Absolute Oils** are the highest possible concentrations of the volatile part of oakmoss extracts. They are used in certain high-cost lotion perfumes where they may impart the most true-to-nature "moss" note without contributing any color at all to the perfume. The absolute oil can be used as a trace additive for topnote effects, or it may constitute a significant part of the body and the dryout notes at higher concentration in the perfume. In odor effect, it is at least twice as powerful as the ordinary absolute.

5) **Resins** are dark and often poorly soluble products. They may contain a significant amount of viscous, odorless solvent (up to two-thirds of the so-called **Oakmoss Resin**) and they are frequently bouquetted with coumarin, deertongue, hydroquinone dimethylether, isobutyl quinoline, clove bud oil, various residues from essential oils, etc. The actual amount of true oakmoss (or treemoss) extract in the so-called oakmoss resin may be as low as 10%. The "resins" are used extensively in industrial perfumes, low-cost soap perfumes, etc. Certain manufacturers know how to make an attractive "resin", others just don't (see **Oakmoss,** summary). Oakmoss resins are excellent fixatives for pine fragrances, low-cost fougères, etc. but they may be insoluble in alcohol. Certain types of oakmoss resin are soluble in mineral oil. These are used in hair preparations, etc.

6) **Resinoids**—so-called. The use is similar to that of the "resin". However, the hot-alcohol extracted "resinoids" represent a special type of oakmoss products (see monograph on **Oakmoss Resin**). Natural extracts of oakmoss contain very little resin. Methyl abietate or abietic alcohols, etc. may be added to produce a "resinous product". Oakmoss resinoids are used in soap perfumes and other perfumes where alcohol insolubility and intense color are no serious drawbacks.

7) **Decolorized Oakmoss Absolutes** are usually amber-colored, pale olive or straw yellow colored liquids. There is a certain loss of odor and change in odor type by the process of decolorizing the green extracts. The decolorized products are used mainly in cases where color is a problem, where a green color must not

appear (to be revealing!), or in high-cost soap perfumes for white soaps. Their particular odor and outstanding power make them interesting for modified oakmoss notes. They are usually higher in cost, by far, than the parent green extracts.

Oakmoss Absolute from Concrète.

One of the most important of all the oakmoss products—if not *the* most important—is the **Absolute of Oakmoss.** It is generally prepared by alcohol extraction of the concrète (see monograph on **Oakmoss Concrète**). A special process involves the addition of solid paraffin or ceresin to the melted oakmoss concrète. The mixture is chilled, comminuted (by grinding or chopping) and subsequently extracted with ethyl alcohol. There are several types of oakmoss concrète, and the corresponding types of oakmoss absolute are produced from these types. Thus, the absolute from a benzene extracted concrète is still a solid or semi-solid mass, while the absolute from a petroleum ether concrète is liquid. The extraction of oakmoss directly with hot ethyl alcohol yields the so-called **Oakmoss Resin** (see monograph).

Oakmoss Absolute is produced by the manufacturers of oakmoss concrète. The processing of oakmoss requires special equipment which cannot be used for anything else due to the extremely penetrating and tenacious odor, the resinous and insoluble coloring matter, etc. that is virtually impossible to remove from the extractors and stills.

The absolute from benzene concrète is a dark green, semi-solid or solid mass (from hot-benzene extracted concrète) or a very viscous liquid or soft, plastic mass (from cold-benzene extracted concrète). White, needle-like or prismatic crystals may grow on the surface or on the inside walls of the container when it has been exposed to significant changes in temperature (sublimation of lichen acids). It is worth mentioning that these crystals are not a direct criterion of either a highly odorous product nor a very genuine one. But it has been established as a fact that these odorless acids contribute greatly to the stability of the highly odorous aldehydes (e. g. **Evernic Aldehyde**). Practically all of the odoriferous principles of oakmoss are chemicals of phenolic, acidic or aldehydic character.

Oakmoss Absolute from petroleum ether con-

crète is a dark, brownish-green liquid, somewhat different in odor from the absolute of the benzene-extraction product. It contains little or no chlorophyll, very few waxes or "resins". It represents one of the purest forms of extracted oakmoss, and is of the highest olfactory value. (See **Oakmoss**—uses of oakmoss products).

Oakmoss Absolute Co-Distillates.

One of the best ways to obtain a good yield of essential oil of oakmoss and, at the same time, produce a colorless distillate is co-distillation of an oakmoss absolute with an odorless, high-boiling solvent, e.g. ethylene glycol, glycerine, isopropyl myristate, etc. The distillation is usually carried out in a comparatively small still, preferably all-glass, and at the best possible vacuum, short column and quick distillation. Molecular distillation is performed by certain manufacturers of these special oakmoss products, e. g. the "anhydrols" (reg. trade name of L. Givaudan & Cie., Geneva). Anhydrols are glycol-extracted or isopropyl myristate-extracted oakmoss products which are distilled in a molecular still. Other products are obtained by special extraction, followed by co-distillation with the high-boiling solvent. It is quite common in these cases *not* to soak the lichen prior to extraction. In fact, some manufacturers claim that it is preferable to extract the absolutely *dry lichen*.

Oakmoss Absolute Co-Distillates are pale yellow or almost colorless, oily or viscous liquids, having various types of oakmoss odor. The odor strength also varies according to the amount of odorless solvent left in the distillate.

These products are not replacements for oakmoss absolutes, nor for the essential oil of oakmoss since few or none of them have this type of odor. Rather, they are new types of oakmoss products, offered with the advantage of great solubility, no color, comparatively great strength, uniform quality, and a reasonable cost compared to that of pure oil of oakmoss. The co-distillates find application in all kinds of fougères, colognes, chypres, modern blends, aldehydic bases, bouquets, forest notes, tabac perfumes, "men's fragrances", etc. They generally cause less trouble in aerosol perfumes than do the extracted oakmoss products.

Oakmoss Absolute Oil.

It is possible to produce an essential oil by steam

distillation of the lichen, **Evernia Prunastri.** The product would be a true **Oakmoss Oil.** But this oil does not represent all the characteristic notes of the extracted moss, nor does it remind one of the lichen itself. Furthermore, the yield is extremely low (less than 0.1%).

A better yield and a more true-to-nature odor are obtained, when oakmoss concrète or oakmoss absolute are steam distilled, preferably under reduced pressure or at atmospheric pressure with superheated steam. Special products are obtained when, in place of steam or water, high-boiling, odorless solvents are used (see previous monograph: **Oakmoss Absolute Co-Distillates**).

Oakmoss Absolute Oil does not contain solvents, and accordingly is the most concentrated form of the volatile oakmoss constituents available. Due to the presence of substantial amounts of crystalline matter (so-called lichen acids), oakmoss absolute oil may deposit crystals or partly solidify on cooling to a semi-solid, crystalline mass. The color is usually pale amber or pale yellow, the odor is characteristic of the top notes of oakmoss: very dry, woody-earthlike, bark-like, almost tar-like, but pleasant, with a leather-like undertone and great tenacity.

Treemoss Absolute Oil (see monograph) is a common adulterant but it is much less fragrant, less dry-tar-like, not very leather-like but rather mushroomy-earthy of odor type. Various seaweeds have been used as adulterants, too (see **Seaweed Absolute**). The French perfumer and oakmoss expert, Pierre Mueller, mentions the Mediterranean shrub, **Inula Viscosa**, as a known adulterant in oakmoss products.

By extraction of oakmoss, and subsequent extraction of the concrète and absolute with selective solvents, other types of **"Absolute Oil of Oakmoss"** are obtained. These oils are pale green or pale olive-yellowish, oily liquids (they have not been exposed to high temperature or distilled), and they present different, although very delicate and interesting, modifications of the oakmoss odor.

Oakmoss Concrète.

True **Oakmoss Concrète** is prepared by hydrocarbon solvent extraction of the lichen, **Evernia Prunastri,** collected mainly from oaktrees in Yugoslavia, France, Italy, Corsica, Morocco, Hungary, and various central European countries. The lichen is often soaked in lukewarm water

24 hours prior to extraction. This operation is not absolutely necessary, but it does facilitate the extraction. However, it also changes the quality of the extract. The solvents used are:

1) petroleum ether (usually cold)
2) benzene (hot or cold)
3) gasoline (cold, but rarely used)
4) trichloroethylene (usually cold, but rarely used at all).

A number of other solvents are used to produce "specialties" of the individual perfume supply houses. Ethyl ether, methylene dichloride, ethyl acetate, etc. are among the more rare solvents. Extraction may be performed at room temperature or in a boiling solvent under reflux. The extractors may be of the "stationary" type in which the solvent by gravity moves through the (stationary) moss, or it may be rotary type where the moss is rotated in the solvent. The most common method has been that of hot extraction with benzene, but during the past five or ten years petroleum ether extraction has become increasingly popular and is now undoubtedly the most important method.

Oakmoss Concrète (hot benzene extracted) is a solid, waxy, dark green mass with a phenolic-woody, slightly tar-like but delicate and pleasant odor, reminiscent of seashore, forest, bark, wood, green foliage and tannery. Cold extracted concrètes are usually viscous or semi-liquid materials. A fair description of oakmoss concrète odor in general is hardly possible since there are so many different qualities, many of which have little or nothing in common with the odor of the botanical material, but most of which have very pleasant notes and pronounced "moss"-effects in perfumery. The dryout notes on a perfume blotter (moistened in a solution of the concrète), the overall odor type and the effect in perfumes, are the three most important virtues to study when an oakmoss concrète (or other extract of oakmoss) is selected.

At sufficiently low concentration, **Oakmoss Concrète** can be used in soap perfumes, that is, if the color is no drawback. The concrète is not clearly soluble in alcohol, but it has very great fixative value and is of comparatively low cost due to the simple one-step processing. The bulk of all oakmoss concrètes, however, are used for further processing into absolutes, etc. (see these monographs).

Oakmoss Concrète (petroleum ether extract) is a viscous, brownish-green liquid whose color is much less intense than that of the benzene-concrète. Its odor is richer, more intense and diffusive than that of the benzene-extracted concrète. The yield of extract is somewhat smaller with petroleum ether than it is with benzene. Accordingly, the former is slightly more expensive.

See also: **Oakmoss**, uses of oakmoss products.

Oakmoss "Resin".

Oakmoss "resin" or **Oakmoss "Resinoid"** are very ill-defined products, and it is apparently entirely up to the supplier to decide what type of product he wants to offer under that label. As the years go by, certain oakmoss "resins" prove to be more successful than others, and the trade will have the interesting experience that the successful (and usually "compounded") oakmoss "resins" become "models" or "standards" for similar extracts from other suppliers.

Basically, the product called oakmoss "resin" or "resinoid" is the hot-alcohol extract from the lichen, **Evernia Prunastri.** The product can be considered as an evaporated alcohol-infusion of oakmoss. Ethyl alcohol is not exactly a selective solvent, and, while the yield of extract is very high with this method, the extract contains also a great deal of chlorophyll and odorless ballast material which is not soluble even in cold alcohol. Its color is almost black-green or brownish-green, more brown when older, but the most important difference from the other oakmoss products is its chemical composition.

The delicate aldehydes (**Evernic Aldehyde**, etc.) in the extract are rapidly decomposed due to the absence of evernic acid which acts as an inhibitor for the protection of the aldehydes in the natural material. The acid is lost because it is esterified under the reflux with ethyl alcohol. The ethyl ester of evernic acid is toxic. It is a liquid, fragrant material which has been prepared synthetically, and is used in the reproduction of oakmoss odors for various well known specialties. It should be noted then, that **Ethyl Everninate** is *not* a natural constituent of oakmoss (compare to **Labdanum "Resin"** which is an alcohol-refluxed product of the crude botanical. **Styrax Resinoid, Benzoin Resinoid,** etc. may all contain ethyl esters of the acids from the botanical starting material).

However, ethyl alcohol produces esters with the oakmoss acids which have more pleasant odors than does e.g. methyl alcohol. The overall result is that the prepared **Oakmoss "Resin"** is a waxy, dark green extract which may produce crystals in the same manner as does the benzene-extracted concrète (see monograph).

Oakmoss "Resin" or **Oakmoss "Resinoid"** is used in perfumery where color and poor solubility present no great problem (colored soaps). They can be extracted further with cold alcohol or with a different solvent, thus producing an "absolute from resinoid", soluble in ethyl alcohol and stronger in odor than the ordinary "resin". A great number of the commercial products known as **Oakmoss Resin** are merely compounds based upon cleaned "resinoids" or alcohol-washed residues from the production of oakmoss absolute. To this basic matter is added coumarin, clove bud oil, deertongue extract, hydroquinone dimethyl ether, phenyl methyl ether, isobutyl quinoline, ethyl everninate, rosemary oil residues, sage oil residues, Texas cedarwood oil, etc. and often substantial amounts of high-boiling solvents such as diethyl sebacate, ethyl ricinoleate, methyl abietate, tetrahydro abietic alcohol, benzyl benzoate, etc.

The total world production of extracted perfume materials from oakmoss is very difficult to estimate since many commercial products are mixtures of oakmoss and treemoss extracts. Large quantities of true and pure oakmoss extracts are sold to companies who "work up" the genuine extract with other perfume materials and sell their own "special" oakmoss extract. A rough estimate of the total production of oakmoss and treemoss extracts would be about 45 to 65 metric tons per year.

Ocimum Canum.

About the heading **Ocimum** in this work, the author has preferred to limit the number of monographs to three:

Ocimum Canum—Ocimum Gratissimum and **Ocimum Kilimanjaricum.**

The three oils, plus the **Basil Oils,** represent all the oils of the **Ocimum** species which have any importance for the perfume industry outside the countries of origin.

Since the two once so popular and interesting types of the **Ocimum Canum** plant have lost most of their importance as sources of **Camphor** and **Methyl Cinnamate,** only a few details shall be mentioned here:

Ocimum Canum is a native of Africa where it grows wild and abundantly over wide parts of that continent. In India, the plant also grows wild, and it has been brought to South America from that part of the world. Similarly to other **Ocimum** species, the ocimum canum is found in at least two physiological forms, usually named: the **Camphor** type and the **Methyl Cinnamate** type. Both types grow in the above areas, but the former seems to prevail in the East African areas (see also **Ocimum Kilimanjaricum**). The author doubts if the oil of ocimum canum, camphor type, will ever find any application as such in perfumery. This oil contains from 50 to 70% camphor.

From a perfumery point of view, the oil of ocimum canum, methyl cinnamate type, is more interesting. Oils of this type produced in various areas (Comoro islands, West Africa, etc.) show some variation in respect to odor characteristics, and only a very general odor description can be given: the oil is usually pale yellow or almost colorless and of intensely sweet, woody-balsamic odor with a rich and tenacious, fruity-balsamic body-note. The topnotes can be more or less coarse, but the dryout is usually very sweet, soft and pleasant. The flavor is at first slightly bitter-burning, but as a whole it is sweet, anisic-fruity, slightly perfumey and herbaceous-woody. It is not likely that this oil will find any application in flavor work. But if it were readily available in sizeable quantities, the oil could be used in soap perfumes, in fougères, chypres, lilac bases, appleblossom, citrus colognes, etc. It blends well with bois de rose oil, lavandin, cinnamic alcohol, geraniol, isobornyl acetate, ocotea pretiosa oil, phenoxyethyl isobutyrate, nitromusks, petitgrain oil, rosemary oil, styrax resinoid, etc.

Ocimum Canum Oil, methyl cinnamate type, is presently produced irregularly and on a limited scale only.

Ocimum Gratissimum.

This stout plant of the family Labiatae occurs in a number of so-called physiological forms, i.e. plants of similar appearance, but different physiological and chemical constitution. This includes a distinct difference in the essential oils from the various physiological forms. To the **Ocimum** species belong also the **Basil** oils, previously described in this work.

Ocimum Gratissimum grows wild in many tropical regions of the world: The South Pacific islands of Tahiti, New Caledonia, etc., the Indian Ocean islands of Seychelles, Comores, Madagascar, in Indonesia, Brazil and West Africa, central and East Africa, southern U.S.S.R., etc. The plant is cultivated on a small scale in the south of France and in North Africa.

The entire overground parts of the plant are steam distilled in the flowering season. There are two important types of ocimum gratissimum: one is distinguished by its high content of **Thymol**, the other by its high content of **Eugenol**. In most cases, the eugenol type is the most interesting for the country of production since there is only one other important source of eugenol: clove oil, and this oil is produced only in Madagascar and Zanzibar. Certain countries have commercial problems, currency exchange problems, etc., which prevent them from buying sufficient amounts of clove oil or eugenol. The eugenol type of ocimum gratissimum oil is of particular economical interest to such countries. Accordingly, the above oils are often produced only in such quantities which may cover the demands of the respective country. No oil is exported, and these oils seem to be rare or even unknown in other countries.

1) **Thymol** type of **Ocimum Gratissimum**:
The oil is distilled in West Africa, Central Africa and, occasionally, in the Comoro islands. Production in Madagascar had been discontinued at the moment of the author's last visit (1955/56). The oil is dark yellow to orange-yellow or brownish in color. Its odor is medicinal-spicy, warm and somewhat herbaceous. The flavor is warm, slightly bitter-aromatic, burning and having a sweet-medicinal aftertaste. It is not conceivable that this oil can compete with **Thyme** oil in Europe or with **Ajowan** oil in India. It may serve as a local medicinal-perfumery oil and as a replacement for the above oils in case of scarcity. The annual production of **Thymol** type of **Ocimum Gratissimum Oil** is fluctuating, usually about a few metric tons.

2) **Eugenol** type of **Ocimum Gratissimum**:
This oil is distilled in the Seychelles, Tahiti, New Caledonia, Brazil, Indonesia, etc. Distillation in Madagascar has been abandoned, and the Comoro islands only distil the oil occasionally. This type of the plant has

attracted much more interest than has the thymol type, and in Brazil recent experiments with selective cultivation have resulted in good yields of an essential oil with about 80% eugenol which is almost comparable to the eugenol content in clove leaf oil.

Eugenol type of **Ocimum Gratissimum Oil** is a brownish-yellow to pale yellow liquid of powerful, warm-spicy and aromatic odor, reminiscent of the odor of clove leaf oil, but having a sweet-woody, almost floral, light topnote. The dryout is more bitter than that of clove leaf oil.

In Brazil, where a certain problem of import of perfumery raw materials exist, the need for eugenol (and for vanillin and other derivatives) has promoted the cultivation of ocimum gratissimum, eugenol type. The plant is locally known in Brazil under its Portuguese name, **Alfavacao.** It is believed that this plant arrived in Brazil with East Indian settlers in the middle of the 19th century. Growing wild in the forests, the plant is now also cultivated for the production of essential oil which in turn serves as a source of eugenol for Brazil. It does not cover the needs in this respect, however. The oil is available to the outside world, but it is not conceivable that it could serve any purpose beyond the scope of clove or cinnamon leaf oils both of which are plentiful and available in other parts of the world.

The eugenol type of ocimum gratissimum has recently been introduced in Formosa. This fertile island already produces several thousand metric tons annually of essential oils from other plants (citronella, camphor, peppermint & mentha arvensis, lemongrass, etc.).

Ocimum Gratissimum Oils (thymol type and eugenol type) may one day disappear from the world market since they represent distinct "replacements" for other essential oils in respect to their main constituents. They are of interest only because of these constituents, and they rarely find any use as such in perfumes or flavors.

Ocimum Kilimanjaricum.

The essential oil which is steam distilled from the overground parts of the flowering plant **Ocimum Kilimanjaricum** is of limited interest to the perfume and flavor industry. The oil is produced irregularly and on a moderate scale in East Africa (mainly Kenya and Tanganyika; the plant is named after the famous volcano), while a regular and com-

paratively large-scale production takes place in India (western Bengal, Kaschmir, etc.). Production in Belgian Congo had been abandoned at the moment of the author's visit in 1955/56.

At this place we should point out that the oil will contain camphor only if the leaves of the plant are included in the distillation material. The camphor can be partially removed from the oil by freezing. The "second" constituent of the oil is **Eugenol,** and the oil thus combines the virtues of the oils from **Ocimum Canum** (camphor type) and **Ocimum Gratissimum** (eugenol type)— (see these monographs).

However, the yield of "total" essential oil (i.e. including camphor) from the plant ocimum kilimanjaricum in India has been very encouraging. The oil is a yellowish to brownish liquid of warm and aromatic, spicy-camphoraceous odor (even when the oil is "decamphorized"). Although the oil blends excellently with lavender, lavandin, rosemary, petitgrain, etc. in the old-fashioned **"Rondeletia"** perfume type, the author does not believe in a future for this oil in perfumery. The oil may serve locally as a good raw material for soap perfumes, etc., and in emergency cases as a source of natural camphor (to be isolated by freezing of the oil).

Ocotea Pretiosa.

Up to a little more than twenty years ago, the **"Brazilian Sassafras Oil"** from **Ocotea Pretiosa** was completely unknown, non-existent. Within a period of 15 years, it climbed to an annual production of nearly 1000 metric tons, bringing the oil into the group of the "Upper Ten" essential oils (in respect to quantity) for perfumes and flavors. Production has since declined somewhat, and other oils have replaced it in the "Upper Ten" group.

Ocotea Pretiosa (earlier known as **Ocotea Cymbarum**) is a medium-sized tree which grows wild and abundantly in the forest regions of southeastern Brazil, Paraguay, as far north as Colombia, and, in fact, over wide areas of South America. Similar to other trees of the family Lauraceae, the ocotea is easily propagated with the aid of the birds who eat fruits from these trees. Distillation of **Ocotea Pretiosa Oil** is concentrated in the southeastern section of Brazil.

The oil is steam distilled from the wood which is of little use for any other purposes. Prior to distillation, the wood is comminuted or made into sawdust on grinding wheels. The essential oil is a pale yellow oily liquid of sweet aromatic, warm-spicy, camphoraceous odor, reminiscent of brown camphor oil or north American sassafras oil. The principal constituent (and this is what we smell) is **Safrole** which constitutes more than 90% of the **Ocotea Pretiosa Oil.** Other components are present in trace amounts, and these have very little influence upon the odor of this oil. It is worth noticing that camphor is apparently *not* present as such in ocotea pretiosa oil. Camphor is a natural constituent of north American sassafras oil (see monograph). This makes adulteration of the latter oil with ocotea pretiosa oil still more difficult to detect since there is no "new" chemical introduced by this adulteration (apart from certain monoterpenes which may be traced in an instrumental analysis).

Due to its very high content of **Safrole,** the oil of ocotea pretiosa can solidify at temperatures below 10°C. However, the oil will usually stay supercooled for a long period, e.g. while shipped during a northern winter. Seeding with a crystal of solid safrole, or even a sudden shock (e.g. mechanical damage to the container) may cause the entire contents of a drum to solidify often under considerable rise in temperature (the heat of fusion). Similar comment may be made with regard to anise oil (star anise, anethole), rue oil, red thyme oil, and certain other essential oils and aromatic chemicals.

Ocotea pretiosa oil is used extensively in the so-called "technical" perfuming (which is a misleading term for the perfuming of industrial products, etc.). Many insecticides, floor waxes, polishes, glues, disinfectants, etc. are perfumed mainly or exclusively with this oil. Its use in glues, gummed papers, library pastes, etc., is partly due to the antiseptic effect of safrole which prevents mold and fungus from deteriorating the glue; simultaneously, safrole acts as a "masking" odor for these materials which are often endowed with a most obnoxious odor when left unperfumed.

Furthermore, the oil is used in soaps, detergents, cleansers, etc. where its great stability, powerful odor and low cost is an advantage. The oil blends excellently with all natural and synthetic materials of the "camphoraceous" type: rosemary oil, white camphor oil, eucalyptus oils, trimethyl cyclohexanol and the corresponding ketone as well as other derivatives of cyclohexanol, iso-

borneol and its esters, lavandin oil, etc. Low cost industrial "perfumes" (or at least "scents") are often simple compositions of ocotea pretiosa oil with citronella oil, coumarin, diphenylether, acetophenone, d-limonene, benzaldehyde, methyl benzoate or other modifiers to the safrole odor.

In flavors, the oil is often used in place of north American sassafras oil for the so-called **"Root-Beers"** which are soft drinks of sassafras-anise-wintergreen flavor with or without licorice extract, etc. By some authorities, safrole is considered toxic, and the safrole-containing oils may be banned for use in flavors some day in the near future. Safrole is chemically related to myristicin which is also considered toxic (see **Nutmeg Oil**).

The major part of all **Ocotea Pretiosa** oil goes into the chemical industry where the safrole is isolated from the oil and subsequently transformed into **Heliotropine, Dihydrosafrole** and other useful perfume materials.

Ocotea Pretiosa Oil is widely used as an adulterant for north American sassafras oil (see **Sassafras Oil** and **Camphor Oil,** brown). The oil is a typical example of a "mono-component" oil which is more important on account of its main constituent than it is for use as such in perfumes. It is representative of the group of essential oils which may remain necessary for the perfume industry and the chemical industry in spite of the rapidly growing aromatic chemical industry and the trend away from essential oils. Safrole can not be synthesized at the same low cost at which it is produced as an isolate from ocotea oil or brown camphor oil (compare eugenol and clove leaf oil, etc.).

Oleo Vermelho.

Years ago, an essential oil was distilled in Japan from the wood of a local tree, **Myrospermum Erythroxylon.** The oil was available in Europe prior to World War II, but the author has been unable to obtain recent samples of this oil. It is known, however, that Japanese farmer-settlers in Brazil have brought the tree along with them to that country. Other Japanese perfume plants have initiated a very prosperous agricultural industry in Brazil (comp. mentha arvensis, etc.).

Myrospermum Erythroxylon is originally a "precious-wood" tree, locally called **"Rosewood"** (see summary of so-called rosewoods in the monograph **Bois de Rose Oil**). But this Japanese tree yields a truly fragrant wood, and the essential oil has been used along with cedarwood and sandalwood in "Oriental" perfumes, etc. More recently, the oil has served as a source for the isolation of the sesquiterpene alcohol **Nerolidol** which is used in perfumery.

Since steam distillation of this high-boiling essential oil involves some difficulties, the method of solvent extraction has also been applied to the chopped wood (compare **Sandalwood Oil, Australasian**). The author has no personal experience with the application of **Oleo Vermelho**, and it is conceivable that the oil may not reappear on the international perfume market. Nerolidol is now produced synthetically at a competitive price, and the oil of myrospermum erythroxylon has little to offer beyond the effect of its nerolidol. See also **Cabreuva Oil**, and **Melaleuca Viridiflora**, variety "A".

Olibanum.

Olibanum is a natural oleo-gum-resin. It is formed as a physiological liquid product in the bark of various **Boswellia** species. These are small trees originating in the mountainous areas of western India, southern Arabia and northeastern Africa. The trees are not cultivated, and collection of the olibanum is made where the trees are most abundant, i.e. Somaliland and Somalia, rarely in south Arabia (near the limestone mountains of Fartak). At least four different species of **Boswellia** are recognized as parent plants of the commercial **Olibanum**.

To increase the production of olibanum from the bark, the natives (mostly Bedouins) make incisions in the bark at regular intervals. The viscous oleo-gum-resin which oozes out will soon resinify, and is either broken off the branches or collected from the ground where it sometimes may fall. The collected material is sorted and graded locally or at the port of departure (Djibouti, Aden, Mogadiscio, Berbera, etc.). The grading is primarily an "appearance" grading, and the author strongly disagrees with published statements, such as, "-- dust and siftings: because of its low price, the most suitable for distillation".

When resinous material is being evaluated, it is of paramount importance to remember that the larger the surface, the more complete the resin-ification, and, consequently, the higher the loss of volatile matter, e.g. essential oil. Usually the dust and siftings give a comparatively low yield of essential oil of a very poor odor (from a perfumery point of view). Furthermore, there is no straight rule as to which color of olibanum "tears" or "lumps" will yield the best oil. The odor of the crude botanical will give certain indications; an experimental distillation will give the best answer. Experience in selecting the correct material for distillation or for the extraction of resinoids or absolutes, is a rare and valuable skill, and is partly based upon years of experimenting with the distillation and extraction of all grades of olibanum.

Olibanum appears as pale yellow or pale amber-colored, tear-shaped or drop-shaped, egg-shaped or almost round lumps, varying from pea-sized to walnut-size. Other grades may be orange-yellow, orange-red or brownish in color, and the tears may be agglutinated into large lumps. For odor and composition, see the monographs: **Olibanum Absolute** (so-called), **Olibanum Oil**, and **Olibanum Resinoid**.

Olibanum Absolute, so-called.

Products offered under this name are usually prepared directly from **Olibanum** by alcohol extraction. The term **"Resin Absolute"** is generally applied to alcohol extracts of the crude botanical. A true **Absolute** should be prepared by extraction of the olibanum resinoid (see monograph) with ethyl alcohol, chilling, filtering and evaporating of the extract. This method will usually yield products of lighter color, particularly if the resinoid has been prepared by extraction with petroleum ether. In this case, the yield is considerably lower than the yield by benzene extraction.

The commercially available **Olibanum Absolutes** can therefore generally be considered to be concentrated tinctures of olibanum. Alcohol will dissolve from 65% to 85% by weight of the crude olibanum. According to the quality and, particularly to the age of the olibanum, and also considering the mesh size, this material contains various amounts of alcohol-insoluble matter. However, the saturated alcoholic solution of olibanum (oil, resin, etc.) will dissolve certain components which would not be soluble individually in alcohol. This is where the difference between the so-called "resin-absolute" and the true absolute arises. The former type will cause more problems in perfume compounding or in the finished goods (e.g. aerosols, lotions, etc.), than will the truly alcohol-washed product. The difference between hot extracted and cold extracted resin-absolutes has been discussed in the monograph on **Myrrh**. It is actually possible to completely exhaust crude olibanum with ethyl alcohol without the application of heat, exclusively by stirring and repeated extraction. If the mixed extracts are chilled and filtered, and then cautiously evaporated at slightly reduced pressure, the resulting absolute will be of superior odor quality and excellent solubility. This type of olibanum extract competes favorably with the two-step-extracted, "true" absolute from the resinoid.

Olibanum Absolute is a solid, but somewhat plastic mass of pale amber color (particularly pale when cold processed), and it has the characteristic odor of olibanum: it is free from terebinthinate or so-called "paint-can"-like odor. It has a fresh-balsamic, yet dry and resinous, slightly green odor with a typical, fruity-green topnote and great tenacity. The oily-green topnote can remind one of unripe apples or certain fruit-esters.

Olibanum absolute is usually prepared by the large users themselves since the preparation demands great knowledge of the raw material, and a strict control of the olibanum to be extracted.

Olibanum Anhydrol and other, similar specialties are produced by molecular distillation of an extract of olibanum prepared with a highboiling, odorless solvent (see **Anhydrol**—Part One of this book).

The absolute is used as a fixative with its distinct lemony-green, dry, fresh-balsamic note as a special effect. In combination with spice oils, particularly with a high grade cinnamon bark oil, olibanum absolute creates quite surprising odor complexes. A typically "powder"-effect in fragrance is obtained with combinations of olibanum, cinnamon bark, cinnamic alcohol, nitromusks and coumarin or coumarin derivatives. Excellent modifications are produced with ionones, methyl-ionones, labdanum extracts or cistus oil (so-called), mimosa absolute, orange flower absolute, muguet bases and numerous other materials or compositions. A truly "Oriental" note can be created basically with sandalwood oil, vetiver oil, olibanum absolute and cinnamon bark oil for further perfume developing work.

Olibanum Oil.

An essential oil is obtained in a good yield by steam distillation of the crude botanical material (see **Olibanum**). The oil is distilled exclusively in Europe and the U.S.A., occasionally in India for local use. No oil is produced in the countries of origin of the botanical material (except the Indian production). The quality and age of the material is largely responsible for the quality of the resulting oil. A good distillation technique, i.e. experience with distillation of oleo-gum-resins, is also essential. As previously mentioned, dust and siftings from the screening of olibanum are generally not suitable starting material for production of the oil. It is true, however, that olibanum of excellent appearance (which is often preferred for **Incense** or **Frankincense** in Catholic churches) may not be a very good starting material for the distillation of essential oil. There is no strict correlation between color and perfumery value of olibanum.

Olibanum Oil is a mobile liquid, pale yellow or pale amber-greenish in color. Its odor is strongly diffusive, fresh-terpeney, almost green-lemon-like or reminiscent of green, unripe apples (peel), but not terebinthinate. A certain pepperiness is mellowed with a rich, sweet-woody, balsamic undertone. Depending upon the method of distillation of the oil (time, vapor pressure, etc.) the odor is more or less tenacious with an almost cistus-like, ambre-type, balsamic dryout note.

The residue from the distillation of olibanum oil is virtually odorless. It consists of resins and a small amount of water-soluble gum. The residue may be extracted with a hydrocarbon solvent to yield a *true* "olibanum resin". This material is not a commercial article, but it finds its way into commercial lots of olibanum resinoid as a "cutting" material, in other words, as a diluent. It improves the fixative value of the olibanum resinoid, but it impairs the odor value of the product.

Olibanum Oil is used in fine perfumery for the notes described above and in the monograph on olibanum absolute. It gives delightful effects in citrus colognes where it modifies the sweetness of bergamot and orange oils. A similar effect is obtained in the rather difficult "fresh" perfume notes such as verbena, citrus, etc. where olibanum and citral form useful bases for further modifying work. Olibanum oil in itself is a base for all the "incense" or "olibanum" type perfumes and specialties, and it is an important ingredient in many Oriental bases, ambres, "powder" type perfumes, floral perfumes, citrus colognes, spice blends, violet perfumes, "men's fragrances", etc.

Various specialties are based upon olibanum oil. The so-called **"Olibanol"** is, in some cases, a partially deterpenized olibanum oil (e.g. alcohol-washed, partially monoterpeneless). In other cases, the term "olibanol" just refers to a compound, suggestive of an olibanum modification.

Olibanum Oil is available in quite sizeable quantities, and the main difficulty encountered by large-scale users is that of obtaining a uniform high quality of oil (or of the crude olibanum).

Olibanum Resinoid.

True **Olibanum Resinoid** is obtained by extraction of the crude olibanum (see monograph **Olibanum**) with a hydrocarbon solvent, usually benzene, rarely petroleum ether, acetone, methylene dichloride, etc. Benzene gives a high yield, but a dark colored product. The most important thing, however, is the choice of raw material. Although not an absolute rule, it is generally true that the reddish-orange colored tears or lumps are poorer starting materials for perfumery use than are the yellowish or whitish lumps. The amount of sand, dust, woodsplinters, etc. should also be considered. A not infrequently used adulterant is the so-called **Dammar Resin**, derived from various **Shorea** species (not, as occasionally claimed, from **Dammara Orientalis**). Dammar resin is practically odorless and contains very little water-soluble matter. Accordingly, it does not form an emulsion with water when triturated. There is a perceptible difference in odor of olibanum resinoids from a hot (= refluxed) extraction process, and those from a cold process (i.e. stirring at room temperature). It is also logical that the manufacturers have switched from hydrocarbon solvents to ethyl alcohol. The latter solvent will mix with the small amount of water (moisture) which is always present in botanicals. This effect of the alcohol facilitates the penetration of the solvent into the particles of olibanum. Accordingly, fewer extractions are necessary and the extraction time is considerably reduced when ethyl alcohol is used in place of a hydrocarbon solvent.

Olibanum Resinoid, when prepared by benzene-extraction, is a dark amber to dark orange or reddish-brown colored, almost solid, but somewhat plastic mass of non-pourable soft-extract consistency. It should contain all the available essential oil from the crude material, and accordingly, should yield about 7 to 10 percent of essential oil on a test distillation. Lighter colored resinoids are obtained in somewhat poorer yields by petroleum ether extraction. The odor of this resinoid is excellent.

Olibanum Resinoid is a valuable fixative, but it also lends its own peculiar odor to the perfume (see odor description under **Olibanum Oil** and **Absolute**). Since the essential oil content is only about 8%, the **Resinoid of Olibanum** has a much more versatile application in perfumery than has the essential oil. However, in order to obtain a true physical fixative effect from olibanum resinoid alone, it would be necessary to use 4 to 6% or even more of this material.

Olibanum Resinoid is often sold in a semi-liquid form, just pourable and handy for compounding without the harmful intermittent heating of the delicate product. The addition of 15 to 25% diethylphthalate or a similar, odorless, high-boiling solvent-plasticizer is a conventional and generally accepted treatment of olibanum resinoid, provided the content of solvent is clearly indicated on the label. See also **Olibanum, Olibanum Absolute, Olibanum Oil.**

Onion Oil.

On account of its medicinal value, the onion of **Allium Cepa** was subjected to steam distillation as far back as late in the 19th century. The essential oil was produced occasionally for use in pharmaceutical preparations and in popular medicine for various ailments, colds, etc.

The plant originated, like so many other plants of the family Liliaceae, in western Asia, the Middle East and middle Asia. Numerous varieties of onion are cultivated all over the world. In France, occasionally in Germany and Egypt, an essential oil is distilled from **Allium Cepa,** the common culinary onion ("red onion", also known in white varieties).

Onion Oil is a brownish yellow, occasionally pale yellow mobile liquid with a very strong odor (when undiluted, it is obnoxiously sulfuraceous) and distinct lachrymatory effect. Chemically, the oil consists of higher sulfides (disulfides) and traces of low-boiling aliphatic aldehydes. The oil is distinguished by the complete absence of terpenes. The flavor of onion oil is warm-aromatic, spicy, biting or pungent (according to the concentration), very similar to the flavor of raw onions.

To the author's knowledge, onion oil is used exclusively in flavors, never in perfumes, although such application is very possible (violet, hyacinth, rose, etc. can benefit from minute traces of onion oil for a distinct part of the topnote). The oil has found an increasing outlet in the canning industry in flavors for soups, meat, table sauces, dressings, etc. There are wide limits for a suggested use-level concentration, according to the acidity and overall type of finished product in which the oil will be incorporated. The **Minimum Perceptible** is about 0.01 mg%.

An onion extract of "oleo-resin" type is produced in France for use in canned food (see **Onion Oleoresin**).

The annual production of **Onion Oil** is still quantitatively small, but easily adjusted to demand. See also **Asafetida, Garlic, Horseradish.**

Onion Oleoresin.

Various extracts of onion (**Allium Cepa**) are commercially available under the name of **Onion Oleoresin** or similar labellings. A true oleoresin is not produced since the extracted material rarely will contain resinous matter. Apart from essential oil, extractive plant matter, plant colors, glycosides and bitter principles, the extracts may also contain certain non-volatile, aromatic flavoring matter. Thus, the "oleo-resin" will not only possess the virtues of the essential oil (sharp, lachrymatory, pungent, aromatic onion-flavor), but also a certain richness and "body" which is highly appreciated, but is rarely present in essential oils of spices and culinary herbs.

Commercial "oleo-resins" of onion are usually dark orange or dark yellow-brown of color. They are more or less viscous liquids or soft pastes of intense onion-odor, but more sweet and subdued than the odor of the essential oil. Onion extracts are produced mainly in France. Extracts are also prepared by the "ultrasonic" method as described in Part One of this book.

Due to the higher yield by extraction, and to the more "true-to-nature" flavor of the extracts as compared to that of the onion oil, the former have become increasingly popular as flavor

materials in the canning industry for pickles, seasonings, meat sauces, etc. The high calorie value of onions (about 50 cal. per 100 g. of onions which contain about 88% water) compared to that of other vegetables has obviously also been exploited in the promotion of the "calorie-free" onion extracts in place of the vegetable itself.

Opopanax.

Another material that has changed in its appearance and odor characteristics within this century is **Opopanax.** The so-called "original" opopanax probably derived from a large plant, **Balsamodendron Kafal**, which grows wild in the southern parts of the Middle East, in southern Sudan and Arabia, etc. The opopanax from this plant is no more a regularly available commercial item, and it is claimed by those who remember that, in respect to odor, this type of opopanax is inferior to the "new" type.

Today, a medium-sized tree, very closely related to the parent tree of **Myrrh** (see monograph) yields the perfumery material, **Opopanax.** This tree, **Commiphora Erythrea** *varietas glabrascens*, grows wild in the interior of Somaliland, eastern Africa, towards the eastern parts of Ethiopia named Harrar province. Apparently the commercial collection of opopanax takes place only in Somaliland. The author was unable to confirm his belief in an Ethiopian production during his visit to that part of Africa in 1956.

Opopanax is a natural oleo-gum-resin, formed as a physiological product in natural cavities or tubular vessels in the parenchym (where most of the activity in trees take place) between the bark and the wood. The natives make incisions in the trunks, but some opopanax flows out by itself. The crude botanical product is dark reddish, rarely dark yellow or brownish, and it occurs in comparatively regular lumps, tear-shaped or bean-shaped, of nut-size to walnut-size. Its odor is sweet-aromatic, reminiscent of spicy soups (a faint resemblance to celery or lovage), a sweet-woody undertone and a peculiar, animal-like, also sweet and root-like note. Although to a certain degree reminiscent of myrrh, the typical difference is that opopanax has a spicy (soup-like) and an animal, root-like note, neither of which is hardly, if at all, distinguishable in myrrh. A test distillation of suspicious-looking lumps will immediately reveal to the experienced perfumer whether the lump is myrrh or opopanax. The difference in odor of the two essential oils is wide. Opopanax is obviously richer in deep-balsamic sesquiterpene type of notes, while myrrh oil has a light, fresh topnote and comparatively little dryout note.

Opopanax Oil.

The essential oil of **Opopanax** (see previous monograph) is produced in Europe or the U.S.A. by steam distillation, occasionally by water distillation. Fine powder would form plastic lumps and hinder the free passage of the mixed vapors. The steam and hot water dissolves a certain amount of the "gum" in the opopanax, and the gum solution acts like a sticky, viscous "glue" on the resinous particles in the still. There are two major prerequisites for the production of a good opopanax oil (just as there are with many other resin oils or spice oils that are distilled from "stable" material):

1) A select raw material (requiring knowledge of the botanical with respect to perfumery quality);
2) A distillation technique which has been developed to perfection by long experience.

A good grade of opopanax can be ruined when distilled by an inexperienced still operator, or by just one small mistake during distillation. A poor perfumery grade of opopanax can never turn out a high grade opopanax oil. This sounds very obvious, but the author has experienced—and so has hundreds of his colleagues—that it is a general conception that poorer grade botanicals are particularly suited for distillation. Occasionally, the economy is used as an excuse, but even this viewpoint can not hold up against a thorough comparison, point for point.

Opopanax Oil is an orange-colored, pale yellow or olive-yellowish to dark amber-greenish liquid, and it possesses an intensely sweet, balsamic, spicy, warm, yet fresh odor, somewhat reminiscent of wine residue ("emptied sherry-wine glass"). If there is but little difference in odor between **Myrrh** and **Opopanax,** the difference between the two oils is quite obvious: the vegetable-soup-like, slightly animal-sweet odor of opopanax oil is entirely different from the medicinal-sharp freshness of myrrh oil.

Opopanax Oil blends well with sage clary,

coriander, labdanum, with woody and heavy-floral perfume bases, chypre, fougère, leather bases (castoreum-labdanum-cananga complex), Oriental bases, bergamot oil, methylionones, nitromusks, patchouli oil, mimosa, phenylethyl phenylacetate, linalyl cinnamate, heliotropine, methyl naphthyl ketone, fir needle absolute, neroli oil, etc. The oil is occasionally used in liqueur flavors for its heavy-sweet body and wine-like notes, spiciness and naturalness. Its power and "growth" in a perfume is often underestimated; unless perfectly balanced with modifying and supporting materials, opopanax oil has a tendency of "showing up" in a rather unattractive manner after a short ageing period of the perfume. The odor of opopanax oil itself is not exactly attractive, and it is the perfumer's job to utilize the effect of the oil without permitting the opopanax notes to show up individually.

Opopanax Oil is occasionally adulterated with myrrh oil, copaiba balsam, traces of lovage oil certain fractions of Siberian pine needle oil, etc. The annual production of opopanax oil is increasing steadily with the interest in the oil, and there is ample supply of raw material available.

Opopanax Resinoid.

In order to prepare a perfumery material from **Opopanax,** it is necessary to remove the mechanical impurities (wood splinters, sand, dust, insects, debris, etc.) and also the "gum" fraction of this natural oleo-gum-resin. Opopanax consists of approximately 5 to 9% essential oil, 15 to 40% alcohol-soluble resins, and 50 to 80% water-soluble gum, insoluble impurities, etc. It is obvious from these figures that it makes a very significant difference in the yield of resinoid whether the starting material contains 80% gum or 50% gum. The yield of resinoid can vary from 20% up to 50%, calculated on the crude botanical.

Opopanax Resinoid can be prepared by extraction of the crude botanical material with benzene, petroleum ether or other hydrocarbons, occasionally with solvents such as dichloro methane (methylene dichloride) or trichloro ethylene. If ethyl alcohol is used directly, a so-called alcohol-resinoid or "resin-absolute" is produced. The commercial "resin-absolute" of opopanax is not a true absolute, extracted with alcohol from a hydrocarbon-solvent-extracted resinoid (compare: **Olibanum Absolute).**

It is customary, towards the end of evaporation of the material, to add a certain amount of an odorless, highboiling solvent or "plasticizer" (see **Myrrh Absolute**) such as diethyl phthalate, deodorized methyl dihydroabietate, dibutyl phthalate, benzyl benzoate (is not quite odorless), isopropyl palmitate or myristate, etc. This addition serves a practical purpose since the true, 100% resinoid of opopanax is not pourable at room temperature. It is almost hard, although slightly plastic due to the content of essential oil (approximately 10 to 20%). No essential oil should be removed from the opopanax when it is transformed into a resinoid or an absolute. Unfortunately, this unwritten law of ethics is not respected by all producers of opopanax resinoid (and other resinoids). Increasing interest in the essential oil will obviously create a surplus of oil-free resin from opopanax. In order to make the production of essential oil more economically attractive, some producers find use for the oil-free resin in products which are labelled **Opopanax Resin**. The term "resinoid" would be positively misleading in this case.

Opopanax Resinoid is a popular fixative in high-class perfumery, if and where its dark color is no drawback. Its warm, powdery, Oriental and spicy effect is utilized in countless combination-fixatives for forest-notes, moss-notes, Oriental bases, "powder" type perfumes, spice fragrances, heavy florals, etc. **Opopanax Anhydrol** is almost colorless and offers certain parts of the opopanax odor gamut. Several other colorless molecular distillation products or decolorized extracts are available as specialties.

Orange Aroma, Sweet.

From selected qualities of sweet orange oil (selected for flavor use), the flavor houses will often make their own "aromas" or aroma-concentrates. A general procedure for the manufacture of citrus oil aromas, aroma-distillates and glycol aromas is outlined in Part One of this book. The "washing" of sweet orange oil with diluted ethyl alcohol yields the so-called orange-aromas; these can be considered as solutions of terpeneless and sesquiterpeneless orange oil in diluted alcohol. A by-product of this process is the so-called **"Washed Orange Oil"** which is a commercial item of some value in industrial perfumery, etc.

A "washed orange oil" is not entirely stripped

of its oxygenated components (aldehydes, etc.), and it still has the waxes and sesquiterpenes which give good fixative effect. Washed citrus oils should be properly dried and kept cool and dark. They tend to become rancid after the shortest exposure to daylight, particularly if moisture is present. The use of antioxidants offers great advantages in this case.

Orange Glycol is produced by liquid-liquid extraction of sweet orange oil with propylene glycol which is subsequently diluted with 15 to 25% of distilled water. The diluted glycol will then contain a terpeneless and sesquiterpeneless sweet orange oil, although the extraction is far from perfect. The glycol-aroma is filtered after standing and chilling, and it now serves as a base for orange flavors for carbonated drinks and other aqueous products to be flavored with a mild, true-to-nature orange: liqueurs, pharmaceutical preparations, etc. This type of orange aroma offers the advantage of excellent solubility in aqueous media. The average use level of these aromas is about 20.0 to 60.0 mg%.

These figures apply to the use in slightly acid media for straight orange flavors. Much lower concentrations can be used with advantage where the orange flavor is a modifier (e.g. ginger ale, etc.). The terpenes which are separated from the glycol-washing of the sweet orange oil are dried and used as "washed orange oil". The term **"Citrus Oil"** is commercially applied to a mixture of distilled or washed oils from grapefruit, sweet orange, lemon, and occasionally other citrus oils. Lemon terpenes are often kept separately since they command a higher price. They find use in the "scientific" adulteration of lemon oil on account of the lower optical rotation of lemon terpenes than that of orange and grapefruit terpenes. The **Citrus Oil** (so-called, commercially) is obtained either by distillation of crushed peels, by evaporation of juice, or by the production of the above types of aroma (washed citrus oil). **Citrus Oil** is a pale yellowish mobile liquid of sweet and comparatively fresh odor, revealing its orange and grapefruit components with a predominant note of monoterpenes. This product also becomes rancid easily. It is used in industrial perfumes, low-cost detergents, etc.

Orange Flower Absolute.

From petroleum ether extracted concrète of bitter

42: Unusually large flowers on a cultivated **Lilac** in Ontario, Canada. *(Fot. S. Arctander, 1959)*

43: **Plumeria Alba,** the overwhelmingly fragrant white "Frangipanni" in East Africa.

(Fot. S. Arctander, 1956)

orange flowers (see **Orange Flower Concrète**), an absolute is produced by alcohol extraction. This process is carried out mainly in France, but many large-scale consumers of orange flower absolute will prefer to produce their own absolute from imported concrète. The latter must be produced very near the plantation of bitter orange trees.

Orange Flower Absolute is a dark brown or dark orange colored, somewhat viscous liquid with a very intensely floral, heavy and rich, warm, but also delicate and fresh, long-lasting odor, closely resembling the odor of fresh bitter-orange blossoms. Although this absolute certainly has notes in common with jasmin absolute, it has a much more versatile application as a floral "fond" when used at a comparatively low concentration. It shows a pleasant, but peculiar and characteristic, sweet-herbaceous undertone, not unlike the one found in jasmin. Orange flower absolute is only slightly cheaper than jasmin absolute, and it may not always impart the same floral strength as jasmin at a similar concentration. But its great advantage is in its freshness which is quite surprising considering that it is an extract with great tenacity. Neroli oil will produce a beautiful "pair" with orange flower absolute. The two products represent altogether different parts of the orange flower fragrance gamut (see also **Orange Flower Water Absolute**).

Orange Flower Absolute is used in countless types of perfumes, heavy Oriental as well as light citrus colognes, chypres and ambres as well as floral bouquets, modern aldehydic fantasy blends, etc. The absolute forms excellent combinations with all citrus oils, petitgrain oils, linalool, linalyl acetate, linalyl cinnamate, methyl anthranilate, various jasmones, myrrh resinoid, etc. It naturally forms an important part of the fixative base in high-class citrus colognes and perfumes of similar type. Orange flower absolute is used in flavors as a very universal "bouquet" material with delightful effects in many types of fruit flavor and even in peppermint or spearmint flavor. It generally masks or rounds off the sharp notes arising from synthetic flavor materials. Often mere traces are necessary to obtain the "bouquetting" effect. The average use level should then be kept just above the **Minimum Perceptible**, which is 0.005 mg% to about 0.020 mg%. These figures apply to the straight material in sugar water, and will only give a very approximate idea of the use level in combination flavors. An indication can be given

through the fact that orange flower absolute usually exerts its bouquetting effect at the level of 0.03% to 0.10% of the main flavor ingredient. Obviously, there is no economical problem in using orange flower absolute in flavors.

The annual world production of orange flower absolute is about 2 metric tons. Adulteration occurs mainly in form of "sophistication", e.g. with the materials mentioned above, or with traces of indole, benzyl cyanide, phenylethyl phenylacetate, orange flower water absolute, beta methyl naphthyl ketone, isojasmone, etc. or various materials which have been identified in the absolute as normal constituents. e.g. linalool, nerol, nerolidol, etc., or with terpeneless petitgrain oil, etc.

Orange Flower and Petitgrain Water Absolute.

Absolute from the distillation waters of bitter orange flowers, twigs and leaves is a rather ill-defined product.

Attempts have been made to exploit the distillation waters from numerous essential oils, but only a few have proven to be useful to the perfumer or to give an attractive yield. One of the most interesting "water oils" is the one extracted from a mixture of orange flower water and petitgrain bigarade water, the so-called **"Eau de Brouts"**. This absolute is produced in the Grasse region of France. The yield is quite good, but the production is not carried out on a very large scale or possibly many distillers use the extracted absolute in their own business to "improve" or "sophisticate" the absolutes or essential oils of orange flowers, etc. Pruning of the bitter orange trees yields a certain amount of "brouts" (= twigs) which are steam distilled with the leaves to petitgrain oil. The distillation waters yield one type of "eau de brouts" absolute by extraction with petroleum ether.

This absolute is a yellowish to orange-yellow or brownish-yellow liquid with a strong but not very tenacious odor, musty, dry, faintly floral, more herbaceous (herb-like) and heavy. The typical notes have been described by perfumers as being "bread-like" or "broccoli-like". The latter term came from an American perfumer who is quite familiar with the Italian vegetable delicacy, broccoli. The author finds that this description is just as striking as "tossed green salad" or "green peppers" is for galbanum resinoid. In any event, it is obviously not a typical floral note. But this material contributes excellently to the naturalness of certain other fragrances, e.g. jasmin, ylang-ylang, neroli(!), gardenia, stephanotis, honeysuckle, etc. It may be an exaggeration to call it "the missing link" between an ordinary floral base of the above type and the perfect, true-to-nature duplication, but this absolute certainly has interesting effects to offer to the creative perfumer. It blends well with chamomile oil, helichrysum oil, bergamot oil, cardamom oil, broom absolute, karo-karoundé absolute, petitgrain oil, myrrh, opopanax, lavandin absolute, etc.

This absolute is produced on a very limited scale, but it can be made available in sizeable quantities upon request. Its area of application is not very wide, and its price is about one-tenth of the price of orange flower absolute. These facts help make the material regularly available from France.

Orange Flower Concrète.

By extraction of freshly picked flowers of the bitter orange tree, **Citrus Aurantium,** *subspecies amara* (see **Neroli Oil**) with a hydrocarbon solvent, a concrète is produced after evaporation of the solvent. Petroleum ether is most frequently used since its low boiling point facilitates removal of this solvent without serious loss of odorous components from the flower extract. The concrète is produced in France, Italy, Morocco, occasionally in Cyprus, and, on a small scale in Haiti, Formosa, the Comores, etc. The main producers are France and Italy.

    Orange Flower Concrète is a dark, brownish or orange-brown paste or soft, unctuous mass. Its odor is extremely strong, floral, deep-sweet, with a peculiar woody-breadcrust-like undertone and great tenacity in floral notes. In high dilution, it is strikingly reminiscent of the odor of fresh orange blossoms.

    The concrète as such is very rarely used in perfumery, but serves as an intermediary in the production of **Orange Flower Absolute** (see this monograph), one of the most important flower absolutes next to rose and jasmin.

    The annual production of orange flower concrète is usually not given, but it can be estimated at several metric tons, judging from the amount of bitter orange flowers harvested and the known

amount of neroli oil distilled. The concrète will yield about 44 to 54% of alcohol soluble absolute. Orange flower concrète is about the same price as a good French or Tunisian neroli oil. Concrète from flowers of the sweet orange tree has been produced, but the odor of this product is distinctly different from that of bitter orange concrète; in brief, it is decidedly inferior to the latter.

Orange Flower Water Absolute.

During the production of neroli oil by water distillation of flowers from the bitter orange tree (see monograph on **Neroli Oil**), significant amounts of essential oil dissolve in the distillation waters, or form a suspension in this water. It is generally estimated that about 25% of the distillable essential oil in the flowers remains dissolved or dispersed in the distillation waters, while about 75% of the distillable oil separates as **Neroli Oil.** More correctly, the total oil in the flower is "extracted" with water during the distillation, the most water-soluble components going into solution while the less water-soluble components will preferably remain in the separated neroli oil. The chemical composition of the "total" or "original" oil in the flowers is thus changed significantly. It should be noted at this point that not only is the yield of absolute by extraction of orange flowers smaller than the yield of essential oil by distillation, but the chemical compositions of the two products are distinctly different. A satisfactory explanation of these facts has not yet been published, and the author regrets that he, too, is unable to answer this question at the present moment. It is understandable that the essential oil contains small amounts of terpenes which inevitably are formed during the slightly acid distillation (in water) of the flowers, containing linalool, linalyl acetate and other esters which are easily hydrolized. The linalool may undergo a molecular rearrangement, and materials are formed which were not present in the flower. But this does not explain the higher yield by distillation, or the tremendous difference in odor type of the two materials, a difference which is evident to any perfumer. This latter fact, however, is partly explained in the above description of the distillation during which significant amounts of oil dissolve in the water and are not included in the final neroli oil. As we shall see in the following description of the odor type of the "water oil", a mixture of the neroli oil and the "water oil" would have at least some notes in common with the odor of orange flower absolute.

The distillation water from neroli oil is extracted with petroleum ether as soon as possible after separation of the neroli oil. The petroleum ether extract is evaporated under gentle vacuum, and the orange flower water "absolute" remains as a residue. Knowing about the chemical composition of neroli oil and orange flower absolute, one can predict the main constituents of the "water oil" to a certain extent. Alcohols are more easily soluble in water than are their esters, and hydrocarbons are poorly soluble, etc. Thus, we will find terpineol, linalool, geraniol, phenylethyl alcohol in higher concentration in the water oil than in the neroli oil. Methyl anthranilate is somewhat soluble in water, and forms an important part of the water oil. Terpenes are practically absent in the water oil, while we find—at least odorwise—significant amounts of eugenol, jasmone, phenylacetonitrile and other powerful odorants.

Orange Flower Water Absolute is a yellowish to orange-yellow or pale brownish yellow colored oil which discolors significantly on ageing; it has a peculiar dry-floral, musty-herbaceous odor, reminiscent of mandarin leaf oil, petitgrain oil, and, faintly, of orange flower absolute.

Being the odorous principle of orange flower water, formerly a very popular household and cosmetic article, the water absolute is occasionally used to prepare "reconstituted orange flower water" or concentrated flavor essences with the flavor of orange flower water. But the water oil has found increasing use in perfumery where its popular notes offer to the perfumer a valuable tool in the creation of neroli bases, jasmin bases, ylang-ylang compounds, etc. and also in the reproduction of certain essential oils. It finds furthermore use in modern colognes, "powder" type perfumes, aldehydic fantasy fragrances, etc.

The **Orange Flower Water Absolute** is available in very limited quantities only, but production has been steadily increasing since orange flower water is no longer a very popular article and actually is a surplus product in the south of France, Tunisia, Italy, and wherever large quantities of neroli oil are produced. See also **Neroli Oil** and **Orange Flower and Petitgrain Water Absolute.**

See **Ylang-Ylang Absolute** for comparison

(extraction product + distillation product are mixed together).

Orange Oil, Bitter.

The "essential" oil from the peel of the almost ripe fruit of the bitter orange tree, **Citrus Aurantium,** *subspecies amara,* is produced almost exclusively by expression. Thus it is strictly not a true essential oil according to current definitions. It contains some non-volatile matter. Like most other citrus fruits, the bitter orange exists in numerous varieties, and bitter orange oil varies considerably in odor and flavor according to its geographical origin. The main producers of bitter orange oil are: Spain, Guinea, the West Indies (Jamaica, Cuba, Haiti, Dominican Republic, Puerto Rico), Italy (Sicily), Brazil, etc., while the U.S.S.R., Mexico, China, Tanganyika, France, etc. are minor producers.

In Italy, the bitter orange tree serves for the grafting of other citrus trees on a wide scale, due to the resistance of this bitter orange tree (trunk) to serious diseases.

After expression of the oil by hand or by machine, some producers submit the peels to steam distillation, thus obtaining a further, small yield of a very poor oil. Unfortunately, this oil is often added to the cold-pressed oil. To the author's knowledge, distillation is never performed in Spain or Guinea, and this fact could be part of the reason for the outstandingly high flavor and odor quality of the bitter orange oils from these areas.

Cold pressed bitter orange oil is a mobile liquid of dark yellow to olive-yellow or pale brownish yellow color. The odor is very peculiar, fresh and yet "bitter" in the sense of "dry", but with a rich and lasting, sweet undertone. There are notes which remind of bergamot, grapefruit and sweet orange, but overall, the odor is distinctly different from that of other citrus oils. It is a different type of freshness, a peculiar floral undertone which occasionally shows indolic notes, and a comparatively good tenacity.

Bitter Orange Oil is used extensively in flavors where it forms the main ingredient in the "orange sec" or "triple sec" liqueur flavors, and also acts as an important modifier and intensifier in common sweet-orange flavors for soft drinks, etc. It lends body and pleasant "twists" to a plain sweet-orange flavor, and its great power makes it economical in use. The average use level would be about 2.00 mg% to 5.00 mg%. Still higher concentrations are recommended for straight bitter orange liqueur flavors. The **Minimum Perceptible** is about 0.02 mg% to 0.04 mg%. These figures are based upon experiments with good Spanish and good Guinea bitter orange oils. Not even the best of the West Indian oils can claim equally low figures. They would be about $1\frac{1}{2}$ to $2\frac{1}{2}$ times the above mentioned figures.

For perfumes, the bitter orange oil finds use among the other citrus oils in all types of colognes, chypres, fougères, fresh fragrances, topnotes, aldehydic citrus bases, etc., and it is one of the most common ingredients in artificial bergamot oil. It blends excellently with lavandin and lavender, rosemary and sage clary, oakmoss and labdanum, linalool and linalyl propionate, etc. and olibanum resinoid is an excellent fixative for the volatile bitter orange oil.

As mentioned above, the quality of this oil varies significantly, and for use in flavors, the author would rate the Guinea and the best Spanish oils highest. Some Italian and West Indian oils would rate second, and the Tanganyika oil is often very good. However, there are large lots of very poor oils on the market, and this fact may have ruined the reputation of the oil and killed many perfumers' and flavorists' interest in bitter orange oil. A thorough organoleptic and olfactory analysis of many samples will usually convince the potential buyer that there are bitter orange oils worth the comparatively high price demanded for this item. Being mainly a cold-pressed and often hand-pressed oil, it is obviously more costly to produce than e.g. sweet orange oil.

Flavor houses often make concentrates of bitter orange oil, and various concentrates are described in the following monograph. Bitter orange aroma and bitter orange aroma-distillate are prepared as described in Part One of this book (see **Aroma** and **Aroma-Distillate**). They are particularly suited for use in liqueur flavoring and in flavors for carbonated beverages.

Bitter orange oil is frequently adulterated with citrus oil terpenes, distilled oils of bitter orange, sweet orange, grapefruit, etc., or with d-limonene. Good oils are often sold out even before they are produced (contracted by the larger flavor houses), and the oil can be almost totally unavailable at some times of the year. The annual world production is fluctuating but averages about 30 metric tons.

Orange Oil, Bitter, concentrated.

For use in flavors, particularly in liqueurs and carbonated beverages, the natural oil of bitter orange offers some disadvantage because of its high content of monoterpenes (over 90%). The monoterpenes produce unpleasant off-flavors (with weak alcohol), and they are not soluble in low-proof alcohol, let alone in water. Many larger consumers of bitter orange oil for flavors will produce their own concentrates according to their special needs. A so-called *ten-fold* **Bitter Orange Oil** is quite common, and offers a "happy medium" between the terpeneless-sesquiterpeneless oil on one side and the natural oil on the other side. Ten-fold bitter orange oils are commercially available. Concentration can be obtained by vacuum distillation, or by a combination of vacuum distillation and extraction with weak alcohol (see chapter on **Terpeneless Oils**, Part One of this book, and **Lemon Oil, terpeneless** in Part Two of this book).

It is also possible to vacuum-concentrate the oil to about one-tenth of the original weight, chill the residual oil, freeze out the waxes, filtrate the concentrated oil and extract the wax with weak ethyl alcohol. After evaporation of the alcohol (and water), this extract is added to the concentrated oil. The resulting mixture is adjusted to a certain concentration (according to special requirements by the manufacturer or the user) by the addition of selected fractions of oil from the vacuum distillation. This concentrated oil is dark orange or yellowish-brown, but it is soluble in 70% ethyl alcohol in the proportions most often required.

Complete deterpenation (see **Lemon Oil, terpeneless**) produces an almost water-white oil. **Terpeneless, Sesquiterpeneless Bitter Orange Oil** is an extremely powerful flavor material, and its good stability makes it useful in all kinds of aqueous foods, candies, beverages, liqueurs, etc. It represents only about 3% by weight of the natural oil, but it is not 33 times stronger in flavor effect. The "lift" from the monoterpenes and their refreshing topnotes are effects which are lost in the terpeneless oils. However, the concentrated (e.g. ten-fold), partially deterpenated oils are much more popular and almost equally stable flavor materials.

Orange Oil, Sweet, concentrated.

For the same reasons as those given under the monograph **Lemon Oil, concentrated** (see this), the expressed oil of sweet orange peel is also further processed to so-called concentrates, e. g. two-fold, five-fold, ten-fold, etc. Concentration is achieved by simple vacuum distillation whereby mainly monoterpenes (pinene and d-limonene) are removed. The distilled d-limonene (an "isolate") is obtained in a similar way from other citrus oils and is used in perfumery similarly to the distilled sweet orange oil. It is also used as a starting material in the synthetic production of **Carvone**, an important spearmint and caraway flavor material.

The above simple concentration leads to very dark, brownish-orange colored oils of powerful and sweet odor, less fresh and less "peel-like" than that of the natural oil. The flavor, too, increases in power, but a five-fold orange oil obviously does not yield 5 times as much flavor as does the natural oil. The lifting effect of d-limonene is typical and is diminished by the concentration of the oil (removal of the monoterpene). The oil is commercially known as "five-fold sweet orange oil, with waxes". The waxes have a fixative effect, and to a certain extent, also exert a preserving effect on the oil. They are poorly soluble in alcohol, and in order to obtain an alcohol-soluble concentrated orange oil, it is necessary to remove the waxes, sesquiterpenes, etc. Such oils are usually called terpeneless sweet orange oils even if they still contain significant amounts of monoterpenes. See monograph on **Orange Oil, Sweet, Terpeneless** and **Sesquiterpeneless**.

Concentrated sweet orange oils are preferably made from the best flavor grades of expressed sweet orange oils of the Valencia type. The concentrate is mainly used in flavors where a pronounced sweet orange flavor is called for, where alcohol-solubility is not a major problem, where good keeping qualities are required and, in general, as an intensifier for the natural oil. It is also used in perfumery for the latter purpose.

A special type of concentrated sweet orange oils is the six-fold, sesquiterpeneless, wax-free and partially monoterpeneless, colorless oil, de-

scribed under **Lemon Oil, Concentrated**. The concentrate of sweet orange oil is prepared in a similar way.

Orange Oil, Sweet, distilled.

The production of distilled orange oil has parallelled the rapidly growing orange juice industry, and has now reached the point where neither the flavor nor the perfume industry can absorb the hundreds of tons of "by-product" from the juice factories.

Distilled sweet orange oil is of very little flavor value, but does have some use in perfumes, e. g. industrial masking odors and low-cost perfumes for household products, cleansers, detergents, etc. The oil is produced

1) by steam distillation of the peels after they have been expressed,
2) by steam distillation of the press cakes of peels (e. g. Spanish method);
3) by steam distillation of sweet orange peels which have not previously been used for expression of oil (not all factories have facilities for cold-expressing the oil);
4) by distillation of the sweet orange juice, since during the evaporation in vacuum (= production of concentrated orange juice), significant amounts of "oil" are collected in the receiver with the condensed juice-waters. The juice also inevitably contains some peel oil from the machine-processed fruit.

Method No. 1 is the main supplier of all distilled orange oils. Method No. 4 yields a different oil, containing the aromatic principles of the juice, including certain aldehydes, and, since these are flavor principles in the oil, this distilled oil may have a higher aldehyde content than the expressed oil. Some manufacturers will "reconstitute" the concentrated juice by adding this oil to the juice concentrate before canning it.

Distilled sweet orange oil is produced in the U.S.A. (Florida, Texas and California) and, to a small extent, also in Italy, Spain and Israel. The oil is a very pale yellow or almost colorless mobile liquid of fresh, sweet, not very rich odor, very poor in tenacity. Only freshly produced or well preserved oils have fresh odors. Distilled oils become rancid or oxidized more quickly than do the expressed oils. It is customary to add an antioxidant to such oils at the place of production. A wide range of effective antioxidants is at our disposal for use in perfumery oils: n-propyl-gallate, dodecyl gallate, butyl hydroxyanisole, butyl hydroxy-toluene, alpha-tocopherol, NDGA, various alkoxy-hydroquinones, etc., supported by trace amounts of ascorbic acid, citric acid, etc. Not all of these materials have been accepted for use in food (flavors) on a world-wide scale. However, certain combinations of the above anti-oxidants are effective (when boosted with one of the acids) at concentrations of about 0.005% in the orange oil. This concentration equals a maximum of about 2 micrograms (0.002 milligrams) of antioxidant per *kilo* of food or beverage. No doubt, we are consuming much more than that quantity of "other, unknown, foreign matter" during the day.

Significant amounts of distilled orange oil are used in the adulteration of expressed orange oil and other expressed citrus oils. For flavoring purposes, such an addition is definitely detrimental. Distilled oils are not suitable for the production of terpeneless oils or other concentrates (a concentrate of distilled lime oil does exist, however).

Distilled sweet orange oil finds extensive use in the duplication of bergamot oil, bergamot compositions, etc. Large quantities of distilled orange oil are re-distilled under vacuum. The "isolated" d-limonene finds extensive use in the chemical industry (synthetic carvone, etc.) and in industrial perfumery.

Orange Oil, Sweet, expressed.

In quantity produced, the oil of sweet orange ranks number one of all the citrus oils. Lemon oil is a close second, and perhaps even outweighs sweet orange oil if we do not include distilled oil in the world production of sweet orange oils.

Expressed sweet orange oil is not truly an essential oil according to our definitions (see **Essential Oil**, Part One of this book). It does contain small amounts of non-volatile matter. It is produced by expression by hand or machine from the peel of the sweet orange, the fruit of **Citrus Aurantium,** *varietas dulcis.*

The tree seems to have originated in the Far East in the area between the Himalayas and southwestern China. It came to Europe in the early part of the 16th century, and soon afterwards was brought to the Americas by the Spanish and Portuguese explorers. Seedlings of the tree

were "landed" in West Africa by Portuguese seafarers long before it was brought to Europe. Thus the Guinea trees are the descendants of the first shipment of orange trees outside Asia. It is possible, however, that orange trees were brought to Polynesia even before the sixteenth century. Sweet orange oil acquired its name "Portugal oil" for the above reasons.

The orange tree grows in numerous varieties all over the world in warm-temperate, semi-tropical and tropical zones. The oil from the peel is expressed in most of these countries, but in many cases only for local use (in carbonated beverages, orangeade, etc.). The main producers for world-wide consumption are: the United States of America (California, Florida, and Texas), Guinea, Cyprus, Italy, Spain, the Union of South Africa, Rhodesia, Brazil, Israel, the West Indies and Algeria. India, Indonesia, China, Japan, Argentina, Greece, Pakistan, etc. produce minor quantities for local consumption. The Japanese sweet orange oil is derived mainly from **Citrus Aurantium,** *varietas natsudaidai,* a local variety. 12 metric tons were produced in 1958 in Japan. This quantity covers only a fraction of the annual requirements of the Japanese flavor industry.

The U.S.A. and Cyprus are the most important producers of modern mechanically expressed oil, while Guinea is the largest producer of hand-pressed oil. Spain specializes in particularly rich-flavored oils, processed in a different way. The total world production of expressed + distilled sweet orange oil exceeds 1,500 metric tons per year. The U.S.A., Guinea, Cyprus, Israel and Brazil will account for 80% of the world production.

The technique of production of expressed citrus oils has been the subject of comprehensive works, and readers who may be interested in the detailed description will have no difficulty in finding expert literature on this subject. It should be mentioned at this point, however, that the wide differences among sweet expressed orange oils from various origins are partly due to the differences in expression technique. Machine expression usually yields oils with high evaporation residue while the various hand-expression methods lead to oils with low residue. The amount of residue in an orange oil has no direct relation to the quality of the oil. It may only affect tenacity, but not odor or flavor type. The particularly high content of oxygenated compounds (which are among the most important flavor and perfume materials) in the Guinea oils is probably due to the fact that these oils are expressed from not fully ripe fruits. There are two main types of Guinea sweet orange oil: perfumery oil and flavor oil. The former is a very volatile, light, fresh-smelling oil, the latter is heavy-rich, sweet and yet fresh, powerful in flavor.

A small percentage of the Spanish production is the so-called "primera" oil; this is the upper layer from the separators in which the crude oil is matured from the date of expression for a period of a couple of weeks. This "primera" oil is of extraordinarily high flavor value, and is much sought after by flavor houses for use in soft drink flavors, etc. The primera oils are usually lighter in color than ordinary Spanish sweet orange oils. These are distinguished by their very intense, orange-yellow color which may be a drawback in perfumes.

Apart from these variations, the sweet orange oils from the same type of fruit from various parts of the world are surprisingly uniform. With strict quality control of the fruits, highly modern machinery, quick packing and proper storage and shipping, oils from farapart sources can be quite similar and are often used interchangeably in perfumery or flavor work. California and Cyprus oils illustrate this fact, the latter perhaps being superior in keeping qualities.

Expressed sweet orange oil is a pale orange-yellow to dark orange or olive-orange, occasionally brownish-orange colored mobile liquid which has a sweet, light and fresh, fruity-aldehydic odor and flavor, distinctly reminiscent of the odor from a scratched sweet orange peel. Machine expressed oils are generally lighter in color, handpressed oils are usually darker (but not always). It is interesting to note that in the case of **Mandarin Oil**, the machine-pressed oils are darker than the hand-pressed. Guinea sweet orange oils may have a slightly olive-yellowish tint. Spanish oils can be very dark (ordinary Valencia oils), but are often the most powerful and rich in flavor.

Expressed, sweet orange oil is used primarily in flavors, often in the shape of a concentrated oil, terpeneless or sesquiterpeneless oil (see these monographs). A certain amount of natural (non-concentrated) oil is a "must" to make an orange flavor true-to-nature. Too much of this oil may cause trouble such as:

1) deterioration and rancidity (off-flavor);
2) bleaching of the flavor due to the formation of peroxides from the monoterpenes;
3) unattractive "oil-ring"-formation in the bottle-neck of carbonated beverages due to the poor solubility and low specific gravity of the monoterpenes.

Orange flavors are among the most popular flavor types all over the world, and they are often superior in masking effect as compared to other fruit flavors. Soft drinks, sherbet ice, candy, pharmaceutical preparations, etc. are only a few of the countless outlets for sweet orange flavor. The oil furthermore enters as a minor constituent in numerous fruit flavors where it lends freshness and sweetness (peach, apricot, berry-flavors, etc.). The average use level could be suggested as 5.00 mg% up to 40.0 mg%. These figures apply to straight orange flavors where orange juice and acid are present, and the sugar content is not less than 10%. Concentrations as high as 40 mg% are found in orangeade and orange sodas, sherbets, fondants, etc. This concentration is beyond the threshold of solubility in aqueous media at the use temperature (usually between $-4°C$. and $+10°C$.). Accordingly, it will be necessary to use solubilizers or emulsifiers in the liquid, aqueous products when the orange oil concentration exceeds 20 mg%. The **Minimum Perceptible** is 0.03 mg% to 0.06 mg%, with significant variations according to the type of oil.

In perfumes, the application is a minor one. Old-fashioned eau-de-colognes, fougères, chypres, aldehydic bases, fruity bases, etc. are among the most common areas of use. As an odor-masking agent, sweet orange oil is quite famous, but it has been substituted in many cases by "artificial" oils, i.e. mixtures of d-limonene, decyl aldehyde, nonyl aldehyde, etc. for masking certain ill-smelling industrial products.

Expressed sweet orange oil is frequently adulterated with terpenes (d-limonene, isolated or "synthetic") or with so-called **"Citrus Oils"**, a mixture of monoterpenes or distilled oils from the citrus fruit juice manufacturers. A flavor test is the best means of evaluating this very important material for flavors and perfumes.

Orange Oil, Sweet, terpeneless and sesquiterpeneless.

Various grades of terpeneless and sesquiterpeneless, wax-free sweet orange oils are obtained from good-quality expressed sweet orange oils. The method of production is similar to that of terpeneless lemon oil (see **Lemon Oil, Concentrated**), with the main difference being that sweet orange oil yields a substantial amount of solid waxes when it is concentrated. Lemon oil contains few or no waxes, but has a certain amount of high-boiling sesquiterpenes, etc.

Terpeneless Sweet Orange Oil (so-called commercially) is often only 15 times concentrated (by weight), and thus still contains substantial amounts of terpenes. But, when wax-free, it is fairly soluble in 70% alcohol. It is a pale yellow to almost colorless, mobile liquid of very pleasant, fresh-sweet odor which keeps the typical notes of orange peel.

A totally terpeneless, sesquiterpeneless and wax-free sweet orange oil is a yellow liquid with a very sweet, but strongly aldehydic-sharp odor, not immediately reminiscent of orange peel. The oil which seems to serve all purposes best is a wax-free, partially monoterpeneless, totally sesquiterpeneless oil at about six to ten times concentration by weight of the natural oil. This oil will have fair solubility, fresh aroma, good keeping qualities and about three to five times the flavor strength of the natural oil. It is almost colorless when prepared as described under **Lemon Oil, Concentrated** (see monograph).

The orange waxes, a by-product of the process of concentrating the sweet orange oil, are often washed and dried to be used in certain perfume compositions. They contain small amounts of odorous sesquiterpene derivatives, etc., and they lend great fixative power to various floral bases, e.g. jasmin, gardenia, tuberose, etc. Orange waxes can not be used in perfumes which must be soluble in low-proof alcohol.

Terpeneless, Sesquiterpeneless Sweet Orange Oil is often produced by the flavor house needing the oil since there are countless qualities on the market, and only few of the commercially available oils are worthwhile using in flavors. For use in liqueurs and finer candies, for high-grade flavors in carbonated beverages, it is of paramount importance to keep a uniform quality. The public is particularly sensitive to any change in the "big" flavors such as the popular orange, peppermint, vanilla, etc. The **Minimum Perceptible** for the truly terpeneless, sesquiterpeneless oil is about 0.0002 to 0.0004 mg%. Use level 0.01 to 0.10 mg%.

Naardenized Sweet Orange Oil is an oil that has been deterpenized by the well-known countercurrent extraction process with selective solvents. It is an "absolute" of sweet orange oil, the highest possible concentrate of the oxygenated components of the oil. Several artificial terpeneless-sesquiterpeneless sweet orange oils are commercially available. Most of them suffer from a pronounced aldehydic note (decanal or nonanal) which completely ruins the flavor effect. Several "branched-chain" aliphatic aldehydes have been developed for use in concentrated orange flavors. Some of these aldehydes have pleasant and natural flavor notes and they are distinguished by their unusual diffusiveness and power. The by-products from the deterpenization of sweet orange oil are all used in perfumery for reproduction of various citrus oils, for masking odors, in industrial perfumes, etc.

Orange Sweet, Petitgrain.

Although not produced regularly on a commercial scale, this oil shall be briefly discussed in order to complete the subject on petitgrain oils. Admixture, contamination or adulteration of true petitgrain oil (from bitter orange trees) is possible and should be considered accordingly when petitgrain oils are evaluated.

In certain areas where labor is not too expensive, and where there are distillation facilities at hand, a surplus of leaves from sweet orange trees, e.g. from the annual prunings, may be steam distilled. During the author's visits to Algeria between 1949 and 1956, he was able to confirm that small lots of sweet orange leaves and twigs were collected to produce a locally distilled petitgrain (sweet orange) oil. The oil was used by the producer and his affiliated house in France.

In Guinea, former French West Africa, the huge areas of sweet orange groves offer another source of leaves and twigs for distillation. Small and irregular lots of the oil are shipped from Guinea, mainly to France.

Petitgrain Sweet Orange is an olive-greenish to green-orange colored, mobile liquid with a peculiar dry, almost bitter undertone after a brief and fresh topnote which is somewhat reminiscent of the topnote of petitgrain bigarade oil. The tenacity is not outstanding, and the odor changes rapidly and significantly during the evaporation on a perfume blotter.

From an olfactory point of view (and a chemical viewpoint, too) the oil is inferior to Paraguay petitgrain oil, by far, let alone the petitgrain bigarade oil. Sweet orange petitgrain oil could serve as a perfume material in areas where other petitgrain oils are not available, and where sweet orange is abundant. Even so, the oil may not have any future beyond that of an academic interest. A number of publications on the subject have appeared from many of the sweet-orange-producing areas. It appears from these publications that the oil usually contains more than 50% monoterpenes. A terpeneless, acetylated sweet orange petitgrain oil has been produced experimentally, but this product did not show any significant advantage in use over a normal grade of terpeneless Paraguay petitgrain oil.

In view of the above facts, it seems most likely that this oil will completely disappear from the perfume and flavor market.

Oregon Balsam.

Oregon Balsam, also called "Oregon fir balsam", is a natural oleoresin of the turpentine type. It occurs as a physiological product inside the trunk of **Pseudotsuga Taxifolia,** the "Douglas fir" or "Western fir" from the mountains of the western United States along the Pacific coast, from California to British Columbia in Canada. The "balsam" was first tapped and brought on the market only 40 years ago. Thus, it is much younger than **Canada Balsam** (see this monograph and **Abies Balsamea**). The Douglas fir is grown in Europe from England to Italy as a lumber tree. To obtain the **Oregon Balsam,** the lumber companies use rather primitive methods:

The "balsam" is collected from felled trees by placing a drum under the end pieces of the trunks. Or, the balsam which flows from natural wounds (e.g. storm damage) is collected by inserting a tube in the wound. The "balsam" is subsequently strained. There seems to be no rational or organized drilling or damaging of the live trees, and the production of **Oregon Balsam** remains at a fairly modest level of tonnage.

Oregon "balsam" is a light amber colored or pale yellow, viscous liquid of pleasant, fresh, pine-type odor. It has been used as an adulterant of **Canada Balsam** (see this), but Oregon balsam is less viscous, slower drying (and does not become hard and brittle like Canada balsam), and it has

a different odor. The "peppery" fresh note of Canada balsam seems to be missing in the Oregon balsam. The lower viscosity of Oregon balsam is also revealed in the higher yield of essential oil by steam distillation of this product as compared to the yield of oil from Canada balsam.

Oregon Balsam is used occasionally in perfumery as a faintly fragrant fixative in pine type perfumes, forest notes, low-cost lemon type perfumes for soaps, and generally as a fixative where the fresh-piney note is justified.

The leaves (needles) of the tree, **Pseudotsuga Taxifolia,** will yield an essential oil upon steam distillation (see **Douglas Fir Needles Oil**). This oil is not a regularly produced material. By steam distillation of **Oregon Balsam** is produced an essential oil, principally a turpentine oil, and this oil is of little or no interest to the perfumer (see **Oregon Balsam Oil,** next monograph). See also **Larch Turpentine.**

Oregon Balsam Oil.

Also called "Oregon fir turpentine oil". The essential oil steam distilled from **Oregon Balsam** (see previous monograph) is of little or no interest to the perfume industry, but the oil will be briefly described here. Since **Oregon Balsam** is plentiful available, the essential oil can be produced on demand, and the oil presents a possible material for the adulteration of various pine needle oils, etc.

Oregon Balsam Oil is a pale yellowish or almost water-white, mobile liquid of a light, pleasant-fresh, turpentine-like odor. It is a very volatile oil with a poor tenacity, but it could find use in the "construction" of artificial pine needle oils, spruce oils, etc. The fresh and natural note of Oregon balsam oil is far superior to that of the pinene which is isolated from ordinary turpentine oil (a common adulterant in pine needle oils). However, Oregon balsam oil is at present not produced regularly, and its use would always be a very limited and local one.

See also **Douglas Fir Needle Oil.**

Origanum Oils.

For a summary of the **Thyme** and **Origanum** oils, see **Thyme and Origanum.**

Origanum oil is steam distilled from the dried, flowering herb of **Thymus Capitatus,** a plant which grows wild in the Middle East, Asia Minor and in Spain. A related plant, **Origanum Virens** and other species of **Origanum,** grow wild in abundance in Morocco where the plant serves for distillation of Moroccan origanum oil. By far, the majority of all origanum oils are derived from the "Spanish" type, **Thymus Capitatus.** This plant is distilled in Spain, Israel, Lebanon, Syria, Turkey (Fethiye region), etc., particularly in the two former countries. Distillation of origanum oil in Cyprus was abandoned a few months prior to the author's last visit there in 1956, and production has not been resumed.

The **Origanum Vulgare** is distilled in the U.S.S.R., Bulgaria and Italy, but this plant yields an entirely different oil (see **Marjoram, Wild**). This plant is a typical garden herb, and it is cultivated for culinary purposes all over the world, including the U.S.A., Central America, South America, India, etc. In Yugoslavia, **Origanum Hirtum** is used for distillation, but the oil is little known outside its country of origin.

Spanish or Israeli **Origanum Oil** is a dark brownish-red or grayish-red or purple to dark orange colored liquid, possessing a strong, tar-like, herbaceous, but very refreshing odor. The topnote is slightly green-camphoraceous, herbaceous, and the body is rich, dry-woody, somewhat reminiscent of cade and phenols ("hospital-odor", "medicinal odor"). On drying out, the odor becomes sweeter, but remains phenolic-dry and woody (as distinguished from the dryout of thyme oil). The flavor is somewhat burning, warm-phenolic ("hospital-like") with a rich herbaceous undertone. The flavor becomes fairly pleasant only in high dilution.

The oil is used in perfumery for its powerful refreshing notes and its spicy-herbaceous effect. The medicinal note is often utilized in soap perfumes of the "medicated" type where this type of odor agrees with the special purpose of the soap. The main constituent of origanum oil is the liquid phenol, **Carvacrol,** and this fact must be kept in mind when the oil is used in perfumes. The phenol will discolor in the presence of iron, and it is also strongly affected by alkali. Strongly alkaline media will "kill" the odor of carvacrol under formation of odorless salts of this phenol. However, the oil is effective in soap perfumes, provided the soapbase (stock) is of low alkalinity. Together with lavandin, ocotea pretiosa oil, amyl salicylate, coumarin, oakmoss products, linalool, cedarwood oil and its derivatives, pine needle oils

or isobornyl acetate, isobornyl propionate, rosemary oil, spike lavender oil, citronella oil, camphor oils, cyclohexanone derivatives, etc., the oil can produce interesting and powerful fragrances and bases for soap perfumes.

Trace amounts of origanum oil are useful for topnote effects in citrus colognes, fougères, forestnotes, chypres, lavender-colognes, spicy-herbaceous after-shave fragrances and lotions, etc. The oil is also used in flavor work, but the milder types of origanum oil are often preferred for this purpose, or, still better, thyme oil is used (see **Marjoram Oils** and **Thyme Oils**).

Moroccan Origanum Oil is quite similar to the Spanish oil in composition and odor. None of the origanum oils are uniform from year to year, probably due to the variety of wild plants growing in the harvesting area, the lack of accuracy in picking one species alone, and the fact that thyme oil stills are used also for origanum oil in many cases.

Rectified or **"White" Origanum Oil** is a redistilled oil which is pale yellow or pale orange of color when freshly distilled. It darkens on ageing and it does not offer any advantage over the natural oil beyond that of the immediate color of the oil. The rectified oil usually lacks the fresh-herbaceous bouquet which seems to mask the phenolic notes in the natural oil to a certain degree.

All **Carvacrol**-types of (i.e. *true*) origanum oil are subject to adulteration or contamination with thyme oil (and vice versa, see **Thyme Oil**). Pure carvacrol is not cheap enough to make an adulteration with this material economical. Carvacrol is produced synthetically from carvone (which can be synthesized from d-limonene) or from paracymene, but the demand for carvacrol is small. The isomer, **Thymol,** is considerably more useful.

The annual world production of **Origanum Oil** has fluctuated between 80 and 150 metric tons during the five-year period 1955/59.

Orris Absolute.

This, one of the most expensive of all natural perfume materials, is on a steady retreat from the perfumer's shelf. This fact is due not only to the high price of orris absolute (about three times the cost of jasmin absolute, or 50% higher than Bulgarian "otto" of rose), but also because of the appearance of a number of fine synthetic chemicals which either reproduce the principal notes in orris absolute, or are actually present in the natural material and have been duplicated in organic synthesis.

Orris Absolute is produced from the "concrète" oil of orris (see following monograph) by alkali washing in ethyl ether solution to remove the myristic acid which amounts to 85–90% of the "concrète" oil. The absolute is also produced from a petroleum ether concrète, which is free from myristic acid. The liquid portion is carefully vacuum distilled. The resulting absolute is a water-white or very pale yellow, oily liquid of extremely delicate, sweet-floral, yet somewhat woody odor which appears very weak at first, but later, or on dilution, displays its full and impressive strength and diffusion. Flavor experiments will easily convince the keen observer that this material has unusual diffusive power and "lift" in spite of its delicate note. In extreme dilutions, the flavor becomes sweet-fruity and reminiscent of raspberries, and it can be used in flavor composing for this effect.

Orris Absolute is occasionally used in trace amounts in raspberry, strawberry, peach and other fruit flavors, and in rum flavor. The average use level will be only slightly higher than the **Minimum Perceptible** concentration which is 0.0005 to 0.0010 mg%. One part of orris absolute is distinctly perceptible in 100 to 200 million parts of sweetened water.

Orris Absolute is mainly used in perfumes, and only in high-class lotion types or similar bases where the price does not prohibit its application. It blends extremely well with all muguet materials, ylang-ylang, mimosa, cassie, cassione, linalool, sandalwood oil, cyclamal, nerol, geraniol, phenylethyl alcohol, phenylethyldimethyl carbinol, heliotropine, etc. or with ambre bases, appleblossom, lilac, violet, tearose bases, etc., and it can be supported by the skillful application of ionones, or better still, methylionones. The so-called deltamethyl ionone (which is beta-iso methyl ionone) is particularly suited for blending and modifying alpha irone in many perfume types.

Orris absolute is offered according to its content of alpha-**Irone** which fluctuates from 55 to 85%. The absolute is thus not truly a "ten-fold" concrète (under which label it is often offered). Some "concrète" orris oils contain up to 18% alpha-irone although the average commercial lots contain from 8 to 15% of this ketone. Adulteration of orris absolute is very common, and even

synthetic alpha-irone can be used with economic advantage. Synthetic alpha-irone sells for about U.S. $ 700 to 800 per kilo, or less than one-third of the price of orris absolute. It is conceivable that such facts will contribute to the complete disappearance of **Orris Absolute** from the market.

Orris (Concrète) Oil.

Orris "Concrète" (so-called) is not a true concrète according to the definitions in Part One of this book. It just happens to be a solid ("concrète") essential oil. It is commercially known as **"Orris Butter"** or **"Beurre d'Iris"**. It is produced by steam distillation of the rhizomes of **Iris Pallida,** one of the most decorative garden perennials. The rhizomes (subterranean stems) are washed, decorticated and dried. They should be stored subsequently, well protected against insect and fungus attack, for three years. The fresh rhizomes are practically odorless. Prior to distillation, the rhizomes are pulverized. Unpeeled orris rhizomes are occasionally used, e.g. in Morocco where the plant is **Iris Germanica** and, more recently, also the **Iris Pallida.**

The distillation of pulverized orris rhizomes demands much experience and involves quite a few problems. The extremely small yield of liquid oil, the high amount of starch in the rhizomes, the volume of the pulverized material, etc. all create problems for the distillers. Production of orris (concrète) oil takes place in France and Morocco, to a lesser degree in Italy where the bulk of the botanical material is still produced. Smaller amounts of the oil are distilled in England and the U.S.A.

The distilled oil solidifies in the receiver to a wax-like, cream-colored mass known as **Orris Butter** or **Orris Concrète.** It is solid because of its high content of myristic acid, a white, stearin-like substance (see also **Ambrette Seed Oil**).

Orris (concrète) oil melts at about body temperature, and has a woody, fatty-oily but distinctly violet-like odor, with a fruity undertone, sweet-floral, warm and tenacious. When freshly prepared and well stored, it should not possess perceptible notes of myristic acid or decomposition products thereof (acid or unsaturated-fatty notes, rancid notes, acrylic notes, etc.). The concrète oil is not soluble in ethyl alcohol at room temperature, and the myristic acid also causes trouble directly because of its acidity when compounded with other perfume materials. Consequently, myristic acid is considered undesirable from a perfumery point of view, although it has certain advantages (fixation of the delicate odor of the irones, etc. It can be shipped in aluminium cans which are unbreakable and thus prevent loss of material; some consumers want to produce the absolute according to their own specific methods and needs).

Orris (Concrète) Oil is used in perfumery as such when the presence of myristic acid is not prohibitive, e.g. in soap perfumes where the weak acid only acts as a fixative. Incidentally, the methyl and ethyl esters of myristic acid are often used as blenders in violet type perfume bases. The isopropyl ester is high-boiling and odorless and is a popular solvent for cosmetic products, or a codistiller for absolute oils. The high cost of orris (concrète) oil limits its application to a certain degree, but even small percentages of this exquisite material lends very fine effects to various perfume types other than the old-fashioned violet: mimosa, cyclamen, freesia, orchid, robinia etc. as well as other delicate florals.

A true Orris Concrète is also produced, and it has become an increasingly popular intermediate in the production of Orris Absolute. The orris rhizomes are extracted with petroleum ether to yield a dark amber colored, viscous extract which is free from myristic acid. This "concrète" which looks more like a resinoid, is then extracted with ethyl alcohol to yield an absolute of orris. Benzene can be used in place of petroleum ether; it gives a higher yield (see Orris "Resinoid", following monograph), but it is darker, and the last traces of benzene odor are very difficult to remove. Petroleum ether can be obtained in a higher grade of purity (free from higher boiling, ill-smelling components) and rarely leaves any residual odor. The annual world production of Orris (Concrète) Oil is in the order of magnitude of one metric ton.

Orris "Resinoid".

The benzene- or ethyl alcohol extraction products of orris rhizome are commercially called Orris Resin or Orris Resinoid, although they are actually concrètes according to the definitions in this work (see Concrète and Resin, Part One of this book). Their consistency is syrupy, very viscous or honeylike, and this fact has probably caused the trade to name them "resinoids". The product

obtained from alcohol extraction is equivalent to a pharmaceutical extract (soft extract).

These products are derived from peeled orris rhizomes, usually the Iris Pallida from Italy, rarely from the Moroccan Iris Germanica. Since alcohol is a particularly good solvent for plant colors and other ballast matter, etc., it is preferable to remove the cortex of the rhizomes prior to extraction and thus obtain a lighter colored "resin". Alcohol extraction gives the highest yield but the hardest "resin"; next comes acetone, while benzene gives a lower yield, a handy viscosity of the extract, and a finer odor of the product. With petroleum ether, the yield is still smaller, but paler and very fine in odor. The honeylike consistency and the amber color of the petroleum ether extract make this an attractive, but also rather expensive "resinoid" of orris rhizome. The petroleum ether extract is mainly used for further treatment into purified "resinoids" (see below) or for Orris Absolute, see that monograph.

Orris Resin (so-called) from alcohol extraction is a low-cost, very hard and rather dark product which is used in soap perfumery for its excellent fixative value and deep-sweet, slightly woody-tobacco-like odor. The alcohol-extracted products are also distinguished by their "winy" topnote (partly due to the ethyl alcohol) and their sweet, root-like undertone. This "resin" blends well with all the ionones, methylionones, cedarwood and cedarwood derivatives, sandalwood, vetiver, cyperus, mimosa, heliotropine, labdanum products, coumarin, bergamot, sage clary, amyl salicylate, linalool, isoeugenol, ethyl cinnamate, anisyl acetone, etc. It gives interesting notes and undertones in "tabac" type perfumes, "warm" bases, Oriental bases, chypres, colognes, "forest" type bases, etc.

The benzene "resinoid" of orris rhizome is of brownish or dark orange color, a very viscous liquid or semi-pourable mass. Its odor is far superior to that of the ethyl alcohol extract. It is customary, however, to purify and solibilize the hydrocarbon extracts further by washing them with alcohol. This leads to an "absolute from so-called resinoid", which is actually the true absolute of orris rhizome according to the definitions in this book. The author disagrees with the frequent statements in literature that these "soluble resinoids are of relatively low price and thus applicable in soap perfumes". The true alcohol-soluble part of the benzene extract from orris rhizome is at least as expensive as geranium oil, but it will not give an appreciable effect in soap at the same low level as does geranium oil. If the odorless myristic acid (which is present in modest amount in the above extracts) is removed by alkali washing, we arrive at a true type of absolute of orris rhizome, consisting of soluble, neutral odorants only (a "purified resinoid"). Various specialties of this composition are offered by the manufacturers of orris extracts. The cost of these purified extracts will inevitably limit their application to high-class lotion perfumes, cream perfumes, etc.; they are hardly used at all in the large brand soap perfumes.

For flavoring purposes, it is still customary to digest the pulverized rhizomes in water or weak alcohol to which a small amount of sulphuric or hydrochloric acid is added. After 24 hours, the mixture is subjected to distillation with or without a previous one-hour period of refluxing. The distillate may then be redistilled to produce an **Orris Aroma** with the correct amount of alcohol.

There are various explanations for the fact that such distillates are more aromatic than those obtained without the use of acid. Chemically, there seems to be an isomerization of the irones, but this should not affect the odor strength significantly. Many flavor houses produce their own **Orris Aroma** or **Orris Distillate** for use in their private formulas. The aromas or distillates are not commercially available products. They may be offered under fancy names in more or less complex compositions for flavors or perfumes (violet-distillate, etc.). These aromas and distillates are still used in the flavoring of certain types of licorice candy, in Sen-Sen, etc. where the sweet, rootlike notes of the orris rhizome seems to blend well with the flavor of the licorice extract. However, this type of licorice flavor has lost its popularity in Europe during recent years.

Orris "Resin" or **"Resinoid"** is very frequently adulterated or rather "bouquetted", sophisticated, etc. with traces of ionones, methylionones, sage clary oil, labdanum absolute, cedarwood derivatives or fractions, amyris oil, methyl abietate, dihydroabietic alcohol, solvents, plasticizers, etc. The number of types of **Orris "Resin"** on the market is so huge that a general description is well-nigh impossible.

Osmanthus Fragrans.

The flowers from a small tree of the family Ole-

aceae (to which also the jasmin and lilac belong) are used in China and Japan as a starting material in the production of a concrète and an absolute.

The flowers of **Osmanthus Fragrans** are extracted with petroleum ether to yield a concrète, which in turn gives an absolute after alcohol extraction. Since the yield of absolute from concrète is only about one kilo per 3,000 kilos of flowers, the enfleurage method or the infusion process have also been applied to these flowers. The perfumed extraction oil (fixed oil) can be used as is (directly) in cosmetic preparations with some advantage.

The production of osmanthus concrète, absolute, pommade and infusion is apparently very local and these products are not regularly available perfume materials outside the producing areas. The author has no personal experience with the use of these flower absolutes, etc. in perfumery.

The flowers of osmanthus fragrans are occasionally used for the perfuming (scenting) of tea in China.

See also **Chimonanthus Fragrans**, the so-called Japanese allspice.

Osyris Tenuifolia.

The essential oil from the wood of a medium-sized East African tree, **Osyris Tenuifolia,** is little known as such, but it occasionally appears as an adulterant in East Indian Sandalwood oil. The tree grows wild over large areas of East Africa, Ethiopia, Uganda, Kenya, Tanganyika, etc. and numerous varieties are found in other areas such as Madagascar, Mozambique, etc.

Distillation is performed by steam on the chipped wood of the trees; there is no regular production of this oil, but occasional lots are distilled in Kenya. Production was long since abandoned in Madagascar at the moments of the author's visits in 1955/56. It is conceivable, however, that the oil is produced whenever there is a demand, and this is why the oil has been briefly described here.

Osyris Tenuifolia Oil is an orange-yellow or dark yellow to brownish colored, viscous liquid of very faint, but pleasant-woody, somewhat sweet odor, not unlike that of araucaria oil. Very crude and dark oils, or freshly distilled oils, may smell dry, tar-like, reminiscent of the odor of Kenya cedarwood oil. It is even possible that the latter oil is used as an adulterant for osyris tenuifolia oil.

Oil of osyris tenuifolia could find use as an excellent fixative in many types of perfume, but it probably does not offer any distinct advantage over **Amyris Oil, Araucaria Oil** or similar, regularly available oils. The future of the **"East African Sandalwood Oil"** (older name for osyris tenuifolia) is, therefore, very doubtful. It should be noted that a "true" sandalwood oil is now produced in East Africa on a small scale (from **Santalum Album**). See also **Muhuhu Oil, Pterocarpus Oil, Santalum Citrinum,** etc.

P

Palmarosa Oil.

Palmarosa Oil is steam distilled or water distilled mainly from wild growing, fresh or dried grass of the plant **Cymbopogon Martini,** varietas motia (see also **Gingergrass Oil).** The grass grows wild in India, particularly northeast of Bombay toward the Himalaya mountains, and to a lesser extent, in Pakistan. The grass has been planted in the Seychelle islands and in the Comoro islands in the Indian Ocean. In Indonesia, particularly in Java, production of palmarosa oil has been resumed at a modest rate after a long lay-off during and after World War II. Cultivated grass is distilled in modern steam stills in Java. India remains the most important producer, and the Indian palmarosa oil is still shipped overseas in the characteristic tinlined copper containers of about 200 lbs. capacity, protected by a net of heavy cord tightly tied around the carboy-shaped copper container. These containers are not very practical for shipping in respect to space, and they are slowly disappearing and replaced by the unromantic 200-liter cylindrical iron drums.

Palmarosa Oil is a pale yellow or pale olive colored liquid with a sweet, floral-rosy odor and various undertones or topnotes according to the quality and age of the oil. Palmarosa oil is the best natural source of geraniol of all essential oils. Only very recently, it has been analytically proved that **Geraniol** in nature is usually accompanied by **Nerol** and perhaps by other alcohols. However, pure **Geraniol** can be isolated from palmarosa oil. Apart from its use as a geraniol-source, palmarosa oil is used as such in many perfumes, particularly in soap perfumes where its greater tenacity, prob-

ably due to its content of farnesol and sesquiterpenes, is of outstanding effect, far beyond the effect gained from commercial geraniol produced e.g. from citronella oil.

Palmarosa oil blends well with all the conventional soap perfume materials and it forms an excellent base with small amounts of geranium oil and oakmoss concrète or absolute. Combinations with cananga oil, bois de rose oil, amyris oil, guaiacwood oil, etc. are excellent bases for further development of soap perfumes. The name **"Geranium Palmarosa"** is a carryover from the days when palmarosa oil was used as an adulterant for Turkish rose oil and was imported into Turkey for that purpose as "geranium palmarosa". The term **"Geranium Palmarosa Turkish"** is completely misleading and obsolete, but is unfortunately still used by dealers and perfumers. There is no such thing as Turkish palmarosa oil, and there is no significant production of geranium oil in Turkey. The term could hardly be more confusing.

On the other hand, **Palmarosa Oil** is now frequently adulterated not only with its close relative, **Gingergrass Oil** (see this monograph), but also with commercial geraniol, obtained from citronella oil or produced synthetically (now from beta-pinene). These geraniol types cost only a fraction of the palmarosa oil price, but they are usually mixtures of geraniol, citronellol and nerol with about 50% geraniol or perhaps even less.

In flavors, **Palmarosa Oil** still finds use in tobacco where it was one of the very first flavoring materials used.

The oil has slowly lost importance, mainly due to the appearance of low-cost isolated or synthetic geraniols, and it is doubtful that palmarosa oil will ever again become a "big" essential oil. The annual production is somewhere between 30 and 50 metric tons, most of which is East Indian. Due to the significant difference in distillation and to the fact that the Indonesian plant material is cultivated while the Indian is wild-growing, the Indonesian oil has certain advantages (e.g. higher ester content) while the Indian oil still claims a better overall odor and highest content of **Geraniol.**

Pandanus.

The **Pandanus Odoratissimus** is a small tropical tree, or, more correctly, a plant. It is presumably a native of the South Pacific Islands, but the exact origin is unknown. A number of varieties of **Pandanus** species are cultivated in the tropics for many and different reasons: it forms a good fence around the house and it does not grow high or shady. The leaves are useful for thatched roofs on native huts, etc. The author found many pandanus plants used as supporting trunks for vanilla vines in Réunion and Madagascar. The plant is known as the **"Screw Palm"**.

For the perfume industry, the flowers of pandanus odoratissimus are highly interesting and very unusual. Not only are the flowers unusually large (single flowers weighing 165 grams are not uncommon), but they are powerfully fragrant with a very characteristic perfume. Accordingly, the creamy-white flowers have attracted the interest of the perfume industry in certain tropical areas where the plant grows abundantly and where extraction facilities are at hand.

In India, particularly in the South Orissa and Ganjam districts, in Pakistan, Burma, Malaya, South Arabia and Iran, and on the Andaman islands, there are pandanus trees in quantity. A regular production of perfume oil from the flowers, however, takes place only in India. The flowers are collected exclusively from cultivated trees. A well developed pandanus plant may carry only about 25 flowers, but this means already several kilos! There are various methods of extraction in practice:

An **"Attar of Kewda"** (i.e. "otto", or "essence" of pandanus) is prepared by maceration of the flowers with sesame seed (of **Sesamum Indicum**) or sesame oil (the fatty oil expressed from the seed). Other flowers may be used simultaneously to produce the fragrant oil which is sold as such for cosmetic purposes. Or, the flowers may be steam distilled into sandalwood oil or other perfume oils in the receiver of the still. This distillate is also called **"Attar of Kewda"** or **"Attar Keora"**.

The flowers can be steam distilled without the addition of other essential oils and with no diluent oil in the receiver, but the extremely small yield makes it necessary to use some sort of a solvent in the receptacle in order to avoid excessive loss of oil. The oil is somewhat soluble in water. The most economic method, and the most common large-scale method today is the hydrocarbon extraction method in which a concrète is first prepared. By alcohol washing of the concrète an **Absolute of Pandanus** is obtained.

The oil or the absolute is particularly interesting for the perfume chemist since the main constituent is about 75% of **Methyl-beta-Phenylethyl Ether**. It is furthermore interesting to see that the odor of kewda absolute has been described (W. A. Poucher, Perfumes, Cosmetics and Soaps, vol. I, page 232, fifth edition 1941) as being reminiscent of **Phenylacetaldehyde Dimethylacetal**. A chemist would probably say: "– yes, and this is exactly the starting material in the synthetic preparation of methyl-beta-phenylethyl ether!" (produced synthetically from phenylacetaldehyde dimethyl acetal by catalytic reduction with hydrogen in the presence of a nickel catalyst at 180°C.).

Pandanus Absolute is a colorless liquid of intensely sharp, very powerful and diffusive, but also very sweet, hyacinth-honeylike odor. It is easier to evaluate this odor in dilutions below one percent. The powerful topnote is of very short duration, leaving only a faint, sweet-floral and fresh tone-out fragrance on a perfume blotter. The absolute blends well with styrax resinoid, cinnamic alcohol, amyl salicylate, phenylethyl phenylacetate, ar-methyl-phenylethyl alcohol, indole, heliotropine, galbanum resinoid, sage clary, bergamot, terpineol, linalool, ylang-ylang, etc. If properly fixed (and this is difficult!), the pandanus absolute can be of great interest to the perfumer in compositions such as honeysuckle, hyacinth, lily, narcissus, etc. and for experimental modifications of rose, lilac, etc.

Only very small lots of **Kewda** or **Pandanus Absolute** arrive in Europe or the U.S.A., but the material is regularly produced for a hungry local perfume market in India where the fragrance is very popular. Published figures of annual treatment of 40 million flowers in the Orissa district seem exaggerated, since this amount of flowers would yield at least 2 metric tons of kewda absolute, and this amount is not available. The author estimates the production (based upon private communication with the producing areas) at about 125 to 175 kilos per year. The absolute is priced about equal to jasmin absolute, the very small yield of pandanus absolute being responsible for the high cost.

Pandanus Absolute is not adulterated as such, but it is difficult to obtain a pure absolute or a pure distillate, free from other essential oils, vegetable oils or diluents which are conventional and accepted additives in India. The main constituent, methyl-beta-phenylethyl ether is produced synthetically, and a Swiss perfume material supply house offers an artificial kewda base. One "sniff" at a true kewda absolute will usually be sufficient to enable the perfumer, permanently, to screen pure from diluted pandanus oils.

Paradise Seed Oil.

Among the very first spices (or "aromatic seeds") to be brought from Africa to Europe was a "pepper" from the countries along the West African coast near Equator. This coast was hence named the "Pepper Coast", but no true black pepper was actually found there.

The seed from **Amomum Melegueta,** a plant related to ginger, is known in medicine as **Paradise Seed** or **Melegueta Pepper.** The seed occurs as an adulterant in black pepper and cubeb, but it is also imported as such as a spice.

When comminuted, the small black seed emits a strong, sweet-fruity odor, reminiscent of strawberry and banana. This may have intrigued the scientists of the 17th century who succeeded in preparing an essential oil from the seed almost 300 years ago.

Paradise Seed Oil is a pale yellow to brownish colored liquid with a spicy-woody, somewhat sweet, faintly peppery odor. The flavor is warm, slightly biting, but not pungent. The essential oil is not a regularly produced item, and it seems to have evaded the noses of the perfumers and flavorists. It is possible that the oil really is of little or no interest to the perfume and flavor industry, but since the seed is commercially available, and because of the peculiar odor of the crushed seed, the author found it worthwhile mentioning this oil. The author has no personal experience with *extracts* of paradise seed. Such preparations do exist, and they do exhibit the same fruity aroma as does the essential oil.

Parsley Herb Oil.

Also known as **Parsley Leaf Oil,** this oil is produced by steam distillation of the top of the flowering parsley plant, **Petroselinum Sativum.** Parsley is a native of the eastern Mediterranean countries, and it has been known and used in food for more than 2000 years. The plant seems to have come to England as late as 1548, and to the U.S.A. about a century later. It was known in northern central Europe in the 13th century.

Since only the leaves have been used for food until the "turniprooted" Hamburg variety of parsley was developed, it is interesting to note that the essential oil of parsley herb apparently was not produced until some time in the 20th century. The yield of oil is very small, but only the oil from the herb (leaves) will reproduce the flavor which is well known in numerous dishes where the delightfully green and decorative garnish yields such a piquant flavor to the food.

Parsley is cultivated all over Europe, in parts of Asia, and in the U.S.A. **Parsley Herb Oil** is distilled in France and Hungary, occasionally in Holland and Germany. The annual world production is probably less than 100 kilos.

Parsley herb oil is a pale yellow or greenish yellow, rarely water-white liquid of a peculiar, warm-spicy, heavy-leafy, yet fresh-herb-like odor. For those who know parsley, it might be easier to describe the odor of the oil as being very similar to that of the fresh cut herb. The flavor, too, is warm, slightly burning and bitter, but it reproduces the natural herb fairly well. The suggested use level is about 2.00 to 4.00 mg% and the **Minimum Perceptible** is 0.04 to 1.00 mg%. Considerable variations in these figures were observed in experiments with oils of different age and origin.

Parsley Herb Oil is used very rarely, if used at all, in perfumery. To the author's knowledge, the oil is used exclusively in flavor work: for seasonings, sauces, pickles, meat additives and various spice blends. The oil could find some use in perfumery for its fine and peculiar green-herb effect, but the limited availability seems to be restrictive to the use of this oil in perfumery.

See also **Parsley Seed Oil,** following monograph.

Parsley Seed Oil.

This oil is produced by steam distillation of the ripe fruit, also called seed, of **Petroselinum Sativum,** the common parsley (see **Parsley Herb Oil,** previous monograph for origin of plant).

The plant is widely cultivated and has been cultivated for so many centuries that it hardly can be found in its wild state any more. Cultivation for the purpose of producing seed for distillation is actually not very common. Most of the seed for distillation is derived from surplus stock, since the parsley fruit loses its germinating power

44: Ornamental **Mimosa** trees in Rabat, Morocco.　　　　　　*(Fot. S. Arctander, 1960)*

45: The delightfully fragrant globoid heads of **Mimosa** flowers on a cultivated, ornamental variety in Morocco.　　　　　　*(Fot. S. Arctander, 1960)*

46: The **Capp et Florale** factory for **Rose Oil** and **Rose Concrète** at El Kelaâ-des-M'Gouna, southern Morocco, looks like a desert fortress from the outside – – –   *(Courtesy Capp & Florale)*

47: – – – but the inside of the beautifully styled factory reveals batteries of modern water-stills for **Rose Oil.** Up to 46 metric tons (= 101,500 lbs.) of rosebuds were treated in one 24-hour period by extractors and stills in this factory.   *(Courtesy Capp et Florale S.a.r.l.)*

48: The fragrance of **Rosa Canina** (the hedgerose or hip-rose) is not extracted from the flowers, but it is often duplicated by the perfumer. *(Fot. S. Arctander, 1956)*

49: A beautiful and very healthy **Sage Clary** ("clary sage") field at Long Melford, Suffolk, England. The essential oil from the flowering top has an inimitable and delightful fragrance.

(Fot. S. Arctander, 1960)

rapidly. Superannuated seed yield almost the same amount and quality of oil as that derived from current year's crop. France, Poland, Holland, Germany and Hungary are the principal growers. Distillation is carried out mainly in France, to a smaller degree in Hungary, Germany and Holland. The exhaust seed is sold as cattle feed, a fact which partly explains the economy of the production of parsley seed oil. Some perfume houses import their own seed (usually from Poland or France) and distil oil to their individual demands.

Parsley seed oil is a yellowish to amber-colored or brownish liquid, more or less viscous. Upon cooling, it may deposit crystals of **Apiole**, chemically a methoxy-myristicin. The oil also contains myristicin, and is considered toxic by many authorities, with approximately twice the hazard of materials such as coumarin. However, parsley seed, nutmeg and many other myristicin-containing natural materials are still widely used in food.

The odor of **Parsley Seed Oil** is warm-woody, spicy, somewhat sweet-herbaceous but, in the author's opinion, not at all reminiscent of parsley *herb* (as described elsewhere in the literature). Its flavor is equally warm-spicy, aromatic, rich and deep, but unfortunately quite bitter. Thus, in flavor compounds, the oil must be well blended with sweeter tasting spice oils in order to exploit the typical and pleasant effects of the parsley oil fully. The suggested use level is 0.60 to 2.00 mg%, and the **Minimum Perceptible** is 0.20 to 0.40 mg%. It is weaker than the herb oil.

Parsley seed oil is used in perfumery for so-called "special effects". It is more spicy-aromatic and less fatty-woody than carrot seed oil. Accordingly, the use of parsley seed oil in perfumery is restricted to such fragrances where a warm-spicy effect is called for: Oriental bases, chypres, "men's fragrances", colognes, certain modern fantasy perfumes, etc. The oil is also used in certain types of rose and orange flower bases. It blends well with anisaldehyde, anisalcohol, cananga oil, coumarin, isoeugenol, linalool, melaleuca alternifolia oil, nerol, oakmoss products, sage clary oil, tetrahydro myrcenol, terpineol etc. However, the main use of parsley seed oil is in flavors for meat sauces, seasonings, spice blends, canned food, pickles, etc. The oil has even been used in tobacco flavoring. The limited availability of this oil puts a certain limit to its use, and it may never become really common in perfumery.

See also **Parsley Herb Oil**, previous monograph.

Passionflower.

Although mainly cultivated for their delicious, edible fruits, or for the beauty of their flowers, the various species of **Passiflora** also include some with very fragrant flowers. The genus **Passiflora** probably originated in South or Central America, but many species are now cultivated in tropical countries all over the world. The **Lilikoi** of Hawaii is a passionflower. Several species are cultivated in Bermuda, tropical west-Atlantic islands, for the purpose of extracting perfume from the flowers by the "enfleurage" method (see chapter on **Pommade**, Part One of this book). Let it be said at once that the perfume produced from these flowers in Bermuda, amount to a mere fraction of the various Bermuda-produced perfumes. The **Passionflower Absolute** as such is not commercially available from Bermuda. The same can be said about the "Bermuda-lily" (see **Lilium Candidum**). An "absolute" of this flower is also produced in Bermuda for the use in special "Bermuda perfumes". The amount of hydroxy-citronellal and other synthetic perfume materials imported to these islands will tell more about the composition of these perfumes.

Since fragrant species of passiflora are plentiful, a production of a true **Passionflower Absolute** is possible, although not presently a reality to the author's opinion.

A number of **Passiflora** species produce edible fruits, e.g. the Australian **Grenadil** fruit (also a native of Brazil), or the giant, cube-shaped **Barbadin** fruit.

Passionflower perfumes are often composed as simple modifications of honeysuckle perfumes from natural and synthetic raw materials.

Patchouli Oil.

This very important perfume oil is produced by steam distillation of the dried leaves of **Pogostemon Cablin** (also known as **Pogostemon Patchouli**), a small plant which probably originated in the Philippine Islands and Indonesia where the bulk of today's patchouli oil still is produced. The plant is cultivated for production of essential oil in Sumatra, Malaya, the Seychelle islands, Nossi-Bé (at Madagascar), Hainan and the adjoining China coast, and, on a smaller scale in Japan, Brazil, Mauritius and Tanganyika. Indonesian patchouli leaves are distilled in Europe and the U.S.A. in modern distilleries, but the oil thus produced is substantially different from the locally distilled patchouli oil.

In order to get a full yield of the essential oil by steam distillation, it is necessary to rupture the cell walls in the leaf material prior to distillation. This can be performed by controlled, light fermentation, by scalding with superheated steam (like the "blanching" process of vegetables before canning), or by stacking or baling the dried leaves, thus "curing" them by modest and interrupted fermentation. If carried out properly, the latter method yields the best perfume oil. The total world production of patchouli oil has increased considerably since 1950 and now exceeds 100 metric tons per year. The price has dropped to about one-third of the 1952 level, and the quality is steadily improving again. Indonesia is the main supplier of patchouli oil.

Patchouli Oil (native distilled) is a dark orange or brownish-colored, viscous liquid, possessing an extremely rich, sweet-herbaceous, aromatic-spicy and woody-balsamic odor. An almost wine-like, ethereal-floral sweetness in the initial notes is characteristic of good oils although this topnote can be absent or masked in freshly distilled, otherwise good oils. The odor should remain sweet through all stages of evaporation. Patchouli oil will remain perceptible on a perfume blotter for weeks or months, and the sweetness is almost sickening in high concentration. Dry or tarlike notes should not be perceptible throughout the first hours of study of the oil on a blotter, and cade-like, dry cedarwoodlike odor which may appear in the topnote should rapidly vanish and give way to the rich sweetness. Thus, it remains a "matter of opinion" what type of patchouli oil is "good" and what type is "poor". Many perfumers have never—or rarely—smelled other types than the dry, phenolic, cade-like type. This type may be their standard of evaluation, or they may actually like to use this type. In both cases it can be said that the bodynotes of patchouli oil should display an outstanding richness, a root-like note with a delicate earthiness which should not include "mold-like" or musty-dry notes. The odor of patchouli oil is often described as "minty", "swampy", "barnyard-like", etc. and there is no doubt that the many types confuse the unexperienced evaluator. Tenacity in odor is one of the typical virtues of patchouli oil, and is one of the reasons for its versatile use.

European or American distilled patchouli oil is a pale orange or amber-colored, viscous liquid of very sweet, rich, spicy-aromatic and herbaceous odor; it bears an overall resemblance to the odor of the native oil, but has a pronounced topnote of fruity, wine-like sweetness, and less pronounced woody-earthy notes. The odor is often more spicy-balsamic and usually more tenacious than that of the native oil. Certain distillers in Europe and at one time in the U.S.A., too, have a reputation for special know-how in the distilling of patchouli. In all cases, whether it is of native or European-American distillation, the odor of the oil improves significantly upon ageing. The sharp-green or "wet-earthy", minty notes are subdued or vanish, and the sweetness rises to the surface of the odor pattern.

Patchouli Oil is used so extensively that it is hardly possible to specify its field of application. It blends beautifully with labdanum, vetiver, sandalwood, ionones, cedarwood derivatives, coumarin, oakmoss, geranium, clove oils, lavender, rose, bergamot, neroli, orris "resinoid", nitromusks, cinnamates, methyl salicylate, cassia oil, myrrh, opopanax, sage clary absolute, borneol, pine needle oils, cyclohexanone derivatives, etc., etc. It forms an important ingredient in Oriental bases, woody bases, fougères, chypres, opopanax bases, powder-type perfumes, etc. It is an excellent masking agent for depilatory creams, e.g. in combination with orange type materials.

In flavors, patchouli oil once was widely used in the **"Sen-Sen"** type of licorice flavoring. Combined with geranium, ionones, orris extracts, nitromusks, anise, clove, etc., it produced a very heavy "Oriental" flavor, popular as a masking agent for alcoholic breath, onion or garlic odors, etc. as an "after-dinner" candy. The rather soapy-perfumey flavor is no longer very popular in Europe; it is slowly disappearing in the U.S.A., but is still used in Asia and South America.

Patchouli Resinoid is, according to the terms of this book (see **Resinoid**, Part One of this book), a concrète extracted from the dried leaves by hydrocarbon solvents. Benzene or petroleum ether are used. The extract is a syrupy or very viscous liquid of dark orange-brown color (benzene extract), or dark amber to pale orange color (petroleum ether extract). Beyond its olfactory virtues which are similar to those of the European-American distilled patchouli oils, it is an excellent fixative. Various so-called patchouli resinoids are available, but some of these materials are heavily adulterated with oakmoss resins, patchouli oil, clove bud resinoid, vetiver oil residues, cedarwood oil residues, etc.

Certain types of patchouli extracts are processed further, e.g. by molecular distillation (**Anhydrols, Resinoines,** etc.) to yield almost colorless, viscous oils of great olfactory value and outstandingly attractive odor type and diffusive power. A second extraction of the petroleum ether extract (of patchouli leaves) with ethyl alcohol yields a true absolute of patchouli, the "heart" of the patchouli odor. Essential oil chemists have investigated the composition of patchouli oil for more than half a century, and it has been claimed that more than 80% of the oil is constituted of odorless or almost odorless chemicals. Consequently, it should be possible to "concentrate" the odor of patchouli considerably. It seems conceivable that the main portion of patchouli oil can be removed by fractional distillation without depriving the small remainder from having the typical patchouli odor. Similar experiments have been carried out with lavandin oil, petitgrain oil, clove bud oil, geranium oil, sage clary oil, etc.

Patchouli Oil is occasionally adulterated with cedarwood oil, clove oil sesquiterpenes, cedarwood derivatives, methyl abietate, hydroabietic alcohols, vetiver residues, camphor oil residues, etc. However, the present price of patchouli, due to the abundance of the oil on the market, has made it less interesting to "cut" this useful perfume material.

See also **Manevoro Oil.**

Pennyroyal Oil, American.

The trade distinguishes between two types of pennyroyal oil. The so-called "American" pennyroyal oil is steam distilled from the freshly harvested, slightly dried, flowering herb of **Hedeoma Pulegioides.** This is a small plant belonging to the same botanical order as peppermint, and it is a native of the eastern and midwestern United States. It is harvested in the midwest and regularly distilled, although the oil has a very limited application.

American Pennyroyal Oil is a pale yellow, mobile oil with a fresh-herbaceous, strong and bitter-minty odor, a rather thin body and a faintly woody dryout which varies according to the age of the oil. The taste is sharp, bitter and somewhat burning.

American pennyroyal oil is occasionally used in industrial perfumes where great strength, masking power and low cost are called for. It blends well with rosemary oil, pine needle oils, lavandin oil, ocotea pretiosa, distilled citrus oils, methyl salicylate, lemongrass oil, citronella oil, dipentene, terpineol and similar materials which are often used in the above types of fragrance. The oil has found some use as an insect repellant in sprays and lotions.

For a short while, the oil was used to some degree in the chemical industry as a starting material for the production of menthol. However, the so-called "European" pennyroyal oil is preferred for this purpose. The main constituent of the two oils, **Pulegone,** is easily transformed into **Menthol** (by reduction, a 70-year old synthesis), but this method is no longer the most popular way of producing "synthetic" menthol.

In view of the above, it is conceivable the "American" pennyroyal oil may slowly disappear entirely from the market.

See also **Pennyroyal Oil "Moroccan",** next monograph.

Pennyroyal Oil, Moroccan.

Pennyroyal, Spanish and Moroccan:

Far more important than "American" pennyroyal oil, is the so-called "European" pennyroyal oil. This oil is steam distilled from the wild growing, freshly harvested, slightly dried herb of **Mentha Pulegium.** Distillation is carried out near the growing areas in the south of Spain, in Morocco and Tunisia, to a lesser degree in Portugal, Italy, Yugoslavia and Turkey. The oil from Moroccan sources is distilled from a different variety of the same plant, but it yields a better oil in respect to **Pulegone**-content. For this reason, it is preferred by the producers of synthetic menthol and related materials.

"European" Pennyroyal Oil is a pale yellow to almost colorless mobile liquid of very fresh, strong, herbaceous-minty, but not very bitter odor (in contrast to the "American" type). The flavor, however, is distinctly bitter, with a slightly cool-minty and strongly herbaceous note. The oil is rarely, if ever, used in flavors. It finds some application in perfumery, e.g. in the reproduction of certain essential oils (geranium, etc.). Furthermore, it is used along with rosemary, lavandin, sage, sassafras, citronella, white camphor and other low-cost oils for industrial perfumes, fragrances for detergents and household products, etc. Its main use has been as a starting material for the production of "synthetic" menthol from **Pulegone** which is present at the rate of up to 96% in the Moroccan pennyroyal oil. Italian, Yugoslavian and Turkish oils contain about 50 to 60% pulegone. Spanish oils are often contaminated at the point of distillation since the wild-growing herb is not picked free from other plants, and because the maturity of the plant material is not uniform.

In the early 1950's, the total production in Spain and Morocco surpassed 100 metric tons, but it has now fallen back to a more modest figure due to lack of interest from the menthol manufacturers.

Peppermint Oil.

One of the largest and most important of all the essential oils is hardly used at all in perfumery. If we add "mint" oil production (see **Mentha Arvensis Oil**) to that of peppermint, the total world production easily surpasses 5,000 metric tons, a fact which almost makes this oil type the third largest (after turpentine and pine oils) and equal to that of citronella and camphor oils. In respect to value, the peppermint + mint oils exceed the two latter oil types by far (see tables in rear of book).

True *peppermint* oil is steam distilled from the partially dried herb of **Mentha Piperita** which is a hybrid from three other species of **Mentha,** all natives of southern Europe. The peppermint plant was brought to the U.S.A. early in the 19th century, and these plants were the foundation of what are today the largest peppermint grwoing centers in the world: first, the northeastern United States, now practically abandoned except for experimental stations, then the midwestern states of Michigan, Indiana, Ohio and Wisconsin, all decreasing their production; the fareastern states of Oregon and Washington are now the main producers of American peppermint oil. The plant is also cultivated in Brazil, Argentina, France, Italy, Morocco, Poland, U.S.S.R., Bulgaria, Holland, Spain, Yugoslavia, Hungary, Germany, England, Rumania, India, Australia and several other countries. The U.S.S.R., Bulgaria, Italy and Morocco are the only countries that produce

either very large quantities or sufficient amounts to make significant exports of the oil.

The production of peppermint oil and all the problems connected with its production are so comprehensively described in literature that the author finds it superfluous to include such details here. It will suffice to say that the plants are all cultivated, and are distilled when fully mature, i.e. in full bloom, at the early blooming rather than at the end of blooming. It is particularly important in the U.S.A. in order to control the content of **Menthofuran,** a characteristic but not highly appreciated ingredient in true peppermint oil. This is a typical *physiological* problem as met with frequently in the production of essential oils. Menthofuran is a derivative of furan with a certain chemical relationship to coumaron.

The essential oil, steam distilled from the rapidly dried herb, is known as "natural peppermint oil". For most flavoring purposes, this oil is "rectified", either by steam distillation or by vacuum distillation. The former method is definitely preferable, provided the distillation is carried out with live steam at atmospheric pressure and under possible fractionation in a column with a minimum of holdup (perforated plate type column). Other commercial oils are labelled "triple rectified" or the like, and may have been further fractionated in order to remove all unpleasantly smelling or tasting fractions, bitter menthone, weedy foreruns, resinous-oily residues, etc.

Natural Peppermint Oil is a pale yellow or pale olive colored liquid of fresh, strong, somewhat grassy-minty odor with a deep balsamic-sweet undertone and a sweet, clean dryout note. The grassy topnote may disappear or fade after proper ageing of the oil (polymerization of the lower aldehydes, etc.). Even the odor gives an impression of coolness, often due to the psychological effect of associating the known flavor with the impression of the odor. Peppermint odor and flavor are well known by practically everybody who brushes his teeth, eats candy, chews gum, uses mouthsprays or gargles, etc. The flavor of the oil appears strong and cooling, but the cooling effect masks some of the delicate, sweet-balsamic undertones of the oil. This is most unfortunate, but it is possible to recall these undertones at certain lower levels of dosage. Below the concentration of one part in 20,000 (or 5,00 mg%), the cooling effect fades away, while the actual *flavor* of the oil remains perceptible at about five to ten times this dilution, strongly dependent upon the medium to be flavored, the sugar concentration, temperature, solvent type, etc. The **Minimum Perceptible** of a good average grade rectified peppermint oil under the experimental circumstances (as outlined under **Flavors** in Part One of this work) is about 0.10 to 0.30 mg%. The coolness is a mouthfeel, a physiological effect, not truly a flavor or an odor. But the coolness is the primary reason for the extensive use of peppermint oil in flavors. Accordingly, the average use level of the oil is usually on the high side of the above figure for minimum perceptible of cooling effect (i.e. higher than 5 mg%). The concentration in certain types of peppermint candy, in chewing gum and in toothpaste is 100 times higher or more (up to 1.00 percent), a fact which gives a good idea of the highly flexible dosage of this oil.

Rectified or "redistilled" peppermint oils are water-white or almost colorless. Their flavor is free from "weedy" topnotes and harsh-resinous or oily residue notes. The oil is more easily soluble in diluted alcohol, and its keeping qualities are superior to those of the natural oil. The loss by rectification amounts to 3 or 4% up to 20%, depending upon the selection of fractions and the type of distillation performed. One advantage of vacuum distillation is that the oil is freed from the water. Even a perfectly clear natural peppermint oil may contain over 1% of water which is harmful to the flavor and chemical composition of the oil, e.g. by hydrolysis or by supporting fungus growth or decay.

Mitcham Peppermint Oil is distilled in England from a **Mentha** species which is a parent of the American peppermints. The English oil, also known as "black Mitcham oil" is known for its unusually high content of menthylesters (gives excellent body and sweetness to the flavor, and indirectly subdues the paralyzing effect of the "cool" menthol), and their modest content of the bitter tasting ketone, **Menthone**. The cool effect of this oil is perceptible only beyond the concentration of 1.00 to 2.00 mg%, while the **Minimum Perceptible** is about 0.10 to 0.30 mg%. The English Mitcham plant has now been introduced into France, Italy, Bulgaria, Argentina and numerous other countries. However, in no country other than England is the typical old-fashioned Mitcham peppermint oil produced. The English production is very small, and does not cover even

part of the United Kingdom consumption, but the Mitcham oil is so expensive that it limits itself to use in high-class candies, etc.

Peppermint Oil is very frequently adulterated outside the U.S.A. The most common adulterant is the essential oil of mentha arvensis (see **Mentha Arvensis Oil**). Modest additions of this oil to true peppermint oil can hardly be detected in chemical analysis, but an organoleptical test by experienced flavorists will usually reveal the fraud. Modern instrumental analysis will, in the hands of expert analysts, offer an efficient tool to provide printed proof of such fraud.

Menthyl acetate prepared from racemic (liquid) menthol, is also used in the adulteration of peppermint oil. Fractions of peppermint oil (foreruns) are used to introduce the positive menthofuran test (see **Mentha Arvensis Oil**); fractions of mentha arvensis oil are used as diluents, and the cruder adulterations include the use of benzyl alcohol, triacetin, nopol, 2-cyclohexyl-cyclohexanone, trimethyl cyclohexanol, etc.

Peppermint Oil is occasionally used in perfumes, e.g. in lavender colognes (lift and freshness), fougères, geranium bases, etc. for its generally "lifting" effects at low concentration. Menthol is used for similar purposes at concentrations of 0.5 up to 2 or 3 percent in certain perfume bases. The peppermint oil has also been used for its cooling effect in certain cosmetics, lipsticks, lipstick perfumes, etc. face creams, shaving creams, hair lotions, etc., but it has greatly been replaced with natural or synthetic menthol for these purposes. In flavors, it is definitely not possible to replace peppermint oil with plain menthol, and there is no indication of peppermint oil losing its popularity as a world-wide accepted everyday flavor material in spite of its comparatively high cost.

Pepper Oil, Black.

The essential oil of black pepper is produced by steam distillation of dried, crushed but not quite ripe fruits of the pepper vine, **Piper Nigrum**. The plant is a native of the damp jungles of southern and southeastern India, possibly also the Indonesian islands known as the Sunda islands. It was cultivated more than 2000 years ago in the same areas, and today, the centers of cultivation are still the Indonesian islands, India, Malaya and Indochina. "Smaller" quantities of the fruit (i.e.

less than 1000 metric tons per year) also come from Madagascar (Nossi-Bé), the Comoro islands and Thailand (Siam). In Madagascar (district of Sambirane in the northwest), in Nossi-Bé and the Comoro islands, smaller quantities of black pepper (and siftings from the cleaned fruits) are steam distilled in local stills. This is one of the very few "on-the-spot" distillations of pepper oil. Little, if any, pepper oil is distilled in the main producing areas of the fruits. The fruits are exported by the tens of thousands of tons to all parts of the world. Although India and Indonesia, China and Japan are large consumers, about 20,000 metric tons are annually shipped to the U.S.A. to cover the American consumption.

Only a very small portion of all the black pepper produced is distilled to yield essential oil. Distillation is undertaken in Europe and the U.S.A., mainly by the specialists in spice oil distillation. The so-called "Lampong" black pepper is generally preferred for distillation. Siftings and unattractive looking black pepper fruits may also be distilled and will yield good oils, provided the siftings are fresh. Thus, the Nossi-Bé oils, distilled "on-the-spot" from siftings, are often very good oils. Two other grades of pepper oil are produced in Nossi-Bé: light and heavy oils. The former consisting of foreruns, the latter of the high-boiling components of pepper oil.

Oil of **Black Pepper** is an almost water-white or pale greenish-gray, mobile liquid which becomes more viscous on ageing. Its odor is fresh, dry-woody, warm-spicy, reminiscent not only of tho odor of dried black pepper, but also of elemi, cubeb and other essential oils of high terpene-sesquiterpene content. The flavor of the oil is surprisingly flat, somewhat dry-woody. At high concentration, the taste is slightly bitter. When more dilute, it presents only a mild spiciness. The essential oil has no pungency at all since the pungent principles of black pepper are not distillable with steam (see **Pepper Oleoresin**, next). The trade distinguishes between at least two types of pepper oil (as mentioned above). The light type presents the typical flavor of freshly crushed pepper (from the grinder, etc.) but it has no tenacity and deteriorates rapidly. The delightfully fresh "top" vanishes after a few months of ageing even under the best storage conditions. The "heavy" type of black pepper oil is inferior in respect to naturalness, but superior in stability

and tenacity. It is this type of pepper oil which is imitated with **Schinus Molle** and similar essential oils.

Oil of **Black Pepper** is used primarily in flavor work as a modifier for other spice flavors where pungency is not wanted or needed. Seasonings, spice sauces and dressings, meat and other canned food are often flavored with black pepper oil and other spice oils. The suggested use level would be about 1.00 to 2.00 mg% with wide limits and variations for the use in various liquid or dry media (thick sauces, vinegars, powder flavors, etc.). The **Minimum Perceptible** is 0.20 to 0.50 mg%. These figures are based upon good grades of European-distilled "total" oils.

In perfumery, the oil gives interesting effects with eugenol and isoeugenol, e.g. in carnation and rose bases, in Oriental fragrances, or in modern, dry-aldehydic bases, ambres, etc. The effect in a rose base is particularly interesting. Although **Phellandrene** is one of the main constituents of the oil, it seems impossible to obtain a similar effect with pure phellandrene (isolated from other essential oils) or with substitutes for black pepper oil.

The oil is often adulterated with phellandrene, pinene, limonene, oil of **Schinus Molle**, atractylis concrète oil, elemi oil, cedrela oil, sesquiterpenes from clove oils, eucalyptus dives oil (particularly the variety "A"), copaiba balsam oil, etc. **Cubeb Oil**, which years ago was a favorite means of adulteration, is no longer used in this way. More often, however, the buyer will just find himself faced with a poor grade of pepper oil. An olfactory and organoleptic test is necessary to evaluate a sample of **Black Pepper Oil**. The latter test can, of course, be left out in the case where the oil will be used for perfumes only. In normal times, the oil is available in almost any quantity required.

Pepper Oleoresin.

Various types of **Oleoresin Black Pepper** are obtained by extraction of the crushed, dried, not fully ripe fruit of **Piper Nigrum** (black pepper) with volatile solvents. The solvent may be a hydrocarbon (petroleum ether), or an oxygenated solvent, e.g. ethyl alcohol, ethyl ether, acetone, etc. These extractions are undertaken in modern installations in Europe and the U.S.A. from imported berries (particularly Malayan pepper).

There are two major characteristics of the oleoresin in comparison with the essential oil:
1) the oleoresin contains two alkaloids, **Piperine** and its stereo-isomer **Chavicine**, which are responsible for the pungency of the spice.
2) the oleoresin does not contain caryophyllene. As are the cases with cloves and cubeb, it seems that caryophyllene is not present in the natural spice, but is formed during steam or water distillation of the crushed spice. The "light" pepper oil (see monograph on **Pepper Oil, Black**) contains little or no caryophyllene because it represents the low-boiling fractions of a total pepper oil. This is one of the reasons for the "naturalness" of the light oil.

Pepper oleoresin is a prepared flavor material. It is usually a very dark green or almost brownish green heterogeneous mass; on standing it separates as a viscous, clear, dark green oil on top of a grainy, black-green, non-pourable mass. The oleoresin must be stirred thoroughly prior to use.

Its odor very closely resembles that of the natural spice, and the flavor has not only the aroma, but also the pungency of the spice itself. Since pungency is a mouthfeel rather than a type of flavor, it is fairly easy to introduce pungency from a source other than black pepper in order to adulterate the latter with a cheaper raw material. Oleoresin of **Capsicum** (see this) is frequently used to increase pungency in black pepper oleoresin and thus to give impression of great strength. Capsicum is, however, almost completely without aroma, and any addition of this material will tend to decrease or impair the pepper aroma. Certain synthetic piperidine derivatives are also used in the adulteration of black pepper oleoresin, but such additions will be detected by the experienced analyst, using specto-photometric determination of the natural and normal concentration of pungent matter in the oleoresin.

Oleoresin Black Pepper is used very extensively in food. Canned food, meat, sausages, salad dressings, pickles, etc. are flavored with the oleoresin which can be standardized according to its flavor performance and rate of pungency, and thus offers a uniform product that is superior to the natural spice in this respect. For food use, it should be kept in mind that the solvent used must be a non-hazardous one since traces of solvent are inevitably left in the oleoresin even after very careful evaporation under vacuum and subsequent "airing" of the extract.

An **Ultrasonic** extract of black pepper is commercially available. Ultrasonic extracts are usually prepared with harmless solvents.

Perilla Oil (from Herb).

An oil which attracted science about a generation ago, is the essential oil steam distilled from the leaves and flowering tops of a Perilla species. It was then claimed that **Perilla Nankinense** was the parent plant, but it seems that the species which is widely cultivated for distillation and also grows wild in Japan (in the Katami region on Hokkaido island) and on the Fareastern mainland, is a variety of **Perilla Frutescens** (according to private communication to the author). Various species are used as culinary herbs in the Oriental household, others yield from their seed a vegetable fatty oil by expression. The expressed **Perilla Seed Oil** is commercially available, and occasionally confuses the customer who orders perilla oil, and soon receives a fatty, drying, nonvolatile liquid that smells of cod liver oil or rancid linseed oil.

The essential oil of **Perilla Frutescens**, *varietas crispa, forma viride* is known in Japan as **Ao-Shiso**. It should be called perilla herb oil commercially in order to avoid confusion.

The oil is a yellowish liquid of very strong and diffusive, fatty-oily-aromatic odor (in fact, with a touch of cod liver oil note!). The odor is so peculiar that it can hardly be compared to any other essential oil except those of similar chemical composition. The author disagrees with statements that the odor of perilla herb oil should be reminiscent of that of cumin oil, but this, of course, is a matter of opinion, subject to endless discussion. However, the principal note in perilla herb oil is actually often encountered in the dryout notes of other essential oils as a faint, but characteristic note. The note is due to an aldehyde, **Dihydro Cuminic Aldehyde**, also called **Perilla Aldehyde**. This aldehyde has been found in another fareastern plant, the Philippine orchid **Sulpitia Orsuami**, the essential oil of which contains about 67% dextro-dihydro cuminic aldehyde and 30% d-limonene. From the wood and roots of a Madagascan tree, **Hernandia Peltata**, comes an essential oil known as **Hazamalanga Oil** which contains from 60 to 90% of this aldehyde. The particular odor of dihydrocuminic aldehyde is the main reason for the perfumer's interest in **Perilla Herb Oil**. The oil can be used in the "construction" of artificial essential oils, e.g. bergamot oil, spearmint oil, etc. and the oil gives highly interesting effects in jasmin, orange flower, ylang-ylang and other floral bases. The tea-like dryout after the oily-fatty topnote is extremely suitable and natural for these compositions. Only minute traces of perilla herb oil are necessary for such effects.

The flavor of **Perilla Herb Oil** is equally strong, warm-spicy, oily, and yet slightly burning. The author can see no immediate use for this oil as such in flavor compositions.

The main constituent, laevo-**Perilla Aldehyde**, is present in the oil at the rate of about 50%. The anti-aldoxim of this aldehyde was known in the 1920's under the name of **Peryllartine**, a sweetening agent which is 2000 times sweeter than cane sugar. However, this sweetening agent has had only scientific interest outside Japan so far (literature: C.F. Walton: International Critical Tables, vol. 1, New York 1926).

The annual production of **Perilla Herb Oil** is at present (1958/59) about 5 to 7 metric tons, all of which is produced in Japan.

Peru Balsam.

Balsam Peru, also called **Peruvian Balsam,** is a true natural resinous balsam according to the definitions in this book (see Part One: **Balsam**). It consists of essential oil and resin, and is thus of the oleo-resin type. The essential oil consists mainly of high-boiling esters of benzoic and cinnamic acids, forming the balsamic part of the natural product.

Peru Balsam is a pathological product which exudes from the trunk of the large Central American tree, **Myroxylon Pereirae**, when the bark is removed sectionwise from the tree. The exudation is collected in a very crude manner, and is only coarsely purified locally by treatment with boiling water. In order to increase the yield of balsam, the native collectors use knives, hatchets or even blowtorches on the bark and the lacerated trunk. The latter sort of treatment may introduce a pronounced "smoky" note in the Peru balsam. Due to the primitive conditions of the purification process, the balsam may acquire a smoky note anaway, namely from the fire over which the water has been boiled with the balsam separating at the bottom.

Practically all of the **Peru Balsam** found in commerce today originates from the Central American state of El Salvador. Peru balsam is a dark brown, viscous but pourable liquid. It is transparent and appears reddish-brown in color when spread in thin layers. The odor is the typical "balsamic" one: rich, sweet, cinnamic-benzoic, soft and very tenacious, showing an increasing vanillin-like note on drying out. Incidentally, the balsam does not truly "dry out" when exposed to the air. If Peru balsam is spilled outside the bottle and not wiped off, the bottle will remain oily, not sticky or stringy. The flavor of the balsam is persistently bitter, warm and biting, not at all as suave or pleasant as its odor.

Peru balsam is almost entirely soluble in perfume alcohol, but only partly soluble in petroleum ether or other hydrocarbons. Chlorinated hydrocarbon solvents (methylene dichloride, trichloro ethylene, etc.) are, however, good solvents for Peru balsam. About two-thirds of the balsam is made up of an "essential" oil (see **Peru Balsam Oil,** next). This is not a true essential oil since it cannot be isolated from the balsam by steam distillation at atmospheric (or higher) pressure. The oil is produced either as an absolute or as a false resinoid (false, since a hydrocarbon is used in the extraction, but no resins are wanted in the extract). More recently, a high-vacuum, dry distillation has been undertaken which can produce a semi-solid "essential oil", directly from the balsam. Molecular distillation produces an **Anhydrol** type product.

Peru Balsam is often used as such in perfumery since the natural resins act as good fixatives. However, the very dark color of the natural product is a disadvantage in many cases. In addition, the insolubility of certain constituents of Peru balsam in other perfume materials presents difficulties. This may cause resins to deposit slowly from the perfume, giving it a poor appearance, or clogging the nozzle of an aerosol can, or making trouble in other ways. In medicinal preparations where Peru balsam is still used extensively for its dermatological (epithel-growth promoting) effects, the recommendation is often made to mix the balsam with equal parts of castor oil prior to incorporating it into the ointment, liniment, etc. This will prevent a separation of resins when the balsam meets sulphur or other active ingredients in the preparation.

Peru balsam blends excellently with cinnamic

alcohol, heliotropine, ionones, isoeugenol, linalool, nitromusks, petitgrain oil, patchouli, sandalwood, ylang-ylang dimethyl phenylethyl carbinol, labdanum products, etc. in floral bases (honeysuckle, tuberose, longoza, etc.), Oriental bases, "powder" type perfumes and numerous types of sweet and heavy perfumes. However, the oil or the resin-free preparations from the balsam find a more extensive use in modern perfumery.

Peru Balsam Oil.

When Peru balsam is steam distilled, it gives a very poor yield of essential oil. This is partly due to the high boiling points of the oil constituents of Peru balsam, partly due to the unfavorable ratio in the binary mixtures of water (steam) and the individual oil-constituents when steam distillation is applied.

Until good and efficient, high-vacuum stills were developed, various so-called Peru balsam oils were available: alcohol extracts, co-distillates, anhydrols, etc. Some of these were water-white, and these products usually diverged considerably from the natural balsam in odor type. An almost "total" oil of Peru balsam is prepared today by several manufacturers who distil the balsam in medium-sized, all-glass vacuum stills at about 2 mm. Hg.-pressure or lower. The heat source may be electrical pads or oil-baths, glycol-baths, etc. The latter type has the advantage of perfect control with the "skin"-temperature which should not exceed 120°C. In order to distil completely at this maximum temperature, it will be necessary to work at pressures below 1 mm. Hg. The main components of Peru balsam oil distil at about 120° to 135° at 2–3 mm. Hg. This distillation temperature demands a "pot" temperature of about 145°C. even when the distillation is carried out with little or no column. At this temperature, dust and other mechanical impurities in the Peru balsam will start charring and decomposing, thus causing an unnatural increase in the "smoky" notes of the distilled oil. A molecular still is in its principle a still without a "pot": the material leaves the heated surface only to move as a vapor over in the condenser and receiver. The balsam can be co-distilled with various odorless solvents which protect the balsam and its oil against superheating. **Anhydrol Balsam Peru** is a molecular distillate of this type.

Peru Balsam Oil is not an essential oil (not entirely volatile in our terms) according to the definitions in Part One of this book. Some of its constituents are solid and a true, total oil of Peru balsam is semi-solid at room temperature. It is a pale yellow or pale amber-colored mass of white crystals in a viscous yellowish colored liquid. The odor is truly balsamic, rich, deep-sweet, slightly spicy and vanillin-sweet. A distinct smoky undertone is natural, but should not be predominant, and may fade away after proper ageing of the oil. The tenacity in odor of this oil is outstanding, making it one of the best fixatives among all essential oils. Its suave odor makes Peru balsam oil a very versatile perfume material which can be incorporated in almost any type of perfume base or perfume at concentrations of from less than one percent up to more than five percent. For delicate floral fragrances such as muguet, lilac, appleblossom, etc., this oil blends excellently with floral as well as with balsamic or spicy notes. With araucaria oil or sandalwood oil it blends to a delightfully sweet "precious wood" type like cabreuva oil. In gardenia, longoza, tuberose and carnation bases or duplications it forms an important part of the long-lasting, sweet undertone with undecanolide, nonanolide, ylang-ylang and other heavy and sweet-floral notes. It imparts depth and natural spicy sweetness to a rose, and warm, balsamic body in ambre or Oriental bases, "powder" type fragrances, etc.

To the author's knowledge, Peru balsam oil has little or no use in flavor work. Its taste is bitter, and it causes at reasonable use level a somewhat burning sensation on the tongue. It might be used in traces in chocolate flavors.

Peru Balsam Oil is usually produced according to demand, and, as mentioned above, there are several quite different types available under various names or trade names. However, very few of the commercially available products are total oils from the crude balsam. Such products are semi-solid at room temperature, and most of the "oils" currently offered are water-white, viscous liquids. This latter type is obviously diluted in some manner. Adulteration with benzyl benzoate, benzyl salicylate, benzyl alcohol, etc. is obvious and tempting, and other high-boiling, low-cost solvents can also be employed in adulteration; vanillin can be added as a fortifier; dibenzyl, ethyl benzoate, ethyl cinnamate, cinnamic alcohol, etc. as blenders and bouquetting materials, etc.

Peru (Balsam) Wood Oil can be obtained by steam distillation of the chopped wood from the tree (Myroxylon Pereirae). Compared to Peru balsam oil, the wood oil is an inferior perfumery material. Those interested in the wood oil should consult Yves-René Naves' publication of his findings in: Helvet. Chim. Acta 31 (1948), pages 408–417.

Petitgrain Bigarade Oil.

"Le bigaradier" is the French term for the "bitter orange tree", the Citrus Aurantium, *subspecies amara*. The tree is cultivated in almost all the mild-temperate, semi-tropical and tropical zones of the world. In the south of France, in Italy, Algeria, Tunisia, Morocco, Spain and West Africa (Guinea), the true bitter orange tree is cultivated, and the leaves and twigs of the tree are distilled with steam to produce the Petitgrain Bigarade Oil. In Brazil, Haiti and the Dominican Republic, the bitter-sour variety of the orange tree is also used, and the leaves are steam-distilled. In Paraguay, only the cultivated bitter-sour variety is used; this oil is described under the monograph Petitgrain Paraguay. In respect to quantity, France is a very small producer, but the quality of the French oil is generally considered superior to all other petitgrain bigarade oils with the possible exception of the Algerian oil which unfortunately has been unavailable or scarce during the past few years. Haiti is the largest producer of petitgrain bigarade oil, but the Haitian oil has a cruder odor than the French oil, partly because of admixture with leaves of the bitter-sour orange tree, partly because of poorer distillation technique.

Petitgrain Bigarade Oil is a pale yellow or amber colored liquid of pleasant, fresh-floral, sweet odor, reminiscent of orange flowers with a slightly woody-herbaceous undertone and very faint, but sweet-floral dryout notes. The "bitter" topnote is possibly an association with the flavor of the oil which is slightly bitter. Bitter—in terms of odor—often refer to a sort of dryness, but it is accompanied by rich and sweet undertones in this oil. The terpenes in the oil are generally held responsible for the characteristic bitterness which in this connection also refers to a certain freshness. The freshness helps to subdue the overwhelming sweetness which would come up from the high content of linalyl acetate in the oil. In other words, one could remove 75% of the components

of petitgrain bigarade oil (the esters, etc.), and the balance of the oil would still smell characteristic of petitgrain (compare lavandin oil, pine needle oil, clove bud oil, etc.).

Petitgrain Bigarade Oil is used in perfumery mainly for its refreshing, sweet-floral notes in citrus colognes, fougères, etc. and very often as a replacement for neroli oil. For this purpose, the Terpeneless Petitgrain Oil (see monograph) is preferable. In flavors, petitgrain bigarade oil finds extensive use—in low concentrations—in fruit and honey flavors or aroma-concentrates where it gives naturalness, bouquet, and rounds off the sharpness of many synthetic components in the flavors. Apricot and peach, apple and pear, banana and pineapple, wine and hop ale bitters and many other flavor types may profit from this interesting natural material.

Petitgrain Bigarade Oil is often adulterated, or, one should say: mislabelled. Redistilled petitgrain Paraguay oils are "doctored up" to simulate the typical notes of true petitgrain bigarade oil. Although it is not yet known as a fact exactly which compound or compounds are responsible for the typical "petitgrain" notes, there are several synthetic chemicals available which to a certain degree can duplicate the "missing links" in a petitgrain bigarade duplication. One of the newest chemicals is Nerone, which is a menthanyl ketone. It is not present in the natural oil, but it does lend a strikingly natural "petitgrain"-like note to compositions in the neroli, petitgrain, orange flower and similar groups.

The annual world production of true Petitgrain Bigarade Oil is less than 10 metric tons.

Petitgrain Bigarade "sur fleurs d'oranger".

Among the better known "co-distillation" products of flowers and oils is the "essential oil" from steam distillation of petitgrain bigarade oil over orange flowers from the same type of tree (bitter orange tree). This product is almost exclusively a specialty of the Grasse houses, but there is no standard in respect to the ratio between petitgrain oil and the amount of orange flowers used in this distillation. A good oil is produced irregularly in Guinea, formerly French West Africa.

The oil should originally be a product from a mixture of leaves, twigs and flowers of the bitter orange tree, but since the trimming of the trees occur in a season when flowers are scarce, this is not very practical. An entirely different type of oil is "composed" by simple mixing of a certain amount of petitgrain bigarade oil with a certain (much smaller) amount of neroli oil. The three methods lead to three different products. The latter is of no interest at all to perfumers. The first mentioned method is the most common in use. The second method—distillation of all three natural parts of the bitter orange tree—yields an interesting distillation water. This water is rich in essential oil, a type of **"Orange Leaf-and-Flower Water Absolute"** which can be extracted by means of a hydrocarbon solvent. This absolute is related to the so-called absolute of "eaux de brouts" (see monograph on **Orange Leaf and Flower Water Absolute.**

The "mixed" essential oil (petitgrain "sur fleurs d'oranger") is a pale yellow liquid of fresh and sweet-floral odor, reminiscent of orange flowers, of terpeneless petitgrain oil, and having a soft, sweet-woody, tenacious undertone. The orange-flowers seem to display themselves particularly in the topnote which attains life and brillance far beyond the effect of an ordinary petitgrain bigarade oil. The roughness of this oil is smoothened out or "rounded-off", and the floral freshness is emphasized, "lifted" to a more elegant level of delicate harmony.

"Petitgrain sur Fleurs" is used in perfumery in the more costly duplications of true neroli oil, in fine citrus colognes, in numerous floral bases, and in light aldehydic perfume types, etc. It blends excellently with all citrus oils, lavender oils, sage clary, rosemary, linalool, hydroxycitronellal, aurantiol, amylcinnamic aldehyde, decanal, anthranilates, labdanum products, oakmoss products, olibanum, etc.

The oil is rarely adulterated directly, but there are countless types and qualities on the market. The evaluation of this product is certainly left to the discretion of the perfumer and his esthetics. One drawback is that it remains very difficult to obtain the same quality of this product from two different suppliers.

Petitgrain Oil, terpeneless.

This oil is prepared from **Petitgrain "Paraguay" Oil** (see following monograph) or, more rarely, from **Petitgrain Bigarade Oil.** The two natural oils do not produce identical terpeneless oils. The deterpenation may be a "topping" of the oil by simple vacuum distillation and removal of only the light, low-boiling and harsh-smelling mono-terpenes, or it may be a total deterpenation by one of the methods described in Part One of this work (see **Terpeneless Oils**).

The most common type is the one obtained from Paraguay petitgrain oil by total vacuum distillation. This yields a practically colorless oil with a loss of about 18 to 35% by weight, calculated upon a good, commercial grade of Paraguay petitgrain oil. Since the production of a deterpenized perfume oil is often a question of esthetics, rather than a question of physical specifications, there are countless types of terpeneless petitgrain oil. The perfumer who selects the fractions to be used in the bulked terpeneless oil from the vacuum distillation, will decide according to his personal experience which of the fractions should be included. This selection is rarely, if ever, done by instrumental specifications and data. The typical "bitter" note of petitgrain should remain perceptible in the deterpenized oil, and it is quite possible that this note is partly due to terpenic compounds. The deterpenized oil will, however, mainly consist of linalyl acetate, methyl anthranilate, linalool, traces of geraniol, nerol, esters of same, etc.

Terpeneless Petitgrain Oil is one of the most indispensible materials in the creation of neroli notes, or in the "creation" or duplication of neroli oils (artificial). For this purpose it is particularly important that the starting material has been a good petitgrain oil, and a bigarade oil is preferable, by far. Ironically enough, in neroli oil it is again the small amounts of certain terpenes which impart the characteristic topnote of this expensive oil. Terpeneless petitgrain oil is furthermore used in citrus colognes, and as a fresh-floral blender in numerous other perfume types. It is an excellent modifier-freshener in Oriental perfume bases, and it is actually used so widely that it would be misleading to point out specific uses of this versatile raw material. It is very stable and offers accordingly an advantage over the natural petitgrain oil. The latter is often used as such in soap, while the terpeneless oil shows inferior power when incorporated in a soap. The greater solubility of the terpeneless oil places it immediately among the useful and versatile materials for alcoholic lotions, aerosols, etc.

Terpeneless Petitgrain Oil finds some application in flavors where it lends sweetness and natural

320

"fond" in peach and apricot, gooseberry, black-currant, etc. and as a modifier in ginger ale flavors, honey-candy flavors, etc.

Petitgrain "Paraguay".

In respect to volume, this is the most important, by far, of all petitgrain oils. The oil is produced in Paraguay and, to a smaller extent, in Haiti. How-ever, only in Paraguay is the oil distilled exclusively from the bitter-sour variety of Citrus Aurantium, *subspecies amara*, the bitter orange tree. This tree grows wild, semiwild and is cultivated on a large scale in the interior of Paraguay. Although there is ample wildgrowing material at hand, distillation is currently carried out almost exclusively with leaves and twigs from cultivated trees of the above variety.

The stills are generally very primitive, and produce a steam-and-water distillation, but there is an increasing number of modern stills in the country. Experiments have shown that modern and rational distillation technique results in better yields of oils with much higher ester content. The better stills (low ratio of steam condensed within the stills) provide for a shorter distillation time, again resulting in reduced hydrolysis of the esters and, subsequently, a higher ester content in the oil produced. A high ester content is not directly synonymous with a particularly good oil since it is generally believed that the "typical petitgrain" notes are due to components other than the esters. However, a high ester content automatically reduces the content of monoterpenes, some of which are unwanted in good petitgrain oils. The annual production of petitgrain oil in Paraguay has fluctuated between 125 and 300 metric tons in the ten-year period up to 1960.

Paraguay Petitgrain Oil (also called Petitgrain, S.A. = South American) is a pale yellow to dark yellow to dark yellow or olive brownish colored, rather mobile liquid of strong, bitter-sweet, woody-floral odor. The topnote is somewhat harsh, but it quickly gives way to a heavy and sweet bodynote of typical petitgrain character: bitter-floral, with a sweet and slightly woody undertone. The dryout, which comes quickly since the odor of this oil is not very tenacious, is sweet and slightly woody-floral, quite delicate. According to the age of the oil, the water content in the oil (or the container).

etc., there are wide variations in the topnote of its odor. Most often, the topnote bears some resemblance to the topnote of crude bois de rose oil, almost nutmeg-like, warm-spicy, but not quite pleasant. The flavor of Paraguay petitgrain oil is bitter, but quite aromatic, bitter-orange peel-like, with a fruity, wine-like undertone. The terpeneless oil is generally preferred for flavors (see mono-graph Petitgrain Oil, Terpeneless).

Petitgrain Paraguay oil is used very extensively in soap perfumery where its great power and versatile application is generally appreciated. It needs solid fixation since the oil itself does not contain natural fixatives to any significant extent. Tolu balsam, labdanum, benzoin, beta-naphthol ethyl ether, methyl betanaphthyl ketone, methyl anthranilate, methyl-N-methyl anthranilate, prop-enyl-methyl anthranilate, aurantiol, isobutyl cin-namate, are common and suitable fixatives, while sage clary, decanal, geraniol, palmarosa oil, citrus oils, clove oils, hydroxycitronellal, amyl cinnamic aldehyde, etc. are excellent blenders or modifiers. Paraguay petitgrain oil is mainly used in the citrus-cologne types of perfume base, but it also lends power and freshness in numerous florals, bouquet perfumes, Oriental blends, etc. Apart from "orange blossom" or neroli types, the oil may be used with jasmin, lilac, lily and similar floral bases as a modifier.

Until a few years ago, the shipments of Paraguay petitgrain oil were far from uniform and often of very poor quality. Not only was the picking of leaf material irrational and careless, but many lots of oil were contaminated or adulterated even before shipping. Lots, exported to Europe were particularly of a very poor grade. Conditions have greatly improved now, and it would be obsolete to mention a minimum ester content of 35/45%. Some oils may have close to 80% esters, but in such cases the linalool content is correspondingly lower (there has been little hydrolysis). Good oils are found mainly in the upper half of the "ester content classes", but not necessarily in direct relation to the ester content. The esters can be removed by fractional distillation, leaving a product ("heads and tails" of the distillation) with a typical petitgrain odor.

The extremely low price of synthetic linalyl ace-tate should remind the evaluating perfumer that this chemical is not the most important odor principle of Paraguay petitgrain oil (compare to similar cases with sage clary oil, lavandin oil, etc.).

Crude petitgrain oils should be properly dried and filtered prior to use in perfume compositions or sale since they arrive from the producing areas in a rather poor condition and often in damaged second-hand iron drums. A water content of several percent is not unusual in a crude oil, and this water is certainly detrimental to the quality of the oil.

Picea Excelsa Oil.

Although a number of widely different oils are offered in Europe under the (translated) name of "fir needle oil", this term should apply only to the oil, distilled from the needles and twigs of **Picea Excelsa** (a pine tree). The tree is known in Scandinavia as **"Red Spruce"** or **"Norway Spruce"**. A related tree, the **Picea Vulgaris** is known as **"White Fir"**. Unfortunately, the distillation of the leaves (needles) of **Picea Excelsa** has not become very popular anywhere. Small quantities of the oil are produced in Tirol (Austria), U.S.S.R., Germany, Yugoslavia and occasionally in France. A similar essential oil is distilled from the **Picea Omorica** in Yugoslavia.

Picea Excelsa Oil is a water-white or pale yellow colored, mobile liquid of very light, fresh, balsamic-pine needle type odor. The dryout is somewhat less sweet, woody, slightly cedarlike. The oil belongs to the group of "low-ester" pine needle oils, and thus has caught less interest among perfumers than have certain other types of pine needle oil (see monograph on **Pine Needle Oil**).

Picea Excelsa Oil is used along with other pine, spruce or so-called "fir" needle oils in air-fresheners, room deodorants, bath-oils, soap perfumes, fougère bases, etc., and as a modifier in colognes, chypres, etc. The oil blends excellently with synthetic materials such as isobornyl acetate, amyl salicylate, coumarin, terpineol, cyclohexanone derivatives, nitromusks, etc. or with naturals such as oakmoss products, labdanum products, lavandin, orange oils, rosemary oil, cedarwood oils, cedarleaf oil, juniperberry oil, etc.

Due to its high content of unstable monoterpenes, the oil should be kept dry, dark and airfree or adequately treated with an antioxidant. The annual production of **Picea Excelsa Oil** is hardly more than 10 metric tons, but the botanical raw material is abundantly at hand.

See also **Fir Needle Oils,** summary.

Pimenta Berry Oil.

Pimenta berry, better known as **"Allspice"**, is a popular household spice, and the layman who is familiar with the odor of all-spice would certainly recognize this odor in pimenta berry oil. The leaf oil, however, would not be identified as "allspice" by the average housewife or cook. This is the same situation as the one we find with clove bud oil versus clove leaf oil or with cinnamon bark oil and cinnamon leaf oil. It is interesting to see that a layman, familiar with a certain product through the frequent use of it, is often better qualified than a perfumer (who may not have been brought up with the true botanical spice in his everyday food or delicacies, etc.) when it comes to discrimination between two closely related essential oils or products.

Pimenta Berry Oil is steam distilled from dried, crushed, fully grown, but unripe fruits of the West Indian tree, **Pimenta Officinalis**. Certain manufacturers insist on water distillation, and and there is reason to believe that this type of distillation yields a superior quality of oil. The tree is a native of the West Indies, and grows wild abundantly on many of the islands, particularly Jamaica. In Guatemala, Venezuela, Honduras and Trinidad, various related species of the tree also grow, and they yield slightly different essential oils. Oils from Jamaican fruits are generally preferred by the flavor houses and most perfume houses.

Distillation takes place on a wide scale in Europe and the U.S.A. from imported berries and in modern stills. There are a few European houses who specialize in this oil and other spice oils, all of which call for a good deal of experience and skill in the field of distillation technique.

Pimenta Berry Oil is a pale yellow liquid with a warm-spicy, sweet odor, presenting a peculiar, but fresh and clean topnote and a long-lasting, sweet, balsamic-spicy bodynote with a tea-like undertone. There is a certain resemblance to clove bud oil in the slightly sour-fresh, fruity topnote. Any dryness in the odor, any lack of sweet freshness and dullness of the dryout, should arouse the suspicion of the evaluator.

The flavor of pimenta berry oil is equally warm, sweet, not burning, slightly peppery, but not dry. The odor of the air over the liquid flavored with pimenta berry oil is initially light and fresh. This is typical of the berry oil. For this reason, the oil is used extensively in fruit flavors of the "heavier" type, e.g. plum, blackcurrant, pineapple, cherry, etc. The main use, however, is in food products such as meat sauces, spice blends for pickles, sausages, etc. The suggested use level would be about 0.50 to 1.50 mg% with wide variations from these figures according to the type of product in which the oil is incorporated (acids, vinegar, sweet sauces, canned food with little juice, etc.). The **Minimum Perceptible** is about 0.25 to 0.50 mg% for a good grade pimenta berry oil. It appears from these figures that the oil is not a very powerful flavor material. Besides, these figures were established as a threshold for the concentration at which pimenta berry oil could still be distinguished from clove bud oil. Upon further dilution, it was no longer possible to distinguish accurately between the two oils.

In perfumery, the role of pimenta berry oil is limited to that of a modifier in the modern "spicy" types of "men's fragrance", fougère, after-shave, etc. and occasionally as a "special note" of warm and sweet-spicy character, e.g. in chypre, Oriental bases, etc. It blends excellently with ginger oil, geranium, geraniol, nerol, neryl acetate, lavender, amyl salicylate, opopanax, labdanum products, isoeugenol, ylang-ylang, methyl cinnamic aldehyde, methyl ionones, patchouli, orris products, etc.

Pimenta Berry Oil is unfortunately very often adulterated with pimenta leaf oil (see monograph), or clove leaf oil, clove stem oil, fractions from the isolation of eugenol, from redistilled eugenol, etc. **Eugenol** is the main constituent of pimenta berry oil. Among the more typical components are methyl eugenol, cineole and phellandrene, all of which are available as partially synthetic or isolated, low-cost materials. Caryophyllene is present in pimenta berry oil, but may not be a constituent of the fruit itself (see **Oleoresin** of **Pimenta Berry**, next monograph). Water-distilled pimenta berry oils contain less caryophyllene than do the steam distilled oils.

Pimenta Berry Oil is produced in quite sizeable amounts, and it is estimated that the total world production exceeds 100 metric tons per year. Exact figures are hard to establish since significant quantities of **Leaf** oil come on the market and are sold by the same houses which sell the fruit (berry) oil.

Pimenta Berry Oleoresin.

The steam distillation of crushed pimenta berries

requires up to 12 hours of operation in order to exhaust the plant material completely. This prolonged exposure to hot steam is not without significant effect upon the chemical composition of the essential oil and other components of the fruits. Under the monograph **Clove Bud Oil**, it was mentioned that this oil contained **Caryophyllene**, a sesquiterpene. Caryophyllene is not present in non-distilled extracts of clove buds. The same can be said about pimenta berries. Since caryophyllene has a distinct dry-woody odor, a rather unpleasant flavor, and tends to depress the odor and flavor of these oils, there are good reasons for avoiding this sesquiterpene. Caryophyllene is present in pimenta berry oil. But when the berries (fruits) are extracted with petroleum ether, benzene or other hydrocarbon solvent, the resulting extract does not contain caryophyllene. Yet, the exhaust material in the extractor is practically odorless.

Pimenta berry oleoresin is a prepared oleoresin. It contains all the essential oil present in the fruits, together with some resinous matter, a bitter tannin derivative (characteristic!), plant colorants (more or less, according to the type of solvent used), a bitter alkaloid and a fatty (fixed) oil which can be eliminated by freezing or by selective solvent extraction (second extraction with slightly diluted alcohol, chilling, filtering and evaporation produces an **Absolute** of pimenta berries). The bitter principles, too, can be removed through the use of selective solvents or chemical treatment. Direct extraction of the crushed berries with diluted alcohol yields a rather dark extract, but leaves out the annoying fatty oil.

Pimenta berry oleoresin (or **Pimenta Berry Absolute**) is usually a dark brown viscous liquid or heterogeneous mass of a grainy paste at the bottom of an oily liquid. In the latter case it should be stirred thoroughly prior to use. In respect to flavor, it is superior to the essential oil by far. The sweetness and naturalness is striking, and the small amounts of resinous matter, etc. give the extract an exceptional tenacity and richness in body. Only very few supply houses offer this product, but a great number of the larger flavor extract consumers prepare their own type of pimenta berry extract according to specific needs for spice blends to the canning industry, etc.

An **Ultrasonic** extract of pimenta berries has been prepared and is available from a well-known Grasse house.

Pimenta Leaf Oil.

The leaves and twiglets of the "allspice" tree (see **Pimenta Berry Oil**) are steam distilled in local stills in the growing regions to yield an essential oil called **Pimenta Leaf Oil**. Distillation takes place in various parts of the West Indies, mainly in Jamaica. Smaller quantities of a slightly different oil are produced in Central America (Honduras and Guatemala) and in Venezuela. The tree grows wild in the West Indies, and leaves can be harvested all year round. The leaves look almost like clove leaves, and the essential oils of the two sorts of leaves are very similar in composition.

Pimenta Leaf Oil is a brownish yellow or pale brownish colored liquid of dry-woody, warm-spicy, aromatic odor, reminiscent of clove leaf oil and crude eugenol. The flavor is warm and aromatic, slightly burning, but also dry and woody, almost sharp or acrid.

The oil is used mainly in perfumery and for the isolation of **Eugenol**, its main constituent. As a perfume material, the oil represents only a modification of the odors of clove leaf oil and cinnamon leaf oil, both of which contain 85-95% eugenol. The warm-spicy eugenol note has become quite popular in fragrances for after-shave, shave cream and other products of the "men's line", etc. However, substantial quantities of pimenta leaf oil are offered on the market under the label "pimenta oil" or even as "pimenta berry oil". It usually requires some experience and a thorough organoleptic test to discriminate accurately between the two oils, particularly since they also occur mixed in all proportions from certain wholesalers. Furthermore, crude eugenol, fractions from the distillation and isolation of eugenol, redistilled or crude clove leaf oil or clove stem oil are all common adulterants in commercial lots of pimenta leaf oil. The tremendous decline in clove leaf oil prices during the late 1950's caused a significant decrease in the West Indian production of pimenta leaf oil. Even the storm and flood disaster in eastern Madagascar in April 1959 did not raise the clove leaf oil price above the level of pimenta leaf oil price. However, the latter has still a good future as a "domestic" source of eugenol for Central and South America, large areas where eugenol-bearing plants are not available in sufficient quantities (see **Ocimum Gratissimum**).

Pimenta leaf oil is a very poor substitute for pimenta berry oil, and any flavorist who is familiar with the aroma of the berry oil would have great difficulty in replacing the berry oil with the leaf oil. The former is well known by his customers, the latter is not, and will hardly be accepted in food flavors.

Pimpinella Absolute.

The roots of **Pimpinella Saxifraga** and **Pimpinella Magna** yield an essential oil which is not commercially available. The plants grow wild in various parts of central Europe and are related to anise, angelica, lovage and many other well-known perfume and flavor plants.

The essential oil is produced occasionally by a few perfume and flavor houses for their own use. The roots are commercially available since they form the raw material of **Pimpinella Tincture**, a well-known pharmaceutical preparation. By gentle evaporation of the tincture, a "resin-absolute" is produced. But since the tincture represents an incomplete extraction, a true absolute of pimpinella root is usually prepared the conventional way:

Comminuted pimpinella root is extracted with petroleum ether (low yield, but light-colored extract) or benzene, acetone or ethyl ether. The latter gives a very low yield of an almost liquid extract (mainly essential oil). The concrète extract is subsequently extracted with alcohol, and the alcohol is removed under mild vacuum.

Pimpinella absolute is a viscous liquid or a sticky, semi-liquid mass of deep orange, yellow-orange or brownish-orange color. Its odor is very peculiar, sweet and extremely tenacious, somewhat spicy, strongly aromatic, herbaceous and woody. The odor and flavor characteristics vary considerably according to the type of solvent used in the first extraction. It is also very difficult to obtain a good pimpinella root material.

Pimpinella absolute (or extract) blends well with labdanum, sage clary, opopanax, benzoin, cinnamic alcohol, nitromusks, isoeugenol, lavender oil, isobutyl cinnamate, rose bases, etc. in heavy Oriental bases, chypres, fantasy fougères, etc. It also finds use, although only rarely, in flavors where its deep-sweet tonalities and great tenacity lend a natural and pleasant bodynote and undertone, rounding off the composition to an attractive and more interesting flavor. Liqueurs and candy flavors are some of the fields where pimpinella extracts occasionally find use beyond the use in pharmaceutical preparations such as throat lozenges, cough drops, gargle concentrates, etc.

Pine Oil.

True **Pine Oil** is obtained by steam distillation of heartwood and stumpwood of **Pinus Palustris** and other **Pinus Species.** The crude oil is then submitted to fractional distillation under vacuum or steam distillation at atmospheric pressure to yield **Pine Oil.** The lighter fractions from this distillation are known as **Wood Turpentine** (see monograph on **Turpentine**). It is customary to extract the wood chips after the steam distillation since the high-boiling and main constituents of **Pine Oil** do not distil readily with steam. A hydrocarbon (a petroleum distillate) is generally used for the extraction of the steam-exhausted wood chips. The hydrocarbon extract is evaporated, and the oil part is submitted to fractionated distillation under vacuum. The residue from this distillation is rosin. All told, true **Pine Oil** comprises less than 2% of all distillable and extractable oil-matter from the wood. The main part is wood turpentine. The trees are felled for lumber, and the wood chips for distillation are obtained only from the waste wood.

Pine Oil is a water-white to pale amber colored, somewhat viscous liquid; it has a sweet, pine-woody, somewhat balsamic-anisic odor with an increasing sweetness in its dryout, followed by a somewhat resinous-bitter undertone according to the type and grade of oil.

Production takes place mainly in the United States of America, particularly in the eastern states from Florida to Maine. Significant amounts of pine oil from related **Pinus** species are produced in China. So-called **Pine Oils** are produced in numerous countries, but these products often consist of fractions or by-products from the terpineol production, starting from alpha-pinene-rich turpentine (European terpineol). These pine oils may present quite similar olfactory, chemical and physical characteristics when compared to the true "natural" pine oil, and their application is frequently that of a replacement for "natural" pine oil.

Pine Oil is used extensively in medicine (in veterinary disinfectant sprays), in paint manufac-

turing (anti-skinning agent), in insecticides as a solvent-carrier, in disinfectant detergents of the American "Lestoil" type (solvent-cleanser), in the mining industry for flotation, in perfumes for soaps and detergents (pine fragrances, low-cost perfumes with citronella oils, ocotea pretiosa oil, lavandin, etc.), as a starting material for the isolation of natural terpineol (in the U.S.A.), estragole, etc. for the production of "synthetic" anethole, etc., etc.

In perfumery, **Pine Oil** blends well with rosemary, cedarwood, cedarleaf, ocotea, citronella, bois de rose, ho leaf oil, camphene, isobornyl acetate, coumarin, oakmoss products, cyclohexane-derivatives, etc.

The main constituents of pine oil are sesquiterpene alcohols (terpineol in particular), ketones, ethers such as estragole, fenchone, fenchyl alcohol, borneol, terpineol, etc. all in smaller amounts but of considerable importance to the odor and disinfectant properties of the oil.

Strictly speaking, the oil is almost terpeneless and it is accordingly soluble in alcohol without turbidity.

The annual production of **Pine Oil** runs into several thousand metric tons in the U.S.A. alone. The figure is close to 100,000 tons if we include all types of pine oils and related products derived from the distillations and extractions of the wood chips from the **Pinus Palustris** and other **Pinus** species. One of the largest outlets for pine oil is in the paper industry where the oil is used in the manufacture of coated paper. The perfume industry absorbs only a few percent of the total production. The appearance and success of the "Lestoil" type household cleansers in the U.S.A. have recently made pine oil an almost "hard-to-get" article. In many uses, however, "synthetic" pine oil can justly replace the natural oil.

Pinus Leucodermis.

The essential oils from the needles of **Pinus Leucodermis** and **Pinus Bor,** are both produced in Yugoslavia and occasionally exported. These oils are, however, mainly of local interest, and they do not present any substantial interest or effect which cannot be obtained by means of the well-known, commercially available pine needle oils, etc. Numerous other similar pine needle oils are produced in various countries on a small scale for

50: A branch with leaves, flowers and tiny, immature fruits of **Schinus Molle**, North-African and Central-American so-called "pepper tree". Morocco, 1960.
(Fot. S. Arctander)

51: Flowering top of American **Spearmint** at harvest time in Michigan, U.S.A. Leaves, stem and flowers contain essential oil.

(Fot. S. Arctander, 1958)

local use as replacements for the European and North American pine needle oils.

See also **Pinus Nigra.**

Pinus Nigra Oil.

The tree **Pinus Nigra** grows abundantly in certain areas of Austria and Yugoslavia. In Austria, it serves mainly for the production of turpentine, while in Yugoslavia, the essential oil from the needles (leaves) is distilled by steam.

The oil is apparently not produced elsewhere; it does not present any unusual odor characteristics, nor does it possess other advantages as a perfume material over the commercially available pine needle oils. Accordingly, the oil is of little or no interest to perfumers outside its country of origin.

Pinus Nigra Oil is a colorless to pale yellow, mobile liquid of pleasant, balsamic-pinelike, refreshing odor. The turpentine-notes (pinene-notes) are, however, rather dominating, and the odor has no tenacity or even faint, pleasant dryout note. The oil could find use in low-cost pine fragrances for household products, bath salts or bath oils, etc. but being a low-ester oil, it has only a thin body and little masking power.

The annual production of **Pinus Nigra Oil** is probably less than 5 metric tons, but could be increased significantly to meet stronger demand.

Pinus Pumilio Oil.

This oil is also known as **Pinus Montana Oil.**

Although belonging to the group of "low-ester" pine needle oils, pinus pumilio oil deserves a good deal of attention since its unique odor is due to trace amounts of substances which apparently are absent in ordinary "pine needle oils". It is generally believed that the characteristic odor of pinus pumilio oil is due to traces of lower aliphatic aldehydes (hexyl-, octyl-, etc.) and perhaps certain cyclic aldehydes.

The oil is steam distilled from the leaves and twigs of **Pinus Pumilio**, also called **Pinus Montana** or **Pinus Mugo**. It is one of many different types of conifer which bears the popular name "mountain pine". The tree grows extensively in central Europe, particularly in Austria (Tirol), Yugoslavia, northern Italy and the Balkans. Tirol (Austria) is the most important producer. It is estimated that between 15 and 30 metric tons of this oil is produced annually, all in Europe. Production in

Denmark covered this country's consumption for a number of years. Distillation in Jutland (Denmark) is irregular, but has reached several tons per year. The oil was used in pine needle bath oil.

Pinus Pumilio Oil is water white (when fairly fresh), and has a very pleasant pine-type odor: balsamic-sweet, faintly woody, also slightly spicy, reminiscent of cypress and juniperberry, with an increasingly oily-fatty, but interesting undertone of great tenacity. The oil is used in perfumery mainly in combination with other pine needle oils, isobornyl acetate, cedarwood oils or derivatives, lavandin oil, rosemary oil, sage oil, aliphatic aldehydes, cananga oil, labdanum products, etc. for room spray perfumes, bath preparations, Christmas fragrances, "leather" type bases, etc.

Pinus Pumilio Oil is frequently adulterated. Pinene, pine oil, pine oil fractions, eucalyptus foreruns, cheaper pine needle oils, camphene, limonene, etc. are among the most common adulterants. The scarcity of the oil outside Europe has greatly encouraged the "cutting" and plain adulteration of commercial lots of this oil.

Pinus Strobus Oil.

"*Canadian white pine needle oil*":

The midwestern **"Weymouth Pine"** grows extensively in the state of Wisconsin, U.S.A., and toward the east into northern New York state. Although the production of essential oil from this pine is practically abandoned, it will be mentioned briefly here since distillation of other pine needle oils take place in the above areas (see: **Spruce Oil**, or **Tsuga Canadensis**).

It serves no purpose to quote any data of this oil since it is no longer a commercially available item. It is quite possible, however, that the needles of pinus strobus are distilled with various species of the so-called hemlock-spruce group (see monograph on **Spruce Oil**). Any significant addition of pinus strobus needles to the spruce material would tend to lower the ester content in the spruce oil significantly.

Pinus Sylvestris Oil.

The **"Forest Pine"** or **"Norway Pine"** (so called in Scandinavia), or **"Scotch Pine"** (in England), the **Pinus Sylvestris** is widely grown all over Europe. This tree also grows in the Baltic states, in the U.S.S.R., central Europe, southern Europe, etc. Distillation is carried out in Austria (Tirol),

U.S.S.R., Sweden (on a small scale, in one distillery and mainly for local pharmaceutical use), in Denmark (irregularly) and in Yugoslavia. In Germany and Scandinavia, it has been customary to produce an aqueous extract from the needles of this tree, for use in bath preparations. As a by-product from this extraction, some essential oil is obtained which is insoluble in the aqueous, very dark brown, viscous extract. On the other hand, the exhaust twigs and needles from the steam distillation of the essential oil can be extracted with water. This is usually done by simple draining of the pot since the "pot water" is a liquid aqueous extract of oil-free needles and twigs. The extract is evaporated to "soft extract" consistency.

The characteristics of **Pinus Sylvestris Oil** vary considerably according to the place of origin (production). The oil is subject to very frequent adulteration, and the label "Oil of **Pinus Sylvestris**" (or **Silvestris**) may be found on the poorest mixtures of camphene, pinene, isobornyl acetate and a few other chemicals and isolates. The true oil is practically colorless, mobile and with a strong, turpentine-type, balsamic pine odor. Its dryout is quick and uninteresting. As a matter of fact, there is rarely any odor left on a blotter after 24 hours or even less. Its characteristic, fresh topnote and the peculiar sweetness in this topnote are the main features of the oil. Apart from that, the oil of **Pinus Sylvestris** does not offer any outstanding or unusual effect in perfumery. Its use is confined to room fresheners (sprays), disinfectants, insecticides, soaps and detergents, vaporizer liquids, etc. Accordingly, it is conceivable that the oil will slowly disappear from the essential oil market. The particularly high quality of the pinus sylvestris oil from Tirol (Austria) cannot compensate for the fact that there is not enough good oil available. There is, on the other hand, an abundance of very poor or coarsely adulterated oils which ruin the reputation of true pinus sylvestris oil. The particular use of this oil calls for such tremendous amounts that one, five or ten metric tons annually may not even satisfy one consumer.

Piper Crassipes.

Among numerous "false cubebs", the fruits of **Piper Crassipes** are probably the best known. And since they occur so frequently in commercial lots of cubeb that they are often distilled with true cubeb, or even distilled *as* true cubeb by unexperienced distillers, a few words should be spent on this adulteration, contamination or confusion.

The selection of true cubebs from so-called "false" cubebs demands considerable experience, and the interested reader should consult special pharmacognostical or botanical works on this subject. The amateur distiller will often find his own method of discriminating true from false fruits, and the author knows of distillers who rely exclusively upon the yield of essential oil by steam distillation. If the yield is better than 9%, the distiller will use the fruits for distillation of "true" cubeb oil (see monograph). This method is obviously unreliable since there are cubebs which yield 16 or 18% essential oil. Such material could be mixed with poor material of false fruits, yielding an average of e.g. 11% essential oil. A thorough study of the general appearance of the botanical material is necessary to ensure a true starting material.

The fruits (berries) of **Piper Crassipes** are generally smaller than true cubebs, and when crushed between the fingers or in a mortar, they emit a sweet, cineole-type odor, in contrast to the spicy-warm, aromatic-woody odor of true cubebs. The color of **Piper Crassipes** fruits is grayish, while true cubebs are brown or reddish-brown in color (when comparatively fresh).

Oil of **Piper Crassipes** is a greenish-yellow, somewhat viscous liquid of faint, but fresh-medicinal odor, slightly reminiscent of niaouli oil and with a dryout of a clove-terpene type odor or cedrela odorata type odor.

Oil of **Piper Crassipes** has no application in perfumery and is not produced regularly on a commercial scale. To the author's knowledge, the oil is without interest to the flavor industry, apart from the above.

Piper Longum.

Of little or no interest as a perfume material, but still occurring frequently as a flavoring agent, is the so-called "**Long Pepper**". It is the fruit of a climbing shrub, a vine closely related to the black pepper plant, and growing wild and cultivated in Indonesia, Ceylon, India and the Philippines. The dried fruit, a conelike cluster of tiny berries, is used as a spice locally and abroad.

It is still a common household spice in Europe where it forms part of the "mixed spices" for the home preparation of pickles, etc.

The essential oil of **Piper Longum** is prepared by steam distillation of the crushed fruits. The yield is rather small, and the oil is substantially different from that of true black pepper. The main and characteristic difference being the complete absence of "light" or fresh-peppery topnotes in the oil of long pepper. The odor of the latter is somewhat reminiscent of the odor of various "false" cubeb oils: warm and faintly aromatic, somewhat woody and cineole-lemon-like.

The fruits of long pepper and the extracts of same have a spicy-pungent flavor. The pungent principle does not seem to be present in the essential oil. Accordingly, it is not conceivable that the oil of **Long Pepper** will have any importance in the flavor industry. Most likely, extracts, e. g. an oleoresin-type, would be of some interest in the compounding of spicy flavor blends for table sauces, seasonings, canned food products, pickles, etc.

To the author's knowledge, the oil of **Long Pepper** is not produced regularly on a commercial scale. The spice is, however, still a common article in Europe and Asia.

It is conceivable that the fresh-aromatic topnotes do exist in the freshly harvested, dried fruits, but there are no distillation facilities in the growing areas. The very large surface of the clusters of long pepper fruits will expose the delicate components of the essential oil to detrimental influence of air during long transportation to users in Europe and elsewhere.

Pluchea Sagittalis.

This plant occurs in Brazil, but the essential oil is not produced in that country at present. According to private communication to the author, the essential oil of **Pluchea Sagittalis** is produced in Argentina on an experimental scale. The author has no personal experience with the use of this oil, and since there is only one potential producer so far, it would be premature to give a general description of "commercial lots" of **Pluchea Sagittalis Oil.**

Plumeria Acutifolia.

One of the most beautiful trees and shrubs of the tropical and semi-tropical zones is the **Frangipanni,** a name given to several species of **Plumeria.** They belong to the genus of Apocynaceae, among which we find very few perfume plants but a number of decorative plants, e. g. the **Nerium Oleander** which grows wild in abundance all over the temperate zones of the world. A botanical cousin, **Acocanthera Abyssinica** was used until very recently by the natives of central East Africa for poison darts and arrows.

In India, the most common **Plumeria** is the **Acutifolia** which is not quite as fragrant as the **Alba** or the **Rubra** (see **Plumeria Rubra,** next monograph). The flowers are about $2\frac{1}{2}$ cms. in diameter, and form an umbel-like cluster at the terminal branches. The five petals are fan-shaped or propeller-shaped, and they open over a period of several weeks, a fact which makes the tree interesting as a decorative plant. Their delightful fragrance is somewhat reminiscent of orange flower, honeysuckle and gardenia, although not strictly indolic of character.

Surprisingly enough, there is no regular production of perfume oil from these flowers. More than 50 years ago, extractions were undertaken on a small and experimental scale. This was at the great perfumery period of Charles Garnier, (although he was not responsible for the extraction of frangipanni).

Further experiments are, however, now being carried out in India of the flowers of **Plumeria Acutifolia,** and in China on the flowers of other species (see following monograph). It is possible that petroleum ether extracts (concrètes) and absolutes may become available in the near future. If so, the **Plumeria Absolute** would undoubtedly find application in fine perfumery along with the absolutes of jasmin, tuberose, orangeflower, ylang-ylang, etc. for sweet-floral, rich and natural notes, in neroli-modifications, fantasy bouquets, Oriental florals, etc. In India, experiments with oil-infusions of the flowers have been carried out. Oil-infusions of various flowers are often used as such in East Indian cosmetic preparations.

Plumeria Rubra.

See also **Plumeria Acutifolia** (previous monograph).

The pink **Frangipanni,** and the white variety **Plumeria Alba** are still more common in the tropical countries all over the world than is their cousin, **Plumeria Acutifolia.**

These trees are often used as decorative plants around official buildings, in private gardens, parks, etc. and they can be seen all over Africa, particularly along the east coast, in Central Africa, along the northern west coast, on most of the tropical islands, all over the West Indies (which may be the origin of the plumerias) and in the South Pacific islands, etc.

The white variety is probably the most common. Its flowers are creamy white, with a fine shading towards the yellowish-orange in the center of the five petals. They emit such a powerful fragrance that one cannot have cut branches with flowers overnight in one's room. Like so many other fragrant tropical flowers, they exhale more fragrance at night than at daytime. The odor is reminiscent of neroli and gardenia, tremendously sweet, yet fresh and suave, but tenacious beyond measure.

In China, the **Plumeria Rubra** has lately been treated with volatile solvents to yield a concrète from the flowers. An absolute is produced from the concrète by alcohol washing. The absolute finds use in finer perfumery as a powerful and versatile floral ingredient for honeysuckle, gardenia, tuberose, lilac, muguet, etc. or in various fantasy-bouquets, heavy-Oriental florals, etc.

The absolute of **Plumeria Rubra** is, however, not yet regularly available to the outside world. If the perfumers find interest in this material, it may very likely be produced in a number of other areas, closer to the big consumers and become more regularly available. Until then, the "**Frangipanni**" perfume must remain a fantasy type with little, if any, relationship to the fragrance of the beautiful and delightfully scented **Plumeria** flowers.

Poplar Bud Oil.

"**Balsam Poplar**" *leaf-bud oil*:

The "balsam poplar" tree, **Populus Balsamifera** (and other **Populus** species) is a native of the northern states of the western and midwestern U.S.A. and of Canada. The tree was introduced in Europe about 200 years ago, and is found growing wild in various countries in central Europe.

Before the leaves open in the spring, they are protected by a hood which is, as in the case of fir and spruce, very resinous (water-proof and airtight) and sticky. The poplar buds themselves are also resinous, and contain a balsamic-resinous substance which can be extracted by means of a hydrocarbon solvent. This produces an oleoresin (occasionally called "concrète"). The oleoresin can be steam distilled to yield an essential oil. Most often, an alcohol-extract of the oleo-resin is produced, or a concentrated tincture prepared directly with alcohol from the leafbuds is used. The essential oil is not commercially available, but the leafbuds are, and so are various extracts from this material.

Balsam Poplar Oleoresin is a viscous, dark brown or dark amber colored liquid of very sweet balsamic coumarinic-cinnamic odor, with a peculiar undertone reminiscent of labdanum extracts. There is a distinct note in alcoholic extracts, reminding one of hop absolute or valerian, but the overall odor is strongly balsamic.

A pale yellow oil has been obtained by molecular co-distillation of the extract with ethylene glycol or similar solvents.

Balsam Poplar Oleoresin and its derivatives are used very rarely in perfumery for their balsamic sweet notes and good fixative effect. They blend well with new mown hay materials, with sandalwood and patchouli, hydroxycitronellal, terpineol and linalool in floral compositions, and in pine fragrances with cypress, pinus pumilio, juniperberry oil, isobornyl acetate, labdanum, lavandin, etc.

The author has been unable to find any connection between the American nickname (American-Indian) "tacmahac" for this balsam or for the tree—and the same name for a Madagascan tree (presumably a **Canarium** species) whose hard, resinous balsam also has a coumarinic-balsamic odor. The two trees are not botanically related.

Porophyllum Lineare.

This plant grows wild in Argentina and Brazil. It is distilled occasionally in Argentina where the essential oil finds some use in local perfumery, while in Brazil the oil is used for medicinal purposes. The production of this essential oil is irregular and very small. According to private communication to the author, it is not likely that the oil will find a market outside the two countries. The author has no personal experience with the use of **Porophyllum Lineare Oil** in perfumery.

Pterocarpus Oils.
See also Sandalwood Oil.

It should be mentioned briefly in this work that the so-called "red sandalwood" is derived from the small tree **Pterocarpus Santalinus** (mainly in India) and that the wood is not fragrant. It does not yield an essential oil upon steam distillation, and it is not used in perfumery or flavor creation. The powdered wood is used as a red colorant in food products, particularly in canned food and spice mixtures, sauces, etc.

Among the countless sorts of so-called "rosewood" for furniture, etc. is also the **"African Rosewood"** from the West African tree, **Pterocarpus Erinaceus**. This wood is faintly fragrant, but it is not used for the distillation of perfume oil to the author's knowledge. See monograph on **Bois de Rose Oil**.

The author has seen a great number of **Pterocarpus** species, many of which have fragrant wood in Madagascar, in East Africa (Tanganyika), and along the West African coast to the savannas of Senegal. The French botanical expert, R.-L. Joly, has reported on a number of these interesting African trees in French perfumery literature during the past two decades.

R

Rapeseed Oil.

Rapeseed from the cultivated plant **Brassica Napus** are used in the industrial, large-scale production of fatty (fixed) vegetable oils, similar to mustard seed oil (expressed), linseed oil, etc. The press-cakes are used as cattle feed, but since many of the above mentioned types of seed contain essential oils which can be harmful to the cattle, the oil is usually removed by steam distillation of the press-cake. In the case of **Rapeseed** it is necessary to introduce an enzyme in order to decompose the "precursor" of the essential oil (a glycosidic substance). The enzyme is obtained from white mustard seed (see monograph on **Mustard Oil**). After steam distillation and extraction of the distillation waters with petroleum ether, an essential oil is obtained: volatile **Rapeseed Oil**.

The oil is almost colorless, mobile and of very pungent, lachrymatory odor and effect upon the mucous membranes. The odor is somewhat reminiscent of horseradish (see monograph).

Rapeseed Oil (volatile) is considered toxic, but the lethal dose has not been published in connection with this statement. It is conceivable however, that the oil is sufficiently harmful as to justify its deletion without hesitation from the list of flavor materials. From a flavor point of view, the oil would not present any outstanding or very useful effects anyway. It should be kept in mind that the term **Rapeseed Oil** may cover two entirely different products: the fatty (fixed), edible oil, and the poisonous, volatile (essential) oil.

Reseda Absolute.

This very rare perfume material is prepared from several varieties of **Reseda Odorata**, a plant of Middle Eastern origin, known since antiquity and cultivated for its potential therapeutic value. The plant is known as an ornamental annual under the name of **Mignonette**. The flowers in particular (but also the entire overground parts of the plant) have long attracted the interest of perfume oil manufacturers. The plant was introduced in France several hundred years ago, and is still cultivated there on a modest scale. **Reseda Odorata** is also cultivated as an annual in northern Europe, but can grow to become a shrub in the south (e. g. in North Africa).

The **Reseda Absolute** is obtained via the concrète which is prepared by petroleum ether extraction of the flowers. These will inevitably include various amounts of foliage from the top of the plant, contributing significantly to the peculiar green note in the odor complex of the absolute. The absolute is prepared by alcohol washing of the concrète. The yield of absolute is about 0.06% calculated upon the weight of dried flower material. Obviously, this absolute is expensive. Today, the annual production of **Reseda Flower Absolute** can be measured in grammes, rather than kilos. It hardly exceeds 5 kilos in France which is the main producer.

Reseda Flower Absolute is a very dark, orange or olive-brown colored viscous liquid which solidifies to a paste slightly below room temperature. The odor is intensely herbaceous-green, with a sweet, watercress-like undertone, and not at all sharp. A peculiar sweetness, reminiscent of roasted chicory-root and with a spicy mellowness, forms the tenacious body, upon which the green note rests.

The author has no experience with reseda flower absolute of recent production. He is inclined to assume that his most recent samples are not exclusively genuine extracts of the flowers of **Reseda Odorata**. It is quite possible, however, that the true absolute still exists, and is used in a few French perfumes where the effect is no doubt extremely important. Its application is somewhat similar to that of violet leaf absolute. The latter material is used as an adulterant in reseda flower absolute along with basil oil, estragon oil, narcissus absolute and various synthetic perfume materials.

Reseda Root has been distilled, and it yields an essential oil of extremely pungent, lachrymatory effect, reminiscent of horseradish oil. Reseda root oil has only academical interest, and it finds no place in perfumery or flavor work.

Rhodium Wood Oil.

Although this oil is hardly available in its original form any more, it deserves some attention since it was once a popular ingredient in colognes, etc. of the 1890's.

Rhodium Wood Oil is distilled from the roots of **Convolvulus Scoparius**, a plant which probably originated in the Mediterranean countries, but now is found most abundantly in the Canary islands and also scattered around in Morocco. Wood from the Canary islands is distilled by steam in France, but very often, the oil sold under the name of **Rhodium Wood Oil** is a "compounded" oil, containing no distillate from rhodium root at all.

This fact, and the one that the oil offers no particular perfume notes which cannot be obtained by other means, are mainly responsible for the disappearance of rhodium wood oil from the perfumery market. Oils offered today under the name of true rhodium wood oils are generally pale yellow to yellow viscous liquids of faint, but pleasant, sweet-woody, somewhat floral odor, reminiscent of nerol, nerolidol, rhodinol and linalool. The author must admit with much regret that he has had no means of confirming the authenticity of the samples which were investigated. However, they represent a fair choice of what is available today under the name of **Rhodium Wood Oil**. The oil could still find some use in

perfumery where its sweet and tenacious notes blend well with all rose materials, lilac, muguet, Oriental bases, etc.

In pharmaceutical preparations, a "rhodium wood oil" is occasionally used which is prepared from 95% copaiba oil and 5% palmarosa oil. This mixture is sold as a rat lure.

Robinia Pseudacacia.

A small tree, a native of the United States of America, was utilized by the early settlers for its solid wood from which were made railway ties, stagecoaches, parts of ships, furniture, etc.

The tree, **Robinia Pseudacacia**, also known as **"False Acacia"**, carries beautiful clusters of creamy white flowers, but it was primarily its useful wood that led the immigrants to send seed and cuttings of the tree back to Europe several hundred years ago. Early in the twentieth century, the very fragrant flowers were ectraxted experimentally in various countries in central Europe. It has been claimed that the absolute is produced at present in Bulgaria. The author has been unable to confirm this (private communication).

For inexplicable reasons, the concrète (or the absolute from concrète) of **Robinia Pseudacacia** has not yet succeeded in catching the interest of creative perfumers. The tree is very common all over the northeastern U.S.A., all over Europe and parts of Asia, etc. The flowers are abundant, and the tree grows even in poor soil. The yield of concrète by petroleum ether extraction is not unusually small, and the product is intensely fragrant and has an individual character.

The odor of **Robinia Pseudacacia** absolute is somewhat reminiscent of the absolutes of mimosa or cassie, but it has an orange flower sharpness, and a sweeter, spicier dryout than the two mentioned materials. The author has based this description upon the study of experimental batches as he was unable to obtain a commercial product.

The outstanding tenacity and highly versatile character of the odor of this perfume material should make it an interesting item for almost all types of floral, floral-aldehydic and Oriental-floral perfume types, particularly lilac, jasmin variations, lily, appleblossom, rose variations, etc. **Robinia Pseudacacia** absolute blends well with ylang-ylang, jasmin, orange flower absolute, mimosa, cassie, sage clary, petitgrain, bois de rose, Peru balsam oil, styrax products, olibanum, labdanum, hydroxycitronellal, isoeugenol, cassione, heliotropine, nitromusks, cyclamal, amyl salicylate, etc.

The author would predict a good future in perfumery for a true absolute of robinia pseudacacia if it were made regularly available in reasonable quantities.

Rose Absolute, Centifolia.

"Rose de mai absolute":

One of the most extensively used of all the floral absolutes is the one obtained from the concrète of **Rosa Centifolia** flowers (see **Rose Concrète, Centifolia**). The processing of concrète into absolute is carried out in Morocco and France, to a small extent also in Italy and China. The yield of alcohol soluble absolute from centifolia concrète is usually better than that from rosa damascena, up to 67% in certain cases.

Rose de Mai Absolute is an orange yellow to orange-brown viscous liquid, which has a rich and sweet, deep-rosy, very tenacious odor. The spicy tonalities are usually less pronounced, while the honeylike notes can be described as similar to those of the damascena absolute. When duly diluted, the flavor is pleasant, delicate, slightly balsamic-sweet with a faint woody-bitter undertone. The flavor effect is unusual in its diffusive power, and this absolute can "round off" and simultaneously "lift" many dull or harsh-synthetic flavor compositions. The suggested use level in flavors is 0.10 to 0.40 mg% (based upon concentration in the end product), and the **Minimum Perceptible** is 0.05 to 0.15 mg%. The presence of large amounts of phenylethyl alcohol in the absolute is responsible for the comparatively high figure for the minimum perceptible. The phenylethyl alcohol is water-soluble and acts as a co-solvent for other flavor principles in the absolute. The more components that go in true solution in the water, the weaker is the apparent flavor. The absolute finds some use in tobacco flavoring, but its main use is that of a flavor "bouquetting" material in countless fruit flavors, etc.

Rose de mai absolute is used very extensively in high-priced and medium-priced perfumes, particularly in floral bases, chypres, Oriental bases, etc., and also generally as a "touch" to round off the sharp corners or rough notes in synthetic compositions. It blends well with jasmin, cassie, mimosa, orange flower and other florals, as well as with most of the synthetic perfume materials

such as geraniol, citronellol, dimethyl octanol, nerol, phenylethyl alcohol, eugenol, nonanol, linalool, phenylethyl propionate, isobutyl phenylacetate, etc. or with modifying essential oils such as bergamot, sage clary, geranium, sandalwood, guaiacwood, patchouli oil, etc.

Its excellent tenacity and soft radiation makes it comparatively economical in use. At less than half the price of the Bulgarian rosa damascena absolute, the centifolia absolute has become increasingly popular as a perfume material in countless bases for use in cosmetics, etc. The conventional perfume for a cold cream or a cleansing cream has long been a rose type, and in face powder perfumes, centifolia absolute also finds wide application.

The rapid growth and expansion of the Moroccan rose cultivation shows that this material is about to become one of the most important perfume raw materials of present times.

Rose de Mai Absolute is frequently adulterated. Small amounts of ethyl alcohol are tolerated, but over 2–3% should not be present. Phenylethyl alcohol is the main constituent, and the amount of this can be increased cautiously so that the nose may not detect it. Instrumental analysis will reveal this fraud. Rhodinol (from geranium oil) is added as another "diluent", costus oil as a "bouquetting" material, clove bud absolute, palmarosa oil fractions, Peru balsam oil, synthetic laevo-citronellol, etc. are among the common additives most of which will be detected during a thorough olfactory examination of the rose de mai absolute sample.

See **Rose Concrète, Centifolia** for production figures, etc.

Rose Absolute, Damascena.

The alcohol soluble extract of the concrète from Bulgarian rose flowers has only recently been produced on a commercial scale in Bulgaria. Previously, the Bulgarian producers had insisted upon making only the essential oil (see **Rose "Otto"**) and the concrète (see **Rose Concrète, Damascena**). A few French and overseas houses, however, have agreements with the Bulgarian producers who will process certain amounts of the Bulgarian concrète to an absolute according to specifications from these customers. Other large perfume houses who use considerable amounts of rose absolute will often buy rose concrète directly from the producer and make their own absolute extract. The yield of alcohol soluble absolute from a petroleum ether concrète extract of Bulgarian rose flowers is slightly better than 50%.

The absolute is also produced in France by the suppliers of perfume raw materials, experienced in the production of flower absolutes. Unknown but smaller quantities of rose absolute are produced in the U.S.S.R. and Turkey from Rosa Damascena Concrète. In China, production is still on an experimental scale.

Rose absolute is an orange-yellow, orange-reddish or slightly olive-yellowish colored, viscous liquid of extremely rich, warm, spicy-floral and very deep rose odor with a more or less pronounced honeylike undertone. Its diffusive power is only realized when the absolute is diluted or used at the concentration of a few percent or even less in a perfume base.

Bulgarian Rose Absolute is used so extensively in high-class perfumes that it is hardly possible to define its field of application. Apart from strictly rosy florals, it forms important parts of the conventional rose-jasmin complex which is found in countless fashion perfumes today. It is used in cassie modifications, carnation bases, chypres, Oriental bases, modern fantasy bouquets, etc. Its unusual radiation compensates for its high cost to a certain degree, so that it can be used in medium priced perfumes as well. The "spent" waxes from the extraction of absolute from concrète usually have a faint odor of rose flowers. These waxes are commercially available and find some application in soap perfumery, but they also present a certain threat to the buyers of rose concrète. Spent waxes are not infrequently added to rose concrète, and it will be necessary to run a test on the yield of absolute from a sample of rose concrète in order to safeguard oneself against this risk.

In flavors, this exquisite material offers interesting effects and bouquet in trace amounts, e.g. in apricot, strawberry, raspberry, bitter almond, apple, etc. Its flavor is somewhat sharp at high concentration, but becomes soft and warm, sweet-balsamic and slightly spicy upon extreme dilution. The suggested use level is just above the Minimum Perceptible which is 0.04 to 0.10 mg%. Due to the high content of phenylethyl alcohol (water soluble) the rose absolute is not a very powerful flavor material.

Bulgarian Rose Absolute is not infrequently adulterated with the absolute from rosa centifolia (see previous monograph), known as "rose de mai absolute". Diluents such as phenylethyl alcohol, ethyl alcohol, rhodinol from geranium oil, diethyl phthalate, etc. are not uncommon in this very expensive perfume material. The major part of the Bulgarian concrète is processed into rose absolute, and the annual production of Bulgarian rose absolute can be estimated at more than 300 kilos. The production is steadily increasing.

See also monograph on Rose Absolute, Centifolia.

Rose Concrète, Centifolia.

Known as "rose de mai concrète", this material is obtained by volatile solvent extraction of the fresh flowers of Rosa Centifolia. The plant is cultivated for perfume oil production in Morocco, France, Italy, Tunisia, Yugoslavia, China, etc. Morocco is by far the largest producer of centifolia rose concrète today. Moroccan production of this material is estimated to exceed 2000 kilos per year. At the time of the author's last visit to Morocco (June 1960) he could confirm that *one* of the larger producers of rose concrète and distilled rose oil had just completed the processing of 1000 metric tons of rose flowers from the 1960-crop. This amount of flowers would yield about 2400 to 2500 kilos of concrète if it were all extracted for that purpose. A certain amount of rose flowers are distilled to yield Moroccan rose oil (see Rose Oil, Moroccan). Extraction is usually carried out with highly refined petroleum ether which leaves little or no perceptible odor in the finished extract (concrète). Mainly due to the good yield from centifolia flowers, partly due to the old and well-established reputation of the Bulgarian damascena concrète, the former is much less expensive than the Bulgarian concrète.

Rosa Centifolia Concrète is a dark yellow or orange-yellow to olive-greenish or brownish-yellow colored, waxy mass which melts at about 45 to 52°C. Its odor is warm, deep-floral, slightly woody-sweet, but the spicy or honeylike notes are less pronounced than those of damascena concrète. Centifolia concrète is used mainly for further processing into absolute (see monograph: Rose Absolute, Centifolia). However, in certain high-class soap perfumes, the Moroccan rose concrète can be used with very interesting results and unusual effect. In cosmetic preparations, where poor solubility in alcohol is of little importance, the concrète finds some application, e.g. in cold cream perfumes, lipstick perfumes, powder perfumes, rouges, bath oils, etc. The concrète will lend a natural body and depth, an inimitable richness to such perfumes, so that the comparatively high cost of rose de mai concrète is easily compensated (present cost, about U.S. $ 200.- to 350.- per kilo in 1960).

A special application of rose concrète (Moroccan) and certain other concrètes is that of perfuming the "solid perfume waxes" which are sold in fancy little containers of wood, china or the like, in eggshape, jarshape or figurines, etc. It is also useful in the perfuming of printed matter (advertising matter, wrappings, postcards, etc.); the rose concrète can be used directly in an unctuous mass with other perfume materials, binders, etc. for a printing paste on the blank paper before the second printing with inscriptions, etc. This is one place where the "spent" waxes from extraction of rose concrète with alcohol (absolute production) is very useful. Unfortunately, the "spent waxes" are frequently used to "cut" good rose concrètes. A test-run on the content of alcohol-soluble matter in the sample of concrète will reveal such fraud.

Rose Concrète, Damascena.

"Bulgarian rose concrète" is produced by petroleum ether extraction of the flowers of **Rosa Damascena**. Extraction on a commercial scale is carried out only in Bulgaria and in Turkey (Isparta region). The plant is cultivated for distillation of rose oil in many countries, see **Rose "Otto"**. The flowers are picked early in the morning when they contain a maximum of perfume. The petroleum ether must be of highest purity so that it will not leave perceptible amounts of unpleasant notes in the evaporated extract (the concrète). Until very recently, the concrète was not further processed in Bulgaria to an absolute. It was sold as such to the consumers all over the world. Small quantities of damascena rose concrète are produced in India, the U.S.S.R. and China. The Moroccan rose concrète (see **Rose Concrète, Centifolia**) is generally considered to resemble the centifolia and not the damascena, although the so-called Moroccan rose may have arrived in northwest Africa as a variety of rosa damascena many

hundreds of years ago (presumably around A.D. 700).

Rose Damascena Concrète is a solid, waxy, orange-yellow or slightly olive-greenish-orange colored mass whose odor is extremely rich, deep and sweetly floral, truly reminiscent of the red or pink rose. A peculiar sweet spiciness on a sweet-woody undertone and an immensely deep-floral and faintly honeylike bodynote are some of the characteristics of this exquisite perfume material. It is occasionally used as is, but more often, it is further processed by the customer or by a perfume house experienced in such preparations, particularly in Grasse, France. The Bulgarian rose absolute is prepared in Bulgaria or in France. The production of concrète is a comparatively new industry in Bulgaria, but the annual production has grown rapidly and is presently (1959/60) estimated at more than 700 kilos.

Rose Concrète comes almost exclusively from one source in original tins with the producer's seal. In that shape, adulteration may be considered almost out of the question. However, unoriginal lots of rose concrète are not infrequently adulterated, e.g. with exhaust waxes ("spent waxes") from the extraction of absolute from concrète. Other adulterants or diluents are: odorless waxes, myristic acid, diethyl phthalate, phenylethyl alcohol, rhodinol, rose de mai concrète, mimosa concrète, guaiacwood oil, etc. It takes more than an average perfumer's nose and experience to discover a skilfully adulterated rose concrète and justly reject it. But with a reliable standard at hand, a few simple apparatus for assaying the content of alcohol-soluble portion (an its odor), an experience with the effect of the above mentioned adulterants, etc. the perfumer should have little difficulty in selecting true and good rose concrète from adulterated and poor products.

Rose Leaf Absolute.

It is not surprising that such a product does exist. As a matter of fact, it is surprising that it was not produced much earlier. When creating (or "constructing") a rose perfume or a rose base, the perfumer is often very interested in notes that will give him the reproduction of the leaves, the fragrance of the foliage which forms such an important part of the rose gamut; the bouquet of roses is not complete without it.

Various chemicals are used, but a good and

true-to-nature product exists in **Rose Leaf Absolute**. It is prepared from a volatile solvent extracted concrète. The concrète is produced by extraction of the leaves of **Rosa Centifolia** in the south of France. Various solvents have been used and experimentally tried, but it seems that chlorinated hydrocarbons (trichloro ethylene or dichloro methane) are the most suitable solvents for extraction of the almost fresh rose leaves. The absolute is obtained by the conventional alcohol washing of the concrète.

Rose Leaf Absolute is a semi-liquid mass of dark green color and intensely "green-leafy", but also sweet, somewhat woody odor, truly reminiscent of the freshly crushed leaves of the rose plant. The absolute is often "bouquetted" with trace amounts of rose de mai absolute, rhodinol, etc. This is merely a "selling note" which has little or no effect in the perfume where the leaf absolute is incorporated.

If it were not such a scarce and very irregularly produced perfume material, the **Rose Leaf Absolute** would undoubtedly catch the interest of all perfumers who work with high-class lotion perfumes, etc. Apart from its application in the type of true-to-nature rose bases, this material would easily find other applications, e.g. that of the introduction of a natural foliage note in lily of the valley where the rose forms a very important part of the floral complex ("muguet"). Or, in numerous fantasy perfumes, chypres, etc., where the rose leaf absolute would blend well with ionones, oakmoss, lavender, mimosa, cassie, narcissus, sage clary, coumarin, linalool, cyclamal, etc.

As mentioned above, **Rose Leaf Absolute** is not regularly available, but it could be produced on a large scale since the botanical material is abundantly present and the extraction facilities are near by.

Rosemary Oils.

The Mediterranean countries are the homes of numerous plants of the family Labiatae, among which are many perfume plants. **Rosemary Oil** is steam distilled (usually by direct steam) from the flowers, leaves and twigs (the twigs are included in Spanish distillations only) of wild-growing **Rosmarinus Officinalis** which is found in numerous forms and subvarieties. The plant grows wild in abundance in Spain, France, Corsica, Italy, Sardinia, Yugoslavia, the U.S.S.R., Turkey, the Middle East, Libya, Tunisia, Algeria, Morocco, etc., and it has even been found in East Africa (Somali and Tanganyika).

Distillation is performed mainly in Spain, Tunisia, Yugoslavia, France, and Morocco. Spain supplies by far the bulk of all rosemary oils, but the quality of Spanish oils varies from the very best to the very poorest of all rosemary oils. One or two Spanish distillers specialize in the so-called "rosemary flower oil" which is distilled exclusively from flower material at full inflorescence. Tunisian oil is very uniform and of high quality. Only flowers and leaves are distilled in Tunisia; the twigs are never included in the distillation. The Tunisian production is in the hands of two large essential oil distillers who are experienced in the field and well equipped to distil or supervise field distillations. At the time of the author's last visit there (1956), Tunis produced about 35 metric tons of rosemary oil per year.

Yugoslavian oils, distilled from flowers and leaves only, are not quite as outstanding as they were in the years between the two wars. French oils are generally of excellent quality, superior to most other rosemary oils, or at least equal to the select material from Spain or Tunis; in fact, many "French" rosemary oils are merely select oils from Tunis or Spain. The total world production of rosemary oils is considerably over 100 metric tons per year.

Rosemary Oil is a pale yellow or almost colorless, mobile liquid of strong, fresh, woody-herbaceous, somewhat minty-forestlike odor. The "high" fresh notes vanish quickly, yielding to a clean, woody-balsamic bodynote which tones out in a dry-herbaceous, but very pleasant and tenacious, bitter-sweet note. There is considerable difference in the odor of the various types of rosemary oil. The above description is based upon average commercial lots of Tunisian oils and select lots of Spanish oils.

Unfortunately, about 60 to 80% of the Spanish production is of a much lower grade. The only advantage in this fact is that the buyer of small and medium-sized amounts can cover his demand with the highest grade of Spanish oil. Certain distillers in Spain even take the trouble of picking the flowering tops of the stalks exclusively ("flower oil", see above), and, upon distillation, this yields a very fine, delicate perfume oil, excellent for use in colognes, lavender waters, etc. Characteristic of poorer oils is the pronounced camphoraceous-cineolic note which is different from the herbaceous: it is coarser, less delicate, less pleasant. These oils usually display a dryout note reminiscent of eucalyptus-residues (oily-resinous-rancid), sweeter and less woody than the note from good oils.

Apart from a very high amount of monoterpenes, rosemary oil contains a significant amount of **Borneol**, a crystalline terpene alcohol, but this is also the main oxygenated component of the oil. Rosemary oil is, accordingly, not very soluble in diluted alcohol (below 80%), but it finds extensive use in perfumery for citrus colognes, lavender waters, fougères, pine needle fragrances, Oriental perfumes (it blends excellently with olibanum and spice oils!), in room-deodorants, household sprays, insecticides, disinfectants, etc. As a low-boiling and fresh-smelling oil it has good effect as a masking agent, particularly for phenolic or tarlike odors. Rosemary oil blends well with lavandin, lavender, citronella oils, origanum or thyme, pine needle oils, coumarin, labdanum, olibanum, elemi, terpinyl propionate, isobornyl propionate, cedarwood oils and derivatives, methyl ionones, petitgrain oil, nitromusks, etc. Occasionally a so-called terpeneless rosemary oil is preferred for colognes and lotions. Terpeneless rosemary oil would be four to five times concentrated if truly deterpenized, but it is customary to "top off" 50% or slightly more in order to produce an oil of greater tenacity and better solubility in diluted alcohol. A select Spanish "flower oil" is an excellent starting material for the production of a good concentrated or deterpenized rosemary oil. The resulting oil is particularly suitable for use in combination with olibanum and cinnamon bark oil, etc. This combination can produce extremely delightful and interesting effects in the line of "Oriental-woody" fragrances for aldehydic and modern "dry" perfumes, ambre-fantasy perfumes, etc.

Rosemary Oil is occasionally adulterated with **Camphor Oil, White** (see monograph) or with head fractions from the rectification of Spanish eucalyptus oil; furthermore, with turpentine fractions, fractions from the production of synthetic terpineol, light cedarwood fractions, etc. In Yugoslavia, contamination has occurred with oil from the plant **Salvia Lavandulaefolia** which in Spain is known as **Spanish Sage** (see monograph **Sage, Spanish**). This oil contains large amounts

of cineole ("eucalyptol"). The plant grows wild in Yugoslavia, but it is not the parent plant of Yugoslavian sage oil (see **Sage Oil, Dalmatian**).

Rose Oil, Moroccan.

The Moroccan rose, presumably a local variety of **Rosa Centifolia**, produces a wealth of flowers and is excellent for the extraction of perfume by solvent (see **Rose Concrète, Centifolia**). The yield of essential oil by steam or water + steam distillation is, however, rather small, and the oil has not attained much popularity among the perfumers until very recently. The production methods have been greatly improved, and it takes time for a "new" material to gain a firm foothold on the perfumer's shelf. The material is regularly available at about half the cost of the Bulgarian **"Rose Otto"**.

Moroccan rose oil is a pale yellow or almost colorless liquid, with a deep-sweet, rich and tenacious floral rose-odor. The peculiar "spicy" undertone found in Bulgarian oil seems to be missing or slightly weaker in the Moroccan oil. The warmth is equal to that of the Bulgarian oil. Overall, the performance of the Moroccan oil shows only a slight deficiency in power, richness and piquancy compared to that of the Bulgarian oil. But the present quality of Moroccan rose oil is a vast improvement over the oil which was occasionally produced in Morocco 20 or more years ago. The Arabs and Berbers of Morocco have known to distil roses and produce rose water since the earliest days of Arab settlement in that country (about A.D. 700). French perfume houses have invested fortunes, experience and skill in the development of this industry which may one day become the world's center of rose oil and rose extract production.

Moroccan rose oil finds increasing areas of application in perfumery where its delightful fragrance adds life, depth, warm notes and naturalness to countless floral and non-floral perfumes, in addition to its use in rose and related bases. In flavors, it is used as a "rounder-off" and bouquetting material, e.g. in tobacco flavoring. It g.ves excellent and delightful undertones in plum and raspberry flavors, etc.

The oil is occasionally exposed to adulteration, although this is rare since the oil is generally sold directly from the producing areas in the southeastern Morocco. The Moroccan rose oil, in turn, has served as a "cutting agent" for the Bulgarian "Rose Otto" (see this monograph under which the Turkish "Anatolian rose" is mentioned).

Rose "Otto".

The so-called "otto of rose" is the essential oil, steam distilled from the flowers of **Rosa Damascena**. In Bulgaria, water distillation is also carried out, but all stills are of comparatively modern design. The rose flowers are distilled quickly after harvesting, and the distillation demands considerable experience. It is common practise to redistil the distillation waters (cohobation process), and to bulk the oils from the two distillations. The yield of cohobation oil is several times higher than that from the first (direct) distillation of the flowering material. The phenylethyl alcohol in "otto of rose" is derived almost exclusively from the cohobation water. It has been claimed that certain buyers were able to procure the first (direct) oil separately. The author has been unable to confirm this rumour. It has also been suggested that the rose flowers should be distilled not with plain water, but with water saturated with phenylethylalcohol (solubility about 1.6 percent in water at room temperature). This should result in the first (or "direct") oil being truly representative of the oil actually present in the flowers. The method remains in the research stage. The yield of oil would obviously increase significantly. The essential oil of **Rosa Damascena** is produced mainly in Bulgaria, but the U.S.S.R., Turkey (the Isparta region), Syria, India and China also produce this oil. The Turkish oil is steam distilled and is known as **"Anatolian Rose Oil"**. Only Bulgaria and Turkey export quantities of any significance. The total world production is fluctuating between 1200 and 2500 kilos per year, equivalent to a value of between 2 and 5 million dollars (U.S.). Considering all products from the rose flower, and considering the fact that these products come from comparatively small areas of the world, the rose oils and extracts are among the most important of all natural perfume materials, and they represent a significant part of the agricultural economy for the countries in question (see tables in the last pages of this book).

Bulgarian "otto of rose" is a pale yellow or slightly olive-yellow liquid which separates white or colorless blades of crystals (the so-called *stearopten*) at temperatures below 21°C. When further cooled, the oil may solidify to a translucent mass, the crystals growing from the surface due to their lower specific gravity. The odorless stearopten amounts to 16 to 22% of the rose oil. The liquid portion is known as the *elaeopten*.

The odor of Bulgarian rose oil is warm, deep-floral, slightly spicy and immensely rich, truly reminiscent of red roses, often with nuances in the spicy and honeylike notes. The taste is slightly bitter at high concentration, biting-sharp, but becomes very pleasant in extreme dilutions. The suggested use level (for bouquetting effect in flavors) is about 0.02 to 0.05 mg%, and the **Minimum Perceptible** is 0.01 to 0.02 mg%. A well-known recent work on essential oils gives the value of 4.00 mg% (one part in 25,000) for minimum perceptible in *unsweetened* water. The author believes that this incredibly high figure must refer to odor perception and not to flavor. But even so, the author observed a perceptible *odor* of Bulgarian rose oil in water at concentrations below 0.05 mg%. A phenylethyl alcohol-free rose oil would obviously show much lower figures.

Bulgarian rose oil is used so extensively that its high cost is almost the only limitation on its use in perfumery. Even traces, fractions of one percent of this oil in many types of perfume bases, can do wonders when correctly used. Carnation is one example of this. Rose oil blends well with many other florals, and jasmin is one of its most frequent companions.

In flavor work, the oil is primarily used in tobacco flavoring and in a number of fruit flavors, e.g. apricot, peach, raspberry, strawberry, plum, etc., where traces of the oil impart a bouquet and a "rounding-off" effect, difficult to obtain with any other material. The wide popularity of the rose flower also greatly contributes to the fact that the oil can be used in trace amounts in unusual places where its presence will merely introduce a non-descript, but "familiar" and therefore pleasant undertone and naturalness.

Obviously, this material has been exposed to adulteration ever since it first appeared on the market. The old-fashioned methods of adulteration have been slowly replaced by clever and artistic "sophistication", etc., but the experienced perfumer with the odor gamut of the genuine Bulgarian rose oil printed in his mind will rarely be fooled. However, additions of a few percent of ethylalcohol, diethyl phthalate, rhodinol from geranium oil, phenylethyl alcohol, etc. are often only detected by means of instrumental analysis. And even a few percent of solvent in a $ 2000-per-kilo-material is an adulteration of substantial economical interest for any "middle-man".

Rue Oil.

Rue Oil is steam distilled from freshly harvested, blooming or fruit-bearing, wild growing plants of Ruta Montana, cultivated plants of Ruta Grave-olens, or other species of Ruta. The plants are natives of the Mediterranean countries, and they grow wild in Spain, Morocco, Corsica, Sardinia and Algeria. Cultivation also takes place in France and Spain, to a small degree in Italy and Yugoslavia. Spain is the largest producer of rue oil, but Algerian oil has been preferred by many perfume houses until it recently became almost unobtainable. A part of all Algerian rue oil is derived from a rue species which yields a substantially different rue oil (the so-called winter rue which does not solidify at temperatures above 0°C.). Occasionally, one can find Spanish oils of this same type.

Rue Oil is a yellow to orange-yellow material, liquid at room temperature, but solid at lower temperature; it usually solidifies at about 10°C. (see above). Its odor is sharp-herbaceous, distinctly fruity-orange-like, with a characteristic bitter-acrid undertone that makes the overall impression an unpleasant one. The flavor is equally sharp-acrid, burning. Rue oil has been used in certain types of flavor, e.g. coconut, to reproduce the peculiar fatty-fruity note in these flavor types. For most people, however, rue oil is harmful to the mucous membranes and will often irritate the skin. On account of certain haemorrhage-producing effects of the oil when taken internally, the sale of rue oil is controlled in a number of countries. For these reasons, backed up by the results of physiological and pharmacological tests, *rue oil should never be used in perfumery or flavor work*. The main constituent of the oil, Methyl Nonyl Ketone (in the so-called "summer rue" oil) is held responsible for the skin-irritating effect, while Methyl Umbelliferone and an alkaloid in the herb are supposed to be toxic. The two latter materials are not readily distillable with steam, but may be present in the essential oil in trace amounts. The ketone has long served as a convenient starting material for the production of Methyl Nonyl Acetaldehyde, a highly appreciated

perfume chemical. The ketone is now produced synthetically, but it is interesting to note that many commercial lots of methyl nonyl acetaldehyde contain as much as 10 or 15% of the above (unreacted) ketone. The latter is responsible for the fruity-orange-like note which is a typical part of the "conventional" description of the odor of methyl nonyl acetaldehyde. This odor description —like many others—will need revision when purer lots of "MNA" become more common on the market.

In view of the above, rue oil may slowly vanish from the perfume and flavor market, although it may maintain its importance as a source of natural methyl nonyl ketone for some time.

Rum.

Rum is included in the monographs of this work as a representative of a group of "aromatic" alcohols which are suitable for use in flavors. Rum is mainly produced as a potable spirit and sold from the factories in various strengths with respect to alcohol content. The lowest alcohol content is 43% (by volume) and this type of rum is often used "as is" in drinks. The highest alcohol content in West Indian or Reunion rums is about 73% by volume. This type is suitable for flavor work. The production of rum has been described comprehensively in works, dealing specifically with potable spirits. Rum originated in the West Indies which is still the most important area of production. Being a by-product of the sugar production from sugar cane, rum is produced in all the sugar-cane growing areas of the world. Australia, South Africa, Réunion, Central America, the U.S.A., etc. are among the more important producers outside the West Indies. The method of production varies considerably from one area to the other, and not all countries produce a truly natural rum. Artificial or natural flavors may be added after ageing of the distilled alcohol in oak vats, but Jamaican and Réunion rums are true distillates with no artificial additions. Their flavor is due to minute amounts of essential oil which is present in the hydro-alcoholic distillate. Rum also contains significant amounts of ethyl- and amyl esters, etc. but these have only an indirect effect upon the flavor of rum ("lifting" effect).

Rum of 72/73% alcohol strength is an excellent menstruum for the extraction of certain natural flavor materials. Freshly roasted cocoa beans can be extracted with rum in place of pure ethyl alcohol to produce a delightfully aromatic cocoa-extract, which, after rectification, yields a colorless, highly aromatic and well-balanced flavor base for cocoa-liqueur flavors, ice-cream flavors, dessert flavors, etc. Coffee beans (also roasted) may be extracted in a similar way. **Sherry Wine** contains only about 20% alcohol by volume, but it can be redistilled gently in an all-glass still to produce a 60%-alcohol distillate which is an excellent menstruum for extraction of cocoa, coffee, vanilla, etc.

The use of rum and sherry in flavor work is thus a secondary one, but the effect is inimitable and valuable. The **Minimum Perceptible** of pure Jamaica rum (72.5% alcohol by volume) is about 200 mg%, and the suggested use level is 200 to 500 mg%. These figures apply to the use of rum in flavors as a "fond", an undertone ingredient, not as a potable spirit (in which state some people drink it straight!). Rum has a perceptible effect in ice cream flavors of the rum, vanilla or coffee type at the concentration of 500 mg%. This concentration is well on the safe side—even for children. It is equivalent to 0.36 grams of pure ethyl alcohol per 100 grams of ice cream. Beer is ten times stronger.

The so-called **"Rum Ether"** or **"Rum Oil, Artificial"** are ill-defined commercial products with little similarity to the flavor of natural rum from fermented sugar cane residues. A very strange and complicated formula for the production of artificial rum ether is still used in Europe and the U.S.A. According to the prescription, a mixture of ethyl alcohol, pyroligneous acid, acetic acid, propionic acid, furfural, fusel oil, diacetyl or acetyl methyl carbinol, St. John's bread, potato starch, manganese peroxide and concentrated sulfuric acid is set aside for digestion in 24 hours. A quicker reaction is started after 1 hour of refluxing (about 90°C.) and subsequently 24 hours of digestion. A certain amount of distillate is then collected under gentle distillation of the reaction mixture. The distillate is sometimes used for a second reaction with similar ingredients (see above), digestion and distillation. The distillate is washed and dried with anhydrous sodium sulfate. Thus produced, the "rum ether" is alcohol- and oil-soluble. It is used as an intensifier in rum flavors for candy, ice-cream, etc. and occasionally in "bay rum" perfumes as a topnote for the bay oil. Vanilla tincture, castoreum tincture, maraniol,

ethyl vanillin, anisyl alcohol, ethyl undecylenate, ambrette seed tincture, pineapple flavor concentrate, etc. may be added for proper fixation and modification of this artificial rum flavor. Very little is known about the identity of the flavor principles in natural rum.

S

Saffron.

The freshly picked botanical material (saffron) is virtually odorless. Steam distillation of the dried botanical material yields extremely little essential oil (see below). However, the **Saffron Oil** has been known for more than a century, presumably because of the interest in the botanical material since time immemorial.

The plant, **Crocus Sativus**, originated in western Asia, Asia Minor and countries of the eastern Mediterranean area. The plant is the autumn flowering cousin of the well known (spring flowering) garden crocus. Most saffron comes from Spain and Turkey, smaller quantities from Greece, Persia, India and the U.S.S.R. **Saffron** is the dried ends (tops) of the three-branched stylus in the flower. When dry, this material presents a most peculiar, intensely sweet, spicy, floral-aldehydic odor with a slightly fatty-herbaceous undertone. The dried botanical material is used in Asia as a condiment in food, and in Asia and Europe it finds use as a coloring agent (textile dye), producing a magnificent and unique orange-yellow color.

The odor is partly due to the presence of an aldehyde, **Safranal** (2,6,6-trimethyl-cyclohexadien-4,6-al-(1). This aldehyde will appear in the botanical material only after decomposition of a glycoside, a so-called precursor to the aldehyde. The glycoside is odorless, hence the absence of odor in the freshly picked material.

Saffron Oil is not commercially available. A tincture of saffron is usually produced by the consumer according to his needs. By petroleum ether extraction of saffron and subsequent decomposition of the glycosidic extract with lukewarm water, the aldehyde is liberated. An essential oil *can* be produced directly from the saffron by water distillation in carbon dioxide atmosphere.

The oil is pale yellow, mobile and possesses a fresh, strong odor, recalling that of the botanical material. However, the essential oil is extremely unstable. It is advantageous to prepare a concentrated tincture from saffron with diluted alcohol under gentle heating (infusion-tincture). A 20% tincture will serve most perfumery and flavor purposes since the penetrative strength of this material is easily underestimated. Minute additions to violet perfumes, narcissus or even neroli bases can produce quite beautiful results, unobtainable by other means.

In flavors, **Saffron Tincture** is a useful and interesting additive to essences for carbonated beverages where it lends a solid, natural body and blends well with other naturals such as hop, ginger, bitter and sweet orange, etc. Interesting effects are obtained with saffron tincture in apple essences, wine flavors, apricot, plum, cherry, etc.

Saffron, as such, is one of the most expensive botanical raw materials, the cost of an average quality being about US $ 90.– to $ 150.– per kilo.

Sage (Clary) Absolute.

Clary Sage Absolute is produced from **Clary Sage Concrète**. The concrète is produced from the clary sage plant (see monograph on **Sage Clary Oil**) by extraction with petroleum ether. As a rule, either flowering tops or tops whose flowers have withered and produced seed are used for extraction. Leaves and stalks are avoided if possible. This may be part of the reason for the six to eight times higher yield by extraction than by steam distillation. Another reason is that non-volatile odorous and non-odorous matter is extracted but cannot be steam distilled. Significant quantities of sage clary concrète are now produced in Morocco from locally cultivated plant material. Smaller quantities are produced in the south of France, but the author is not aware of any production of the concrète in the U.S.S.R. although that country is the world's leading producer of clary sage oil (steam distilled).

Clary Sage Concrète is a solid mass of green to pale olive-green color and an extremely rich, delicately sweet, yet bitter-winy and somewhat herbaceous odor of great tenacity. Th slightly bitter undertone is utilized with good results in ambre perfume bases, while the rich and sweet body blends extremely well with citrus colognes, lavender fougères, chypres, etc. The concrète is occasionally used as such in high grade soap perfumes, etc., where high fixative power is imperative.

Although poorly soluble in alcohol, the concrète is clearly miscible with most perfume materials, and it finds increasing use in modern perfumery, e.g. for aldehydic perfumes, fougère bases, chypres, colognes, after-shave lotion perfumes, ambre bases, etc.

Through the usual alcohol washing method, the concrète may be processed into an absolute. About 50% of the concrète is alcohol-soluble matter. **Clary Sage Absolute** is also green, solid or paste-like, and may separate crystals on prolonged storage under uneven temperature conditions. The crystals are presumably **Sclareol,** a solid, odorless, non-distillable terpenealcohol which contributes strongly to the fixative effect of the extracted products from clary sage. It is technically possible to produce **Clary Sage Concrète** at about half the price of the essential oil. Concequently, the absolute can be produced at almost the same price as the steam distilled essential oil.

The odor of the absolute closely resembles that of the concrète, but there is a perceptible difference in the intensity of the odor of the two materials. The absolute has a somewhat finer, less resinous odor, more balsamic-sweet than the odor of the concrète. **Clary Sage Absolute** is an extremely interesting perfume material and, since the yield is three to four times the yield of essential oil by steam distillation, the absolute can be produced at a very attractive price, and the demand for this material increases steadily.

Clary Sage Absolute is an excellent modifier, fixative and natural "body" for colognes, lavender-fougères, chypres, ambre bases, conifer fragrances, forest notes and even floral notes like muguet and jasmin. It blends well with ionones, methyl eugenol, cedarwood derivatives, nitromusks, labdanum products, citrus oils, lavender and lavandin, phenylethyl alcohol and numerous other common perfume materials.

The annual production of **Clary Sage Concrète** is limited to less than one metric ton (1960) and the material comes mainly from Morocco. Smaller quantities are produced in France and Italy. Most of the concrète is processed further to the **Absolute,** but increasing amounts of **Concrète** are now used as such in soap perfumery, etc.

Sage (Clary) Oil.

Known under the French name of "essence sauge sclarée", **Clary Sage Oil** is steam distilled from the flowering tops and foliage of **Salvia Sclarea**, a tall perennial plant, often cultivated in gardens or occasionally growing semiwild sporadically in the neighborhood of previous cultures of the plant.

Salvia Sclarea originates in countries bordering the Mediterranean sea, but is now cultivated in central Europe, the U.S.S.R., England, Morocco and the U.S.A. In the southernmost parts of the U.S.S.R., Crimea and Kaukasia, the plant is cultivated and the oil distilled on a very large scale. Production of the essential oil in this area exceeds 100 metric tons per year. Part of this quantity is used domestically in Russia, but considerable quantities are exported to France, the U.S.A. and the Far East. During the late 1950's, the Russian oil has dominated the world market and made distillation of clary sage oil in France, Italy and England economically unattractive. The creative perfumer can enjoy a price decrease from about 375/– sh. per kilo in 1955 to about 220/– in 1960. The French and English oils, and, more recently, the Moroccan oils enjoy a reputation of fineness and delicate notes, superior to those of the Russian oil. Morocco, France, Italy, Germany, Hungary, Rumania, Yugoslavia and, lately, the far-western states of Oregon and Washington in the U.S.A. are producing modest quantities of clary sage oil. American production is still on an experimental scale in the farwestern peppermint area.

Clary Sage Oil is a colorless to pale yellow or pale olive-colored liquid, sweet-herbaceous, tenacious in odor, soft and somewhat reminiscent of ambra in its bitter-sweet undertone. Apart from the initial linalylacetate—linalool notes, there is a very characteristic note in the odor of clary sage oil. The note remains in the dryout odor on a perfume blotter. Some perfumers describe it as tobacco-like, others as balsamic or tea-like. It also has something in common with the odor of **Cistus Oil** and **Moroccan Chamomile** (see these monographs).

Since **Linalool** and **Linalyl Acetate** are the main constituents of this fairly expensive essential oil, adulteration frequently takes place by the simple addition of these synthetic materials or by addition of **Mentha Citrata** oil, etc. Such additions obviously affect the above-mentioned characteristic note, but may not affect the physico-chemical properties

of the oil. It is therefore of paramount importance to rely upon a strict olfactory test on this oil prior to any significant purchase. The characteristic notes coming from constituents other than linalool and linalyl acetate should be studied carefully.

Clary Sage Oil is used in perfumery as an individual body or as a modifier for bergamot oil, lavender, etc. and for ambra notes with labdanum extracts, cistus oil, olibanum resinoid, cinnamic alcohol, nitromusks or synthetic ambergris materials, etc.; in chypre bases, fougères, Oriental and "tabac"-type fragrances and in modern fantasy creations with aldehydic notes or even in woody bases. In the classical type of cologne perfumes it lends unique tenacity and acts as a very fragrant fixative, particularly in combination with labdanum products and musks. It blends beautifully with coriander, cardamom, citrus oils, lavandin and lavender, geranium oil, sandalwood oil, eugenol and derivatives, cedarwood derivatives, methylionones, phenylethyl alcohol, etc. In flavors, the coriander-like notes of clary sage oil are exploited in liqueurs, wine essences, grape flavors, etc. Furthermore, it is useful as a modifier in spice compounds.

See also **Sage (Clary) Absolute** and **Concrète**, previous monograph.

Sage Oil, Dalmatian.

The trade distinguishes between the flavor material **Sage Oil**, the perfume material **Spanish Sage Oil**, and the perfume material **Clary Sage Oil**. The three oils are distilled from different species of **Salvia**.

Sage Oil, usually known as **Dalmatian Sage Oil**, is steam distilled from the dried leaves of wild growing **Salvia Officinalis** in Yugoslavia. Smaller quantities are produced in Bulgaria, Turkey, Malta, France and Germany, while Cyprus sage has unfortunately vanished from the market since the house of Lanitis, in 1954, abandoned production of a large number of herb oils from this sunny and fertile Mediterranean island. The author himself enjoyed using Cyprus sage oil up to that year, and regrets very much that this oil is no longer available. In Morocco, the wild-growing local variety **Salvia Maurorum** is occasionally distilled. It yields an oil of thujone-cineole type, similar to the Dalmatian sage. **Sage Oil Spanish** and **Sage Clary Oil** are discussed in separate monographs in this work.

52: La Vallée du Dadès, the Moroccan valley of **Roses** at the fringe of the Saharan desert.

(Fot. S. Arctander, 1960)

53: Cultivated Moroccan **Rose.** This variety is larger than the Dadès rose and the Centifolia imported
rose.   *(Fot. S. Arctander, 1960)*

Dalmatian Sage Oil is a pale yellow, mobile liquid, having a fresh and strong, warm-spicy herbaceous and camphoraceous odor, somewhat reminiscent of artemisia vulgaris oil. The flavor is equally cineolic-herbaceous, warm and burning. A peculiar sweetness, reminiscent of tansy flowers, is characteristic in the top note of the Dalmatian sage oil. The oil finds extensive use as a flavor material: in liqueurs, canned meat, spice sauces, pickles, sausages, etc. The dried leaves are among the most popular culinary herbs in southern Europe and the U.S.A., and they are an important ingredient in the flavoring of Vermouth (wine) and other "bitters" or "aperitifs" in spite of the content of Thujone in the leaves (see below).

In perfumery, Dalmatian Sage Oil is used for its power, partly as a topnote material, partly for its relatively good tenacity. The fadeout of the odor of the oil is sweet-herbaceous and very pleasant. The oil blends well with lavandin, rosemary, citrus oils, bois de rose oil, etc.; it introduces fresh notes in fougères, chypres, aldehydic perfume bases, colognes and spicy "men's fragrances" for after-shave lotions, etc.

Dalmatian Sage Oil is occasionally adulterated with other essential oils which contain similar odorants such as cedar leaf oil (the so-called thuja oil, distilled from the leaves and twigs of the Virginian cedar Juniperus Virginiana). Other adulterants include thuja oil fractions or fractions of Spanish sage oil, rosemary oil, various artemisia oils, etc. In turn, Dalmatian sage oil finds its way into other essential oils, partly as an adulterant, partly as a necessary component in the composing of artificial essential oils such as tansy, wormwood, etc.

Like most other spices and herbs, Dalmatian Sage has also been marketed as an extract for flavoring purposes. In the case of Dalmatian sage, however, the extract—sometimes called Oleoresin of Sage— is a kind of a by-product. The exhausted plant material (after steam distillation of essential oil) is extracted with boiling hot water (compare to Fir Needle Extract). The aqueous extract is evaporated and used with or without the essential oil in flavoring extracts. The aqueous extract is not a true oleoresin, but it does contain some flavoring matter (but no Thujone), and it greatly improves the tenacity and stability of sage oil in spice blends.

Strange as it may seem, Dalmatian Sage is a very popular herb for food seasoning, although part of its flavor is due to the presence of Thujone, a ketone which is also present in wormwood oil and which was the main reason for the banning of "absinth" in France some years ago. Thujone was decreed toxic and harmful to human beings.

Due to its content of thujone, Dalmatian sage oil is considered somewhat toxic and skin-irritating. The fairly good bactericidal value of the oil is illustrated by the fact that Dalmatian sage herb infusions are still used as effective mouth washes and gargles in household medicine.

Dalmatian Sage Oil is readily available, and is produced in quantities of five to fifteen metric tons per year. The dried leaves rank among the quantitatively largest condiment herbs imported into the U.S.A.

Sage Oil, Spanish.

From the wild growing herb of Salvia Lavandulaefolia in Spain an essential oil known as Spanish Sage Oil is steam distilled. The oil is produced in many of the districts where the Spanish spike oil (see this monograph) is produced, and, unfortunately for the latter, contamination or even deliberate adulteration of spike oil with sage oil occurs quite frequently. This fact also has an adverse effect on the reputation of the Spanish sage oil, and lessens the consumer's interest in it. The consumers are left confused about what they are actually getting when they buy either of these oils. Obviously, good and genuine oils are obtainable from certain houses. In fact, if genuine oils were not available, the above remarks could not be made as they would have no justifiable basis and would be of little or no interest.

A related species, the "Greek Sage", is distilled in the Fethiye province of Turkey from the Salvia Triloba plant. The essential oil has a harshrosemary like odor and is used locally for pharmaceutical purposes.

Spanish Sage Oil is a pale yellow mobile oil with a fresh-herbaceous, eucalyptol-camphor like odor, a rather sharp pine-like topnote and little or no sweetness on drying out. The oil is used in soap perfumery and in the "reconstitution" of other essential oils, e.g. Spanish spike lavender oil. In fact, the two oils have many common constituents.

Spanish Sage Oil blends well with the related oils of rosemary, lavandin, spike lavender, pine needle oils, citronella oils, etc., and is used generally as a freshener in industrial perfumes, soap perfumes, detergent fragrances, etc.

The annual production of **Spanish Sage Oil** varies from three to ten metric tons, but it is believed that significant quantities of the herb are distilled along with rosemary and Spanish spike lavender. Thus, exact figures on the exploitation of Spanish sage are not obtainable.

Wild growing **Salvia Lavandulaefolia** plants in Yugoslavia occasionally contaminate the Dalmatian rosemary oil (see monograph on **Rosemary Oils**).

Sandalwood Oil, Australasian.

Next to East Indian sandalwood oil, the west Australian oil is the most important of the various types of "true sandalwood oils" in perfumery. The oil is obtained by a combination of solvent extraction and steam distillation of the wood from a small west Australian wildgrowing tree, **Eucaria Spicata**. Since the wood is also suitable for woodcarving and incense making, the better lumber is exported as such to India and other eastern countries where it is used as "sandalwood" equal to the East Indian sandalwood. The Australian tree is a close relative to the parent tree of East Indian sandalwood oil (see next monograph). The essential oil from **Eucaria Spicata** is produced in western Australia only. The oil is occasionally rectified further in Australia prior to shipping.

Australasian Sandalwood Oil is a pale yellow viscous liquid whose odor is soft, woody, extremely tenacious and somewhat balsamic in its delicate sweetness. Its topnote is distinctly different from that of the East Indian sandalwood oil, not sweet but rather dry-bitter, slightly resinous like myrrh oil, although not very pronounced. On drying out, the odor slowly becomes very similar to that of the East Indian oil. Apart from this characteristic topnote, there is very little difference in the overall odor between the East Indian oil and the Australasian oil. Redistilled Australasian sandalwood oil competes favorably with commercial grades of East Indian sandalwood oil.

Australasian Sandalwood Oil is used mainly as a replacement for East Indian sandalwood oil although the price difference is not very great. The Australasian oil is very suitable for the isolation of santalol, the main constituent. It should be kept in mind, however, that the conventionally given figure of 90/95% "**Santalol**" in

this oil refers to "total alcohols", out of which perhaps 10% are not santalol. Fractionated distillation will eliminate the head fractions of hydrocarbons and other non-alcoholic components, while the main fraction will consist of "total alcohols", generally named "**Santalol**" in perfumery and having the odor of East Indian "santalol".

Australasian Sandalwood Oil is also used in perfumery for its balsamic-woody notes and great tenacity (fixative value). It blends well with linalool or bois de rose oil, hydroxycitronellal, geraniol, citronellol, geranium oil, isoeugenol, vetiver oil, bergamot oil, oakmoss products, labdanum products, benzoin, ionones, methylionones, phenylethyl alcohol, etc. Its characteristic topnote often makes it unsuitable for direct replacement of the East Indian oil. Finally, the Australasian oil is still used in the Far East for pharmaceutical purposes, particularly as a disinfectant for the urinary tract, a use which has practically been abandoned in Europe and the U.S.A.

Australian Sandalwood Oil is rarely adulterated, but there are various qualities on the market. Years ago, cutting of the oil was accomplished with an essential oil, derived from a south Australian tree related to the **Eucaria Spicata**. The oil from the south Australian tree does not contain significant amounts of santalol.

An entirely different oil is obtained from the wood of a small southeastern Australian tree, **Eremophila Mitchelli**. Neither of the two oils are commercially produced or regularly available (see also monographs on **Osyris Tenuifolia** and **Santalum Citrinum**). The annual production of Australasian sandalwood oil fluctuates widely; it has been as high as 60 metric tons (in the early 1930's). It is presently between 3 and 15 metric tons. With respect to quantity, it presents no threat at all to the East Indian oil.

Sandalwood Oil, East Indian.

Sandalwood is one of the oldest known perfume materials, and it has at least 4000 years of history and uninterrupted use. It is believed that the *oil* of sandalwood was known in Ceylon over 1000 years ago, but it is only within the past century that the oil has appeared in European and American perfumery.

The oil is steam distilled or water distilled from

the coarsely powdered wood of billets and roots of **Santalum Album**, a comparatively small tree. The tree originates in India, Ceylon, Indonesia and surrounding islands, and it grows wild in the Portuguese island of Timor and on Celebes, among other places. Today, practically all Indian sandalwood oil is derived from the wood of cultivated trees, although cultures outside the native areas of the tree have never attained any importance. India exports some quantities of wood, but 80 to 90% of all the wood is distilled in India. Timor exports all its wood, and many of the smaller islands also have no distilleries at all.

Sandalwood Oil, distilled in Europe or the U.S.A., may derive from Indian wood (most often), from New Caledonian wood (certain French sandalwood oils), or it may be distilled from Timor wood (one Dutch producer seems to specialize in this oil). Of an estimated annual world production of over 100 metric tons, about 75 to 80% is produced in India under government control (Mysore, etc.).

A sandalwood tree must be over 30 years old before its wood is suitable for distillation. Comminuting of the wood is not an easy job (3 progressive steps often required: sawing or cleaving, chopping, grinding), and the distillation also requires considerable experience, many hours of operation per batch, large amounts of steam or heating of the water, etc. For such reasons, it is understandable that the cultivation of the tree has remained an Indian tradition through thousands of years. Very recently, small lots of East African sandalwood oil (from Kenya) have reached the world market, but this production is still on an experimental scale.

East Indian Sandalwood Oil is a pale yellow to yellow, viscous liquid, having an extremely soft, sweet-woody and almost animal-balsamic odor, presenting little or no particular topnote, and remaining uniform for a considerable length of time due to its outstanding tenacity. The oil blends so excellently with rose, violet, tuberose, clove, lavender, bergamot, etc. etc., that it is almost a common "blender"-fixative in countless woody-floral and Oriental-floral bases, chypres, fougères, clover, carnation, origan-types and other perfume types. Furthermore, the oil is used as a base for co-distillation of other essential oils, e.g. the most delicate florals: rose, mimusops elengi, anthocephalus cadamba, pandanus, etc. (see these monographs). In India, the so-called "attars" are made with sandalwood oil distilled over such flowers, or by distillation of these flowers into a receiver with sandalwood oil.

As a background note and sweet fixative in ambre perfumes, in opopanax and "precious wood" types, it is almost obligatory, and it blends beautifully with the ionones, methylionones, oakmoss and labdanum products, patchouli oil, vetiver oil, natural and artificial musks, geranium oils, mimosa absolute, cassie, costus, clove bud oil or eugenol, linalool, geraniol, phenylethyl alcohol, hydroxycitronellal, bucinal, cyclamal, etc.

As a flavor material, sandalwood oil is of little or no importance. It has a slightly bitter, resinous taste, and requires skilful blending in order to become attractive. The oil is still used in certain types of the old-fashioned "Sen-Sen", a sickly-sweet tasting, "Oriental"-smelling licorice candy which is used for the masking of bad breath (see monograph on **Patchouli Oil**).

East Indian Sandalwood Oil is not infrequently adulterated with Australasian sandalwood oil (lowers the laevorotation), with araucaria oil, copaiba oil, heart fractions of aged Atlas cedarwood oil, amyris oil or various rare East African wood oils (e.g. the Brachyleana Hutchinsii, see **Muhuhu Oil**), with bleached copaiba balsam or with various odorless solvents such as benzyl alcohol, benzyl benzoate, diethyl phthalate, isopropyl myristate, liquid paraffin, etc. etc.

For pharmaceutical purposes, the oil is usually rectified in Europe and the U.S.A. Rectification includes steam distillation and drying of the oil. Although of some therapeutic value, the disinfectant use of sandalwood oil has been largely abandoned in most parts of the world.

Sandarac.

Somewhat misleadingly called "**Juniper Gum**", the **Sandarac** is a natural oleo-resin, although it has resemblance to a turpentine in which most of the essential oil has already resinified to resin acids, etc. In our present definitions, sandarac would therefore be considered a natural resin, containing minute amounts of essential oil of the turpentine type.

Sandarac is a physiological product of **Callitris Quadrivalvis**, a small conifer, originating in and growing wild in the mountains of northwest

Africa (Algeria, Morocco). The tree is found in Malta and sporadically in Tunisia.

The resin is obtained only by incisions in the trunk and branches, whereby the viscous sandarac flows out and quickly solidifies when exposed to the air. Native people then peel off the small tear-shaped, pale yellow resin drops. The main part of all sandarac is used in fine lacquers, varnishes (also medicinal), while small amounts are used in perfumery as a fixative in woody perfumes, pine fragrances, incense or Oriental bases, etc. The essential oil can be obtained either by steam distillation directly on the resin (usual method), or, the resin acids being soluble in aqueous potassium hydroxide, it is possible to isolate the essential oil from a neutralized alcoholic solution of sandarac. The alcohol is evaporated, and the alkaline solution is extracted with ethyl ether. After removal of the ether, a small amount of essential oil is left, unharmed by the exposure to high distillation temperatures. This method has hitherto had only theoretical interest, and there is, all told, very little interest in the essential oil of Sandarac.

Sandarac Oil is a pale yellow or almost colorless mobile liquid of a turpentine-like, fresh-resinous and slightly balsamic odor. Tinctures of sandarac are used with some advantage since sandarac is almost entirely soluble in alcohol.

Essential oils have been prepared from the wood of the sandarac tree, and from the leaves of that tree. None of these oils have yet attained any commercial interest, and they are not available at the present moment.

Sanna Oil.

Closely related to Longoza (see monograph) is a Far Eastern plant, Hedychium Spicatum, cultivated in India and Japan for its flowers and very fragrant roots (rhizomes). In India, an "Attar Ekangi" is prepared from the rhizomes, while in Japan the rhizome is known as "Sanna".

The essential oil is produced by steam distillation of the comminuted rhizomes. Distillation takes place locally (only) and the yield of oil is good.

Sanna Oil is a viscous, pale yellow to amber colored liquid, occasionally showing a deposit of a crystalline mass. The crystals are usually odorless when purified. The liquid part of the oil consists almost entirely of cinnamates and

1,4-Methoxy-Cinnamates of lower aliphatic alcohols. This makes the oil quite interesting and unique.

The odor of freshly prepared Sanna Oil is woody-spicy with a camphoraceous-fresh-woody topnote and an increasingly spicy, cinnamon type of body note of immense richness and tenacity. On dryout, it becomes again less sweet, but remains spicy-woody. The author has no experience with the application of this oil in perfumery (samples too small), but it is obvious that the oil could find use in balsamic, woody and heavy-floral bases, in hyacinth, lavender and lavandin perfumes, etc. and that it will blend well with styrax, cinnamic alcohol and its derivatives, terpineol, linalool, benzoin, sandalwood oil, nitromusks, ionones, etc.—a very versatile material.

Unfortunately, Sanna Oil is not regularly available outside its countries of origin.

See also Kaempferia Galanga and Longoza.

"Santalum Citrinum."

Under this name is sold an essential oil, distilled in Grasse, France, from the wood of an East Indian tree. Since the oil is produced by one manufacturer only, it is very possible that the source of raw material is much better known than the above name reveals. Whatever the botanical source is, the oil deserves some attention and the author prefers to discuss it under the above trade name.

The oil of "Santalum Citrinum" is a very pale yellow or almost colorless, viscous liquid of very pleasant sweet-woody odor, reminiscent of sandalwood. Judging from the odor, however, it resembles still more that of santalol with a truly woody-balsamic undertone. The tenacity of this fragrance is quite outstanding, and the uniformity of the odor is unique. For such reasons, one is ready to excuse for almost any kind of "undercover" names for a perfume material.

Although the cost of the oil does not prohibit its general use, "Santalum Citrinum" Oil will mainly find application in high-class lotion perfumes, face-powder perfumes, etc. where it blends beautifully with bruyère, cis-para-tertiary butyl-cyclohexanyl acetate, cyclamal, methylionone, olibanum, opopanax, sage clary, treflol, ylang-ylang extra, etc. and it may form an important "fond" in chypres, fougères, Oriental bases, origan perfumes, orchid bases, rose "thé" bases, or in various floral and woody creations.

To the author's knowledge, the oil is produced on a limited scale only, but there has been no difficulty so far with respect to availability.

Sarsaparilla.

Highly famed in advertising as an important flavor ingredient in the so-called "root-beer" (a carbonated, non-alcoholic beverage), is the extract of **Sarsaparilla**. The name sounds intriguing, exotic, perhaps it is a good advertising slogan. The other side of the story is, that sarsaparilla does not contribute any important flavor note to the complex of sassafras, wintergreen, etc., called "root beer", nor to any other flavor. As a matter of fact, it has very little flavor at all. But the name sounds perhaps better than that of sassafras, the main flavor principle of that beverage.

Sarsaparilla root comes from various **Smilax** species in Mexico, Honduras, Brazil and elsewhere in Central America. The root was brought to Europe in the 16th century, and great therapeutical value was attributed to the preparations from the drug. It has since become evident that **Sarsaparilla** is without any therapeutical or pharmacological value.

The root has been submitted to steam distillation, but it yields less than 0.01% of essential oil. The olfactory characteristics of the oil have been described (Journ. of the Royal Chem. Society of London, 1914, vol. 105, page 205) and are apparently without interest to the perfumer or the flavorist. The author is unable to give personal comments on the odor and flavor of this essential oil.

The author has deliberately included this monograph in order to enlighten some of the very confusing informations, usually given in popular discussions on the subject of **Sarsaparilla**. The fact remains that sarsaparilla extracts are still used in certain types of soft drink (without any flavor effect), and are still used in pharmaceutical preparations (also without any effect). Apparently to satisfy the die-hard laymen among the public.

Sassafras Oil.

"North American Sassafras Oil":

The true **Sassafras Oil** is steam distilled from the roots or rootbark of **Sassafras Albidum**, a medium-sized North American tree. The tree is a native of the eastern United States and the southern midwestern states where it grows wild and in abundance, often like a weed in mountainous areas and on poor soil. The tree has been known since the very first landings of the Spaniards in Florida early in the 16th century. The tree is practically unknown beyond the limits of southeastern Canada and northern Mexico. The essential oil from the root has been known for more than 300 years.

Distillation takes place mainly in the southeastern states where fairly modern installations now are at hand. The essential oil exists in the root-bark tissue right beneath the cork, but the root-wood itself also contains some oil. The roots or stumps are comminuted into chips and steam distilled. The oil is heavier than water and, to a significant degree, soluble in the water. The oil solidifies at about 4 to 5°C. It must be completely melted and stirred prior to use or transfer from one container to another.

Sassafras Oil is a yellowish to pale brownish yellow oily liquid of sweet-spicy, fresh and slightly camphoraceous odor with a long-lasting, woody-floral and very sweet undertone. A short, fresh-peppery topnote is characteristic of the odor of this oil. The flavor is sweet, somewhat woody, usually described as "root-beer"-like; this description refers to the use of sassafras oil (and other components of root-beer), and therefore is a poor terminology. Due to the high content of **Safrole**, a phenolether closely related to myristicin, the sassafras oil may some day in the future be removed (banned) from all food products. Many physicians consider that safrole is so toxic and hazardous that its use should be prohibited by law.

Up to now, however, safrole and sassafras oil (as well as other safrole-bearing oils) have been used as the main constituents of most root-beer flavors for candy, carbonated and non-carbonated drinks, toothpastes, mouthwashes, etc. There are no substitutes for safrole as a flavor material at present (apart from dihydrosafrole, isosafrole and similar closely related chemicals). The suggested use level for sassafras oil in finished goods is about 0.30 to 0.50 mg%, while the **Minimum Perceptible** is 0.03 to 0.08 mg%. The water-solubility of this oil prevents it from showing its apparent strength.

In perfumery, the cheaper oils of camphor and

ocotea pretiosa (see these monographs) have substituted for sassafras oil for a long time. The two oils are richer in safrole than is the sassafras oil. Ocotea pretiosa oil lacks the peppery topnote and the camphoraceous freshness, while camphor oil (or fractions thereof) usually presents a more pronounced camphoraceous note, no fresh peppery topnote, and a more woody bodynote than the North American sassafras oil.

North American Sassafras Oil is frequently adulterated with the Brazilian oil of ocotea pretiosa or with fractions of camphor oil. The two oils are cheaper and are produced in far larger quantities than the sassafras oil. The Brazilian oil can be identified by simple instrumental means, while detection of adulteration with camphor oil usually requires an organoleptic test. Due to the above facts, North American sassafras oil has lost much of its importance and, if safrole is banned as a flavor material, it is very conceivable that true sassafras oil will completely vanish from the market. The present production of North American sassafras oil is about 50 metric tons per year, or less than 3% of the world production of the two other safrole-bearing oils.

Savin Oil.

This oil is steam distilled from the twigs with leaves of a wild growing small tree or bush from Central Europe, the Juniperus Sabina. Distillation takes place mainly in Austria (Tirol). Irregular lots of oil come from France and Yugoslavia. In France only little, if any, true savin oil is produced. Other species of Juniperus are used in the distillation, yielding oils of entirely different odor.

Savin Oil is a pale yellow or pale olive-greenish to almost colorless, oily liquid which becomes more viscous upon ageing. The odor is quite unique, very unpleasant, nauseating but also slightly reminiscent of juniperberry oil and cypress oil. The initial unpleasant notes could remind one of the odor of wormseed oil, while the undertone is more camphoraceous and turpentine-like. The taste is bitter, repulsive, camphoraceous-medicinal. The oil is banned from sale to the public in many countries, due to its toxic effects (nerve poison and blood circulation stimulant). It is conceivable that this oil will disappear slowly from the market, and the very rare examples of its application in perfumery (pine fragrances,

oakmoss bases, woody and peppery effects, etc.) may easily find replacements among other perfume materials.

Savin Oil is characterized by its high content of high-boiling constituents and the nearby absence of the common, low-boiling "pine"-type monoterpenes. Thus, the oil would find a place among fixatives if it were not for the above significant drawbacks.

Savory Oil.

See also summary of correct denominations of this and related oils under Thyme Oil.

Various species of Satureia are steam distilled to yield essential oils known as "Savory Oils". In France, the Satureia Hortense is cultivated, while the Satureia Montana grows wild. The latter is also found extensively wild growing in Yugoslavia, Turkey, and to a lesser degree in Hungary, Austria, Germany, Bulgaria, the U.S.S.R. and Italy. In Spain and particularly in Morocco, the Satureia Montana is quite common and it is the only savory used for distillation there. The plant is a small labiate, and the essential oil is obtained by steam distillation of the entire overground plant with its flowering stalks. The plant has been used as a culinary herb since Antiquity in the Mediterranean countries.

The oil is distilled in France (mainly Satureia Hortense), Yugoslavia, Spain, Morocco (Satureia Montana). The two oils are quite similar, although not identical in odor and flavor.

Savory Oil is a pale yellow or almost colorless liquid of fresh medicinal-spicy odor, reminiscent of sage and thyme, but with a sharpness recalling that of cumin oil, although not distinctly green. The dryout is rather phenolic-harsh. Of flavor, the Savory Oil is disappointingly sharp, biting or burning, almost bitter. At low concentrations only, the flavor can be recognized as pleasant, herbaceous, reminiscent of the culinary herb. The oil is used mainly in flavors for sauces, seasonings, canned meat, pickles, vinegars, etc., but occasionally, the fresh-herbaceous, medicinal effect can be useful and interesting in perfumes of the forest-type, chypres, fougères, or as a modifier in lavender bouquets and colognes along with citrus oils and oakmoss products. The oil blends well with amyl salicylate, coumarin, lavender, pine needle oils, rosemary oil, etc.

The annual production of Savory Oils is less

than 10 metric tons, but confusion (and adulteration) with origanum and thyme oils (see these monographs) gives the impression of a higher production figure.

Schinus Molle Oil.

This oil illustrates a typical example of an essential oil which came into the limelight more because of the shortage of another essential oil (oil of Black Pepper) than because of great interest in the Schinus Molle Oil itself.

The oil is steam distilled from the fruits (berries) of a small or medium sized tree which seems to have originated in northern South America. The tree is also known as "Peruvian Pepper Tree", "Peruvian Mastic", "Californian Pepper Tree", etc. and it grows wild in Mexico, Guatemala and other tropical areas. An intoxicating beverage is produced from the fruits of this tree in Central America. The tree has been introduced in North Africa where the author has had repeated opportunities to study it, knowing that its fruits served locally as a substitute for black pepper. It is known as "faux poivrier" in the French-speaking parts of North Africa. The tree grows now in most Mediterranean countries including Spain, and it is also found in South Africa. It is possible, however, that the tree actually originated in North Africa since there is no record of its ever having been introduced there.

The fruits are collected for distillation mainly in Mexico, Guatemala and Spain. Leaves and flowers have been distilled experimentally in Algeria and Italy. The leaf oil resembles the oil from the berries.

Schinus Molle Fruit Oil is a pale greenish or pale olive colored, oily liquid whose odor is fresh, woody-peppery, warm-spicy with a somewhat sharp or dry, smoky-woody undertone. The odor becomes less pleasant upon ageing of the oil. The flavor is warm, somewhat biting although not pungent, but less rich than that of black pepper. The overall organoleptic picture of the oil calls to mind the odor and flavor of the tail fractions of black pepper oil (the "heavy" fractions) with some resemblance to angelica seed oil, juniper berry oil and elemi oil. The peppery note is undoubtedly due to the presence in the schinus molle oil of large amounts of the unstable monoterpene, Phellandrene, and perhaps also caryophyllene (a sesquiterpene).

Apart from its individual character and possible use in perfumery for woody-spicy, warm and powdery notes which blend excellently with oakmoss products, clove oils, nutmeg, cinnamic alcohol, ionones, nitromusks, aldehydes, etc., the oil of Schinus Molle has served as a replacement for (or adulterant in) black pepper oil. The sudden interest in Schinus Molle Oil during the years of the black pepper scarcity even caused cases of adulteration of schinus molle oil with eucalyptus dives oil, clove oil sesquiterpenes, etc. Eucalyptus dives oil was at that time produced in large quantities for the mining industry. Back to normal conditions again, we find that schinus molle oil does not offer any sensational new notes for the working perfumer and flavorist, and the oil will probably remain a small item, while the berries will continue to serve as a local substitute for black pepper in the growing areas.

"Seaweed Absolute".

Although rarely offered under the above name, there are several perfumery products which consist entirely or mainly of extracts of one or more species of seaweed.

Very little concise information has ever been published with respect to the odorous constituents of various seaweeds. And when perfumers generally are looking for a "marine" or "seashore" type of odor, they will often turn to ambergris, nerol, geraniol, iodinecomplexes, ozone-notes, etc. However, several different extracts of seaweed are common commercial articles in the pharmaceutical industry: e.g. the extract of Fucus Vesiculosus (the bladder seaweed) which is a mild laxative. The brown algae Dictyota Dichotoma which is quite common in Scandinavian waters has, when dry, a typical "seashore" odor. In Ireland, certain seaweeds are collected along with the harvesting of Carragheen (Irish moss) which is itself occasionally extracted for perfumery purposes. These and other (to the author unknown) seaweeds are processed in England for a perfume manufacturer. No doubt, the typical notes of seaweed will remind the perfumer of iodine, nerol, cresol, furfural, cymene, ambergris, etc. Some of the above algae or seaweeds have been submitted to steam distillation and yielded essential oils.

So-called Seaweed Absolute is often a deep-green or greenish-brown liquid (petroleum ether extracted) of intensely green-herbaceous, phenolic-woody and "dry" odor type, distinctly recalling the odor of seaweed drying on a salt water beach after a heavy storm or surf. Obviously, the appearance and odor of these products are strongly affected by the nature of the starting material. Many different seaweeds are used.

Seaweed Absolute is an extremely powerful perfume material. Its penetrative effect is partly due to its unusual type of odor. It finds use in mossy-woody, herbaceous, aldehydic or "green" perfume types, or in fantasy bases, etc. It blends excellently with oakmoss products, patchouli oil, spice oils, cedarwood oils and cedarwood derivatives, lavender, musks, labdanum products, castoreum, pine needle oils, galbanum resinoid or oil, geraniol, nerol, cedrela odorata oil and other dry-woody oils, cyperus oils (Cypriol in particular), etc.

The annual production of Seaweed Absolute is probably less than 100 kilos, but an increased demand could easily be met.

Siam Wood Oil.

Before World War II, significant amounts of this oil were produced in France from wood imported from the former Indochina. Various cypress trees from the mountainous regions of northern Indochina were used for their fragrant wood in the manufacture of finer woodcarvings, handcarved figures, boxes, etc. Waste wood from this production was steam distilled (trunk wood and roots) to yield an essential oil, known as Siam Wood Oil. The oil was also known as Fokiena Oil, since one of the sources of wood was the tree Fokiena Hodginsii, while another well known Fareastern species is Dacrydium Elatum, both belonging to the Conifers (see also Huon Pine Wood Oil). It is most likely, however, that the greater part of all Siam Wood Oils consisted of oil, distilled from Fokiena Hodginsii (the tree originated in the province of Fokien or Fukien in Indochina).

Siam Wood Oil (from Fokiena hodginsii) is a pale yellow to amber-colored, rather viscous liquid of a very pleasant, woody-balsamic, opopanax-cedar-like, mild and almost floral odor which tones out in a cleaner, woody note, reminiscent of the odor from rectified Texas cedarwood oil. The author has studied samples of oil, presumably from Dacrydium Elatum, and this oil

smelled more typically like rectified cedarwood oil. The oil was crude and of a color similar to that of crude Texas or East African cedarwood oils (reddish-brown).

Siam Wood Oil could find use as a fixative in woody perfume types, pine fragrances, Oriental bases, etc., but the perfumer is already blessed with a wealth of natural oils in this odor group. If Siam wood oil should disappear entirely from the perfumery market as a result of the postwar development in the area of origin, this may not present any great loss or deprivation to the creative perfumer.

Snakeroot (Canadian) Oil.

This oil is produced by steam distillation of the dried, comminuted rhizomes and roots of Asarum Canadense, a wild growing plant from the northeastern U.S.A. and Canada. The oil should not be confused with the so-called "Virginian snakeroot oil" or serpentaria root oil. The latter is derived from the roots and rhizomes of Aristolochia Serpentaria (same botanical order) which grows in the southeastern U.S.A. (Virginia to South Carolina).

Canadian Snakeroot, also called "Wild Ginger", is a small plant which has been used in folk medicine for centuries. The essential oil is produced in the U.S.A. by only a few distillers, and in very limited amounts (there is no cultivation of the plant).

Canadian Snakeroot Oil is a yellowish to amber-brownish colored liquid whose viscosity increases on ageing. Its odor is warm-aromatic, woody-spicy, yet rich and sweet with a minty-gingerlike undertone, and a pronounced tealike, lasting dryout. The flavor is equally warm, slightly pungent or biting and spicy-aromatic. This oil is occasionally used in perfumes where it blends well with amyl salicylate, bergamot, costus, ionones, methyl eugenol, oakmoss products, patchouli, pine needle oils, sage clary and even florals such as cassie and mimosa, etc.

The main use, however, is in flavors where it acts as an excellent blender and modifier with ginger, clove, coriander, hop, and numerous spicy or herbaceous flavor materials. Its warmth and natural richness lends body to the flavor, and rounds off chemical notes where synthetic materials have been used.

Since the chemical composition of this oil has

been quite thoroughly investigated, it has been possible for many suppliers to offer **Canadian Snakeroot Oil** in larger quantities and at lower prices, than the actual production of true oil would indicate.

The oil of **Asarum Europaeum** (see monograph) differs from the above oil in that the former contains **Asarone** and is considered toxic. Hence the European oil should not be used in flavors or as a substitute for **Canadian Snakeroot Oil.**

Soybean.

Although the flavor known as **Soy Sauce** is only a minor derivative of the soybean, it should be mentioned briefly at this point in view of the tremendous importance of the soybean for the world nutrition problem.

Soybeans are the seeds from the pods of **Glycine Soja**, a Far Eastern plant, now cultivated all over the world in tropical, semitropical and temperate zones. The milky emulsion that is formed when soybeans are ground with water can be fermented by means of a fungus, **Aspergillus Oryzae**, which the Japanese and Chinese people keep on hand in their households, cultivated on a riceball. Due to this fermentation, certain flavor materials are formed; among them is one of the most powerful and pungent flavor chemicals known: gamma-**Methyl Mercapto Propionaldehyde,** commercially known as **Methional**. It is one of main flavor principles in the well known Chinese or Japanese **Soy Sauce**. In this sauce is also present the corresponding alcohol, gamma-methyl mercapto propanol and the related delta-methyl mercapto butanol and the well known **Maltol** (also known under the brand name of "palatone"). Similar materials have been isolated in an "essential oil" steam distilled from the press cake of the soybean, a very common cattle feed and by-product from the soybean oil factories (vegetable, fixed, edible oil).

The very comprehensive studies of soy sauce have contributed significantly to the advance of modern food flavoring. One of the largest selling "spices" (truly a seasoning or food-additive, the so-called "third spice", following salt and pepper) is MSG, *monosodium glutamate*, consumed today in tens of thousands of tons all over the world as a flavor improver, salt synergist, chicken or meat flavor, etc. The annual consumption in the U.S.A. is estimated at a figure between 10,000

and 15,000 metric tons. MSG is actually present in soy sauce. This sauce is, incidentally, the main source of salt (sodium chloride) for the people of the Eastern countries.

Soy Sauce is a very dark brown liquid of a sweet, meat-extract-like odor and extreme pungency, but also salt-sweet and spicy taste. At proper dilution, it enhances the flavor of many kinds of food, e.g. meats, soups, vegetables, fish, rice dishes, etc. The sauce is sold as such, but smaller amounts are also used in the spice industry for combination sauces, seasonings, etc.

Spearmint Oil.

The story of the spearmint is quite an amusing one. The plant—**Mentha Spicata**—originated in Europe, was introduced into the U.S.A., and is now one of the most important essential oil bearing plants of the U.S.A. The amusing part is that while it never was popular anywhere in Europe, the flavor of spearmint immediately became popular with the American public. Only recently, the oil seems to be appearing more and more and, as a modifier of peppermint flavor, it has been slowly regaining a foothold in Europe where peppermint always was the "only" acceptable flavor type for toothpaste, chewing gum, hard mint-candy, etc. There are still certain countries in Europe where it is virtually impossible to sell spearmint-flavored toothpaste or chewing gum. However, certain countries have used "mint" (**Mentha Viridis** and other wild spearmints) as a culinary herb in food and beverages for several hundred years (see below).

Thus, we find the world's main producing areas of spearmint in the midwestern U.S.A. (Indiana – Michigan – Wisconsin), and in the far-western states of Washington and Oregon. The midwestern American spearmint is still considered the best and, until recently, it also was the largest in quantity. In Europe, smaller quantities are produced in Hungary, Spain, Yugoslavia and Germany (almost abandoned), also in the U.S.S.R., India and, to an increasing degree, in China. Chinese spearmint oil is arriving in Europe at half the price of American spearmint, and it presents a serious threat to the American exports of the oil to Europe. All producing areas combined, the world production of spearmint oil exceeds 1000 metric tons per year. Due to a sudden increase in demand, the price of spearmint oil went up to twice the normal level during the spring of 1960.

Furthermore, the plant is cultivated in many areas for use as a culinary herb, e.g. in Egypt (distillation abandoned in 1955) and in a number of European countries. In culinary terms, the word "mint" always refers to one of the spearmint varieties. The "na'na'" of the Moslem countries is an almost non-hairy variety of spearmint, related to **Mentha Viridis.** It is cultivated in hundreds of thousands of small private gardens and used extensively as a tea ("shai") mixed with Chinese tea as a tonic and popular infusion. At least three glasses of hot and heavily sweetened "shai" is a must for guests, travellers and friends at Moslem homes or camps all over the Mediterranean countries far into Sahara and in the Middle East.

Spearmint Oil is produced by steam distillation of the flowering tops of the plants, which are partially dried prior to distillation. The distillation is carried out in the fields in fairly modern or very modern stills. The oil is sold as such, or it may be rectified according to the buyer's specifications. The oil obtained right from the field stills is known as *natural* spearmint oil. It is a pale olive or pale yellow, mobile liquid with a very warm, slightly green-herbaceous odor, penetrating and powerful, truly reminiscent of the odor of the crushed herb. The flavor is equally warm, almost biting, spicy-herbaceous, somewhat bitter. Rectified oils are less bitter or not bitter at all, more burning-biting, and they have a much sweeter, balsamic taste in dilution. The suggested use level would generally be about 0.50 to 2.00 mg%, but the oil is actually used in toothpaste flavors up to a concentration of 300 mg%. There are children who "eat" toothpaste, and this fact must be kept in mind when the flavor materials are selected. The **Minimum Perceptible** for a good, rectified spearmint oil is about 0.10 to 0.20 mg%. In view of the penetrative odor, the flavor of this oil is surprisingly weak, a fact which is due to the water-solubility of carvone.

Spearmint Oil is used primarily in flavors for toothpaste, chewing gum, candy, mouthwashes, etc. where it has attained great popularity as a modifier for peppermint (e.g. "doublemint", etc.). In perfumery, the oil finds some use for its peculiar herbaceous-green effect in lavender-fougère or even in jasmin compositions. The chief constituent of spearmint oil, **Carvone,** blends well with certain notes of the jasmin complex. The oil has a good and powerful effect in soap perfumes and is surprisingly stable in soap (carvone itself is a very delicate and unstable material).

So-called terpeneless spearmint oil is often merely an isolated or a synthetic carvone. A synthetic **Carvone** has now been prepared on a very large commercial scale from d-limonene, a readily available monoterpene from the citrus oils. The d-**Carvone** (typical of caraway oil) as well as the l-**Carvone** (typical of spearmint oil) are both prepared from d-limonene. Even on the synthetic carvones, it is possible to distinguish by taste and odor between the dextro- and the laevo-rotatory form. The natural isolates of carvone from the two oils obviously have some "carry-over" taste and odor from the parent oil.

In view of the above, it will be quite evident that adulteration of spearmint oil is not only possible but even a common occurrence. However, the Chinese spearmint oil is now on the market at such a low price that one cannot produce an artificial oil from synthetic carvone at a competitive price. Carvone was in 1960 sold at about half the cost of American spearmint oil (crop 1959 offered in the spring of 1960). If the cost of synthetic carvone drops further, there will again be an abundance of "artificial" spearmint oils on the market. A thorough flavor test should be included in any evaluation of spearmint oils prior to purchase.

The American production of spearmint oil has steadily increased during the past ten years, and is still increasing with no significant drop in price (or demand).

Spike Lavender Oil.
Aspic Oil:

Spike lavender oil, also called **Lavender Spike** or just **Spike Oil** (= Spanish spike oil) is known in France as **Aspic.** The oil is steam distilled from the flowering tops of the stout plant, **Lavandula Latifolia** which, together with true lavender, are the parents of the hybrid **Lavandin.**

The spike or aspic plant grows wild in or around its homeland, the Mediterranean countries, particularly in Spain, France, Yugoslavia, Italy, and scattered in many places in North Africa and the eastern Mediterranean countries and islands. Italian plantations in Ethiopia have not been very successful in that the oils produced were substantially different in composition. The main producer is Spain, with France following far behind in quantity, but producing an oil of more delicate odor. The Spanish oils are generally produced by a water-and-steam distillation, while all French oils are steam distilled. It seems likely that Spanish plant material is collected with less respect to uniformity in botanical specimens than the French.

Spike Lavender Oil is a pale yellow (most Spanish oils) to almost water-white (most French oils), mobile liquid of transitory camphoraceous (eucalyptus-like), fresh and herbaceous odor, reminiscent of lavandin and rosemary oils and with a somewhat dry-woody undertone.

Until the appearance of large quantities of lavandin oil in the 1930's, the oil was one of the most popular soap perfume materials. It has power, good stability, radiation and a generally popular freshness, applicable in a multitude of perfume types, varying from lavender over fougère and "new mown hay" to pine and woody, Oriental and aldehydic or cologne-like fragrances. It seems conceivable that if lavandin oil remains at less the half the cost of spike oil, the latter will slowly be forced out of soap perfumes. With cineole, eucalyptus oil or rosemary oil added to lavandin oil, effects can be obtained which are similar or even superior to those obtained from spike oil in soap perfumes. This suggestion refers mainly to the Spanish spike oil. The French oil —more delicate, uniform and, usually more expensive—is used in room sprays, deodorants, air fresheners, disinfectants, insecticides, etc. Spike oil blends well with all the related oils, e.g. rosemary, sage, lavandin, eucalyptus, lavender, bois de rose oil, petitgrain oil, and also with countless other common perfumery materials: spice oils (clove oils in particular), pine needle oils, amyl salicylate, isobornyl acetate, coumarin, etc. Cedarwood oil, oakmoss products, patchouli oil, etc. are important and necessary fixatives.

Partly because of its comparatively high price, partly because of the availability of tempting substitutes, **Spike Lavender Oil** is very often adulterated or "cut" with e.g. Spanish sage oil (grown in the same areas in Spain), rosemary oil, lavandin oil, eucalyptus oil, fractions of these oils, fractions from terpineol production or from Chinese camphor oils, saponified lavandin oil, etc., etc. Besides, there are a number of other lavandula species which yield essential oils of composition similar to that of spike oil, and most of these plants grow in the Mediterranean area.

The annual production of spike oil exceeds 100 metric tons, but if the price cannot be brought down to a reasonable level in comparison to lavandin oil, it is quite likely that spike oil will meet a decreasing demand on the world market.

Spikenard Oil.

Also known as "false" **Indian Valerian Root Oil.** It should not be confused with the essential oil of various **Ferula Species,** an oil which is known under the name of **Sumbul Root Oil** (see monograph). See also **Valeriana Wallichii Oil.**

Spikenard Oil is derived from the roots of **Nardostachys Jatamansi,** a plant of the Valerianaceae. The plant grows wild and is occasionally cultivated in India (northern mountain regions), China and Japan (also Formosa).

The dried, comminuted root (rhizome and root) is steam distilled in India or in Europe or the U.S.A. Unfortunately, there are a number of **Nardostachys** species and also other plants, not only to the valerian family but also to quite different families which yield roots, sold commercially as "Indian valerian root". Consequently, there are different opinions on the odor and flavor of **Spikenard Oil.** As a general description it can be said that the oil is a pale yellow to amber colored liquid with a heavy, sweet-woody and spicy-animal odor, reminiscent of valerian, ginger, cardamom and Atlas cedarwood oils. The flavor is warm-spicy, root-like in sweetness, somewhat pine-wood-like and slightly bitter-burning, powerful.

Spikenard Oil is not regularly produced outside India and Japan, but when the oil is available, it can be used with advantage in perfumes such as Oriental bases, heavy florals, fougères, woody bases, animal-ambre types, etc. It blends well with amyl salicylate, cedarwood oil and its derivatives, coumarin, ionones, labdanum products, lavender, oakmoss products, patchouli oil, pine needle oils, vetiver oil, etc. In flavors, it can be used as a modifier for valerian, hop, ginger, calamus, cardamom, etc., and its warm and rich body will help rounding off the sharp notes from chemical additives in the flavor composition.

The oil has been used as a substitute for **Valerian Oil** (see monograph), but the reverse case has also occurred since **Spikenard Oil** is now a scarce oil. Adulteration takes place frequently with additives such as borneol, patchouli oil, isobornyl valerianate, terpinyl valerianate, terpineol, eugenol, cajuput oil, etc.

Spiraea Oil.

The wild growing plant or cultivated garden shrub, **Spiraea Ulmaria** (or **Filipendula Ulmaria**), also known as **"Meadow Sweet"** or **"Meadow Goat's Beard"**, etc., is well known in most temperate and cold-temperate countries for its wealth of tiny cream-colored flowers which exhale a very strong odor; the odor is to some people quite repulsive in its sickly sweetness. Quite obviously, an essential oil has been distilled from the flowers by steam, but the oil has never attained any importance in perfumery, mainly because of the fact that its main odor principles are readily available and low-cost, synthetic chemicals: **Salicylic Aldehyde,** methyl salicylate, heliotropine, etc.

The oil of **Spiraea Ulmaria** is briefly mentioned here, mainly to report that little or no true essential oil from this plant is produced or commercially available today. Various oils, sold under the name of **Spirea** (or **Spiraea**) **Oil,** are merely mixtures of the above synthetic chemicals and other perfume materials.

In view of the skin-irritating effect of salicylic aldehyde, it is conceivable that also the artificial spiraea oils will disappear entirely from the perfume market.

The odor type of the artificial oil also limits the application to certain technical preparations, masking odors, etc. since its sharpness and harshness is difficult to blend into ordinary perfume types. Minute additions of salicylic aldehyde, etc. could be useful in lily, ylang-ylang, lilac, new mown hay, fougère, etc., but the aldehyde is unstable in soaps and, as mentioned, it is skin-irritating. Acetophenone, methyl acetophenone, methyl benzoate, benzaldehyde, etc. have replaced spiraea oil in the rare places where it was ever used.

Spruce Oils.

Under the name of **Spruce Oil** or **Hemlock Spruce Oil** an essential oil is marketed in the United States of America. The oil is usually derived from several different botanical sources.

It is steam distilled from the leaves (needles) and twigs of **Tsuga Canadensis,** also known as the **"Eastern Hemlock"** since it grows all along the east coast of the U.S.A. Other sources of spruce oil are:

Picea Mariana, the **"Black Spruce"** in the northern United States and, to a smaller degree, **Picea Alba** and

Tsuga Heterophylla, the latter yielding an oil which is substantially different from the three others.

Spruce Oil is distilled in the eastern U.S.A., particularly in the states of Vermont, New York, New Hampshire, Tennessee, Virginia and in the midwestern state of Wisconsin.

The oil is pale yellow or almost colorless, and has a very pleasant, balsamic-fresh odor with a peculiar sweet-oily and slightly fruity undertone. The odor characteristics can vary significantly, according to the origin of the oil and to the nature of the botanical species used.

Spruce Oil is used extensively in the U.S.A. for room spray perfumes, bath preparations, air fresheners, disinfectants, in liquid detergents, cleansers and other household products, etc., and it finds a natural application in "pine" fragrances, not only because of the previous shortage of "true" Siberian pine needle oil, but also because of the excellent individual performance of spruce oil in "fresh" perfume types. It blends excellently with all pine needle oils, with oakmoss products, isobornylacetate, terpineol, cedarwood oils and their derivatives, coumarin, galbanum products, benzoin resinoids, lavandin oil and lavandin concrète, amyl salicylate, rosemary oil, etc. Spruce oil is fairly stable in soap, and it can be used in "pine" type fragrances for soaps, detergents and all kinds of household products where this fragrance seems to be generally accepted.

Although the oil is produced regularly on a fairly large scale, it is not available in quantities that would allow for a liberal use in the everyday household products. This application could easily result in a demand which would far exceed the 15 to 50 metric tons of annual production of the spruce oils.

See also **Abies** oils and **Picea Excelsa Oil.**

Star Anise Oil.

Star Anise Oil is steam distilled from the fresh or partly dried whole or comminuted fruits of

Illicium Verum, a tall, slender tree which is a native of southeastern Asia. The leaves are co-distilled not infrequently, or the essential oil of the leaves may be produced separately but added to the fruit oil on the production place. Distillation takes place in the Tongkin province of Indochina (Viet-Nam) and in the neighboring southern parts of China. There are a few modern distilleries which undertake the rectification of the oil, crudely distilled from native stills. The tree is cultivated, but old and abandoned plantings, semiwild trees, etc. yield a significant quantity of fruits for distillation.

During World War II, the star anise oil distillation was almost brought to a standstill and, after the war, serious political troubles in these areas prevented a full come-back of this important flavor material. A synthetic anethole was finally produced at an attractive price and in a sufficiently pure grade for flavor purposes. This anethole completely compensated for the lack of true star anise oil in the United States of America and several other markets. However, it should be remembered that a "synthetic star anise oil" or a "synthetic" **Anethole** (usually produced from methyl chavicole which is isolated from pine oil fractions) may be harmful to human beings due to the presence of *cis*-**Anethole** in some of the "synthetic" anetholes. Those interested in the toxicity of *cis*-anethole compared to the harmless *trans*-**Anethole** (naturally occurring anethole) should study the publications of Y.-R. Naves, Favre and Ardizio in the Bulletin de la Société Chimique de la France, April, 1958, page 566, and also later publications in various technical periodicals (S.P.C. Sept. 1959), etc.

Star Anise Oil is a pale yellowish or almost water-white liquid whose odor is intensely sweet. The conventional odor-flavor description "like licorice" is just as erroneous as the description "chocolate-like" for the odor of a vanilla bean. Anise oils are used for the flavoring of licorice, but they have nothing else in common with the pure licorice root or extract of licorice. The two materials have a sweet but widely different flavor.

Due to the high content of **Anethole** (up to 90/95%), star anise oil is also strongly reminiscent of "true" anise oil (see **Anise Oil**). Most Pharmacopoeias allow the use of both oils indiscriminately, provided the assays are kept.

Although the flavor of star anise oil does not immediately appear very powerful, it has certain unusual characteristics. The use-level (recommended concentration of star anise oil in a finished product where anise is the main flavor principle) can be varied quite substantially without any distinct change in the overall flavor, and without causing the flavor to become unpleasant, biting or pungent. Briefly, overdosage is not easily performed. On the other hand, when the oil is used in the "wrong" places (i.e. where anise is either not wanted or where it should be a trace component or a sweetener only), overdosage is very likely. Trace amounts of star anise oil in e.g. bitter almond oil, rose compounds, lavender oil, etc. may easily ruin a composition. In combination with sweet orange oil or with sweet orange terpenes, star anise oil produces excellent masking effects for putrid odors such as sulfides, etc. (cold wave lotions). In pine needle fragrances, traces of star anise oil are often very helpful, although the anise note in certain cases is quite detrimental to the pine needle odor.

The suggested use level and **Minimum Perceptible** for star anise oil are practically identical to the figures mentioned under **Anise Oil.**

Star Anise Oil is used almost exclusively as a flavor material in candy, licorice, toothpaste flavors, carbonated drinks, alcoholic beverages, pharmaceutical preparations, etc. Minor amounts are used in soap perfumes, but low-cost synthetic anethole has largely substituted for the unavailable star anise oil for such purposes. Star anise oil is occasionally adulterated at the place of its production with the essential oil from the leaves and twigs of the same tree **(Illicium Verum).** That oil contains less anethole, but has a composition similar to that of star anise fruit oil. "Artificial" star anise oils have flooded the market for some time. They are based upon synthetic anethole, with trace amounts of phellandrene, para-cymene, estragole, safrole, etc. as "bouquetting" additives.

Crude star anise oil in the original drums is often very dirty, and may contain water, sand, fruit residues, etc. Filtration and rectification is then recommended. Anethole can be isolated from the oil by freezing. This anethole is an important ingredient in the very popular French "anisette" flavored brandy. This beverage is a 43 to 45% alcoholic and saturated solution of anethole. It separates anethole and becomes "cloudy" when chilled below room temperature.

The annual production of star anise oil in

Indochina is estimated at from 300 to 500 metric tons during the five-year period of 1955/60.

Stirlingia Latifolia.

From a small, wild growing plant in the west Australian coastal districts, an essential oil can be obtained by steam distillation of the entire overground parts of the plant. The material is distilled without being dried first.

Stirlingia Latifolia Oil has very little importance or application in perfumery, but deserves a brief mention because of the peculiar fact that it consists almost entirely of Acetophenone. This material is readily available as a synthetic chemical at a very low cost and, furthermore, it can be used in perfumes only in trace amounts because of its power and harshness in odor.

The oil of stirlingia latifolia is not regularly produced or commercially available. Occasional lots of the oil offered on the perfumery market may well consist of synthetic acetophenone with minute additions of other perfume materials. It serves no purpose to use such artificial oils in perfumery.

A true oil of Stirlingia Latifolia is pale yellow when freshly distilled, and smells strongly herbaceous, sweet and floral-haylike, not nearly as repulsively sharp or harsh as pure acetophenone. Materials, suitable for "rounding-off" the odor of synthetic acetophenone are, e.g.: heliotropine, cassione, anisyl acetone, anisic alcohol or anisyl acetate, cinnamic alcohol, methylcinnamic alcohol, vanillin, zingerone, anethole, dihydrosafrole, isoeugenol, mimosa concrète, ylang-ylang oil, etc., but the fact remains that Mother Nature can camouflage the presence of 95 to 98% of acetophenone in an essential oil to such a degree of perfection that one must smell it to believe it. We have numerous examples of this natural art of perfumery in essential oils.

Styrax.

I: Asian Styrax:

Styrax, occasionally called Storax, is a natural balsam (see Part One of this work: Balsam), formed as a pathological product in the sapwood and bark tissues of Liquidambar Orientalis, a medium-sized tree native to Asia Minor and the surrounding islands. The name Liquidambar is derived from the French "liquid ambre". The tree is wildgrowing, and does not have to be felled in order to yield styrax. The bark is removed spotwise, and the sapwood is deliberately injured. Styrax is formed and collected in cans below the wounds or scraped off the wound. The peeled bark can be boiled in water to yield an additional amount of styrax. The entire yield is "cleaned" by washing in boiling water. The water is decanted, and the heavier styrax collected on hairsifts or linen filters. However, when packed in cans, the styrax still contains up to 25% water. The water is usually found on top of the styrax. A sandy, grayish mass will deposit at the bottom, consisting mainly of dirt, sand, etc. Obviously, such matter is unwanted in a perfumery material, and various methods of further cleaning or "clarifying" the styrax have been suggested:

1) Drying with anhydrous sodium sulphate, prior to extraction with benzene. This yields a true resinoid of styrax.

2) Extraction with alcohol (ethyl alcohol or, rarely, methyl alcohol). Several extractions are necessary if the water content is high. The alcoholic extracts are subsequently dried with anhydrous sodium sulfate or the like prior to evaporation of the extract in mild vacuum. This leads to a so-called "resin-absolute" of styrax.

3) Direct extraction of the crude styrax with an odorless, high-boiling solvent, e.g. diethyl phthalate. Prior to this extraction, a test is run on the raw material in order to determine the exact content of "oil-soluble matter" in the crude styrax. Then, a calculated amount of diethyl phthalate is added, e.g. exactly enough to make e.g. a 50% solution of the "resinoid" in diethyl phthalate. The water will separate, and the dirt remains undissolved. The viscous liquid can be warm-filtered, yielding a clear and pourable 50% styrax resinoid, soluble in all conventional perfume materials, but not in paraffin oil, and not soluble without turbidity in alcohol. For further details, see monograph on Styrax Resinoid.

Asian Styrax is a very viscous or semiliquid mass of greenish-gray to brownish gray color, usually showing water on the surface and a heterogeneous semi-solid mass of darker color at the bottom of the container. The styrax itself is sticky and usually non-pourable at room temperature. The water-free portion is almost completely soluble in alcohol. It contains substantial amounts of cinnamic acid (which should be considered when styrax is used in soap perfumes). Also, when the styrax is extracted with hot alcohol or with alcohol under reflux, it must be remembered that significant amounts of ethyl cinnamate are formed and carried over in the extract. This type of extract is thus not truly representative of natural styrax.

Asian styrax is rarely used as such in perfumery. Only well cleaned products or extracts are suitable for perfumes. See the monographs on **Styrax Oil** and **Styrax Resinoid.**

II: American Styrax:

A product similar to the above Asian styrax is produced from certain varieties of the large tree, **Liquidambar Styraciflua,** wild growing in the eastern and southern U. S. A., in Mexico, Honduras and Guatemala. This balsam is collected in Honduras and, to a lesser extent in Guatemala, Central America. The balsam is a pathological exudation which accumulates in "pockets" in older trees. Incisions in the bark or other damaging of the trees thus is not necessary. The pockets are tapped on the living trees. There is little or no cleaning operation of the collected balsam.

Like the Asian styrax, the Honduras balsam is shipped in 5-gallon kerosene tins. Shipments in 55-gallon second-hand iron drums is becoming more common. The balsam is usually darker, but cleaner than Asian styrax. The odor of American (Honduras) styrax, however, is more "gasoline-like" (styrene-odor), covering the balsamic sweetness of the main ingredients of the balsam. The two products are used for quite similar purposes in perfumery. On account of the subdued styrene odor, the Asian balsam is generally preferred. However, when resinoids are prepared, the two products become almost identical since the styrene is partially or totally lost during the evaporation. Some perfumers even prefer the pronounced styrene note because of the apparent power displayed by this unsaturated hydrocarbon.

Styrax balsams are occasionally adulterated with odorless, high-boiling solvents, but adulteration of the crude material is rare. More frequently, the resinoids, etc. are "cut" or "stretched" with diluents such as diethyl phthalate, benzyl benzoate, benzyl alcohol, cinnamic acid, various cinnamates,

deodorized hydrogenated methyl abietate, isopropyl myristate, etc.

Styrax Oil.

Apart from the acids (mainly cinnamic acid), most of the components of crude styrax balsam are volatile with steam. The essential oil obtained by steam distillation of the crude styrax is the true styrax oil. However, there are numerous perfume materials on the market under names which seem to indicate that they are true essential oils from styrax, although these products are often quite different from the true essential oil. One fact that immediately strikes the alert observer is that styrax "oils" or "essences" are available at prices ranging from little more than twice the cost of natural styrax balsam up to 15 or 20 times this figure. The most expensive ones are often the most "compounded". It is customary to saponify the crude styrax prior to distillation when the so-called "styrol" or natural cinnamic alcohol is wanted. By steam distillation after saponification is obtained a mild-smelling, neutral perfume material which finds some use in floral perfumes, etc. for its tenacious and balsamic, mild and floral sweetness. This "natural" cinnamic alcohol is several times more expensive than the synthetic material.

True steam distilled styrax oil is a pale yellow to almost water-white, viscous liquid with an odor that is very rich, balsamic-sweet, floral and somewhat spicy, reminiscent of lilac, hyacinth, etc. although it has a distinct topnote of hydrocarbon character, unpleasant and actually not wanted. The topnote can be disposed of by leaving out the "heads" of the steam distillate but, on the other hand, many customers expect this styrene note and it also mellows in to a great extent after some time. **Styrax Oil** can be considered a neutral (non-acidic) concentrate of styrax balsam. It has all the floral-balsamic notes of the balsam, but none of the drawbacks from acids, water or color. It is clearly soluble in alcohol and all common perfume materials, and its comparatively low cost makes it one of the most interesting perfume materials. Even the tremendous drop in the price of synthetic cinnamic alcohol during the past 10 years has been unable to kill the interest in natural styrax and its derivatives.

Styrax Oil is used in numerous types of floral

perfumes, e.g. lilac, hyacinth, appleblossom, carnation, etc. In spite of its deep sweetness, its dry-floral note makes it suitable for cassie, mimosa, violet, carnation and hawthorn (spicy notes!), lavender and fougère (sweetness and tenacity), rose, etc. It blends excellently with coumarin and its derivatives, with cyclamal, linalool, terpineol, anisaldehyde, ylang-ylang, jasmin bases, ionones and methylionones, etc., etc. The spicy note is derived from cinnamic alcohol and its esters, and from traces of cinnamal formed by oxidation of the cinnamic alcohol in the oil. Styrene, the hydrocarbon topnote material, eventually polymerizes and becomes odorless. This is no drawback at all.

Numerous of the so-called "Styrax Oils" on the market are nothing other than more or less successful compounds of cinnamic alcohol, cinnamic esters (acetate, formate, propionate), cinnamates (methyl-, ethyl-, cinnamyl-, benzyl-, phenylpropyl-, etc.), with traces of cinnamal, vanillin, etc. added.

Other and far superior products are true distillates obtained by e.g. high-vacuum distillation, co-distillation or molecular distillation (anhydrols, alva-essence styrax, etc.). These products contain more components of the crude styrax than does the steam distilled oil. They are closer to the natural styrax in odor type, but they may not be neutral or entirely soluble. They usually lose the unpleasant styrene topnote during distillation which inevitably involves temperatures high enough to decompose the styrene. The amount of so-called styrax oil annually offered on the market is far in excess of the theoretical amount of true styrax oil in the combined world production of Asian and American styrax balsams.

Styrax Resinoid.

Natural (crude) styrax is so impure that it cannot be used directly in perfumes. It contains substantial amounts of water, and it is a heterogeneous mass which cannot be dispensed without thorough and troublesome stirring. Therefore, only cleaned products, e.g. resinoids, are used in perfumes. A summary of the conventional methods for production of cleaned styrax is given under the monograph Styrax.

Benzene extraction leads to a true resinoid, free from water and producing a dark olive to brownish colored, very viscous liquid, hardly pourable at room temperature. The resinoid is clearly soluble in most perfume materials, but causes turbidity with alcohol.

Direct alcohol extraction leads to a so-called resin-absolute. Water must be removed in order to complete the solution in alcohol. Hot extraction causes severe changes in the composition of the extract (formation of ethyl cinnamate, etc.) while cold extraction and low-temperature evaporation leads to a true-to-nature alcoholic extract of styrax. The alcoholic extract is somewhat darker than the benzene extract, but this depends also upon the quality and type of the styrax.

Alcohol extraction of the benzene resinoid leads to a true **Absolute** of **Styrax**. This product is alcohol-soluble, comparatively pale in color, and truly representative of the natural raw material in odor.

Petroleum ether extraction yields a pale olive or greenish-brown colored resinoid in a slightly lower yield, but with a sweeter, more balsamic odor. It is available as a "neutralized" (purified) extract, the acids having been removed from the petroleum ether solution by alkali washing prior to evaporation. Benzene extracts are sometimes treated in a similar way.

Acetone is now rarely used for extraction of styrax. Like ethyl alcohol, it is miscible with water, and before it can be evaporated without loss of odorous components, the acetone extract must be dried.

Direct "extraction" with high-boiling solvents (which are not removed from the "extract"), e.g. diethyl phthalate yields a viscous, diluted extract of styrax, clear and comparatively pale in color, pourable and handy for use. Extraction tests prior to diethyl phthalate addition will tell the manufacturer exactly how much diethyl phthalate he must add to obtain, e.g. a 50% styrax resinoid solution in the diethyl phthalate. Such resinoids should, of course, be duly labelled "Styrax Resinoid, 50% solution in D.E.P." and not, as it is often the case: "Styrax - - - -" (brand name for this company's resinoids). There is unfortunately no standard prescription for the production of styrax resinoid (or other resinoids), and it is left to the manufacturer's discretion to produce—and to the perfumer's experience to evaluate these products.

54: A single **Tuberose** left after the cutting of a 15-acre field near Mâaziz, Morocco.

(Fot. S. Arctander, 1960)

55: Moroccan **Tuberose** flowers. For extraction of the concrète, the flowers are picked immediately before the buds open.

(Fot. S. Arctander, 1960)

Sumbul Root Oil.

See also **Spikenard Oil** and **Valerian Oil, Indian.**

Various species of a plant of the Umbellifer family, and native of the mountainous regions in Iran, India, southeastern U.S.S.R. and Afghanistan, are known for their fragrant roots, the **Sumbul** roots. The best known of these plants is **Ferula Sumbul** which probably is the original, so-called **Musk Root.** Other species have roots of different odor type. The fact that the root from **Ferula Sumbul** is difficult to obtain in a state free fom admixture of roots of other **Ferula** species, is partly responsible for the lack of interest in this material.

Sumbul Root is steam distilled in Europe and occasionally in the U.S.A., rarely in India, to yield **Sumbul Root Oil.** The constituents of the oil are, however, very high boiling, and a prolonged distillation or an increased steam pressure may seriously affect the olfactory quality of the oil. A so-called oleo-resin or, according to the definitions in Part One of this work, a concrète extract of sumbul root is occasionally prepared by certain European perfume houses, see **Sumbul Root Resinoid** (next monograph).

Sumbul root oil is a very viscous, dark amber to brownish liquid with a warm-woody, orris-like and very faintly musky ("animal") type of odor, remotely reminiscent of valerian, de-sulphurized asa foetida, costus and elecampane. There is a certain balsamic sweetness in the dryout, but the most outstanding virtue of the oil is the fixative effect. In chypre, Oriental bases, musk bases, "precious wood" notes, etc., the oil of **Sumbul Root** may find some application. The poor availability, as pointed out above, almost prohibits the use of this oil.

Due to the irregular appearance on the market, **Sumbul Root Oil** is frequently adulterated, and without previous solid knowledge of a genuine oil, an evaluation of this rare oil is quite a difficult task.

Sumbul Root Resinoid.

Various extraction methods and solvents have been applied to produce tinctures, concrètes, resinoids, "oleo-resins", etc. from **Sumbul Root** because of technical difficulties in the distillation of the root with steam.

Alcohol extraction directly on the comminuted root yields tinctures which are applicable in perfumery as good fixatives of comparatively little odor value. The root material is imported from the country of origin of the plant (see **Sumbul Root Oil**), and according to the author's knowledge, no extraction is carried out in the countries where the plant is grown.

Benzene extraction will yield a so-called resinoid (a concrète extract) of sumbul root. This product is a dark brown, semi-solid, non-pourable mass of a pleasantly warm-woody, slightly sweet-balsamic odor. Hydrocarbon solvent extraction usually gives a much lower yield than alcohol extraction, but the odorous components and the resins are carried over into solution by both types of solvents. The alcoholic products are generally darker and more solid of texture. They may be preferable in colognes or weak alcoholic lotions where the oil-soluble, hydrocarbon-extracted products would not be clearly soluble.

Due to the scarcity of true **Ferula Sumbul** roots or closely related species of **Ferula**, the **Sumbul Root Resinoid** remains a very rare perfume material which is not commercially available or regularly produced by the supply houses. The root is still imported by a few French, English and American perfume houses for use in "private" perfume compositions. The tinctures and resinoids find application as fixatives in the same types of perfume as those mentioned under **Sumbul Root Oil.**

Sweet Pea.

Lathyrus Latifolius and other species of **Lathyrus** are very popular garden flowers (climbing vines), cultivated for their wealth of fragrant flowers in white, pink, pastel blue, rose-red, mauve and striped and many other colors. The origin of the plant has not yet been determined but it is believed that the plant came from southern Europe. Although there is some difference in the fragrance of the various colors and species of **Lathyrus** (flowers), the difference is not nearly as wide as in the case of e.g. rose varieties. **Lathyrus** species are cultivated all over the world in cold-temperate zones and in semi-tropical zones. The islands of Bermuda are famous for their sweet peas (as the plant is also called), and a local Bermudan perfume industry claims the rare use of **Lathyrus** flowers in their perfume production.

Lathyrus flowers could be extracted by the

enfleurage method or by direct solvent extraction. The latter method is occasionally applied in Europe. However, true and exclusively natural products from **Lathyrus** flowers are not regularly produced anywhere.

The fragrance of the flowers recall that of freesia, certain roses (e.g. the wild rosa canina, also called hip-rose or hedge-rose) with a very delicate touch of orange blossom or hyacinth. However, the most typical feature of the fragrance of lathyrus is its suave lightness, almost balsamic (like the non-aldehydic part of hyacinth), sweet (like rose-freesia) and yet honeylike sweet, subdued floral (like orange flower) with a bouquet and top of mild greenness.

Lathyrus perfumes are accordingly based upon other natural perfume materials with addition of various synthetic perfume materials, e. g. tuberose, orange flower absolute, jasmin absolute, rose de mai absolute, vanilla absolute, terpeneless petit-grain bigarade, styrax products, benzoin products, tolu products, cinnamic alcohol, methyl cinnamic alcohol, terpineol, phenylethyl alcohol, linalyl anthranilate, beta-gamma hexenyl acetate, hydra-tropyl acetone, phenylethyl monochloroacetate, etc.

Sweet Pea perfume bases are used in perfume creation as floral, sweet and light bases to be blended and modified with other perfume bases.

Syringa.

A very common and popular garden shrub is **Philadelphus Coronarius,** a native of northern and temperate zones in Europe and Asia. The shrub is cultivated in Europe and the U.S.A. as an ornamental plant, and it is known for its wealth of strongly fragrant white flowers. The orange-flower-like odor of these flowers is probably the reason for the common name **"Mock Orange"** for the shrub. The name **Syringa** is somewhat confusing and erroneous since it truly is the generic name for the lilacs (see monograph on **Lilac**) while the **"Mock Orange"** truly is a **Philadelphus** species.

Small amounts of philadelphus coronarius flowers are extracted in the south of France, and an absolute is marketed under the name of **"Absolu de Seringe".** This material is an amber colored, very viscous liquid of rich and sweet-floral odor, reminiscent of honeysuckle, gardenia, orange flower, etc. The odor is soft and very tenacious without any indolic notes.

Syringa Absolute would no doubt find some application in floral perfume bases, in modern aldehydic-floral colognes, in jasmin modifications, in ambre and cassie bases, etc., if the material would become freely available. Its reasonable cost (less than jasmin and orange flower absolutes) should indicate that a large-scale production could bring the price further down to a very attractive level and thus result in a more general and wide use of this interesting perfume material.

T

Tagetes Absolute—and Tagetes Oil.
(See also **Marigold** (calendula absolute) and **Tagetes Patula**).

From the overground parts of the plant, **Tagetes Glandulifera,** harvested just after the inflorescence, an essential oil (by steam distillation) or an absolute (from concrète by extraction) is obtained. The plant grows wild in south Africa, East Africa and Nigeria (west Africa), often in such abundance that it is considered a weed. It is presumably of South American origin, and has followed war transports to south Africa and Australia, and then further expanded its domain to Europe, Asia and North America. The oil is distilled in the Union of South Africa, in Kenya, Nigeria and France, occasionally in Australia. The absolute is produced in Nigeria and France. It is thus one of the few perfume plants which are distilled in all five continents of the world.

Tagetes Absolute is an orange-green or dark greenish-brown colored, semi-liquid mass or viscous liquid. Its odor is intensely herbaceous-green, with a sweet-fruity undertone and a somewhat bitter-herby dryout. Some people find the odor very pleasant; others find it highly disagreeable. In perfumery, it is necessary to work it up into high dilution in order to obtain pleasant and useful effects. It blends well with sage clary, flouve, tobacco extracts, bergamot oil and other citrus oils, linalool, phenylethyl alcohol, anthranilates, etc., all representing fruity-herbaceous and tobacco-like notes.

The essential **Oil of Tagetes Glandulifera** is a mobile, dark yellow to orange-yellow colored liquid which solidifies upon exposure to air, daylight and moisture. It can be kept in diethyl phthalate solution when it is well protected against ultra-violet light and moisture, and preferably under antioxidant protection. The main constituent, **Tagetone,** an unstable ketone, is presumably responsible for the peculiar odor and for the resinification and unstability of the oil.

The production of **Tagetes Oil** in Nigeria is of fairly rexent date, but the total world production is still at a very low figure (estimated for 1959 at less than 100 kilos). There is no suitable substitute for true **Tagetes Oil** or **Tagetes Absolute,** and once these materials are established in perfume formulas, the oil must be procured somehow. In spite of the typical apple-like note in highly diluted preparations of **Tagetes,** the oil has not found significant use in flavors. It is quite possible that **Tagetone** is harmful to the human organism.

Tagetes Patula.

While the European "marigold" (calendula officinalis) is used in perfumery as an absolute, the Indian variety, **Tagetes Patula,** can be steam distilled to yield an essential oil.

(See also monographs on **Marigold** (for calendula absolute) and **Tagetes Absolute** (for tagetes glandulifera oil).).

Various tagetes species grow wild and abundantly in India, and several species are used in the production of perfume oils. **Tagetes Patula** is a tall perennial plant with orange-colored flowers. It grows semiwild and is cultivated on a comparatively large scale in the western parts of India, particularly in the northern highlands. It should be noted at this point that the well known **Tagetes Glandulifera** and other species also grow in India.

The flowers, occasionally the entire overground part of the plant (the herb), are distilled with steam to yield a yellowish-amber-colored essential oil which is mobile when freshly distilled, but soon oxidizes and resinifies and becomes very viscous when exposed to air and moisture. Old oils are viscous, dark amber or brownish colored, and lack the typical fruity topnote. Fresh oils are characterized by a very powerful fruity topnote, somewhat reminiscent of green apples. The bodynotes are strongly herbaceous, somewhat sharp, like the non-floral part of the lavender fragrance. The oil finds use in certain types of herbaceous fragrances, e.g. fougère, lavender, etc., and occasionally in florals such as jasmin, gardenia,

chypre, violet, etc., where the herbaceous-green notes play an important role. Modern aldehydic bases, "tabac"-bases, etc., may also benefit from trace additions of tagetes patula oil. When the flowering tops of the tagetes patula plant are distilled into a receiver which contains a solvent, e.g. sandalwood oil or liquid paraffin, a so-called **"Attar Genda"** is obtained. The genda attar is a well known Indian perfume material, but has attracted very little interest outside of its country of origin. It is weaker and less natural in odor than the essential oil.

The absolute of **Tagetes Patula** is not a commercially available item, but in Europe an absolute is prepared from **Calendula,** a related plant (see this monograph). In Nigeria and France, other **Tagetes** species are extracted, see **Tagetes Absolute** (and **Tagetes Oil**).

Tagetes Patula is occasionally used for the adulteration of **Saffron** (see this monograph) since the dried outer petals of tagetes have an appearance similar to that of true saffron. However, the latter produces a much more intense color when extracted with water.

Tangerine Oil.

While **Mandarin Peel Oil** (see this monograph) is well known and is produced on a fairly large scale, the peel oil of the closely related **Tangerine** is a comparatively rare oil. The tangerine tree, **Citrus Reticulata,** grows in Florida, Texas and California (U.S.A.), and is actually the American variety of the East Asian **Mandarin.** The tangerine has recently been introduced in Guinea, West Africa. Small amounts of oil are produced there by hand ("écuelle" method, or "spoon scraping method"). Algeria produces a machine pressed mandarin oil. The tangerine is much larger than the mandarin, almost globoid, and its peel is usually yellow or pale yellow to reddish. It is cultivated mostly for sale as a whole fruit and for the canning of cleaned sections.

Tangerine Oil is machine pressed from the peel of the ripe fruit in the canning factories. The oil is orange colored, mobile and with a fresh, sweet odor, reminiscent of bitter orange and of Valencia orange oil, rather than of mandarin oil. It completely lacks the characteristic dryness and "perfumery" notes of mandarin oil, and it is also much "thinner" in body. **Tangerine Oil** can not be used as a replacement for mandarin oil in perfumery or flavor work. It constitutes a particular citrus note, but it is not sufficiently characteristic to become very interesting. It is used to some degree as a modifier in colognes, as a topnote material in aldehydic perfumes, etc. In flavors, it is a popular modifier (in the U.S.A.) for orange and lemon-lime combination flavors. As a "five-fold" concentrate or similar concentrated (evaporated) oil, it is used in candy flavors, soft drink flavors, ice cream flavors, etc.

The peculiar "fishy" amine note of freshly expressed mandarin oil (probably due to a nitrogen compound derived from the anthranilates in this oil) is never present in tangerine oil. The latter may not contain any anthranilates at all.

Annual production of American tangerine oil is now over 10 metric tons, but the oil may only become more popular if the growers succeed in producing fruits with closer resemblance to the mandarin fruit.

Tansy Oil.

The essential oil, steam distilled from the flowering herb of **Tanacetum Vulgare,** is at present of little or no interest to the flavorist. The perfumer may still use it occasionally, and it deserves some attention for its peculiar odor characteristics. The plant is a very common wild-growing perennial, probably originating in Central Europe, and brought to the United States by the European immigrants. It is found in almost every temperate and cold-temperate zone in the world. It is cultivated for the purpose of harvesting the herb (pharmaceutical purposes); the oil is distilled in France, Germany, Hungary, Poland and the midwestern U.S.A.

Tansy Oil is a yellowish to orange-olive colored liquid with a warm, almost sharp and spicy, dry and herbaceous odor. The taste is very sharp, pungent and bitter at high concentrations. Due to the high content of **Thujone** (a toxic ketone) in the oil, it should not be used in flavors or any food preparations, although it has been used for a long time as an important ingredient in bitter-flavors for alcoholic beverages, etc. Earlier, the oil was used as an anthelminthicum in pharmaceutical preparations. In this respect too, it is related to wormwood oil (see this monograph) which is the flavor principle of the old type of "absinth".

Tansy Oil can add interesting notes to perfumes of the fantasy type, chypres, fougères, etc. where it may appear as a topnote of good tenacity and original effect. It is not infrequently adulterated with cedarleaf oil or Dalmatian sage oil. Tansy oil is far less stable than these materials, and has never achieved the wide application of the two other oils. It will undoubtedly remain a minor item on the perfumer's shelf, turning dark and viscous before the bottle is empty.

See also **Balsamite.**

Tea Leaf Absolute.

See also **Maté.**

Certain perfumery materials which are sold under the name of **Tea Absolute,** etc. are obtained from the cured, dried leaves of various forms of the true tea-tree, **Thea Sinensis** (or **Camellia Sinensis**). By hydrocarbon solvent extraction of the leaves, a concrète is obtained which in turn yields an absolute by alcohol extraction. Such extractions are performed in France and the U.S.A. However, the best known extracts are those which are molecularly distilled or co-distilled from the direct extraction product (first extract). These products are known as **Anhydrols** (L. Givaudan & Cie.) or **Resinoines Incolores** (P. Robertet & Cie.), etc. True absolutes are also available, but they are usually strongly colored. The distilled products are viscous, amber-colored liquids of a faint, but rich and delicately dry, somewhat herbaceous, yet sweet and woody odor. On dilution, the odor becomes slightly reminiscent of the odor of dry and cured tealeaves.

Tea Leaf Absolute (or Anhydrol or Resinoine incolore, etc.) are used in perfumery to produce sweet-herbaceous notes in certain floral perfumes, e.g. jasmin, orange blossom, gardenia, sweet pea, freesia, and to produce new effects in woody or aldehydic perfumes of non-floral type in general. As an intensifier of clary sage, melaleuca bracteata, michelia leaf oil, or other tea-like fragrances, it is unsurpassed in naturalness. Artificial "tea" bases are available, but they represent the perfumer's conception of a tea-perfume, rather than the fragrance of the tea itself.

Being of comparatively low flavor strength, the alcoholic tea leaf absolute finds very little use in flavors. Occasionally, aqueous extracts of tea are used, and they are certainly much cheaper.

An essential oil has been produced by steam distillation of the tea leaves, and this oil has been thoroughly investigated by the worldwide tea industry. However, the oil is not produced commercially, and may not be of any perfume or flavor interest. There is ample literature on the subject of the flavoring principles in tea leaves.

Templin Oil.

See also **Abies Alba Oil.**

By water distillation or steam distillation of the crushed cones of the European **"Silver Fir"**, **Abies Alba,** an essential oil is produced which is different from that of the leaves and twigs of this tree (see **Abies Alba Oil**).

The cones consist of seeds with a heavy protective tissue. The seeds contain the **Templin Oil.** The trees grow wild, and there is a certain limit to the amount of cones that can be collected. The oil is regularly produced in Austria, Switzerland, Germany and Yugoslavia, but only on a very modest scale. Annual production fluctuates between 2 and 10 metric tons.

Templin Oil is an almost water-white, mobile liquid of fresh and sweet odor, at the same time reminiscent of pine needles, balsam and sweet orange oil. The woody undertone could almost be said to resemble bitter orange oil. It is used as a "freshener" in colognes, fougères, "leather" notes, ambres and, above all, in better pine fragrances for room sprays, bath oils, etc. A peculiar application is as a corrective agent in "artificial" Siberian pine needle oils. Templin oil has an extraordinarily high laevorotation which is useful in the reproduction of all the correct "specifications" (physical data) for Siberian pine needle oil.

Although one of the "low-ester" pine type oils, the oil of **Templin** is quite interesting, and good oils can introduce very pleasant effects in perfumes. Its poor solubility in alcohol is a drawback for its use in fougère-colognes, lotions, after-shave perfumes, etc. where its fragrance is truly at home.

Thuja Plicata Oil.

"Pacific Thuja" oil:

Two different essential oils are produced from this tree.

1) **Wood Oil:** Although not a regularly produced or commercially available essential oil, the oil of American **"Western Red Cedar Heartwood"** deserves some attention. Through Scandinavian and American research, it has been found that this oil contains quite interesting chemicals. At this point, it should also be mentioned that the oil is poisonous, due to the presence of a ketone, *gamma-***Thujaplicin.** It should be remembered that another oil from a tree of the family Cupressaceae, savin oil, is also toxic.

Thuja Plicata Wood Oil can be produced by steam distillation of the heartwood of this tree. Among the interesting constituents of this oil is **Methyl Thujate**, a crystalline material which has a fresh, sweet and green-woody odor, great power and richness of fragrance, and apparently a versatile field of application. Those interested in further scientific data should consult Acta Chemica Scandinavica, 1952, vol. 6, pages 690 and 854, (and possible later publications by Herr J. Gripenberg). It is stated in these publications that the material was once thought to be methyl dehydroperillate, but it has been clearly determined to be the methyl ester of 4,4-dimethyl-cyclohepta-2,5,7-triene-1-carboxylic acid (and this acid is not identical with the so-called dehydroperillic acid).

2) **Leaf-and-twig Oil:**

A distillation of leaves and twigs of this tree gives an even better yield than the heartwood. Once produced in tens of tons annually in the northwestern U.S.A., the oil is now a rarity and is not regularly available.

Thuja Plicata Leaf Oil is a pale yellow to almost colorless, mobile liquid of strong, Dalmatian-sage and bitter-fennel-like odor, terpeney and camphoraceous with a sweet-woody undertone. A powerful masking agent, this oil can not compete with the so-called "thuja oil" (see monograph on **Cedarleaf Oil**). The odor of the former is cruder, harsher, and its availability is uncertain. However, the oil is, occasionally, offered as **Thuja Oil** (true).

Thujopsis Dolobrata Oil.

"Hiba oil":

Among numerous varieties of thuja all over the world is the Japanese **Thuja Dolobrata** (or **Thujopsis Dolobrata**). This tree grows also in certain parts of Asia and in the southern parts of the U.S.S.R. In Japan, the leaves and the wood are used for the distillation of two oils:

1) **Hiba Leaf Oil,** steam distilled from the leaves of the above tree, is of little or no interest. It is not regularly available on the perfumery market.

2) **Hiba Wood Oil,** steam distilled from the chips of the wood, is quite important. Recently, the annual production has surpassed 20 metric tons in Japan (1959). The wood is a popular construction wood, due to the excellent resistance of this wood to fungi and bacteriae. The fungus-growth inhibitor in the wood is a ketonic substance. In this respect, the wood resembles the wood of **Chamaecyparis Obtusa** (see this monograph).

Hiba Wood Oil is a yellowish to brownish-amber colored, somewhat viscous liquid of dry, woody odor with a peculiar sharp or pungent undertone. There are various types of the oil available (with or without the above ketonic fungistat-bacteriostat), and the odor of these types varies slightly. The ketone-free oil-fraction is used in Japan as a cedarwood oil in soap perfumes, detergent perfumes and industrial perfumes. So far, the oil has found no market outside of its country of origin, but the oil is available from Japanese supply houses in limited quantities.

The author has no personal experience with the use of **Hiba Wood Oil** or **Hiba Leaf Oil** in perfumery. It is conceivable that these oils will remain local materials.

Thyme Absolute.

A small amount of thyme herb (**Thymus Vulgaris**) is extracted in France, particularly by one manufacturer who specializes in extracted perfume materials, ultrasonic extracts, etc.

The dried herb is extracted with petroleum ether or other hydrocarbon solvent. The extract is a concrète of thyme. This is extracted with alcohol and yields an absolute. A diluted, liquid extract, obtained by direct hydro-alcoholic extraction (percolation) of the coarsely pulverized thyme herb, is known in pharmacy as **Thyme Fluidextract.** The use of diluted alcohol results in a much darker extract than when pure alcohol is used. For perfumery purposes, it is an advantage to use the two-step extraction which eliminates most of the chlorophyll and other coloring matter.

Thyme Absolute is a very viscous, dark green liquid or a semi-solid mass. Its odor is very

deep-herbaceous, sweet and somewhat green with a rich, spicy undertone and a faintly medicinal, but pleasant bodynote. This product is useful in perfumery for its peculiar effect which is entirely different from that of the thyme oil. In traces, the absolute can introduce beautifully natural notes in jasmin, hyacinth, violet, etc., and it lends a rich herbaceous note in fougère, chypre, colognes, etc., where it blends well with citrus oils, lavender, oakmoss, patchouli, isobornylacetate, etc.

In flavors, **Thyme Absolute** may be used as an improvement over thyme oil in all kinds of sauces, seasonings, and other food products, providing its green color is not prohibitive.

It is possible that **Thyme Absolute** may be produced on an increasing scale if, for example, Morocco will go into production of this item. The thyme plant is not too plentiful in France and, in Spain where there are numerous varieties of thyme plants, there are very few extraction facilities.

See also **Thyme Oil,** next monograph.

Thyme Oil.

The perfume and flavor trade distinguishes between two types of **Thyme Oil: Red** and **White.** Only the former is a natural distillate. The latter will be discussed at the end of this monograph.

Red Thyme Oil is water-and-steam distilled from the partially dried herb of the wild growing **Thymus Vulgaris, Thymus Zygis** or related species, mainly in Spain. The plant grows abundantly in Spain, Morocco, Turkey, Israel, the U.S.S.R., China and, to a smaller extent, in Italy, Hungary, Yugoslavia, Syria, France and various parts of Central Europe.

The plant is cultivated all over Central Europe and in many other countries for use as a dried culinary herb. Distillation is undertaken mainly in Spain and Israel. Production in Cyprus was abandoned in 1955 before the time of the author's last visit there. It is regrettable that this outstandingly fine quality of thyme oil is no longer available. Moroccan oils were distinguished by the fact that they were steam distilled from *flower* material. They were accordingly sweeter, but less herbaceous in odor and flavor. It is a matter of personal opinion as to which of the two types is the "best". At the time of the author's most recent visit to Morocco (June 1960), the distillation of thyme oil had been discontinued. The

Moroccan thyme grows in an area almost 500 kilometres from the nearest still.

Red Thyme Oil is a brownish-red, orange-red or grayish-brown colored liquid, rich and powerful, sweet, and warm-herbaceous in odor, somewhat spicy and distinctly aromatic. The flavor is equally warm, somewhat biting, but not bitter or tarry. A sharp and lasting mouthfeel is accompanied by a spicy-herbaceous taste and an outstanding richness in body. There should be no bitter-phenolic, cadelike or tarlike notes detectable, but there may be a short bite of terpeney, cymene-like topnotes in poorer oils. The suggested use level is 0.50 to 1.00 mg%, and the **Minimum Perceptible** is about 0.05 to 0.10 mg%. The oil is used extensively in flavors for food products, in sauces, dressings, pickles, canned meat, etc. In pharmaceutical preparations, the excellent germicidal properties of the oil are exploited in mouth waters, gargles, dentifrices, and for numerous types of disinfectants. Cough syrups, lozenges, etc. are often activated with thyme oil in combination with peppermint, eucalyptus, etc.

In perfumery, the oil finds some use in soap perfumes where its power and freshness can introduce a hint of medicinal notes, often desirable in certain types of soap or detergent. The oil exerts an excellent masking effect over tarry odors and thus illustrates brillantly an example of "distracting" odor effect. Added to lotion perfumes or colognes in trace amounts, thyme oil may lend body and sweet freshness in lavenders, fougère-colognes, citrus-colognes, spicy after-shaves, etc. The oil is highly interesting as a topnote material. Due to its phenol content (the solid phenol, **Thymol**), it discolors rapidly in contact with iron, even iron in trace amounts in other essential oils. Larger concentrations of thyme oil in soap perfumes may also prevent the perfume from being used in white soaps.

The oil is not infrequently adulterated—perhaps contaminated—with origanum oil or with fractions of various Spanish essential oils. Commercial lots of origanum oil may be offered under the name of thyme oil merely because of lack of knowledge from the broker's side.

Red Thyme Oil is produced in fluctuating quantities of 40 to 100 metric tons per year in the main producing areas. Little or no thyme oil is produced in France today, although large quantities are exported from that country.

White Thyme Oil, when correctly produced and genuine, is a pale yellow liquid similar in odor to the above-described red thyme, yet somewhat sweeter, less terpeney or sharp. It is also less herbaceous. Truly, it should be a redistilled red thyme oil. But frequently the commercial white thyme oil is merely a "compound" of pine oil fractions, terpineol fractions, rosemary fractions, eucalyptus fractions, red thyme oil fractions, para-cymene, pinene, limonene, caryophyllene, origanum oil fractions, etc. The Thymol content i commercial lots of so-called white thyme oil varies from about 20% to over 60%. A redistilled red thyme oil will usually contain about 60% thymol.

Ajowan Oil (see this monograph) is produced almost exclusively in India, and the terpenes from this oil are no more occurring as a common adulterant in Spanish or Moroccan thyme oils.

Thyme and Origanum Oils.

Summary:

To reduce further confusion in the nomenclature of **Thyme** and **Origanum**, the author proposes to outline briefly the names under which the various oils are listed in this work:

Thyme Oil: is produced from **Thymus Vulgaris, Thymus Zygis** or other species of **Thymus**, producing thymol-type of essential oil.

As **Thyme Oils**, the author will consider only those oils distilled from the above plants, and in which the phenol content is over 40%, and where more than 90% of the phenols is thymol.

Origanum Oil: is produced from **Thymus Capitatus** (also called **Coridothymus Capitatus** in Spain and the Middle East) while in north Africa various carvacrol-bearing plants of the **Origanum** species are used. Bulgarian and Italian so-called origanum oils are produced from **Origanum Vulgare** and other species, (see monograph on **Marjoram Oils**).

As **Origanum Oils**, the author will consider only those oils distilled from the above species, and containing over 55% phenols, exclusively or almost exclusively consisting of carvacrol (liquid).

Wild Marjoram Oils are either produced from **Origanum Vulgare** (see above) or, in Spain, from **Thymus Masticina**.

Sweet Marjoram Oils are produced from cultivated plants of **Majorana Hortensis.** They contain no phenols.

White Thyme Oil is not a natural oil, but it may be a redistilled "red thyme oil". Commercial lots of "white thyme oil" show heavy cutting and adulteration and rarely a true, redistilled thyme oil.

The German **"Feldthymian"** oil, also called **"Wild Thyme"** is produced from **Thymus Serpyllum** in many countries. It is known under the name of **Serpolet** in France.

Savory Oil is produced from **Satureia Montana** or **Satureia Hortensis.** The oil resembles Spanish origanum to a certain degree.

Thymus Hiemalis produces the so-called "Spanish verbena oil" (see monograph on **Verbena**).

True **Verbena Oil** is produced from **Lippia Citriodora,** but there is no regular production of this oil.

The main confusion arises from the fact that Spanish thyme oils are often origanum oils and vice versa. Mixtures of the two oils are also commercially offered under one or the other name.

Thyme, "Wild".

Of very little interest to the perfumer, and of decreasing interest to the flavorist is the oil, steam distilled from the flowering herb of **Thymus Serpyllum.** The plant grows wild in various botanical forms in the U.S.S.R., Central Europe, Asia and Africa. It is also known in many states of the northern U.S.A. The plant is collected in France, Germany, Yugoslavia, Italy and Poland. In France, it is known as **"Serpolet"**, in Germany as **"Quendel".**

"Wild Thyme" oil is a pale yellow, mobile liquid with an odor that is fresh, but somewhat sharp-terpeney, and a burning sharp, woody-herbaceous taste with a spicy-phenolic undertone. There are many different types of this oil, but the author has yet to meet one which is outstandingly pleasant or very interesting beyond the scope of thyme oil, origanum oil or marjoram oils.

Wild Thyme Oil is used in its various countries of origin as a food condiment and, to a very limited extent, in perfumery where its fresh, sometimes almost lemony notes can be helpful in citrus-colognes, fougères, etc.

Oil of **Thymus Serpyllum** is rarely offered as a genuine oil, and it may slowly disappear from the perfumery and flavor market. Oils offered under the above name may be "constructed" from thyme oil fractions, linalool, origanum oil fractions, etc.

Tobacco Flower Absolute.

Certain species of the tobacco plant, **Nicotiana,** have flowers which are very fragrant, and for this reason have attracted not only horticulturists, but also perfumers. It will be remembered that the flowers of several species of **Coffea,** the coffee bush, have attained a similar reputation for fragrance. However, perfumery products of these botanicals are very rare and hardly ever offered commercially in significant amounts. A few perfume houses may process their own absolutes from the concrète extracts of flowers from **Nicotiana Affinis, Nicotiana Petunoides** or various species of **Nicotiana** from the Middle East.

The author has no personal experience with the use in perfumery of true extracts of fragrant tobacco flowers, but he has studied various species, including **Nicotiana Affinis,** in nature. The fragrance of this flower is extremely delicate, yet rich and sweet, spicy-floral, somewhat reminiscent of carnation with a fresher note, almost fruity. The white/pink phlox and the "sweet William", well known garden perennials, may even better describe the main odor type of the tobacco flower.

Because of its inavailability, the absolute of tobacco flower is a well-nigh unknown perfume material, and the inclusion of the material in this book may only serve as a completion of the monograph on **Tobacco Leaf Absolute** (see the following monograph).

Tobacco Leaf Absolute.

From various species of **Nicotiana** (the tobacco plant) come the leaves which, in the cured state, are known as tobacco. An infinitely small percentage of the world production of these cured leaves ends up in the perfume raw material factories to be processed into concrète by petroleum ether or benzene extraction. The concrète is then extracted with alcohol to yield an absolute. This extraction is carried out in France and in the U.S.A., occasionally in other countries. The "Virginia" type of tobacco leaves is generally preferred, although other types have been used.

Latakia Absolute is presumably produced from the Turkish or Syrian Latakia tobacco leaves.

Tobacco Leaf Absolute from Concrète is a dark brown, semi-solid mass of strong, almost repulsive odor, faintly reminiscent of cigar tobacco. The color is somewhat prohibitive for the extensive use of this material, but there are several decolorized or almost colorless products available. By extraction of the tobacco leaf material with special solvents, and subsequent co-distilling the extract with a high-boiling, odorless solvent in a molecular still, a pale amber-colored, viscous liquid is obtained. In dilution, it has a typical cigar-tobacco fragrance. Anhydrol Tobacco (Givaudan) is a product of this type, however somewhat diluted due to the special method of distillation. It yields similar odor effects. Resinoine Incolore Tabac (P. Robertet & Cie.) is another product of this type, a powerful concentrate of the tobacco leaf odor.

Steam distillation of the cured tobacco leaves has been attempted. It yields an essential oil which, on dilution, produces an odor fairly reminiscent of the tobacco odor. Due to the tremendous size of the tobacco industry, there has been extensive research on this subject, and those interested will easily find ample literature about the aromatic principles in the cured tobacco leaves. It is interesting to note that *phenylacetic acid* is a major constituent. This material has been used for half a century in artificial tobacco flavors (for shag and cigarettes).

Tobacco Leaf Absolute (or Anhydrol or Resinoine Incolore, etc.) are used not only in the "tabac" type of modern or aldehydic perfumes, but also for "dry" and "masculine" effects in fantasy types, in Oriental blends, etc. These materials blend well with sandalwood, castoreum, labdanum, clary sage, vetiver, bergamot, methylionones, cedarwood derivatives, etc., and they produce effects which are very hard to imitate or match (with other materials).

Tolu Balsam.

Tolu balsam is a *balsamic* type of a natural oleo-resin. Its content of essential oil is so low that the product could justly be called a balsamic resin or a Balsam. Balsam Tolu is a pathological product, formed after injuries in the trunk of Myroxylon Balsamum, a tall tree, native of the jungles of northern South America, particularly in Colombia and Venezuela. The tree also grows wild in Cuba.

After making incisions in the bark of these trees, the natives collect the viscous balsam which slowly solidifies on ageing. At present, practically all of the commercially available Tolu Balsam comes from Colombia. It is usually shipped in 5-gallon kerosene cans. When the balsam reaches the American or European market, it is hard at room temperature, plastic by hand heating and pourable at about 60°C. It is generally believed that the merchandise which is sold under the name of Tolu Balsam today is significantly different from the pre-war material, and distinctly inferior to this.

The balsam is a brown, orange-brown or dark yellowish brown mass, brittle when cold, and the fracture is glasslike or flintlike. Its odor is sweet-balsamic, cinnamic in type, faintly floral and with an undertone of vanillin. Its taste is slightly bitter-burning and rich-aromatic, spicy-cinnamic in overall flavor type.

The balsam itself is rarely used as such, but various cleaned products are employed in perfumery and pharmaceutical preparations (see the following monographs: Tolu Balsam Oil, Tolu Balsam Resinoid and Tolu Balsam Absolute). Tolu balsam is almost completely soluble in 95% alcohol. It is also soluble in most perfume materials, but not in all essential oils (turbidity with citrus oils, pine needle oils, etc.). The alcoholic solution is acid to litmus. A Tolu Tincture is occasionally used in perfumery, but if tolu balsam must act as a fixative it will be necessary to use from 2 to 5% or even more of the balsam. The tincture is only 20%, and it would thus be difficult to use the tincture as a fixative (solution). A neutralized absolute (alcoholic extract) is then preferable (see Tolu Balsam Resinoid). Tolu Balsam is occasionally adulterated with rosin or resinous residues from other balsams, copaiba balsam, peru balsam, acaroid, colophonium, etc. By extracting the tolu balsam with petroleum ether, one can usually identify such foreign matter since this solvent will extract little or no solid matter from a true tolu balsam. The annual world production of tolu balsam is about 100 metric tons. Considerable amounts of "de-aromatized" tolu balsam are offered on the market. The pharmaceutical industry uses certain amounts of tolu balsam for an aromatic syrup. The exhaust tolu balsam from the production of this syrup is strikingly similar to the true tolu balsam in appearance, but it is considerably less aromatic.

Tolu Balsam Oil.

By steam distillation of tolu balsam (see monograph), an essential oil is obtained which is truly **Tolu Balsam Oil**. However, the product which is turned out has quite variable properties according to the method of production, the steam pressure in particular. It has therefore become increasingly common to submit tolu balsam to a vacuum distillation. Very low Hg-pressure is necessary to prevent "burning" of the high-boiling components, and various "wiping-film" stills, molecular stills, etc. have been used in the production of distilled oils from tolu balsam.

The composition of dry distilled tolu balsam is significantly different from that of the steam distilled oil. Cinnamic and benzoic acid, together with high-boiling alkoxyphenols are present in the dry-distilled oil and make this material a good, but not neutral fixative in perfumery. **Anhydrol Tolu** (or similar specialties representing concentrates of the aromatic principles in tolu balsam) may be preferred for their neutral reaction and uniformity.

Tolu Balsam Oil (steam distilled) is a viscous oil of a sweet-floral odor with a rather sharp, peppery topnote which fades away quickly, giving way to a faintly fruity-floral, sweet-spicy, long-lasting, balsamic dryoutnote.

Tolu Balsam Oil (dry distilled) is an amber colored or yellowish, viscous liquid which solidifies into an amber colored, crystalline mass on standing or cooling. The odor of the melted homogeneous mass is very rich balsamic, occasionally somewhat creosolic, sweet and floral, outstandingly tenacious, and more uniform than the odor of the steam distilled oil. This material gives excellent effects in hyacinth, tuberose, gardenia, honeysuckle, stephanotis and numerous other sweet-floral fragrances; it blends well with hydroxycitronellal, linalool, sandalwood oil, terpeneless bergamot oil, isoeugenol, labdanum, heliotropine, mimosa absolute, opopanax, ylang-ylang, orange flower, and it is, in general, an interesting item for use in all types of "fantasy" perfume, "tabac", "leather", aldehydic perfume, etc. It produces interesting "powdery" effects with patchouli, ionones, musks, cedarwood ketones, etc.

In flavors, it is a useful fixative for rum (which contains many low-boiling and highly volatile materials), or in flavors for baked goods where the fixative effect of tolu balsam oil protects the flavor from evaporating during the baking at elevated temperatures (e.g. caramel flavors, etc.).

Tolu Balsam Oil is often produced by the consumer according to his specific needs, but there are countless qualities of this oil offered from the usual producers of natural perfume materials. Adulteration is very possible and likely to occur, partly due to the fact that the main ingredients of the oil are well-known, readily available, low-cost synthetic materials.

Tolu Balsam Resinoid.
Tolu Balsam Absolute.

Tolu balsam (see this monograph) can be extracted to yield various "cleaned" products. The crude balsam is soluble in alcohol, benzene, acetone, ether, chloroform, trichloro ethylene, methylene dichloride, etc., but not in petroleum ether. An alcohol extraction thus yields from 65% to over 90% of a product which is commercially available under various names, e.g. "resin absolute tolu", tolu resinoid, purified tolu, etc. Benzene extraction products are also commercially available, and are generally called tolu resinoid. The term "resin tolu" truly refers to the extracted, resinous matter from which the essential oil has been removed. Such a product is obviously a by-product from the suppliers who distil tolu balsam (see also **Tolu Balsam Oil**, adulteration). The resin has very little odor value, and is only a mediocre fixative since it has a high percentage of acids (benzoic and cinnamic in particular). These are not appreciated in perfumery or in soaps.

Tolu Balsam Absolute should be prepared from the benzene resinoid of tolu balsam by alcohol washing. However, it is customary to prepare the "absolute" by cold alcohol extraction of the crude tolu balsam. Due to these facts, it is not possible to give a firm description of these products. They appear on the perfumery market in a wealth of qualities and under scores of fancy names. Neutralized extracts of tolu balsam are produced by alkali washing of the benzene extract. The resin acids, cinnamic and benzoic acids, and other free acids are thereby removed. Such neutral tolu extracts are often very light colored, and they are excellent materials for soap perfumery where they simultaneously lend floral and fixative effect without affecting the alkalinity of the soap, or acid-hydrolizing eventual delicate perfume materials in the soap perfume.

Tolu Balsam Resinoid or **Tolu Balsam Absolute** are used primarily as fixatives in citrus-colognes, Oriental perfumes, chypres and floral bases, etc. Along with Peru balsam products, they are among the most interesting modifiers for "exotic" floral fragrances.

"Tombacco Absolute".

The name of this material does not reveal the botanical origin, and the sole producer of the material would probably not publish such information.

Tombacco Absolute (so-called) is produced in Grasse (France), from one or more flowering plants of local origin by extraction the usual way. The absolute is a soft, unctuous, non-pourable, dark olive-green material with a very rich, deep-sweet and floral-herbaceous odor which displays most surprising undertones, such as a sweet-fruity, prune-like, delicately floral and woody, tobacco-hay-like note, etc. There are notes which resemble **Flouve** and **Hay** absolute, **Clary Sage** absolute, **Cassie** absolute, **Carob** flowers, **Boronia**, **Ulex Europeaeus**, **Chloranthus Spicatus**, etc. Indeed a material of the floral tea-like odor group.

"**Tombacco Absolute**" is used in high-class perfumes for various purposes. It imparts by itself a warmth and slightly spicy floralness which is often requested for the lipstick perfume types and other sweet-fruity fragrances. It is an excellent fixative for certain types of floral perfume bases, e.g. muguet and honeysuckle, and it has an outstanding ability of rounding off the inevitable rough notes which accompany some of the conventional synthetic materials in a perfume. Its tenacity and uniformity in odor is particularly useful in face powder and rouge perfumes where many perfume materials show surprisingly little effect and poor stability.

A 50% solution of **Tombacco Absolute** in ethyl alcohol or diethyl phthalate is pourable and liquid.

The product is very stable and blends excellently with the aldehydes, e.g. in the "powdery" type of perfume bases where the aliphatic aldehydes, cinnamic alcohol (or styrax products), musks and

ionones form the body note, modified with woody or spicy notes.

The author is not convinced that this product is derived exclusively from one botanical raw material, but he finds it sufficiently interesting that it should be mentioned among the *processed* natural perfume materials.

Tonka Absolute.

A tincture can be prepared from dried comminuted tonka "beans" with ethyl alcohol (see monograph on **Tonka "Bean"** next). The strength of the alcohol may vary from 70% to 85% by volume. A tincture is a cold-processed, one-step extraction product and does not contain all of the aromatic principles of the tonka bean. After the evaporation of a tincture of tonka bean, some fats and waxes are left in the residue. Consequently, the best way of producing an alcohol-soluble extract (an **Absolute**) of tonka bean is the conventional two-step extraction via the **Concrète** (see **Tonka Concrète**).

Through the use of sufficiently diluted alcohol, or by freezing the alcoholic washings, it is possible to eliminate the fats and waxes (from the concrète), part of which are carried over in the alcohol washings. After removal of the alcohol under gentle vacuum, the **Tonka Absolute** is left.

Tonka Extracts may also be prepared by direct hydro-alcoholic percolation of the crushed seeds, usually without the application of heat. This leads to so-called **Absolutes** (or "**Resin-Absolutes**").

Tonka Absolute is a semi-solid or crystalline mass of pale amber or pale brownish-yellow color. Its odor is very rich, sweet and warm, distinctly coumarinic-herbaceous, with a prune-like or caramellic-sweet undertone. The odor description "tobacco-like" is somewhat confusing since tonka tincture has been used quite extensively in the flavoring of cured tobacco leaves. The absolute consists of from 20 to 45% **Coumarin**, but the effect of a true tonka absolute goes far beyond that of the coumarin contained in the absolute (see also **Vanilla**). In this fact lies the explanation for the continuous use of tonka absolute today, almost a century after the appearance of synthetic coumarin on the perfume and flavor market.

Tonka Absolute is used as a fixative and non-floral sweetener which introduces warm notes in chypres, fougères, new mown hay bases, lavender bouquets, Oriental bases, etc. It blends very well with lavender, lavandin, clary sage, flouve, phenylacetates, salicylates, cinnamates, styrax products, heliotropine, bergamot, oakmoss products, geranylesters, citronellylesters, menthylesters, etc.

An adulteration with synthetic coumarin is not always easy to detect, but comparing samples with home-made standard extracts prepared in the perfume laboratory will usually tell the perfumer whether an offered tonka absolute is genuine or not.

Tonka Absolute can not be used in flavors in those countries where a coumarin ban exists (U.S.A. and others).

Tonka "Bean".

Tonka "Beans" are the seeds from the fruits of a large tree, **Dipteryx Odorata** (and other species of **Dipteryx**) which grows in western and northeastern South America, particularly in Venezuela, the Guianas and Brazil. The tree also grows in Nigeria, West Africa, but production of beans for export has been irregular and remains unimportant in Nigeria.

The seed is removed from the ripe fruit and is dried and soaked in alcohol or rum for 12 to 24 hours. The seeds then swell and, when they are removed from the alcohol bath, they shrink on drying, and on the surface appears the well-known crystalline frosting of coumarin. This treatment is partly a curing, partly a conventional "sales promotion" process. The customers expect this particular appearance of tonka beans although the "frosting" is no criterion of high quality. Rum is used mainly because it is the cheapest form of local alcohol.

Tonka Beans are shipped via the seaports of, Maracaibo, Port of Spain (Trinidad is a transit station, not a producing area) and Belem (the Brazilian **Para**-tonka beans). After curing in the country of origin, the beans are not processed further, but are shipped to Europe and the U.S.A.

Tonka Beans do not yield any appreciable amount of aromatic oil upon steam distillation, but they are extracted with various solvents to produce tinctures, concrètes and absolutes (see the monographs on **Tonka Absolute** and **Tonka Concrète**). Under the first heading, the tincture is described; under the latter the so-called resin or resinoid of tonka, which is a concrète according to the terms of this work, is described.

In order to evaluate tonka beans, it is necessary to perform a test extraction. Even if he has solid knowledge and good experience in the trade of tonka beans, it is not possible for the perfumer to judge the quality directly. Adulteration is practically out of the question when the consumer buys the whole beans. However, "artificial" frosting with a solution of synthetic coumarin is not an unknown sophistication.

Due to the coumarin ban since 1953 in the U.S.A., tonka beans are no longer used in flavors for food or candy, beverages, etc., but they still find use in tobacco flavoring in a number of countries. The masking effect of tonka bean fragrance is well known. Cod liver oil, iodoform and other strong smelling pharmaceutical products were once perfumed with these odorous seeds. The use of tonka beans as an insecticide (against moths in clothes cabinets, etc.) is practically obsolete.

Since the tonka "bean" does not contain any significant amounts of resinous matter, the author prefers to use the term **"Concrète"** for the hydrocarbon- or acetone-extracted products of the bean. Benzene, acetone, ethyl ether or petroleum ether are used in the extraction of the coarsely pulverized, dried tonka "beans". Hot extraction is not advantageous since it draws out waxes and fats which are solid at room temperature and must be eliminated anyway. Percolation gives good results. The extract is evaporated under gentle vacuum until all solvent is removed. The resulting residue is **Tonka Concrète.** and its appearance varies according to the solvent used. A considerable amount of fixed (vegetable, fatty) oil is present, and the concrète is rarely a homogeneous mass. Its color is amber to brownish yellow, and it will form a white or creamy-colored deposit of crystallized coumarin, which is present in such amounts that it is not soluble in the oil.

When acetone is used in the extraction, the moisture which is enevitably present in the "beans" will go into the acetone and impair its solvent action. It will also result in the fatty oil separating from the acetone-extract before or during the evaporation. This can be of some advantage to a quicker elimination of the fixed oil. But this fatty oil has a considerable amount of coumarin and other aromatic substances in solution, and must be thoroughly washed (with ethyl alcohol) before it can be disposed of as useless. Some producers even take advantage of this aromatic fixed oil by producing a "tonka oil" which is used as an oil-soluble tonka flavor of suave sweetness and excellent tenacity and stability e.g. in baked goods. This oil can turn rancid on prolonged storage unless it is properly treated with an antioxidant (permitted in food products).

Petroleum ether extraction leads to a pale amber colored and very attractive concrète of a true-to-nature aroma, and free from water. The yield is slightly smaller than by benzene extraction which gives a somewhat darker concrète.

Tonka Concrètes are used in tobacco flavoring in countries where a coumarin ban does not exist. For perfumery, the **Absolute** (see this monograph) is preferred for better solubility and absence of fixed oil. **Tonka Resin** is a conventional term for a solid extract of tonka "beans", usually by means of benzene. The fatty oil may be eliminated, but the so-called resin still contains natural waxes. It is not infrequently adulterated with synthetic coumarin. It does not contain natural resins from tonka in any significant amount. Methyl abietate, deodorized dihydro methyl abietate, hydroabietic alcohols, Sumatra benzoin extracts, etc. may be added to tonka bean extracts to give them an appearance of "resins". Similar compounded products are offered under the name of **Tonka Resinoid.**

Treemoss Absolute.

By alcohol washing of **Treemoss Concrète**, an absolute is obtained which is more or less viscous and dark colored according to the solvent that was used in the first extraction of the moss. Benzene concrète gives an almost solid absolute, greenish-brown in color, while petroleum ether concrète yields a semi-solid mass or viscous liquid of dark brown color. The odor is woody, dry, forest-like or seaweed-like, herbaceous-green and of great tenacity. The yield of absolute from concrète is good, much higher than in the case of oakmoss. Accordingly, treemoss absolute is much cheaper than oakmoss absolute. However, there is a significant difference in odor characteristics, particularly in the absence of the powerful, yet delicate topnote which is found in true oakmoss.

The trade offers countless types of treemoss absolutes and similar extracts, tinctures, concentrates, ultrasonic extracts, integral extracts, fractions, etc. Thus, it would be impossible to give more than a very general description of the odor and appearance of treemoss absolute.

Treemoss Absolute is used extensively in perfumery. In fact, this material has become one of the most important natural fixatives and odorants next to the essential oils. It is now produced on a very large scale in France, mainly from imported mosses. Germany, Hungary and other countries produce smaller amounts of treemoss extracts. The admixture of treemoss to oakmoss occurs already at the point of harvesting, and it cannot always be considered an adulteration. Moss from the cork-oak (le chêne-liège) is collected in the Atlas mountains in Morocco. It is not identical to the oakmoss from the "royal oak" (le chêne royal) in France. On the other hand, treemoss collected from firs, cedars and spruces is rarely mixed with true oakmoss. The treemoss products present the earthy-woody, dry forestnotes and part of the leather-like notes of true oakmoss. But treemoss has little or no topnote, delicate freshness or elegance. By the addition of various amounts of oakmoss to treemoss, all grades of intermediate products and qualities are obtained.

An essential oil (**Treemoss Oil**) is obtained by molecular distillation of treemoss concrète. Similar products are obtained by co-distillation of the concrète with a high-boiling solvent (see **Oakmoss Anhydrol**, etc.). These products are distinguished by their pale color and good solubility. The essential oil is pale yellow or almost colorless, and usually shows a deposit of white crystal needles. The oil is the most concentrated form of the treemoss odor, but it has less fixative effect than the absolute or the concrète.

Treemoss (and oakmoss) **Absolute** are occasionally used in the adulteration of the so-called **Patchouli Resinoid** (patchouli concrète). Treemoss products are generally used to "cut" true oakmoss in order to reduce the cost.

Treemoss Concrète.

See also **Oakmoss.** The lichens, **Evernia Furfuracea** and **Usnea Barbata,** known as treemoss, firmoss or pinemoss grow on the trunks and branches of spruces and firs in the humid parts of the forests in central and southern Europe (France, Italy, Spain, Morocco, Hungary, Czechoslovakia and Yugoslavia). The curing and extraction of treemoss is quite similar to that of oakmoss as described under the **Oakmoss** monograph. However, although the yield of extract is larger in the case of treemoss, the quality is considered much inferior. The trade has become accustomed to the fact that "Oakmoss" products are mixtures of oakmoss and treemoss products (with the exception of a few European oakmoss extracts from factories who claim the use of botanically pure oakmoss), and that true oakmoss products, obtained exclusively from **Evernia Prunastri** are very rare (with the above exceptions). Accordingly, a description of the two individual products may serve as a lead in the evaluation of so-called oakmoss products.

Treemoss Concrète is a solid mass at room temperature. The benzene extraction product is dark brown or greenish brown, while the petroleum ether extract is dark brown and usually is just about pourable at room temperature, or it may be a sticky mass. The odor of these extracts is more woody and tar-like than that of the oakmoss extract, and they usually lack the delicate topnote, the fresh "seashore"- or seaweed-like note which is so characteristic of true oakmoss (and of seaweed extract!). The chemical composition of treemoss is distinctly different from that of oakmoss, particularly in that the former does not contain evernic acid or related compounds. The chemical composition also varies according to the solvent used and the extraction method applied in the production of the concrète. **Treemoss Resin** (so-called) is obtained by direct *hot* alcohol extraction of the treemoss, as described under **Oakmoss**. It is a *chemical* and physical derivative of treemoss, not directly representative of the natural botanical with respect to odor and composition. The ethyl alcohol reacts with the acids in the moss during the reflux and forms various esters. These have a significant influence upon the odor of the extract.

Treemoss Concrète and **Treemoss "Resin"** are used in soap perfumery for their excellent fixative effect and pleasant woody-forest-like note which blends well with coumarin, rosemary, lavandin, amyl salicylate, isobornyl acetate, geranium oil, cedarwood oils and derivatives, clove and nutmeg oils, pine needle oils, lavandin concrète, etc. The cost of treemoss being lower than oakmoss, it is more generally applicable, but its lack of fineness limits its use to the more robust perfume types.

The annual world production of treemoss concrète can only be estimated very approximately to 25 or 30 metric tons.

Tuberose Absolute.

There are various types of products, commercially named **Tuberose Absolute**: the **Absolute** from **Concrète** is produced by alcohol washing (extraction) of the petroleum ether extract (concrète) of the flowers from the tuberose plant (see below). The **Absolute** from **Pommade** is produced by alcohol washing of the "pommade" which, in turn, is prepared from the flowers by enfleurage. (For details of this process, see monograph on **Absolute** in Part One of this book). The flowers are picked immediately before the petals open. Finally, the **Absolute** from **Châssis** is prepared by alcohol washing of a hydrocarbon extract of the "spent" flowers of the "chassis" from the enfleurage process, (see monograph on **Absolute**).

The tuberose plant is a tender, tall, slim perennial, **Polyanthes Tuberosa**, a native of Central America where wild growing species can be found. Its name refers to its bulb (it is *tuberous*) although this is not truly a tuber in botanical terms. It has no reference to "rose" at all. The plant is related to the **Narcissus, Jonquil** and other popular garden plants. The tuberose is cultivated for perfume oil production in the south of France, in Morocco, China (Formosa) and Egypt. Production in Egypt is irregular; in France it is slowly vanishing. The Chinese product is substantially different from the conventional products from France or Morocco. No absolute is prepared in Morocco, but the Moroccan concrète is shipped to France for processing to absolute.

For several reasons, the most common form of tuberose absolute has always been the enfleurage product:

The tuberose flower is one of the flowers which continue to *produce* and exhale perfume long after it has been removed from the plant. Even without this advantage, the yield of absolute from pommade is higher than the yield by solvent extraction. It is only very recently that solvent extraction has been developed to such a point of perfection that it has become economically attractive and generally practicable. Until a few decades ago, hand labor was still available at a cost which was no obstacle to an economical production of perfume oils (by enfleurage, etc.). Times have changed, however. Petroleum ether extraction has become a very interesting method of isolating flower absolutes, etc., and hand labor has become very expensive. Only the fact that the yield of tuberose absolute by enfleurage is *ten to fifteen times* higher than the yield by the solvent extraction keeps the old method of enfleurage alive in the case of tuberose.

The annual production of **Tuberose Absolute** from concrète (petroleum ether extracted) is very small, and has been less than 5 kilos in some years. It takes 3600 kilos of flowers to produce one kilo of tuberose absolute from concrète. It is understandable that, at a price of U.S. $ 4000 to $ 8000 per kilo, the absolute from concrète finds itself in competition with the enfleurage product although, from a perfumery point of view, the two products are distinctly different. Moroccan tuberose flowers are extracted with petroleum ether to produce a concrète. No enfleurage process is undertaken in Morocco.

Tuberose Absolute from **Pommade** is a soft paste or semiliquid mass of dark orange to brown color. The odor is extremely heavy-sweet, floral-honey-like with a distinct oily-fatty undertone that is partly due to the method of production.

Tuberose Absolute from **Concrète** is a dark orange to brown colored, viscous liquid with a heavy floral, almost nauseatingly sweet, heavy and somewhat spicy odor, reminiscent of honey-suckle, peru balsam, orange flower absolute, ylang ylang residue fractions, stephanotis flowers, etc. The odor also has some resemblance to that of **Longoza Absolute** which is probably the closest natural approach to the tuberose fragrance (see monograph on **Longoza**).

Although tuberose absolute has been analytically investigated during the past 60 years, nothing has come up to shed light on the question of what causes this oil to have such an outstanding floral sweetness and power. Only well-known and very common chemicals have been identified.

Tuberose Absolute is used—when available and when the cost allows for such extravagance—in high-class floral perfumes of the heaviest and sweetest types: frangipanni, stephanotis, caprifolium, lilac, heliotrope, gardenia, violet, and in heavy Oriental types, opopanax, in fantasy perfumes, etc.

With an annual world production measured in kilos and never in tons, and being one of the most expensive of all perfume materials, **Tuberose Absolute** is subject to extensive adulteration.

Absolutes of longoza, narcissus and ylang-ylang, Peru balsam oil, helichrysum oil, methyl benzoate, methyl anthranilate, methyl para-toluate, methyl salicylate, undecanolide and a multitude of other natural and synthetic perfume materials, solvents or diluents have been (and are still) used in this profitable fraud. It takes more than average experience to pick out a true 100% tuberose absolute, if such a product exists commercially at all.

Turpentine.

Although the essential oil from turpentine is not used as such to any great extent in perfumery, the product deserves some attention in a work on natural perfume materials since **Turpentine Oil** is the largest of all essential oils (by volume) in the world (see tables in the rear of this book). **Turpentine Oil** is discussed in the next monograph.

Turpentine is a natural oleo-resin, formed as a physiological product in the trunks of **Pinus Palustris** and other species of **Pinus** (see also **Larch Turpentine**). The tree grows so extensively that it would take pages of this book to specify all places of production. From Norway to New Zealand, from Portugal to Japan, in the U.S.A. and India, France and Greece, hundreds of thousands of tons of this important oleo-resin is tapped from pines by simple methods, comprehensively discussed elsewhere in literature.

The turpentine consists of an essential oil, known as turpentine oil, and a resinous substance known as **Rosin**. The latter is a mixture of various resin-acids and resin-acid anhydrides, commercially known as **Abietic Acid**. By steam distillation of turpentine, about one-sixth of the weight of the natural oleoresin distils with the water as turpentine oil, while five-sixths are left as rosin. Thus, the annual world production of natural rosin is between one-half million and one million metric tons.

Turpentine (oleoresin) as such is not used in perfumery. Derivatives of rosin are used as fixatives in certain types of perfume. Some of the well-known derivatives are:

Abitol (a mixture of dihydro- and tetrahydro abietic alcohols),

Abalyn (methyl abietate)

Hercolyn (methyl dihydroabietate)

Hercolyn D (same, but distilled and deodorized), etc.

These are all very high-boiling, almost odorless viscous materials, readily miscible with all conventional perfume materials. **Abitol** and **Hercolyn D** have comparatively low odor levels, but even the faint odor of "pine derivative" limits the use of these products to pine fragrances, woody notes, industrial perfumes, masking odors, etc., or they may be used at a low concentration only. For their physical fixative effect, these products are among the very best of all low-cost, readily available solvent-fixatives (see monograph on **Fixatives** in Part One of this work).

Turpentine Oil.

Turpentine Oil, the "world's largest essential oil", shall be discussed briefly here since it is a basic raw material in the production of so many important perfumery materials: camphene, citronellal, citronellol, geraniol and geranylesters, hydroxycitronellal, isoborneol, isobornyl esters, linalool and esters, menthol and esters, myrcene and derivatives, nerol and esters, nopol and esters, terpineol and esters, etc., etc. The annual world production is probably more than five times the total world production of all other essential oils combined (see tables in the rear of this book).

The main producers are the U.S.A., France, the U.S.S.R., Portugal, Spain, India, Greece, etc. More than half the world production comes from the U.S.A. The turpentine (oleoresin) is steam distilled to yield the turpentine oil and the rosin (as a residue).

There are several types of so-called turpentine oil, apart from the steam distilled "balsam turpentine" which is described under this monograph:

DD Wood Turpentine is obtained by dry distillation of the chopped wood and roots from the pines. The oil may be redistilled or fractionated during a second distillation.

Steam Distilled Wood Turpentine is steam distilled from the pine wood, or from the extracts of the wood by solvents.

Sulfate Turpentine is a by-product from the production of sulfate-cellulose. It separates an insoluble layer on top of the sulfate lye, but it carries a typical by-odor from this lye.

Sulfite Turpentine is a by-product from the sulfite-cellulose production, similar to the above. None of these two turpentines can be used for the production of terpineol or other derivatives of alpha-pinene. The same can be said about **DD** wood turpentine.

From a perfumery point of view the most important is the steam distilled wood turpentine which is rectified to yield **Pine Oil** (yellow and white), and the so-called wood spirits of turpentine. Pine oil yellow and white are used in perfumery for detergents, household cleaners, insecticides and various sprays, and they serve also as basic raw materials in the isolation of such important components as: fenchyl alcohol, methyl chavicol, terpineol, etc., and these chemicals are, in turn, further processed into a large number of important perfume and flavor materials: anethole, borneol, fenchone, fenchyl acetate, menthone, etc. (see **Pine Oil**).

Steam Distilled Turpentine Oil from the natural oleoresin ("balsam turpentine") is a water-white or almost colorless, mobile liquid with a peculiar warm-balsamic, refreshing odor, reminiscent of all the everyday products from where we meet it: paint, stain removers, insecticides, solvents, etc. However, in many of these uses, the true turpentine oil has been replaced by wood turpentine spirits, etc. (see previous summary of "other" turpentine oils).

American turpentine oil contains 25–35% beta-pinene and only about 50% alpha-pinene, and is thus uneconomical for production of terpineol. European and East Indian turpentines are rich in alpha-pinene, but very low in beta-pinene. They are excellent starting materials in the production of terpineol. Beta-pinene is a starting material in the production of camphene, nopol, nopyl acetate, etc., and it is an important basic material in the production of certain insecticides. Consequently, European terpineol is partially a synthetic product, while the American terpineol is an "isolate" (from pine oil).

Turpentine oil is also available as a rectified oil which evaporates without the slightest residue. This oil is used to some extent in perfumery, e.g. in the compounding of artificial pine needle oils, pine fragrances, etc., and in smaller amounts as a freshener. Due to the instability of the monoterpene, **Pinene**, turpentine oil does not keep well unless it is absolutely dry and in well filled and stoppered, cool-stored containers. Oxidation leads to the formation of peroxides, similar to the decomposition products of citrus oils. Older oils may even resinify and become viscous and odorless. The formation of peroxides is used to advan-

56: The tuberose-like flowers of **Stephanotis Floribunda** in Madagascar are extremely fragrant. The perfume oil is not extracted from the flower, but it is often imitated by the perfumer.

(Fot. S. Arctander, 1956)

57: Cultivated as an ornamental shrub in England, the **Syringa** (Philadelphus coronarius) exhales its delightful orange-blossom-like fragrance, occasionally extracted from the flowers of cultivated **Syringas** in France.

(Fot. S. Arctander, 1960)

58: The mature **Vanilla** flower is ready for hand pollination in the Antalaha-region, northeast Madagascar.
(Fot. S. Arctander, 1955)

59: A full year later, the cured Bourbon **Vanilla** fruits undergo a final inspection before they are shipped to the customers. Île de La Réunion, 1956.
(Fot. S. Arctander)

tage in oil paints where the release of oxygen from the peroxides will speed up the drying of linseed oil (and other fixed oils) by affecting the unsaturated carbon atoms in the chief components of these paint oils.

Turpentine oil is, partly due to its world-wide distribution, not infrequently used as an adulterant in various essential oils, e.g. eucalyptus, pine needle, rosemary, spruce, etc.

U

Ulex Europaeus.

This is a plant or small shrub of the family Leguminosae, and it is known in various parts of Europe under the name of **Gorse** (England), **Ajonc** (France), **Gaspeldoorn** (Holland), and other names, often referring to the thorny leaves of the plant.

Perfume materials derived from the creamy or yellowish colored flowers of this plant are not commercially available, but several attempts have been made in order to start a regular production of an essential oil or an absolute from ulex europaeus. For samples and detailed information, the author is indebted to Mr. Henry A. Kobus, pharmacist and perfumer in England. Mr. Kobus has produced various materials from the flowers of **Ulex Europaeus:**

1) An absolute, extracted by petroleum ether, then alcohol-washed.
2) An essential oil, steam distilled from the flowers. The oil has a very delicate, woody-rosy odor of the clary sage—tobacco type, clean and fresh with a sweet undertone reminiscent of high-quality tea leaves, verbena and zdravetz oil.

Since the shrub grows on extremely poor soil only, it would seem to be a good idea to exploit this sturdy plant in the perfume industry. If made available in attractive quantities, the oil or the absolute would certainly find enthousiastic perfumers who could utilize the pleasant and interesting notes in modern-aldehydic fantasy fragrances, citrus colognes, "men's fragrances", muguet bases, ambre bases, new mown hay bases and other floral and non-floral bases, fresh perfume types, etc. The oil blends well with fougère bases, linalool, citrus oils, lavender, clary sage,

mimosa, geraniol, ionones, nerol, phenylethyl alcohol, etc.

V

Valerian Absolute.

In the preparation of valerian extract for pharmaceutical purposes, certain methods lead to the isolation of the (essential) oil of this botanical. Separated by solvent extraction, this oil is not truly an essential oil, but it does resemble an absolute from a perfumery point of view.

Ether-extracted valerian oil is available from various producers of pharmaceutical valerian extract. It has certain advantages over the steam distilled essential oil (e.g. little or no heating involved in the preparation) and shall be briefly mentioned here. For details on the botanical source, see monograph on **Valerian Oil.**

Valerian "Absolute" is an olive-brown or pale brown colored liquid with a very powerful, balsamic-green, sweet-woody, yet somewhat sour odor. The sour notes are practically absent in fresh absolutes. Characteristic is a green-woody undertone of great tenacity, reminiscent of hops (beer), balsam poplar buds and pine forests. Valerian absolute is used in perfumery (although very rarely) in combination with oakmoss and patchouli, rosemary, lavender, pine needle oils, etc. for special effects in forest notes, chypres, fougères, etc. The power of this perfume material is easily under-estimated.

In flavors, its richness and peculiar root-like, herbaceous-green taste gives interesting effects in apple flavors, beer flavors, tobacco flavors, liqueurs, etc.

When exposed to moisture or air, the absolute (oil) turns acid and its odor is ruined by the appearance of isovaleric acid notes. In a way, **Valerian Absolute** is a by-product in the manufacture of the pharmaceutical, odorless extract of valerian rhizome, and is not regularly available. Its high price is compensated for by the outstanding power of the material.

See also **Valeriana Wallichii** and **Valerian Oil.**

Valeriana Wallichii.

Somewhat similar to the essential oil of the European valerian is that of **"Indian Valerian"**, the perennial herb of **Valeriana Wallichii**. The plant grows wild and is cultivated in the northern mountainous parts of India.

An essential oil is obtained by steam distillation of the comminuted, dried rhizomes. The oil finds some application locally, but little use overseas as a perfume material.

Indian Valerian Oil is a pale brown or amber-yellow colored liquid of a balsamic-woody, slightly spicy-root-like odor with a distinct note of valerian acid, more or less pronounced according to the age of the oil. The musk-like and patchouli-like, camphoraceous notes are quite characteristic of the odor of this oil.

Generally considered poorer in odor than the European valerian oil, the oil of Indian valerian is used in certain flavors, e.g. for tobacco, honey, root-beer types, etc. In perfumery, the oil could be used in pine needle fragrances, chypres and moss types. It blends well with oakmoss and lavandin, rosemary, isobornyl acetate (or valerate!), amyl salicylate, fenchone, isocyclocitral, isobutyl quinoline, coumarin, hydroquinone dimethyl ether, etc. and it can present interesting effects as a modifier in all types of woody fragrances. **Indian Valerian Oil** is produced on a very limited scale only, and it is not always available. The rhizome may be imported and distilled by the consumer himself in order to assure the production of fresh batches with little or no acid notes.

A "**Concrete**" has been prepared experimentally by petroleum ether extraction. It is a viscous, syrupy, brown mass of high ester content and very low acid content. A semi-solid extract has been prepared with alcohol from the rhizome. The two products are both very true-to-nature in odor, sweet and pleasant smelling with an exceptional depth and richness. They are not yet commercially available.

See also **Spikenard Oil**.

Valerian Oil.

From the rhizomes of the so-called European valerian, an essential oil is produced which is generally known as **Valerian Oil**. Under the monograph **Valerian Absolute** another product is described; the latter is occasionally marketed under the name of valerian oil, but actually being a product of extraction, it is not a true essential oil.

The plant **Valeriana Officinalis** is a native of Asia, and it grows wild in most parts of Asia and Europe. For the purpose of producing pharmaceutical extracts from the rhizomes, the plant is cultivated in the U.S.S.R., the Baltic states, Belgium, Germany, France, and occasionally in Scandinavia, England, Hungary and Yugoslavia.

The steam distilled **Valerian Oil** is an olive-green to olive-brown colored liquid of a warm-woody, balsamic-rootlike odor with a distinct animal undertone of musklike character and great tenacity. A fresh-green, slightly camphoraceous topnote is also typical in the odor of a good oil. Under poor storage conditions and on ageing, the oil turns darker, becomes more viscous and acquires an objectionable odor of isovaleric acid. This acid is also present in the distillation waters, which should be quickly separated from the oil, or by gentle and continuous neutralization be kept harmless and insoluble in the oil.

Valerian Oil can be used in perfumery for its musky-woody, balsamic notes which give interesting effects in combination with patchouli, costus, oakmoss, cypriol, etc. in modern chypre variations, and it blends well with all pine materials, lavenders, methyl ionones, cedarwood derivatives, mandarin petitgrain oil, nopyl acetate, quinoline derivatives, isocyclo citral, etc.

In flavors, the oil is occasionally used for tobacco flavoring and in combination with hop or lupulin flavor extracts in beer or rootbeer flavoring, apple flavors, etc.

Another valerian oil is obtained from the so-called **Kesso Root**, the rhizome of the Japanese variety of **Valeriana Officinalis**. The odor of **Kesso Root Oil** is much drier, more woody-borneolic than that of "European" valerian oil. The Japanese oil is much less expensive, and is often used to adulterate the European valerian oil.

Synthetic bornyl isovalerate is available and can be used in the adulteration of the above valerian oils, but the characteristic sweetness and musky undertone is obtainable only from the true oil. The annual world production of **Valerian Oil** (even including the **Kesso Oil**) is much less than one metric ton.

Vanilla.

One of the most intriguing and inimitable flavor and perfume materials is **Vanilla**. The story of vanilla is a tale in itself, and the process of curing the immature green capsules into the deliciously fragrant chocolate-brown vanilla "beans" is no less fantastic. Literature is abundant on the subject of cultivating, curing and extracting vanilla, but a few brief details should be mentioned a this place. To the author's opinion, literature on vanilla extraction leaves much to be desired yet.

The vanilla plant is an orchid, a climbing vine that needs a supporting tree or trunk into which the vine sends tiny, but strong "hooks", often mistaken for suction roots. But the plant is not a parasite. It takes all its nourishment from the soil and the air directly. The plant **Vanilla Planifolia** is a native of Central America or Mexico where a local insect with a particularly long trunk takes care of a natural pollination of the flower. When Fernando Cortez brought the plant to Europe shortly after the discovery of America, it remained for a long time a mystery that the plant did not produce fruits outside its native country. More than 300 years later, a method of hand-pollination of the flowers of vanilla plants in the island of La Réunion in the Indian Ocean resulted in the plants producing fruits. From then on, methods of curing were developed, based upon experience from the natives in Central America, and before the end of the 19th century, cured vanilla "beans" were among the most appreciated flavoring materials. About that time, synthetic vanillin sold for U.S. $ 1100.- per kilo. "Natural" vanillin could hardly be produced from vanilla fruits today at that price. Synthetic vanillin from lignin (a wood pulp derivative) is today available at less than one percent of the above price. The vanilla plant is cultivated for the production of fruits in Mexico (one of the native areas of the plant), in Madagascar, La Réunion, Tahiti, the Comoro islands, Guadeloupe, East Africa, Indonesia, the Seychelles, etc. Madagascar is the largest producer by far (up to 80% of the total world production), followed by Mexico (different curing process yields a different quality), La Réunion (same process as Madagascar, and considered the best quality vanilla), Comoro islands (rapidly growing industry), and Tahiti (considerable production, but the plant is a different hybrid and yields a distinctly different vanilla aroma). Other producers turn out a few tons or less of cured fruits annually.

The vanilla flowers are hand pollinated (even in Mexico where the growers cannot expect the local insects to do a 100% effective job), and the flower produces a fruit which reaches maturity after 8 to 9 months on the plant. Immediately prior to maturity, the fruit is harvested, and the green, odorless, bitter tasting and somewhat poisonous "pods" now face a long and troublesome curing period, not unlike the curing of tea and tobacco. The curing leads to enzymatic processes within the fruits which slowly turn brown and become aromatic. The curing of vanilla fruits is performed locally, except in the Andapa (inland jungle) district of Madagascar where no experienced curers are at hand, although many hundreds of tons of green pods are harvested there. The fruits are airshipped to the coastal district for proper curing.

After three months or more curing time, the "pods" (botanically the fruit is a capsule) are ready for shipment. Before being shipped, they are sorted according to length and appearance. The trend is towards a drier export material. The greatest bulk of all vanilla ends up in extraction units in Europe and the U.S.A. The old-fashioned, glossy, soft and attractive fruits with their very high moisture content (occasionally up to 70%, but usually 30 to 50% water), cause considerable trouble in the extractors, diluting the solvent, giving a poor yield, etc. Today, a rather unattractive, unsorted (with respect to appearance), but selected aromatic quality of low moisture content is preferred by the large consumers. After tedious experiments in Madagascar, "chopped" fruits, dried under infra-red lamps are also available now. The drier the fruit, the faster will the vanillin crystals appear on the outside of the fruit. It may take a year or more on whole, moist fruits. It is, however, no sign of high quality, since this "frosting" can be attained by sprinkling the vanilla fruits with an ethereal solution of synthetic vanillin (compare **Tonka Bean**).

From Madagascar and La Réunion comes the so-called **Bourbon Vanilla,** named after the island of Bourbon (La Réunion) where the curing method was developed. Mexican vanilla is also derived from **Vanilla Planifolia** (a hybrid of other vanilla plants), but the Mexican curing method is slightly different from the Réunion curing. The Mexican vanilla is somewhat sharper or more pungent in its aroma. **Réunion** or **Bourbon Vanilla** appears as chocolate-brown, semi-dry or somewhat moist, dull or glossy. 14 to 22 cm. long "sticks", which may be bundled in different ways according to origin, or may be sold "en vrac" (i.e. loose in box).

The aroma is extremely rich, sweet, somewhat woody and animal (castoreum-like), tobacco-like and very deep in its balsamic, sweet-spicy body-note. Actually, the odor of vanillin is *not* one of the characteristics in the aroma of Bourbon vanilla. However, the odor varies considerably according to the moisture content of the fruits; thus, the odor of very moist fruits is usually more to the vanillin side. The drier the fruits become, the more perceptible is the odor of the non-steam-volatile, high-boiling aromatic principles.

Tahiti Vanilla is generally shorter in length and mostly a bundled, moist fruit. Its odor is almost perfumey-sweet, not tobacco-like, not very deep or woody, nor distinctly animal. Some people find it more attractive, perhaps because it reminds them more of the everyday (artificial) vanilla flavors in ice-cream, candies and baked goods.

A certain type of **Guadeloupe Vanilla** is called **"Vanillons"** and the fruits are derived from **Vanilla Pompona**, a different species of vanilla. The fruits are short (8 to 14 cms.) and wide (up to $2\frac{1}{2}$ cm. flat measure). They have a peculiar floral-sweet fragrance of the anisic, heliotropine-isosafrol type, and are more perfumey than all other vanilla types. Vanillons are considered poor quality vanilla for flavoring purposes.

The cured vanilla fruits do not yield any appreciable amount of essential oil by distillation. Even the molecular distillates of vanilla extracts do not represent the rich and typical gamut of vanilla flavor. No "aroma distillate" (see this monograph in Part One of the present work) can be made from vanilla fruits. The following perfume and flavor materials are manufactured from cured vanilla fruits: **Vanilla Absolute**, **Vanilla Extracts** (with various solvents and in various concentrations), **Vanilla "Resinoid"** (also called "oleoresin"), **Vanilla Tincture** and several other types of aroma concentrates. The following monographs will describe the most common products of vanilla fruits.

Vanilla Absolute.

The highest concentration of vanilla aroma (perfume and flavor) is found in the so-called **Vanilla Absolute**. It must be mentioned at this point, however, that this absolute is not representative of the total aroma of the vanilla fruit. Certain aromatic materials, particularly flavor ingredients, are lost in the attempt to produce an alcohol-soluble extract of this botanical. The conventional

way of washing the hydrocarbon solvent extract (in this case: the **"Oleoresin of Vanilla"**) with alcohol does not yield a satisfactory result. If the vanilla fruits are extracted with hot alcohol (e. g. infusion), and the resulting extract is evaporated, we will find that the extract is not soluble in ethyl alcohol. Even if the infusion is set aside for several weeks and filtered before the alcohol is removed, it will not be alcohol soluble. Hydrolysis and other processes continue to work in the extract. Certain resinous substances will remain in clear solution for a considerable length of time before they finally "fall out" as a gummy precipitate in the extract.

The so-called selective extraction method has recently been applied to vanilla fruits with good results. It is important that the moisture content is very low in the starting material (see the general remarks under the monograph **Vanilla**). It is possible to eliminate the alcohol-soluble resinous matter, etc. and obtain a truly alcohol-soluble absolute of vanilla. Other manufacturers have tried to reach this goal by use of co-solvents, a method which is less than perfect and not universally useful.

This absolute is about 7 to 13 times stronger in flavor effect than vanilla fruits of average moisture content, while the alcoholic extract prepared with diluted alcohol is only $3\frac{1}{2}$ to 5 times stronger than vanilla fruits (see monograph on **Vanilla Extract**). **Vanilla Absolute** is a dark brown, clear and viscous liquid of very rich, sweet and true-to-nature odor. An odor-flavor description of this product would not be correct without the remark that the flavor is strongly dependent upon the type of vanilla used in the extraction.

Vanilla Absolute from **Vanilla "Oleoresin"** is commercially available, usually prepared from the benzene extract of vanilla. In that case, it should be used for perfumes only (even traces of benzene are harmful to the human organism). The absolute is very dark brown and semi-solid, just about pourable at room temperature. It is less rich in odor than the direct alcohol- (or hydro-alcoholic) extraction products, and the perfumery effect is not proportional to its concentration over the vanilla tinctures.

Vanilla Extract.

It is interesting to see that the United States Pharmacopoeia uses glycerine, water and ethyl alcohol as a menstruum for extraction in the preparation of "pure vanilla extract". The surprising thing is that vanillin with glycerine forms an alcohol-insoluble condensation product. The author has no explanation for this contradiction.

Under the monographs of **Vanilla Absolute,** **Vanilla "Resinoid"** and **Vanilla Tincture,** it is mentioned that a hydro-alcoholic extraction of the cured vanilla fruits is the method that yields the best and richest extract from an odor-flavor point of view. It is quite possible that, during the treatment with hot ethyl alcohol and water, certain chemical processes take place among the components of vanilla (transesterification, hydrolysis, etc.). Since the cured vanilla contains some oily and resinous matter, the most practical method of total extraction is the following:

The vanilla is extracted once with petroleum ether or dichloromethane. This extract is evaporated per se, and kept separate till later. Extraction is then continued with 70% ethyl alcohol, then with 60% alcohol, with 50% alcohol and perhaps with 40% or 30% alcohol. Finally, one extract is made with hot, distilled water. The alcoholic extractions are carried out under one hour reflux, or they may be simple percolations. The water extraction is usually a percolation whereby adherent alcohol is flushed out of the exhaust plant material. The combined extracts are evaporated gently. Towards the end of alcohol take-off, propylene glycol is added to the extract so that the water can be distilled off under gentle vacuum (pot temperature about 40°C.). It is adviseable to extract the distillation water with petroleum ether since traces of delicate aromatic matter are steam distilled with the water. By weighing the completely exhausted and dried vanilla, it is possible to calculate the exact amount of non-aqueous extracted matter. The water content in the vanilla fruits prior to extraction must be determined in advance. Thus, it is possible to add exactly the right amount of propylene glycol so that the resulting extract is e. g. 1 = 1. At this point, the first petroleum ether extract is added or an alcohol extract from it is prepared and added. The extract from the distillation water is also added here. In other words, one part of extract corresponds to one part of vanilla. This preparation is a dark brown viscous liquid, and it is truly a **"Ten-fold Vanilla Extract"** in commercial (American) terms (see monograph on **Vanilla**

Tincture). The extract will inevitably separate small amounts of oily liquid after standing or cool storage. This oil can be separated without significant loss of extract or flavor. The clarified extract is primarily a flavor material since it is not miscible with essential oils or most synthetic perfume materials. The miscibility could be improved by the use of triethylene glycol, heptylene glycol, hexylene glycol or triacetin in place of propylene glycol. However, such preparations would be banned from use in flavors in most countries.

Vanilla Preparations, use of –

In spite of tremendous competition from the inexpensive synthetic vanillin, the various vanilla extracts manage to maintain a sufficient interest to keep their production profitable. The production of 600 to 1400 metric tons of cured vanilla fruits per year is, from the point of view of aroma-effect, only a tiny fraction of the combined world consumption of so-called vanilla flavor extracts based upon vanillin, "ethylvanillin", "vanitrope" (propenyl guaethol, Shulton) and a number of other synthetic vanilla materials. One of the facts to be remembered is that the conventional advertising of vanillin as being 50 times stronger than vanilla (fruits) is just a classic example of miscalculation based upon analytical findings. Vanilla contains about 2% vanillin, but a true 1 = 1 (see **Vanilla Extract**) vanilla extract yields about 8% of the flavor strength of vanillin. Besides, the two cannot be compared directly as flavor materials.

Unfortunately, vanilla extracts are adulterated to such an extent that most housewives, bakers, ice cream manufacturers, candymakers, etc. hardly know what true vanilla extract tastes like. In addition, the cost problem has again been to the advantage of the synthetic vanillin. **Vanilla Extracts** are primarily used in flavors: ice cream, soft drinks, pharmaceutical preparations, chocolate manufacture, tobacco, hard and soft candy, baked goods and household essences (rarely the true extract!), liqueurs (e. g. "crème de cacao à la vanille"), etc.

In perfumes, the extracts are often substituted for by absolutes, tinctures or special concentrates. These products lend an unsurpassed richness and depth to many types of sweet-floral or heavy ambre bases, Oriental perfumes, etc., where they blend excellently with sandalwood, vetiver, opopanax, spice oils, etc. The vanilla note can be modified or supported by materials such as zingerone, castoreum tincture, cassione, vanillin, "ethylvanillin", "vanitrope", longoza absolute, ortho-diethoxybenzene, anisalcohol, anisyl formate, veratraldehyde, etc., while heliotropine, isosafrole, cyclotene, frambal, maltol, etc. are definite modifiers which tend to change the typical note of natural vanilla.

The tenacity of a true vanilla extract is quite outstanding, and the unusual uniformity of the fragrance all through the very slow evaporation make vanilla extracts highly interesting perfume materials which are, in the author's opinion, not nearly common enough on the perfumers' shelves.

Vanilla "Resinoid".

The hydrocarbon (or other volatile solvent) extracts of vanilla are often called "Resinoid", "Resin", "Resinoine", or the like, but they are actually more closely related to Oleoresins or Concrètes from a raw material and processing point of view. They do contain some resinous matter, but they are viscous liquids, pourable at room temperature, and they are derived from formerly live plant matter, not from a resinous exudation. The amount of steam-distillable matter in the extract is negligible. Thus, it would not even be correct to use the term Oleoresin which, however, is the most common. For solvents, benzene, petroleum ether, acetone, trichloro ethylene, dichloromethane, etc. may be used. Acetone will dissolve water from the moist fruits, and this fact makes acetone a troublesome solvent. The same goes for methyl alcohol, isopropyl alcohol or other "hydrophilic" solvents.

The yield of "oleoresin" with the above solvents is considerably lower than the yield by ethyl alcohol extraction. Furthermore, the aromatic properties of hydrocarbon vanilla extracts are generally much poorer than those of alcohol extracts.

Vanilla "Oleoresin" (resinoid, concrète) is usually a viscous, dark brown liquid with a sweet and vanilla-like odor, but without the rich tobacco-like extractnote, without the animal undertone, and less rich in body than the alcoholic extracts. The hydrocarbon extracts are oil-soluble and miscible with most perfume materials, but not with alcohol, tinctures, glycerine, propylene glycol, etc. They are accordingly limited to use in preparations where alcohol, tinctures, etc. are not present, and they cannot be used in perfume bases intended for lotions, colognes or other alcoholic dilutions.

For flavors, the "oleoresins" have the advantage of being oil-soluble, an ability sometimes requested in flavor preparations.

Generally speaking, Vanilla "Oleoresins" are less important than the alcoholic and hydro-alcoholic extracts of vanilla (see also Vanilla Extracts).

Vanilla Tincture.

This is a prepared perfume and flavor material. In most countries, the alcohol control is extended to such uses of alcohol as in the preparation of tinctures. Consequently, the vanilla tinctures for perfumery use are made with "perfume alcohol", i.e. ethyl alcohol denatured with diethyl phthalate, brucine sulfate or the like. These tinctures can not be used in flavors. Furthermore, it is generally necessary to maintain a high alcohol percentage in tinctures for perfumes since other perfume materials are not soluble in diluted alcohol. The aromatic principles in the vanilla fruit are more soluble in diluted alcohol than in concentrated (pure) ethyl alcohol. Accordingly, the vanilla tinctures for flavors and for perfumes are two different products, in solvents and in composition.

Perfume Tincture: The classic vanilla tincture was prepared from 125 grams vanilla fruits and 1000 grams of 95% ethyl alcohol. The chopped or coarsely ground vanilla was macerated with the alcohol for 14 days, then filtered. The resulting tincture contained considerably less than 95% alcohol since it had absorbed the water from the vanilla fruits (see Vanilla). With little or no standard for moisture content in vanilla fruits, such tinctures were far from uniform. For ordinary use in perfumery, a convenient tincture is that of 10% vanilla in alcohol of 95% strength. If the vanilla is of average moisture content, the resulting tincture will not fall below 90% alcohol strength which is sufficient to dissolve all the common perfume materials, too.

Certain perfume houses still use the old-fashioned "infusion" method of extraction: the vanilla is extracted with alcohol under reflux, i.e. while the alcohol is boiling. The rate of fruit to alcohol is either 12½ to 100 or 25 to 100. The resulting infusion may be filtered either immediately or after cooling. In both cases, it will become cloudy and show additional precipitate on standing. The alcohol strength in the infusion 25/100 may be too low for certain perfume materials (vetiver oil, cedarwood oil, sandalwood oil, etc.) because of the 8 to 15% of moisture introduced with the fruits. In view of the above, the author would conclude that a 10/100 tincture or a 12½/100 infusion are the most promising and practical preparations for perfume use. However, the "oleo-resins" or absolutes described in the previous monographs may be preferable in cases where extensive use is made of vanilla in a composition.

Flavor Tinctures: In certain flavor compositions, it is necessary to maintain a higher alcohol content in order to keep the other flavor ingredients in solution. Tinctures or infusions can be used, made with pure ethyl alcohol as described under Tincture in Part One of this book. A conventional tincture of today is the so-called 1-10 tincture which is prepared from 100 grams vanilla, 200 grams of sugar, and ethyl alcohol and water to make 1000 grams of a tincture which measures 38-40% alcohol by volume. Obviously, such a preparation can not be used in perfumes without causing precipitation of other ingredients. A Ten-fold Vanilla is a preparation of which one gram is equivalent to one gram of vanilla bean (compare pharmaceutical standard fluid extract).

It should be kept in mind, however, that certain flavor components of the vanilla fruit are not extracted at all with high-proof alcohol, and that the 1-10 tincture above mentioned thus will have a richer flavor than the tinctures prepared with pure ethyl alcohol. (See also Vanilla Absolute and Vanilla "Oleoresin" (resinoid)). Vanilla tinctures are used to a decreasing degree since they are not sufficiently standardized. Most large consumers prefer to prepare their own tinctures or extracts after thorough analysis of the purchased lots of vanilla fruits, particularly with respect to moisture content. Unfortunately, Vanilla Tinctures are so extensively and commonly adulterated that many consumers have completely forgotten what a true tincture smells and tastes like, a fact that makes this business difficult for the vanilla growers as well as for the manufacturers of true tinctures and extracts. See also: Vanilla Preparations, use of –.

Verbena Oil.

The "true" verbena oil is produced by steam distillation of the freshly harvested herb of Lippia Citriodora, a tall perennial which is presumably a native of Chile and Argentina in South America. It grows semiwild and it is cultivated in many countries around the Mediterranean: France, Tunis, Algeria and in Kenya and China. The yield of oil is very poor, and the cultivation of the plant involves considerable problems with respect to climatic conditions, etc. The essential oil does not offer any unique notes, or notes which are unobtainable by means of other and better known perfume materials. Accordingly, the oil has become almost obsolete, and is unknown to most perfumers of today.

However, since the name "Verbena Oil" still appears on most pricelists from supply houses, a brief mention of the oil is justified: True Verbena Oil is a pale yellow to yellow or olive-greenish colored, mobile liquid with an intensely fresh, lemon-like odor which slowly changes into a sweet, almost fruity bodynote and fades out almost unchanged, sweet floral-fruity, slightly rosy. The oil contains usually about 30 to 35% citral. Verbena oil found some use in the "old-fashioned" citrus colognes where it offered a delightful freshness and clean topnote, superior to the effects that could be obtained with lemon oil 30 or 40 years ago. A special "Eau de Verveine" is still known and is fairly popular in France and Central Europe, South America, etc. For this purpose, the verbena oil was blended with citrus oils, neroli oil, palmarosa oil, heliotropine, ionones, nitromusks, aldehydes, spice oils, olibanum, tolu or elemi resinoid, etc.

But with the appearance of lemongrass oil and oil of Thymus Hiemalis (see "Verbena Oil, Spanish, so-called"), countless duplications of the true verbena notes were produced. Some of them attracted the consumers' attention, and the true verbena oil lost an uneven battle. The true oil is simply too expensive for what effect it has to offer.

The author has not seen verbena distillation in Algeria since his very first visit there in 1937. It is conceivable that production has been completely abandoned. In 1956 however, the author noted that an Algerian botanical drug house still purchased the fresh verbena herb from nearby farmers. The dried leaves were sold as "folium verbenae" to French drug houses. The verbena leaf is part of the popular French "tisane", a medicinal household tea for universal puposes. The plant is cultivated in many private gardens all over the Mediterranean area.

See also **Verbena Oil**, so-called (**Spanish**), next monograph.

Verbena Oil, Spanish, so-called.

Spanish Verbena oil:

Odorwise somewhat similar to the true verbena oil (see previous monograph) is the essential oil steam distilled from the dried herb of **Thymus Hiemalis,** a perennial which grows wild in Spain, Portugal, Italy and North Africa. Irregular lots of this oil are produced in Spain, and the oil is sold under the name of **Verbena Oil, Spanish.** This oil is also related to the oil from wild-growing Spanish **Lemon-Thyme.** The latter is rarely seen on the perfumery market. Spanish verbena oil is a yellow liquid of a powerful and fresh lemonlike, herbaceous odor with a rich and sweet, somewhat sage-like undertone. It has the freshness of lemongrass oil, and the herbaceous-sweet undertone of e.g. sage clary, yet without the delicate teanotes of this oil. Overall, the Spanish verbena oil is a rough or crude version of the true verbena oil which is very rarely produced and sold in its natural shape.

Spanish verbena oil is produced only on a very modest scale, but when available it could be used in colognes, chypres, after-shave lotion perfumes, etc. since it blends well with all citrus oils, methylionones, isosafrole, lavender, geraniol, eugenol, petitgrain oil, etc. Like most other citralbearing oils, it needs good fixation which can be obtained by benzoin, olibanum, labdanum, elemi, oakmoss products, guaiacwood oil, araucaria oil, bruyère absolute, etc.

Lemongrass oil, litsea cubeba, eucalyptus staigeriana, synthetic citral and other inexpensive sources of citral have greatly contributed to the lack of interest in Spanish verbena oil, and it is quite possible that this oil may disappear from the perfumery market in the very near future.

Vetiver Oil.

Although the essential oil of vetiver rootlets apparently is a product of comparatively recent times, the rootlets themselves have been used for their fragrance since antiquity. The parent plant is a grass, **Vetiveria Zizanoides,** a tall perennial which originates in India, probably also in Indonesia and Ceylon. The grass grows wild in India, Ceylon, Burma, the Malayan Peninsula, etc., but little essential oil is derived from the wild growing grass. For the purpose of distilling oil, the grass is cultivated in southern India, Indonesia (particularly in Java), the Malay states, Philippines, Japan, Réunion island, Angola (West Africa), the Belgian Congo, Haiti, the Dominican Republic, Brazil, Argentina, British Guiana, Jamaica, Mauritius, Martinique and, on an experimental scale, in many other tropical regions.

The grass also serves as a soil protecting plant since its abundant lacework of rootlets will secure the soil on mountainous slopes against excessive erosion during the torrential tropical rains. Vetiver grass has been introduced in many volcanic islands and mountainous tropical countries as a soil protector. In India, several other grasses serve similar purposes, and some of them are simultaneously used for the distillation of perfume oil from the rootlets (see monographs on **Cyperus** oils).

Vetiver Oil is steam distilled from cleaned and washed rootlets which are dried, cut and chopped, then again usually soaked in water prior to distillation. The distillation is undertaken near the place of harvesting with exception of small lots which are distilled in Europe or the U.S.A. from rootlets that have been imported from India, Indonesia or, very rarely, from Haiti. In the Belgian Congo, the distillation is centralized at one modern distillery in Kivu (eastern province). The cleaned rootlets arrive at this distillery from hundreds of kilometers away. The author has no reports of the distillation being abandoned during or after the July 1960 events in Belgian Congo.

Réunion and Haiti are the largest producers of vetiver oil with India as a strong third. Most of the East Indian production is absorbed by this huge country's local soap and perfume industry which is not saturated in any way by the 10 to 25 metric tons of vetiver oil annually produced in India (mainly in the northern India). Réunion produces 35 to 48 metric tons annually, while the Haitian production fluctuates (10 to 35 tons) according to the political situation. All other producing areas turn out less than 10 tons each annually. Indonesian production is increasing, and so is the Japanese. Belgian Congo oil is usually dark and may be slightly turbid, but of good quality (high alcohol content, and almost free from green-earthy, "potato-peel"-like top-notes). Angola oils come in two entirely different types: one is quite normal in odor and color, the other is very pale and attractive, grayish-amber colored and of dry-woody, almost cedrela-like odor, reminiscent of certain types of Cyperus oil. The pale Angola vetiver oil is distilled on a new plantation, and another oil, distilled in France from the same root material, has a similar odor and also the same peculiar laevo-rotation (hitherto found only in Indian vetiver oils) as well as very high alcohol + ester content. Thus, a general description of Vetiver Oil is not easy to give. The following suggestions for the use of vetiver oil apply to the "Bourbon type" (Réunion, Congo) and to the Haiti type of oil, totalling about 75% of the world production:

Vetiver Oil is an amber colored to grayish brown, olive brown or dark brown viscous liquid whose odor is sweet and very heavy woody-earthy, reminiscent of roots and wet soil, with a rich undertone of "precious wood" notes. Oils distilled from too young rootlets and very freshly distilled oils may display some "green" potato-peel-like or asparagus-like topnotes. These are not appreciated by the perfumer, but the peculiar topnote is exploited in flavor work (see below). There is no definite rule to confirm the saying that dark oils are superior perfume oils, nor that the optical rotation will indicate the quality of the oil. The consumer who wishes to use his vetiver oil for isolation of vetiverol (a mixture of sesquiterpene alcohols in the oil) will soon find out during a test distillation how much vetiverol is in the oil. Vetiverol is responsible for the very faint, but tenacious, suave and sweet-woody odor, while the Vetiverone (corresponding ketone mixture) seems to lend bitter earthiness—and also tenacity—to the odor of the oil. Esters of vetiverol are still higher boiling and may have very little odor value, but they are excellent fixatives. Only the lower boiling "head fractions" are definitely undesirable from a perfumery point of view. If an oil has been improperly distilled, that is, if the distillation was "pushed" too far at insufficient steam pressure, the oil will usually have poor odor qualities.

Vetiver Oil is used extensively in perfumery not only as a fixative, but also as an odor contributor in bases such as fougère, chypre, modern woody-aldehydic or ambre-aldehydic bases, Oriental bases, moss and wood notes, opopanax bases, rose bases, etc. It blends well with ionones, linalool, cinnamic alcohol, patchouli, sandalwood, oakmoss products, amylsalicylate, lavender, clary sage, mimosa, cassie, opopanax, isoeugenol, etc.

The oil also serves for the isolation of Vetiverol and Vetiverone, the former again being used to produce Vetiveryl Acetate. This ester is also produced by direct acetylization of vetiver oil, but the method leads to a much inferior vetiveryl acetate since it is difficult to separate vetiverone and vetiveryl acetate by fractional distillation, and since vetiverone is affected by acetic anhydride in the process. Vetiverone is also used in perfumery.

"Vetiver Acetate" is a commercial term for acetylated vetiver oil, more or less rectified. True vetiveryl acetate, also known under a number of brand names, is a very viscous, almost colorless liquid of faint, fresh-sweet, slightly woody odor, absolutely free from earthy, grassy, musty or fungus-like notes. This description unfortunately fits very few of the commercial products. Similar comments could be made for guaiacwood oil and guaiyl acetate, amyris oil and its "acetate", etc.

Haiti-, Réunion- and Congo vetiver oils are usually considered best for the isolation of Vetiverol. Indian and Angola oils often have a very high content of vetiveryl esters in their natural state.

The "foreruns" ("heads" of distillation) from the vacuum distillation of vetiver oil can be used in flavor work. When extracted with weak alcohol or propylene glycol, the foreruns yield an "aroma" (see Aroma, Part One of this work) with a very striking resemblance to asparagus flavor. The taste is not very powerful, but resembles asparagus (or certain green peas) to such a degree that this soluble aroma may be used in food preserves (vegetables, etc.) to reinforce the flavor of asparagus.

Vetiver Oil is occasionally adulterated with oils from roots of other grasses (see Cyperus oil), or it may be "cut back" with fractions from the isolation of vetiverol. After arrival in Europe or the U.S.A., Réunion oils may be cut with Haitian oil, Caryophyllene, Cedarwood derivatives, Amyris oil, etc.

The annual world production of all vetiver oil types is about 90 to 130 metric tons. At least 20% of this quantity is tied up for "domestic purposes" in the countries of production (India, Brazil, etc.).

Vetiver "Resinoid".

Due to the fact that vetiver rootlets yield almost exclusively high-boiling components on steam distillation, obviously other methods of isolating the aromatic constituents of the botanical material have been tried. By benzene extraction of the comminuted, dried rootlets and subsequent removal of the solvent under gentle vacuum, a concrète of vetiver is obtained. Because of its resinous appearance, the product is most often called Vetiver Resinoid. In composition, it is very closely related to the essential oil, but it seems that extraction leads to a product which contains few or no low-boiling constituents, but does contain a high amount of the components which are difficult to distil even in a modern high-pressure steam still. It is conceivable that steam distillation decomposes some of the constituents (perhaps the esters) of the natural oil to a certain degree, thereby producing an essential oil with very high acid number (this is indeed true about vetiver oils), and with a certain amount of lower boiling constituents which are usually classified as "unwanted notes" by the perfumer. Thus, the extracted concrète ("resinoid") will represent a truer picture of the natural constituents of vetiver roots. The author agrees that the mere fact of being "natural" is by no means always synonymous with "being superior in perfumery value". However, a customer will often, consciously or subconsciously, prefer a fragrance in which he recognizes natural scents or odors which are already registered in his mind from earlier experience (in nature, etc.).

Extraction of vetiver rootlets is carried out experimentally in the Belgian Congo (perhaps the only "on-the-spot" production, and last reported in 1959. The author has no report of a 1960 production, nor has he reports of the production being discontinued since the July 1960 events in Congo.).

On a modest scale, extraction is undertaken in Europe and the U.S.A. from rootlets imported from India or Indonesia, rarely from Haitian rootlets. Benzene is the most common solvent used. The yield by petroleum ether extraction is much lower than that from benzene extraction, but the product is pale and attractive. Vetiver "Resinoid" is a semi-solid, plastic mass of dark brown or dark amber color, and faint but extremely persistent odor, reminiscent of the best grades of vetiver oil: sweet-woody, root-like,

with an almost balsamic and very rich undertone. Obviously, this material has an excellent fixative effect, but it also lends a suave softness and rich body to perfumes of the heavier Oriental type, fougères, chypres, crèpe de Chines, etc. where it blends with practically all the same materials as were mentioned under vetiver oil. In certain types of rose base, vetiver "resinoid" is unsurpassed as fragrant fixative.

More recently, various processed extracts of vetiver rootlets have been marketed. Anhydrol Vetiver is a molecular distillate of a vetiver extract, produced in the absence of water. During the co-distillation (with glycols or isopropyl myristate), a residue is obtained. This residue may appear on the market as "Vetiver Resin", and it is a good fixative, but it has little or no odor value. By-products and residues from the production of vetiverol and vetiveryl acetate (and "vetiver acetate") are also commercially available, but are erroneously named "vetiver resin".

Molecular distillation of vetiver oil and other high-boiling essential oils has become more and more of a common practise. In the case of vetiver, oils with very high content of vetiverol are obtained, and the color is often straw yellow or pale amber. Being residue-free, they offer better solubility in alcohol and better miscibility with other perfume materials.

A Vetiver Absolute has been prepared experimentally from the above mentioned concrète ("resinoid"), but the absolute is not a commercial or regularly available product.

Violet Flower Absolute.

This material is now obtained almost exclusively by alcohol washing of the petroleum ether extracted concrète from the flowers of Viola Odorata. The plant is cultivated on a large scale in the south of France and in Italy for the production of Violet Leaf Absolute (see following monograph). Extraction of flowers has become more and more uneconomical and rare. The availability of excellent synthetic materials, reproducing the main odors of the violet flower, and the fact that violet as a fragrance type is not a very popular perfume any more, has resulted in the disappearing of this exquisite flower absolute from the perfumery market.

Violet Flower Absolute is a greenish-olive colored

or creamy-green, viscous liquid of very delicate, sweet-floral odor, truly reminiscent of the violet flowers only when diluted below one percent in an odorless solvent. The author will not guarantee that the samples upon which the above description is based, are true and genuine extraction products, obtained exclusively from violet flowers. It is quite possible that the true products will disappear from the market since their effect is not sufficiently appreciated by the perfumers that it compensates for the high price of the absolute. Prior to World War II, the price of violet flower absolute was about U.S. $ 10,000.- per kilo.

True violet flower absolute could be used in high-class perfumes along with cassie absolute, mimosa, boronia, costus, orris, clove bud absolute, ylang-ylang absolute, "gamma"-methyl ionone, "delta"-methyl ionone, sandalwood oil, bergamot oil, dodecanal, myristic aldehyde, isopropyl nonylate, vanoris, vertenex HC, etc.

A production in China of violet flower absolute has brought small lots of this rare material to the Asian and European markets since 1958. It is still too early to predict any future for this new item.

Violet Leaf Absolute.

Far more important in perfumery than the flower absolute (which is hardly available any more) are the extraction products of violet leaves. The leaves are derived from **Viola Odorata**, the so-called Victoria variety which is cultivated extensively in the coastal region south of Grasse, France. The plant is also cultivated in northern Italy for the extraction of leaf absolute and, more recently, China has started production of this interesting perfume material.

Violet Leaf Absolute is produced by petroleum ether extraction of the freshly harvested leaves. The resulting extract is the concrète of violet leaves. By alcohol washing, chilling and filtration of the alcoholic extract and subsequent evaporation in vacuum, an absolute is obtained. This is a viscous liquid, intensely dark green and possessing a very powerful and peculiar odor, truly a greenleaf odor, but with an indisputable floral and delicate note which makes it immediately reminiscent of violets in a bouquet (flowers, stems, leaves).

Although the annual production must be estimated at only 100 to 250 kilos, **Violet Leaf Absolute**

is used extensively in perfumery where its tremendous diffusion and delicate naturalness is obtainable at very low concentrations of the absolute in a perfume or base. In certain floral bases, e.g. hyacinth, muguet, reseda, violet, and in high-class chypres, in aldehydic-woody fragrances and in many fantasy types, it lends an unsurpassed elegance when skilfully used. It blends excellently with tuberose, narcissus, tea leaf absolute, michelia leaf oil, anthocephalus cadamba, boronia, clary sage absolute, estragon, cumin, basil, and with numerous synthetic materials. It was used with cyclamal, cuminal, dimethyl heptenal, hop absolute, beta-gamma hexenal, isononyl acetate and propionate, and with certain other synthetic materials for the once fashionable "cucumber"-green note.

In flavors, violet leaf absolute finds some application, but the absolute suffers from the disadvantage of being very unstable in the presence of water (which is the condition ruling in most flavor concentrates, etc.).

Violet Leaf Absolute is occasionally adulterated with synthetic 2,6-nonadien-1-al (this is one of the odor principles in the absolute), with chlorophyll extracts (obtained from odorless botanical material), and with amyl heptine carboxylate, methyl heptine carboxylate, ethyl octine carboxylate, ethyl decine carboxylate, dibutyl sulfide, dimethyl heptenal or other synthetic materials. These have not yet been identified in the natural absolute extract of violet leaves.

W

Wallflower Absolute.

The decorative perennial plant **Cheiranthus Cheiri** has been known in the eastern Mediterranean countries for more than 2000 years, and was mentioned along with violet in ancient greek history. The small plant grows wild in the south of France, Italy, Greece and the Middle East. It is widely cultivated in numerous varieties in Europe as a garden perennial (known in Germany as **Goldlack**).

Occasionally, small quantities of flowers are extracted with petroleum ether in the south of France. The resulting concrète is washed with alcohol to produce an **Absolute** of **Wallflower.** This absolute is a brownish-orange or olive-brown colored, viscous liquid of intensely swet floral fragrance, reminiscent of jasmin, honey, orangeflower, ylang-ylang and with a narcissus-carnation-like, green topnote.

Wallflower absolute is no more produced on a commercial scale, and only very rarely are sizeable lots offered on the open market. The author has no personal notes of its odor description since 1953, and it is quite possible that a true wallflower absolute is now an obsolete article.

When available, wallflower absolute could be used in high-class lotion perfumes of the floral and heavier type where it would blend well with jasmin, ylang-ylang, tuberose, petitgrain, Peru balsam oil, benzoin Siam resinoid, linalool, methylionones, nerol, nerylacetate, phenylethyl cinnamate, phenylacetates, isoeugenol, etc.

Walnut Leaf Oil.

Perfumers who have owned or seen walnut trees, will probably have wondered why the delicious fragrance of the leaves has not been exploited and made accessible for the industry in the form of an essential oil, an absolute, or the like.

The essential oil of the leaves of **Juglans Regia,** the walnut tree, has been produced in several European countries, e.g. Germany and France, but the oil is presently not commercially available. A few, rare, users may have the oil or an absolute from the leaves prepared for special purposes. With the abundance of walnut trees in the south of France, Germany, Italy and southeastern Europe, it is conceivable that the oil could become a regular, commercially available product, if sufficient interest were in evidence.

The leaves of the walnut tree are particularly fragrant in the mid-summer when the fruits are still small (pea-size to cherry-size). The leaves are frequently used as an insect repellant by the local population where the walnut trees grow, and where flies or mosquitoes are a nuisance at night. A few leaves or a twig at the headpiece of one's bed should keep the insects away.

Walnut Leaf Oil is a pale yellow, mobile liquid of a powerful, warm-spicy, sweet and rich tealeaf-like odor with a labdanum-like, intensely herbaceous-sweet, balsamic undertone. The odor bears some resemblance to nutmeg, ginger, myrtle, laurel berry and Moroccan chamomile. The

author has no experience with respect to the chemical composition of this oil but, judging from the odor, cineole, myrcene, methyl eugenol, geraniol, etc. could be some of the components. The characteristic labdanum-like sweetness must, however, derive from materials other than those suggested here.

Walnut Leaf Absolute is reported produced upon demand in France, but the author has no personal experience with this material. The essential oil of walnut leaf could find use in colognes, chypres, aldehydic bases, fougères, etc. where it might well introduce fresh topnotes and a warm, rich, natural body, roundness and fixation at higher concentrations. It blends very well with citrus oils, lavender, spice oils, linalool, coumarin, pine fragrances, labdanum, oakmoss products, nerol, vetiver oil, etc., and it would no doubt be an interesting "carrier-note" in a "men's fragrance" for after-shave lotions or the like.

Walnut Leaf Oil could become an interesting flavor material since it blends extremely pleasantly with sage oils, nutmeg and clove, pimenta berry, laurel leaf, etc. for meat sauces, pickle spice blends, seasonings, etc.

Wintergreen Oil.
Gaultheria oil:

The once popular and well known essential oil of **Wintergreen,** also called **Gaultheria Oil,** is about to become obsolete on the perfumer's and flavorist's shelf. More correctly, it has been replaced by synthetic **Methyl Salicylate.**

Wintergreen oil is a typical American essential oil, derived by water distillation of the leaves of **Gaultheria Procumbens,** a small plant of the heather family. Prior to distillation, the leaves are exposed to enzymatic action in warm water. During this process, the methyl salicylate is formed as a decomposition product from a glycoside in the plant material. Traces of other volatile constituents are either present in the leaves, or they are formed during the water distillation as decomposition products (diacetyl is a possible trace component in the oil, as is formaldehyde, etc. These materials are presumably derived from carbohydrates in the re-used distillation water).

The leaves are practically odorless, and methyl salicylate makes up more than 95% of the water-distillable oil.

The plant is a native of eastern North America, and grows wild abundantly in the eastern states from the southern part of Canada to Georgia in the southeast of the U.S.A. The production of wintergreen oil is steadily decreasing, and is often closely connected with the distillation of oil of Sweet Birch (see monograph on Birch Bark Oil). The actual production of pure and genuine wintergreen oil may not be counted in tons any more, but merely in hundreds of kilos.

Wintergreen Oil is a pale yellow to yellowish or pinkish colored liquid of intensely sweet-aromatic odor and flavor, often displaying a peculiar creamy-fruity topnote and a sweet-woody dryout which may have a tarlike note in poorly distilled oils. The suggested use level in finished flavored goods is about 0.20 to 0.50 mg%, and the Minimum Perceptible is 0.05 to 0.10 mg%. (There are toothpastes, however, in which the synthetic methyl salicylate is used at a concentration of 300–700 mg%) The oil is still used in pharmaceutical preparations as a flavor corrector. In candy, toothpaste, industrial products, etc. the oil has been replaced by pure synthetic methyl salicylate which is much less expensive and is readily available in car-loads. Methyl salicylate is not exactly toxic, but it is harmful to human beings in larger dosages. Many people, particularly children, die from accidental intake of industrial preparations that have been flavored with this all-American popular chemical. Its use in "root-beer" (American carbonated beverage) has made the methyl salicylate flavor still more popular, and this flavor may attract the curiosity of children if they meet the odor in certain industrial (and non-edible) products. Hence the many accidents. Methyl salicylate is the main flavor ingredient in several large brands of toothpaste, and it is a "must" in many types of candy and chewing gum. It blends excellently with anethole, safrole, vanillin, menthol, spearmint oil, linalool, estragole, etc. Methyl salicylate is a natural constituent of the extract of coca-leaves (decocainized) which is used in the world famous coca-cola flavor complex (see monographs on Cola, Sarsaparilla and Sassafras, North American).

Methyl salicylate (or "wintergreen oil") is useful in perfumery where traces of this powerful odorant can add natural notes to ylang-ylang, tuberose, narcissus, lily, gardenia, etc. and it is used frequently in fougères and other forest notes.

Woodruff Absolute.

The small perennial, Asperula Odorata of the botanical family Rubiaceae, grows wild all over Central Europe and Scandinavia. It is known as "Sweet Woodruff" (England), "Waldmeister" (Germany), "Asperule" (France), "Bukar" (Sweden) and "Skovmaerke" (Denmark). The tiny flowers open up in late April to mid-May before the beech and oak trees cast their deep shadow on the floor of the forest. The woodruff is almost odorless when freshly picked, but the herb develops upon drying a rich, sweet, herbaceous-coumarinic fragrance reminiscent of deertongue or melilotus (see these monographs).

It is customary to make wreaths of the plant in these countries. The wreaths are pinned to the wall at home or they are kept in a dresser-drawer where the fragrance is slowly released over a period of many months. In Germany, certain wines are flavored with the herb.

Similarly to the other coumarin-type herbs and botanicals, the Woodruff does not yield an essential oil upon steam distillation. Tinctures have been prepared and they are still used in pharmaceutical preparations in the countries where coumarin is permitted in flavors. By petroleum ether extraction, a concrète is prepared; the concrète yields an absolute after alcohol-washing. Woodruff Absolute (or "oleoresin") is very rarely offered from the regular suppliers of perfume raw materials, but it is occasionally prepared by the individual users. The dried herb is available all over Europe.

Woodruff absolute (from concrète) is a viscous dark green liquid of a heavy-sweet, herbaceous-tobacco-like odor, reminiscent of hay, dry tea leaves, tobacco, melilotus, etc.

This product blends excellently with lavender and lavandin concrète and absolute, clary sage concrète, oakmoss products, labdanum products, pine needle oils, cedarwood oils, "tombacco" absolute, isobornyl acetate, nitromusks, cinnamic alcohol, ionones, methyl cinnamate ,etc. for "powdery" notes, fougères, new mown hay bases, chypres, forest notes, lily of the valley (very interesting modifier), etc.

Woodruff absolute is obviously very likely to be adulterated with coumarin, lavandin concrète, deertongue extract, etc.

Wormseed Oil (American).

The so-called "American" Wormseed Oil is steam

distilled from the dried herb of mature **Cheno-podium Ambrosioides,** *varietas* **Anthelminthicum** plants. The plant grows wild in the eastern and southeastern United states of America and in India (Bangalore and Mysore), Hungary and the U.S.S.R. (see also the monograph on **Chenopodium Ambrosioides,** under which the Brazilian variety is discussed).

American wormseed oil is distilled almost exclusively in the states of Maryland and Ohio. The oil is produced for its anthelminthic (worm-exterminating) effect in human and veterinary medicine, and it is quite hazardous if used without the directions from a physician. For these reasons, the oil should never be used in flavor work, and it can easily be avoided in perfume formulation. The author wants to mention the existence of this oil briefly since he has occasionally noted its use in various perfume compounds during the past 20 years. Isolated cases of confusion with **Wormwood Oil** (see following monograph) can only encourage to more caution and to a total ban of wormseed oil from use in perfumes and flavors.

Wormseed Oil, American, is a pale yellow or almost colorless, somewhat viscous liquid with a heavy, unpleasant, nauseating odor, a sharp, camphoraceous topnote and a woody-sweet under-tone. The odor faintly recalls that of savin oil.

While the Russian **Wormseed Oil** (derived from **Artemisia Cina**) contains **Cineole** ("eucalyptol") as its main constituent, the principal and active ingredient in "American" wormseed oil is **Ascaridol,** another terpene oxide, chemically related to cineole. American wormseed oil is used for its content of ascaridole. The annual production of this oil is in the order of magnitude of 50 metric tons. It should be noted that ascaridole, like certain terpene peroxides, may explode under dry distillation if the temperature exceeds 125°C. In the presence of acids, the ascaridole is liable to explode without heating. Wormseed oil (American) is in many respects a very hazardous oil.

Wormwood Oil.

See also the monographs on **Artemisia Alba, Artemisia Annua** and **Artemisia Vulgaris.**

Wormwood oil is steam distilled from the dried herb (leaves and flowering top) of the plant **Artemisia Absinthium.** It is known in the U.S.A. as **Mugwort.** It should not be confused with the Chinese so-called mugwort. Chinese megwort oil

is derived from a different species and the oil contains about 40% borneol.

Artemisia absinthium is a native of central and southern Europe where it grows wild in abundance. It is also cultivated in France, Holland, Belgium, Germany, Hungary, Yugoslavia, the southeastern U.S.S.R., North Africa and Brazil. Besides being a common weed in the U.S.A., the plant is cultivated in the midwestern peppermint-spearmint area of Michigan-Indiana-Wisconsin, where the oil is locally distilled.

Along with angelica root, anise seed, marjoram herb and numerous other herbs, the dried herb of wormwood is an important ingredient in the flavoring of **Vermouth,** the Italian aperitif (vermouth = wormwood).

Wormwood Oil is a very dark green, brownish-green or bluish-green colored liquid with an odor that is intensely herbaceous-green, warm and deep, and a sharp and fresh topnote, reminiscent of cedarleaf oil. The body-note is very warm and dry-woody, long-lasting and highly interesting as a unique perfume note. The flavor of wormwood oil is intensely bitter, and it has an astringent mouthfeel and a long-lasting, unpleasant after-taste. The flavor is pleasant, green-herbaceous, somewhat reminiscent of hop and chamomile only in very high dilution.

The bluish or greenish color of wormwood oil is due to the presence of an **Azulene.** These colored hydrocarbons are often found in the essential oils from plants of the family Compositae. However, certain of the **Artemisia** species yield colorless oils upon distillation (e. g. the "armoise", the French and North African **Artemisia Vulgaris,** see this monograph).

Wormwood Oil is used quite extensively in flavor work in spite of the fact that the herb itself was responsible for the ban in France in 1915 of the production of "absinth" with this herb. It was claimed that the **Thujone** in the plant acts as a narcotic in greater doses, and that it was habit-forming. Thujone is the main constituent of wormwood oil, and this ketone is also responsible for the similarity in odor to the oils of tansy and cedarleaf, partly also to Dalmatian sage oil. The European distillers and wine producers are using several other species of **Artemisia,** but all of these plants contain some thujone.

Wormwood Oil Fractions:
Considering the fact that more than half the oil

is made up of **Thujone,** it is quite surprising that wormwood oil still has an odor so distinctly different from that of cedarleaf. A number of essential oils have been thoroughly investigated during the past 10 or 20 years, particularly with respect to isolating and identifying the characteristic odor principles in the oils. It has often been found that the major constituent (by volume) is not responsible for the characteristic odor of the oil, and that the major constituent can be removed from the oil (e.g. by fractional distillation, isolation by chemical means, etc.) without the oil losing its typical odor (see **Clove Bud Oil, Geranium Oil, Lavandin Oil,** etc.). Consequently, it is logical that several perfume houses have endeavored to prepare fractions of wormwood oil in order to isolate the more interesting notes, e.g. the intensively green-herbaceous note, the dry woody note, and the leatherlike, sweet and tenacious notes. These notes are found in the higher boiling fractions of wormwood oil, thujone being a comparatively low-boiling component. A partially "de-thujonized" wormwood oil thus presents an extremely interesting perfume material which can be utilized in a multitude of new combinations. It blends well with oakmoss; it introduces a true-to-nature herbaceous note in a jasmin, orange-flower or hyacinth; it lends enormous richness to a chypre or a lavender compound; it gives life, warmth and topnote to modern fantasy bases, particularly in combination with a selected oak-moss product.

Wormwood Absolute has been prepared experimentally, but it is not regularly available. It has been recommended that wild growing plants be used for perfumery purposes since these plants contain less thujone but, to the author's knowledge, this practice is not yet a common one.

X

Xanthoxylum Alatum.

Various species of **Xanthoxylum** are known in the tropics, and used for their spicy or pungent fruits. The plants belong to the family of Rutaceae. One of the species is **Xanthoxylum Alatum** which grows wild in Kaschmir (India) and produces a pepper-like fruit. This plant is known in the Far East as **"Chinese Wild Pepper"** or **"Tumru".**

An essential oil can be obtained from the dried fruits by steam distillation. This essential oil is produced on a limited scale in the northwestern part of India (Himalaya). The plant is at hand in abundance, and the oil could be produced in ton-lots annually if sufficient interest were in evidence.

The essential oil of the fruits of xanthoxylum alatum is a pale yellow to olive-yellow colored, mobile liquid of a warm-woody, green-peppery, spicy odor, reminiscent of cubeb, guaiacwood, etc. with a faint resemblance to the odor of wild roses (rosa canina). The dryout is deep-floral and somewhat similar to the odor of cabreuva and araucaria oils. The tenacity of the fragrance makes the oil interesting as a fixative in woody-floral or aldehydic-woody, modern fragrances. It blends excellently with "gamma"-methyl ionone (alpha-iso-methyl ionone), hydroxycitronellal, linalool, geranium oils, cinnamic alcohol, clove bud oil, etc.

The comparatively good yield of oil by steam distillation, the abundance of wild growing botanical material and the fact, that distilleries are close at hand, are all in favor of a good future for this oil, in case it should be made available outside its country of origin. Its interesting odor characteristics and valuable perfume effects will no doubt arouse the interest of creative perfumers beyond the borders of India.

Y

Ylang-Ylang Absolute.

One of the most delightful floral absolutes is the one obtained by alcohol washing of the concrète from **Ylang-Ylang.** This process is performed almost exclusively in France, from concrète imported from Nossi-Bé or from the Comoro islands (see also monograph on **Ylang-Ylang Concrète** for origin and production).

The concrète yields a very high amount of absolute (75 to 82%), and the resulting absolute is a pale yellow to straw yellow, oily liquid of intensely sweet-floral, very diffusive odor. With an unusual power in its topnote, the fragrance fades out very slowly and most elegantly in a long-lasting, floral-spicy and very sweet note, truly reminiscent of the fragrance of the flower. It is a typical *balsamic* floral note, and it is distinguished from the odor of the oil ("extra") by its lightness and uniformity. Considering its relatively low cost and versatile application, it is surprising that this material is not used much more frequently in perfumery than the production figures seem to show. The annual world production must be considerably less than one metric ton.

Ylang-Ylang Absolute is one of the finest floral materials in high-class muguet perfumes (type "Diorissimo", etc.), where its power and (yet) very delicate undertone blend excellently with jasmin and rose materials, hydroxycitronellal, dimethylbenzyl carbinyl acetate, dimethyl phenyl-ethyl carbinol, phenylethyl isobutyrate, nerolidol, Peru balsam oil, indole, isoeugenol, rhodinol, sandalwood oil, cassie and mimosa, vertenex HC, alpha isomethyl ionone, etc. It is used in carnation, lilac, lily, narcissus, gardénia, violet, hyacinth, honeysuckle, peony, freesia, sweet pea, and countless other floral bases. Furthermore in Oriental perfumes with rose, sandalwood, opopanax, spice oils, nonanolide, undecanolide, anthocephalus cadamba, costus, etc.

The absolute finds occasional use in flavors of the intensely sweet type, e.g. peach and apricot. It is obviously an interesting bouquet for methyl salicylate flavors ("wintergreen") through its olfactory and chemical relationship. **Ylang-Ylang Absolute** has a slightly bitter taste but, with proper blending and very low concentration, it gives quite pleasant and interesting notes in fruit flavors, etc. The suggested use level is 0.02 to 0.10 mg%, and the **Minimum Perceptible** is 0.01 to 0.02 mg%.

Selling at less than one-fifth the price of jasmin absolute, **Ylang-Ylang Absolute** should have a very good future in perfumery.

A steam distilled or steam-vacuum distilled concrète of **Ylang-Ylang** is commercially available under various brand names. The product can be considered as a type of an **Absolute Oil**. It represents the highest possible concentration of the volatile (and extractable) constituents of the flower. Its odor is even more refined than that of the absolute, but the tenacity is slightly inferior.

Ylang-Ylang Complete Oil.

It was a very good idea (and who was actually the originator?) when, in the mid-1950's, a "new" ylang-ylang oil was marketed under the name of **Ylang-Ylang Complete**. It was claimed that the

oil was a natural distillate. To be quite true to its name, the oil should be the total result of an uninterrupted water-and-steam distillation of ylang-ylang flowers (see also **Cananga Oil**). The distillation was carried out in the Comoro islands by a large French company which had good and modern equipment at its disposal. If such an oil was ever distilled on a commercial scale, the undertaking was rapidly abandoned. Consumers were not willing to pay the high price which obviously has to be high enough to include the equivalent of "extra" oil contained in the total distillate (see **Ylang-Ylang Oil**). The true "complete" oil would cost about half the price of the "extra" oil. Consequently, another "complete" oil was "produced" on the spot: a mixture of all the fractions which were difficult to sell at the same rate as the quick-selling "ylang-ylang extra" (particularly the oils ylang-ylang I and II).

Thus, a new means of economical distillation was set up. A "medium quality" ylang-ylang oil was made available at a reasonable price. However, the profound studies of the chemical composition of ylang-ylang oil proved disadvantageous to the natural oil: countless artificial "complete" oils appeared on the market, and today it is hard to find the natural mixture among the abundance of artificial oils, many of which are quite good from a perfumery point of view. They are available at less than half the theoretical cost of a true and genuine complete ylang-ylang oil.

Ylang-Ylang Complete Oil is usually a yellowish, somewhat oily liquid, with a powerful and intensely sweet, but also soft-balsamic floral odor and an unusual tenacity in its floral-woody undertones. The oil is useful in soap perfumes and in general perfumery as a floral additive of extremely versatile application. It blends with almost any other floral natural or synthetic material, and gives good effects in a concentration of 0.5% up to about 5% of the perfume base. In view of the above remarks on the genuineness of ylang-ylang complete oil, it is not possible to give any useful production figures.

Ylang-Ylang Concrète.

From the flowers of cultivated **Cananga Odorata** trees (see **Ylang-Ylang Oil**) in Nossi-Bé and the Comoro islands, a concrète is produced by petroleum ether extraction. Installations for extraction are at hand in these islands. As a matter of fact,

60: **Vetiver** field in south-western Réunion. Main roots ready for replanting. Secondary rootlets collected for distillation. The grass in the background is the **Vetiver** plant. *(Fot. S. Arctander, 1956)*

61: Modern high-pressure steam still for **Vetiver** rootlets in Goma, eastern Belgian Congo (Kivu province). *(Fot. S. Arctander, 1955)*

62: A single flower of **Ylang-Ylang** displayed by the foreman of a Réunion distillery. Flowers must be distilled within a few hours after early morning picking. *(Fot. S. Arctander, 1955)*

50 years ago the first extractors were brought to La Réunion which, at that time, was about to become the world's leading producer of ylang-ylang oil. After the economic collapse of the ylang-ylang industry in Réunion, the installations were moved to Nossi-Bé, a tiny island off the north-west coast of Madagascar. Comparatively modern equipment is now in operation in the two island areas (Nossi-Bé and the Comores). In Nossi-Bé, it is customary to water-and-steam distil the extracted flower material, and thus obtain an additional yield of oil which is added to the extracted concrète. The steam-and-water distilled oil is of rather poor odor value, but has a certain fixative effect and adds to the mellowness of the concrète. Thus two products are sold under the name of **Ylang-Ylang Concrète:** 1) the true extraction product, and 2) the combined extract and distillate (from exhaust flowers). Certain sesquiterpenes seem to be insoluble in petroleum ether, but they are distillable with water. Benzene has been suggested as a better solvent, but although the yield is far better with benzene, the odor of the benzene concrète is inferior to that of the petroleum ether concrète. Again we find an example of the detrimental effect exerted by boiling water on certain components in essential oils, often resulting in the formation of sesquiterpenes or other materials of low odor value.

Ylang-Ylang Concrète is not a "concrète" in appearance. It is a brownish-yellow or dark amber colored liquid with a bottom deposit or suspended precipitate of cream-colored or grayish-yellow, waxy grains or flakes. At slightly higher than room temperature, the waxy and insoluble precipitate melts and dissolves in the liquid which then becomes homogeneous. The odor is rich, sweet and intensely floral with an outstanding tenacity and uniformity. Considering the fact that the concrète contains up to 85% alcohol-soluble matter (ylang-ylang absolute), it is surprising that the sharp and very "high" topnote of the absolute is rounded-off so elegantly in the concrète without affecting the naturalness or the rich body.

Ylang-Ylang Concrète is primarily used for the production of absolute (see that monograph), but an increasing number of perfumers have visualized the concrète as a potential perfume material in better soap perfumes where the waxes most often will dissolve and cause no further trouble. The effect of *one percent* of of ylang-ylang concrète in

a floral soap perfume (e. g. lilac) is so obvious and, most often, so definitely an improvement that the question of economy is eliminated and the use of the concrète is justified.

The concrète blends well with isoeugenol, hydroxycitronellal, bucinal, cyclamal, cassione, vertenex, ionones and methyl ionones, cinnamic alcohol, anisalcohol, amyl salicylate, benzyl salicylate, phenylethyl salicylate or cinnamate, linalool and esters, isosafrol, heliotropine, mimosa and cassie absolutes, sandalwood oil, alpha terpineol, etc., etc. In floral soap-perfume bases such as lilac, muguet, hyacinth, carnation, appleblossom, sweet pea, etc. and in heavy Oriental soap-perfume bases, etc., ylang-ylang concrète lends a richness and natural mellowness with its soft, balsamic-floral bouquet, whose tenacity is hard to obtain by other means.

The annual production of ylang-ylang concrète is still measured in hundreds of kilos, but the increasing interest in this material will undoubtedly encourage the producers in the Indian Ocean islands to turn out a tonnage of this exceptionally fine perfume material.

Ylang-Ylang Oil.

So much has been written about this important perfume oil that the author is inclined to limit this monograph to a number of references to the literature. On the other hand, this book also aims at giving condensed and yet concise information on all the available natural materials for perfumes and flavors.

Ylang-Ylang Oil has been called "the poor man's jasmin", a nickname which the author strongly resents. He would rather call it "everybody's ylang-ylang". A good ylang-ylang oil need not be compared to any other perfume oil. It is so unusual in itself, so simple and yet so complex of odor, so generally popular a fragrance, that it easily finds its own place in perfumery, not merely as a replacement for jasmin, but as an improvement to almost any type of floral fragrance. However, one might say that the essential oil is poorer than the absolute of ylang-ylang from a viewpoint of floral fineness and magnificence.

The oil is produced by water distillation or water-and-steam distillation of the freshly early-morning-picked flowers from **Cananga Odorata,** a tree which is native to Indonesia and perhaps the Philippines. All ylang-ylang oils of today are produced from flowers of cultivated trees. Cultivation is most extensive in the Comoro islands, in Nossi-Bé, northwestern Madagascar, while the plantations in the Philippines and Indonesia are of minor importance. Smaller cultivations are found in Haiti, in Zanzibar, in a few of the French South Pacific islands, in Réunion (where two producers turn out about one metric ton per year), and in some of the West Indian islands. About 80% of the world production is derived from the Comoro islands and Nossi-Bé. All trees in these two areas are topped at an early age, causing the branches to grow horizontally. This facilitates the harvesting of the tender yellow flowers, tedious but very important handwork.

Distillation is carried out in rather small stills since the flower material would suffer considerably by the weight and pressure of a heavy charge of flowers. The distillation of the oil (or, the collection of condensate) is usually interrupted, the first distillate being collected separately, and then a second distillate being collected over a longer period. Finally, a third distillate is collected over a period of 24 hours or even more. By controlling the specific gravity of the distillate, the various producers make the interruptions at the moment when they feel that the oil can be classified within one of these groups. The specific gravity is often over 1.000 in the very first distillate, then it slowly decreases. Although the "extra" quality is usually standardized at a specific gravity of 0.975 to 0.985 (at 25°C.), this specification is no guarantee of the genuineness of the oil (see below).

Adulteration or contamination of the ylang-ylang flowers with flowers of Artabotrys Suaveolens (see this monograph) occurs not infrequently in the oils from Indonesia and the Philippines. The first distillate of ylang-ylang oil, usually the first 30 to 45% of the total distillate, is called Ylang-Ylang Extra. There is no standard as to the physico-chemical properties of "Extra" or any of the other grades, but it is left to the distiller's discretion to make the correct fractionation during the distillation. After the "extra" quality comes Ylang-Ylang First ("première"), then the Second ("seconde") and finally Ylang-Ylang Third ("troisième") (see also monograph on Ylang-Ylang Complete).

Obviously, there are various qualities of "extra" which is the most wanted grade. On the other hand, the economy of the entire production of ylang-ylang oils is based upon a sale of all the grades. Accordingly, the "extra" is by far the most expensive even if it amounts to almost half the yield of oil. The chemist will often judge the oil according to its ester content, but this figure is unfortunately an easy one to "arrange" by the addition of synthetic esters. Consequently, ylang-ylang oils can only be evaluated properly by an experienced perfumer who has a standard of odor in his mind (or perhaps, if necessary, on his shelf).

The author finds that the classical grading of ylang-ylang oils in "extra", "first", "second" and "third" has become so inconsistent that it serves no purpose to describe the individual grades. Furthermore, there is little or no interest for the "second" and "first" grades. Most consumers want a good "extra" oil and a good "third" oil. With the latter, they often make a replacement for Cananga Oil (see this monograph) which was unavailable for many years until recently. The unfortunate "first" and "second" oils form the major part of the so-called Ylang-Ylang Complete (see monograph).

Ylang-Ylang Extra is a pale yellow oil with a very powerful, floral and intensely sweet odor and a cresylic and benzoate-like topnote of limited tenacity. The fadeout is more pleasant, soft and sweet, slightly spicy and balsamic-floral. A high-grade "extra" oil resembles the absolute of ylang-ylang in odor type very closely. The former is, however, often more sharp-cresylic in its topnote. A peculiar creamy-sweet note is characteristic of good "extra" oils; this note appears very early in the evaporation, although it seems to be present also in the higher boiling fractions (in good "third" oils), and it definitely is missing in the first fractions when "extra" is vacuum-redistilled. This suave, soft and persistent note is very difficult to reproduce in artificial ylang-ylang oils.

Ylang-Ylang Extra is used mainly in high-class perfumes of the floral and heavy-Oriental type, but mere traces of the oil can do wonders in medium-priced floral bases. There is hardly any floral type, where ylang-ylang "extra" would not fit in. The oil blends excellently with bois de rose, vetiver, amyl salicylate, opopanax, bergamot, hydroxycitronellal, mimosa, cassie, methylionones, cinnamic alcohol and esters, benzoates, para-cresyl esters (ethers), nerolidol, Peru balsam oil, vertenex HC, etc. and with gardenia bases, stephanotis bases, tuberose bases, etc.

Ylang-Ylang Oil "Extra" is produced in quite substantial quantities per annum. The exact amount is difficult to give since many "borderline" ylang-ylang No. 1 oils are sold as "extra". The annual world consumption of "extra" quality may be estimated at over 20 metric tons. It is understandable that this quantity is of vital importance for the economy in the very small areas of production (see tables in the rear of this book).

Adulteration is a frequent occurrence, and the added materials are countless: the "extra" oil is first of all adulterated with the No. 1, 2 and 3 oils, with vanillin (a bouquetting material), para cresol methyl ether (to give power), methyl benzoate or methyl para-toluate, ethyl benzoate, geraniol, iso-eugenol, isosafrol, benzyl alcohol, benzyl benzoate or salicylate, benzyl propionate and cinnamate, anisyl acetone and anisyl alcohol, copaiba oil, Peru balsam oil (mainly in the "second" and "third" grades of ylang-ylang oil), and other natural or synthetic materials, many of which are known and identified in the natural oil of ylang-ylang.

Ylang-Ylang Oil "Third" is a yellowish oily liquid of sweet-floral and balsamic-woody odor, with a tenacious and very sweet-balsamic undertone. This oil was once used in place of Cananga Oil (see this monograph), but such a replacement is unjust to both oils. They are not interchangeable, either in floral type nor in fixative effect. With its tenacity and fair stability, the ylang-ylang No. 3 is useful in soap perfumery and as a comparatively low-cost floral material for hyacinths, lilacs, etc. if cost is a major problem.

Ylang-Ylang "third" is also frequently adulterated, mainly with high-boiling materials such as benzyl benzoate, cedarwood oil fractions, anis-alcohol, copaiba balsam, isosafrol, amyris oil, benzyl salicylate, etc. The oil is the second largest ylang-ylang product next to the "extra" oil.

Ylang-Ylang "First" and "Second" are "inbetween-qualities", poorly defined, and slowly disappearing from the market. They are used in "cutting" of the other grades of ylang-ylang (upgrading or downgrading!) and in the production of the so-called Ylang-Ylang Complete Oil (see this monograph).

Z

Zdravetz Oil.

Much has been written about Zdravetz Oil, Zdravetz Absolute and Zdravetz Concrète, and the author almost felt like leaving this monograph out of the present work. It appears that there is no production at all of the two latter items, and that the Zdravetz Oil is produced only upon demand. The term "concrète" is occasionally applied to the essential oil since this is a solid mass at slightly below room temperature.

The plant Geranium Macrorrhizum (the last name means "big root") is a small, but very hardy perennial which grows wild on rocky soil at high and medium altitude in the Balkans and southeastern Europe. The oil is distilled in Bulgaria. The name "zdrave" means "health", and the plant is used extensively in these areas as a popular medicinal herb. It is cultivated for this purpose in various countries in Central Europe.

The overground parts of the plant are water distilled, but the yield of oil is extremely small, even smaller than the yield of geranium oil from pelargonium plants (see Geranium Oil).

Zdravetz Oil is a pale olive-green or pale yellowish, somewhat viscous liquid from which a considerable amount of large white crystals will separate on standing and on cooling. Most oils are semi-solid at room temperature, and some oils contain paraffin in such amounts that they become entirely solid at room temperature. The paraffin is of no perfumery value, and the author is inclined to believe that larger amounts of paraffin in this oil is not a natural occurrence. The crystals are, however, of a certain perfumery value. Although virtually odorless, they are useful for their excellent fixative effect (compare Sclareol in clary sage absolute) and the crystals seem to be necessary for the perfect balancing of the peculiar odor of this oil.

The odor of zdravetz oil is sweet-woody with a floral and faintly herbaceous undertone, reminiscent of clary sage, tobacco, broom absolute (fruity notes), tea leaves and ulex europaeus. The floral notes are of rosy-woody character, delicate and tenacious. The odor does not strike one with power, but the effect of zdravetz oil in a perfume is often perceptible at concentrations around one percent.

Only the irregular availability and the immediate

impression of weakness could be reasons for the apparent lack of interest in this oil among perfumers. The oil has an excellent fixative effect which can be utilized in fougères, chypres, crèpe de Chines, Oriental bases, colognes and fantasy fragrances. It blends excellently with oakmoss, labdanum, olibanum, sandalwood, sage clary absolute, lavender or lavandin, bergamot, etc.

Quantities of 50 or 100 kilos can be produced upon demand with due notice, but the oil is rarely offered in sizeable lots on the perfume market.

Zedoaria Oil.

A perennial plant of the family Zingiberaceae, **Curcuma Zedoaria,** is a native of Ceylon, Indonesia and the East Indian islands. The plant grows wild, and is also cultivated since its rhizomes are used locally as a household spice. Furthermore, the leaves are occasionally used, but their flavor is entirely different from that of the rhizomes. The leaves, when crushed, smell somewhat lemongrass-like and fresh, while the rhizomes have a warm-spicy, woody and camphoraceous odor.

The essential oil is distilled from the dried rhizomes by steam. Little or no oil is produced in the growing areas, while smaller quantities are distilled in Europe from imported roots. Like many other spice oils, **Zedoaria Oil** belongs to the oldest known distilled oils. It has now lost most of its importance in pharmacy, and the perfume industry has very little interest in this oil. It is still used to some extent in flavors.

Zedoaria Oil is a viscous liquid of olive-brown to greenish-amber color, often hazy or opalescent. Its odor is warm, woody-spicy, camphoraceous-cineolic in its initial notes, later sweet and warm, very tenacious. It does not present the lemon-orange-like note which is found in ginger oil (after proper ageing), but apart from this, the odor of zedoaria oil is strikingly resemblant to that of ginger oil (particularly oil of African ginger).

The flavor is equally warm-spicy, but somewhat bitter in its predominant, camphoraceous note which is accompanied by a slightly biting-bitter aftertaste. In a way, it is a poor edition of ginger, but the zedoaria oil does present some attractive flavor notes which are not immediately perceptible in ginger oil. **Zedoaria Oil** is used, although very rarely, in spicy flavor blends, and also as an appetizing tonic in aromatic bitters. In perfumes, the oil could find some use in the powdery-Oriental types, ambre types, chypres, etc. It blends well with lavandin, coumarin, clove, ionones, cedarwood derivatives, bay leaf oil, terpinyl acetate, ocotea pretiosa oil, isobornyl acetate, etc.

Zedoaria Oil is not produced regularly, and it may slowly disappear from the perfumery market. Its importance in flavors is also rapidly decreasing.

TABLES

Tonnage of World Production
of important natural perfume and flavor materials.

The figures are based upon actual production figures from the sources of the individual materials, not from export or shipping stations. Consequently, several figures are slightly higher than certain figures for exported quantities, published for outside buyers.

	approximate quantity in metric tons annually during 1955–1959
Turpentine oil—all types..........	200,000
Pine oil—all types...............	100,000
Citronella oils, "Java" type (1955: 2,100 t.).....(incl. China)	5,400
Camphor oil—all types (less camphor)................	5,000
Mentha arvensis oil..............	3,000
Mentha piperita oil..............	2,000
Lemongrass oil (1955: 1,000; 1957: 2,200)........(incl. China)	1,500
Sweet orange oil.................	1,300
Lemon oil......................	1,200
Clove leaf oil...................	1,000
Vanilla (cured fruits) (1959: 1,200 t.)	1,000
Eucapharma oils................	1,000
Lavandin oil (still increasing)......	800
Ocotea pretiosa oil..............	800
Citronella oil, "Ceylon"..........	800
Bois de rose oil (1957: 450 t.; 1955: 800 t.).................	700
Spearmint oil (increasing)........	600
Lime oil (incl. local consumptions).	500

For comparison it can be mentioned that the figures for

Sandalwood oil is about....	180 tons
Lavender oil..............	80 tons
Ylang-ylang oils...........	50 tons
Rose oil + Rose concrète...	10 tons

The production of turpentine and pine oils amounts to more than 80% of the production of all essential oils combined.

Value of World Production
of important natural perfume and flavor materials.

	approximate value in million U.S.$ in the years 1958–1959 annually:
Turpentine oil—all types..........	40
Pine oils......................	30
Mentha arvensis oil..............	25
Mentha piperita oil..............	20
Vanilla (cured fruits), fluctuating figures......................	14 (1959)
Rose oils and concrètes (fluctuating)..................	12
Geranium oils—all types (1960 = 12 mill.)..............	9
Spearmint oil (increasing).........	9
Lemon oil.....................	6.6
Citronella oil, Java-type..........	6.5
Camphor oils, less camphor.......	5
Jasmin extracts.................	5
Lime oil......................	5
Sweet orange oil................	4.5
Sage clary oil (not incl. concrète)...	4.5
Bergamot oil...................	4
Sandalwood oil.................	4
Neroli oil and Orange flower concrète.....................	4
Civet (extracts from crude)........	4

Total value of essential oils produced in 1958: approximately U.S. $ 240 mill. (including $ 70 mill. of turpentine and pine oils).

For comparison it can be mentioned that the value of

Black Pepper (about 65,000 tons, 1958) was U.S. $.....................	70 mill.
Cloves (about 26,000 tons, 1959) was U.S. $.....................	20 mill.
Nutmeg (about 8,000 tons, 1958) was U.S. $.....................	8 mill.

—and that the largest synthetic flavor material was Monosodium Glutamate (1958: 14,000 tons) approximately U.S. $ 35 mill.

Location of the most important Centers of Production
with respect to quantity.

	approximate production in kilos per capita/year
Zanzibar and Pemba (incl. clove buds)..............	85
Zanzibar and Pemba (essential oils only)............	1
Grenada (mainly whole nutmeg) . . .	50
Nossi-Bé (mainly black pepper)....	40
The Moluccan islands (whole nutmeg only)...........	5
U.S.A. (including turpentine and pine).......................	2
Madagascar (excluding coffee, including clove bud, vanilla, pepper, etc.)..................	2
Réunion island..................	0.7

The largest production of an essential oil in one isolated area is that of **Clove Leaf Oil** in northeast Madagascar: 1000 metric tons on 130 square miles with approximately 36,000 inhabitants. The production of essential oil in this isolated area is thus about 27 kilos per capita per annum.

The largest production of essential oil from imported (not locally grown) botanical material is that of:

Clove Bud Oil:
approximately 250 to 500 tons per year, produced exclusively outside the countries of origin of the clove bud.

Nutmeg Oil:
approximately 75 to 125 tons per year, produced mainly outside the countries of origin of nutmeg and mace.

Location of the most important Centers of Production
with respect to value for the local community.

	approximate U.S.$ per capita/year
Grenada (Fed. of West Indies) (including whole nutmeg).......	100
Zanzibar and Pemba (incl. whole clove buds).........	80
Zanzibar and Pemba (essential oils only)............	4
Nossi-Bé (mainly ylang-ylang oils) .	60
Comoro islands (including cured vanilla)......................	20
Comoro islands (essential oils only).	8
Réunion island (including cured vanilla)......................	16
Madagascar (without Nossi-Bé) (including clove buds and vanilla)	7
Madagascar (without Nossi-Bé) (essential oils only)............	0.5
Madagascar (if coffee production is included)..................	20
The Moluccan islands (whole nutmeg only).................	5
Morocco (essential oils and concrètes only)...............	2
Jamaica.......................	2
Formosa (mainly citronella).......	1
Brazil........................	1
U.S.A. (including turpentines and pine oils)....................	1

In the **Dadés** valley, southeastern Morocco (north-western Sahara) the annual production of **Rose Concrète** and **Rose Oil** amounts to a value of approximately U.S. $ 200 to U.S. $ 400 per capita per year in this isolated region. The entire harvest and extraction is completed within a period of five to six weeks in April/May every year.

GROUPING

of the natural materials according to
odor type and suggested use

All materials that are described in Part Two of
this book have been grouped according to odor
type from the point of view of use, confusion,
adulteration or "cutting". The grouping is not
strictly a chemical or a botanical one, but it
inevitably includes groups of materials which
have a main constituent in common or materials
which are derived from closely related botanical
species. After most of these groups, there is a
reference to related groups. The grouping includes
a cross-reference in all cases where the author
finds it justified. The list may be useful for quick
reference to modifiers, adulterants, etc. Through
the use of the references to related groups, the
list can be reduced to a minimum of odor types.
The grouping itself, however, remains strictly
subjective and should only be considered as a
summary for special purposes.

Group No. 1
Fresh-balsamic Conifer-odors

Abies alba
Abies sp.
Balsam fir needle oil
Chamaecyparis obtusa leaf oil
Douglas fir needle oil
Fir needle oil "Siberian"
Myoporum crassifolium
Picea excelsa
Pinus leucodermis
Pinus nigra
Pinus strobus
Pinus sylvestris
Spruce
Related groups: No. 8, 43, 66, 76, 78.

Group No. 2
Sweet-balsamic resins

Acaroid
Benzoin
Styrax

Group No. 3
Sweet wood and root odors

Agarwood
Calamus
Costus
Cyperus
Elecampane
Orris "resin"
Vetiver
Related groups: No. 11 and Angelica

Group No. 4
Floral and woody, tealike

Agleia odorata
Boronia
Carob (flower)
Cassie
Chloranthus spicatus
Elderflower
Hennaflower
Lilium candidum
Mimosa
Robinia pseudacacia
Stirlingia latifolia
Tombacco
Related groups: No. 17, 26, 47, 56.

Group No. 5
Thyme group

Ajowan
Ocimum gratissimum (Thymol type)
Savory
Thyme
Thyme, "wild"

Group No. 6
Bitter almond group

Almond, bitter
Cherry laurel
Spiraea

Group No. 7
Phenolic leather odor

Amber oil, crude
Birch tar oil, rectified
Cade oil
Leather (tinctures, etc.)
Related groups: No. 19, 39.

Group No. 8
Pine oil group

Amber oil, rectified
Cedarwood, Port Orford
Pine oil
Related group: No. 1.

Group No. 9
Ambra group

Ambra
Cistus
Labdanum
Olibanum
Poplar bud oil
Related groups: No. 55, 66.

Group No. 10
Winy-sweet-floral

Ambrette seed
Nigella damascena
Related groups: No. 61 and Cognac oil.

Group No. 11
Rooty-sweet, animal

Ammoniac gum
Sumbul
Related groups: No. 3 and Angelica root oil

Group No. 12
Mild or sweet woody, faint

Amyris
Araucaria
Bruyère
Camphor oil, blue
Copaiba balsam
Guaiac wood
Gurjun balsam
Illurin balsam
Osyris tenuifolia
Pterocarpus sp.
Related groups: No. 36, 40, 50, 52.

Group No. 13
Sweet, non-floral, candy-flavor

Anise fruit oil
Clausena anisata
Fennel, sweet
Star anise
Related groups: No. 28, 29, 34, 42.

Group No. 14
Caraway group

Anethum sowa
Caraway fruit oil
Dill fruit oil
Lippia carviodora
Spearmint
Related groups: No. 68, 77.

Group No. 15
fresh, spicy-woody

Angostura
Cascarilla
Laurelberry
Laurel leaf
Mace
Melaleuca alternifolia
Marjoram, sweet
Myrtle
Nutmeg
Ocimum Kilimanjaricum
Walnut leaf
Related groups: 16, 41.

Group No. 16
sweet spicy, powerful and warm

Anona squamosa
Cardamom
Lovage herb
Related group: No. 15.

Group No. 17
delicate and sweet, leafy-floral

Anthocephalus cadamba
Artabotrys odoratissimus
Artabotrys suaveolens
Camellia
Cananga
Champaca
Cymbidium virescens
Hamanasu
Lily of the valley
Magnolia
Saffron
Sweet pea
Ylang-ylang
Related groups: No. 4, 9, 56.

Group No. 18
woody-camphoraceous

Apopin
Camphor oil, white
Chamaecyparis obtusa root oil
Marjoram, wild, Spanish
Ocimum canum (camphor type)
Thujopsis dolobrata root oil
Related group: No. 79.

Group No. 19
bitter-herbaceous, phenolic or medicinal

Arnica
Betel
Ivy leaf
Marigold absolute
Maté
Mistletoe absolute
Origanum oil
Porophyllum lineare
Reseda
Rose leaf
Tobacco leaf
Related groups: No. 7, 73, 84.

Group No. 20
Thuja group

Artemisia alba
Artemisia annua
Artemisia capillaris
Artemisia herba-alba
Artemisia mendozana
Artemisia vulgaris
Cedarleaf
Davana
Hyssop
Iva
Lippia daunensis
Milfoil
Sage, Dalmatian
Tansy
Thuja plicata
Wormwood
Related groups: No. 27, 35, 87.

Group No. 21
sulphuraceous, non-lachrymatory

Asafoetida oil
Garlic oil
Related groups: No. 74 and Galbanum oil

Group No. 22
sweet-balsamic

Asafoetida balsam (oil-free)
Peru balsam
Tolu balsam

Group No. 23
peppery, rootlike, woody

Asarum europaeum
Snakeroot, Canadian
Related groups: No. 3, 11, 24, 62, 64.

Group No. 24
peppery

Atractylis
Pepper, black
Schinus molle
Related groups: No. 23, 62.

Group No. 25
grassy, fresh, lemon-like

Backhousia citriodora
Eucalyptus staigeriana
Lemongrass oil
Leptospermum citratum
Litsea cubeba
Melissa
Verbena
Verbena, so-called (Spanish)
Related groups: No. 53, 57, 69.

Group No. 26
sweet-wood and dry-tea-like

Backhousia myrtifolia
Birch bud oil
Huon pine wood oil
Melaleuca bracteata
Palmarosa oil
Related groups: No. 4, 17, 47, 73 and Gingergrass oil.

Group No. 27
fresh minty-herbaceous, bitter

Balsamite
Pennyroyal
Related groups: No. 20, 35, 87.

Group No. 28
sweet-camphoraceous, green-herbal

Basil "exotic"
Parsley herb oil
Related groups: No. 13, 29, 34, 42.

Group No. 29
sweet-herbal, faintly green

Basil, French
Dictam
Goldenrod
Estragon
Related groups: No. 13, 28, 34, 42.

Group No. 30
dry-woody, pronounced spicy

Bay leaf oil
Cinnamon leaf oil
Clavel moena
Clove leaf oil
Clove stem oil
Eugenia jambolana
Lawang oil
Ocimum gratissimum, "eugenol type"
Pimenta leaf oil
Related group: No. 58.

Group No. 31
Rose group

Beeswax absolute
Rose absolute (and oil).

Group No. 32
Fresh citrus

Bergamot
Cedrat
Lemon
Lime
Related groups: No. 63, 82.

Group No. 33
Petitgrain group

Bergamot petitgrain
Louro nhamuy
Orange flower water absolute
Petitgrain Paraguay
Petitgrain sweet orange
Related group: No. 80.

Group No. 34
Wintergreen group

Birch bark
Fern leaf
Wintergreen
Related groups: No. 13, 28, 29, 42.

Group No. 35
warm-phenolic, fresh-herbaceous

Blackcurrant
Calamintha
Fennel, bitter
Related groups: No. 20, 27, 87.

Group No. 36
Rosewood group

Bois de rose oil
Ho leaf oil
Ho wood oil
Homalomena rubescens
Linaloe seed oil
Linaloe wood oil
Related group: No. 12.

Group No. 37
medicinal, nauseating, sweet-conifer

Boldo leaf
Chenopodium ambrosioides
Savin
Wormseed

Group No. 38
warm-herbaceous, sweet, dry-herb-like

Broom
Chamomile "German"
Chamomile "Roman"
Everlasting absolute
Flouve absolute (and oil)
Hay oil
Helichrysum oil
Related group: No. 67.

Group No. 39
Sharp minty, bitter-herbaceous

Buchu leaf
Matico
Pluchea sagittalis
Related groups: No. 7, 19, 27, 72, 86 and Xanthoxylum alatum.

Group No. 40
Floral-sweet, "precious wood"

Cabreuva
Melaleuca viridiflora, var. "A"
Oleo vermelho
Rhodium wood oil
Sandalwood
Siamwood
Related group: No. 12.

Group No. 41
Eucalyptus group

Cajuput
Eucapharma oils (see index)
Melaleuca linariifolia
Niaouli
Related group: No. 15.

Group No. 42
Sassafras group

Camphor oil, brown
Ocotea pretiosa
Sassafras oil
Related groups: No. 13, 28, 29, 34.

Group No. 43
Turpentine "balsam" group

Canada balsam
Larch turpentine
Oregon balsam
Turpentine
Related groups: No. 1, 8, 85.

Group No. 44
Cinnamon group

Canella
Cassia
Cinnamon bark

Group No. 45
dry-woody

Cangerana
Carrot seed
Cedrela odorata
Cryptomeria japonica
Machilus
Nigella sativa
Related groups: No. 3, 51, 62.

Group No. 46
balsamic-floral

Capé
Heliotrope
Hyacinth
Lilac
Néflier
Osmanthus fragrans
Pandanus
Peru balsam oil
Related groups: No. 4, 17, 56, 61, 71, 75.

Group No. 47
Carnation group

Carnation
Cestrum nocturnum
Tobacco flower
Wallflower
Related groups: No. 4, 26 and Xanthoxylum alatum.

Group No. 48
Hop group (woody-herbaceous and animal)

Carob bean
Hop
Lupulin
Spikenard
Valerian
Related: Galbanum and Sumbul.

Group No. 49
True animal notes

Castoreum
Civet
Musk

Group No. 50
Sweet cedar

Cedarwood Atlas
Cedarwood Himalaya
Cedarwood Lebanon
Muhuhu
Related group: No. 12.

Group No. 51
dry cedar

Cedarwood East Africa
Cedarwood Texas
Related group: No. 45.

Group No. 52
Oily cedar

Cedarwood "Virginia"
Dacrydium elatum
Related group: No. 12.

Group No. 53
Lemon-petitgrain group

Cedrat petitgrain
Karna
Lemon petitgrain
Related group: No. 25.

Group No. 54
Celery group

Celery seed oil
Fenugreek extract
Lovage root oil
Maple
Opopanax
Pimpinella

Group No. 55
fresh-herbaceous, dry-ambra-like

Chamomile "Moroccan"
Erigeron
Related groups: No. 9, 66.

Group No. 56
Jasmin group

Chimonanthus fragrans
Honeysuckle
Jasmin
Karo-karoundé
Murraya paniculata
Nyctanthes arbortristis
Orange flower absolute
Passion flower
Syringa
Related groups: No. 4, 17, 26, 46, 83.

Group No. 57
Citronella group

Citronella Ceylon
Citronella Java (Formosa)
Combava petitgrain
Eucalyptus citriodora
Related groups: No. 25, 53.

Group No. 58
warm, sweet spice

Clove bud oil
Pimenta berry oil
Related group: No. 30.

Group No. 59
mild, oily

Coconut absolute
Linseed oil absolute

Group No. 60
Cola group (bitter, woody, tonic)

Cola
Guarana

Group No. 61
sweet, delicately floral

Coriander oil
Orris absolute
Violet flower absolute
Related groups: No. 10, 46 and Cognac oil.

Group No. 62
Woody, warm-peppery (Cubeb-group)

Cubeb
Louro brasileiro
Paradise seed
Piper crassipes
Piper longum
Related groups: No. 23, 24, 45.

Group No. 63
Sweet citrus (Orange group)

Curaçao peel oil
Grapefruit oil
Orange, bitter
Orange, sweet
Related groups: No. 32, 82.

Group No. 64
Ginger group

Curcuma
Galanga
Ginger
Zedoaria
Related group: No. 23.

Group No. 65
powerful oily-herbaceous, green

Cymbopogon connatus
Inchigrass oil
Perilla oil
Related: Cognac oil, Cumin oil, Gingergrass oil.

Group No. 66
balsamic-ambre-like

Cypress oil
Juniperberry oil
Pinus pumilio oil
Related groups: No. 1, 9, 10, 43.

Group No. 67
coumarinic-herbaceous, warm

Deertongue absolute
Fir needle absolute
Hay absolute
Melilotus absolute
Tonka absolute
Woodruff absolute
Related group: No. 38.

Group No. 68
fresh-peppery, warm, light

Dill weed oil
Elemi oil
Eucalyptus australiana var. "B"
Eucalyptus dives, var. "A"
Eucalyptus dives type
Eucalyptus numerosa type
Evoulimba oil
Kuro-moji oil
Related groups: No. 14, 78 and Xanthoxylum alatum.

Group No. 69
fruity-rosy, herbaceous and tea-like

Eucalyptus macarthuri
Nindi oil
Related groups: No. 25, 26, 72.

Group No. 70
Oakmoss group

Fig leaf absolute
Oakmoss
Seaweed absolute
Treemoss

Group No. 71
Tuberose group

Gardenia
Longoza
Mimusops elengi
Plumeria
Tuberose
Related groups: No. 46, 56 and Neroli and Vanilla.

Group No. 72
Geranium group

Geranium
Mawah
Related groups: No. 27, 31, 39, 69.

Group No. 73
dry tealeaf odor

Hamamelis leaf
Henna leaf
Jaborandi leaf
Tea leaf
Related groups: No. 19, 26, 88.

Group No. 74
sulphuraceous, lachrymatory

Horseradish
Mustard
Onion
Rapeseed
Related group: No. 21.

Group No. 75
floral, green-leafy, light

Jonquil
Narcissus
Violet leaf
Related groups: No. 46, 56, 71.

Group No. 76
Turpentine group

Juniperus macrocarpa
Juniper wood oil
Oregon balsam oil
Turpentine (oil)
Related groups: No. 1, 8, 43, 66.

Group No. 77
warm-woody, balsamic-spicy

Kaempferia galanga
Sanna
Parsley seed
Related group: No. 14.

Group No. 78
lemony-turpentine-like

Kauri-kopal
Templin oil
Related groups: No. 1, 8, 43, 66, 68, 76.

Group No. 79
warm-woody, cineolic-herbaceous

Lavandin oil
Rosemary
Sage, Spanish
Spike lavender
Related groups: No. 18, 80.

Group No. 80
Lavender group

Lavender
Linaloe husk oil
Mentha citrata
Ocimum canum (methylcinnamate type)
Petitgrain bigarade
Related groups: No. 33, 79, 88 and Neroli.

Group No. 81
faint, sweet-rooty

Licorice
Sarsaparilla

Group No. 82
Mandarin group

Mandarin
Mikan
Tangerine
Related groups: No. 32, 63.

Group No. 83
musty, dry-floral, herbaceous

Mandarin-petitgrain
Orange flower and petitgrain water absolute
(Bitter orange leaf water absolute)
Related groups: No. 46 and 56.

Group No. 84
Patchouli group

Manevoro
Patchouli
Related group: No. 19.

Group No. 85
Resin group

Mastic
Sandarac
Related group: No. 43.

Group No. 86
Peppermint group

Mentha arvensis
Peppermint

Group No. 87
sharp-fruity, herbaceous

Rue
Tagetes
Related groups: No. 20, 27, 35.

Group No. 88
sweet-herbaceous, balsamic tea and ambrelike

Sage clary
Ulex europaeus
Zdravetz
Related groups: No. 9, 17, 72, 73, 80.

The following materials have been left unclassified, but they are mentioned in connection with the above groups:

Angelica root – Angelica seed – Cognac oil – Cumin – Galbanum – Myrrh – Neroli – Vanilla – Xanthoxylum alatum.

Alphabetical order is introduced throughout the first listed material in each group.

INDEX

to Part One

Definitions and Methods of Processing

INDEX
to Part Two
Monographs

French-German-Spanish condensed index:

Part One:

English	French	German	Spanish
balsam	baume	Balsam	balsamo
essential oil	huile essentielle (essence)	Aetherisches Oel	aceite esencial
flavors	essences alimentaires (arômes)	Geschmackstoffe	
fruits	fruits	Früchte	frutas
gum	gomme	Gummi	goma botanica
gum resin	gomme-résine	Gummi-Harz	
odor description	odeur, déscription	Geruch, Beschreibung	olor, descripción
resin	résine	Harz	
spices	épices	Gewürze	especias
tincture	teinture	Tinktur	tintura

Part Two:

Almond oil, bitter	amande amère	Bitter Mandel Oel	aceite almendras amárgas
amber (oil)	ambre jaune	Bernstein	ambár
ambrette seed	ambrette, graines	Moschuskörner	ambarilla
artemisia	absinthe	Wermuth	absintio
asafoetida	ase fétide	Asant	asafetida
basil	basilic	Basilikum	basílicon
bay leaf	bay, feuilles	Bay	bay-malagueta (bahia, hojas)
beeswax	cire d'abeille	Bienenwachs	cera de abeja
benzoin	benjoin	Benzoe	benjúi
birch bud	bouleau, gemmes	Birkenknospen	bétula, yemas
birch bark	bouleau, écorce	Birkenrinden	bétula, corteza
birch tar	bouleau, goudron	Birkenteer	bétula, brea
blackcurrant (bud)	bourgeons de cassis	Johannisbeer Knospen	grosella negra yemas
bois de rose	bois de rose	Rosenholz	palo de rosa
broom	genêt	Ginster	
cade	cade	Kade (Wachholderbeer Teer)	
calamus	calamus	Kalmus	cálamo
camphor	camphre	Kampfer	alcanfor
capsicum	poivron rouge	Cayenne Pfeffer	pimienta cayenne
caraway	carvi	Kümmel	comino
carnation	oeillet	Gartennelke	clavel rojo
carob bean	caroube	Johannisbrot	pan San Juan
carrot (seed)	carotte	Möhren (Samen)	zanahoria
cassia	canella de Chime	Kassia	casia
castoreum	castoreum	Bibergeil	castóreo
celery	céléri	Sellerie	apio palustre
chamomile	camomille	Kamille	manzanilla
cherry laurel	laurier-cerise	Kirsch-Loorbeer	laurél cerézo
cinnamon bark	ecorce de canelle de Ceylan	Zimtrinden	canéla, corteza

English	French	German	Spanish
civet	civette	Zibeth	civeta (algalia)
clove bud	clous de girofle	Nelkenknospen	clavos (clavel, flóres)
clove leaf	girofle, feuille	Nelkenblatt	clavos, hojas
clove stem	girofle, tige	Nelken Stiel	clavos, cabillos
cognac	lie de vin	Kognak	coñac
copaiba	copahu	Kopaiva	copaiba
cumin	cumin	Kumin	comíno románo
dill	aneth	Dill	anéto
elderflower	sureau, fleurs	Holunder Blüte	
elecampane	aunée	Alant	enula campana
fennel	fenouil	Fenchel	hinójo
fern	fougère	Farn	helecho
fig	figue	Feigen	higo
fir (needles)	pin (aiguilles)	Fichten (Nadel)	pine (pinóchas)
galanga(l)	galanga	Galgant	
garlic	ail	Knoblauch	ajo
ginger	gingembre	Ingwer	gingibre
grapefruit	grapefruit (pampelmousse)	Pompelmus	toronja
guaiacwood	galac (bois)	Guajak Holz	guayacol (guayaco, palo)
hay	foin	Heu	heno
henna	henné	Henna	colorante henna
honeysuckle	chevrefeuille	Geissblatt	madreselva
hop	houblon	Hopfen	lupolo
horseradish	raifort	Petersilienwurzel	rabano picante
hyacinth	jacinthe	Hyazinthe	jacinto
hyssop	hysope	Ysop	hisópo
ivy	lierre	Efeu	
juniperberry	genièvre baies	Wachholderbeer	enebro (bayas)
laurel berry	laurier baies	Lorbeeren	(frutas de) laurél
lavender	lavande	Lavendel	alhucéma (lavanda)
leather	cuir	Leder (Juchten)	cuero
lemon	citron	Zitron	limón
lemongrass	lemongrass	Lemongrass	canita de limon (lemongraz)
licorice	réglisse	Lakritz	orozuz
lilac	lilas	Flieder	lilas
lily of the valley	muguet	Maiglöckchen	lirio de los valles
linseed (oil)	lin, huile de graines de	Leinsamen (Oel)	linaza (aceite)
lovage root	livèche, racine	Liebstock Wurzel	levistico, raiz
maple (sugar)	érable (sucre d')	Ahorn (Zucker)	maple
marigold	calendula (souci)	Morgenfrau	calendula
marjoram, sweet	marjolaine	Majoran	mejorana
mastic	lentisque	Mastix	almaciga
milfoil	mille-feuilles	Schafgarben	aquílea
mistletoe	gui	Mistel	muerdago
musk	musc	Moschus	almízcle
mustard	moutarde	Senf	mostaza
nutmeg	muscade (noix)	Muskat (Nuss)	moscada (nuez)
oakmoss	mousse (de chêne)	Eichenmoos	musgo de encina (musgo de roble)

English	French	German	Spanish
olibanum	encens	Weihrauch	olibano (incienso)
onion	oignon	Lauch (Zwiebel)	cebolla
orange oil, sweet	orange douce	Apfelsinenoel (Pomerantzenoel) süss	naránjas dúlces
orange flowers	orange, fleurs	Orangenblüten	azáhar (naranjas flores)
orange, bitter	orange amère	Pomerantzenschalenoel bitteres	naranjas agria
origanum	origan	Dosten (Oel)	origano
orris	iris	Iris	íris
parsley herb	persil, feuilles	Petersilien Kraut	peréjil, hojas
parsley seed	persil, fruits	Petersilien Samen	perejil, semilla
pennyroyal	poley (menthe pouliot)	Polei	poléo
peppermint	menthe poivrée	Pfefferminz	mentha pimienta
pepper, black	poivre	Pfeffer	pimienta negra
poplar bud (oil)	peuplier, gemmes	Pappelknospen (Oel)	
rapeseed	navette	Rapssamen	nabina
rosemary	romarin	Rosmarin	romero
rue	rue	Rauten	ruda
rum	rhum	Rum	ron
saffron	safran	Safran	azafran
sage clary	sauge sclarée	Muskateller Salbei	salvia esclárea
sage	sauge	Salbei	salvia
sarsaparilla	salsepareille	Sarsaparillen	zarzaparilla
savin	sabine	Sadebaum	sabina
savory	sariette	Bohnenkraut	saturéja
seaweed	varech	Meeralgen (-gras)	alga marina
soybean	soja	Sojabohne	soja
spearmint	menthe crépue	Krauseminz	méntha créspa
spike lavender	aspic	Spik	espliégo
spruce	sapin	Tanne	pruche
star anise	badiane	Sternanis	badiána
styrax	styrax	Storax	estoréque
sweet pea	pois de senteur	Wicke (wohlriechende)	alelí
tansy	tanaisie	Rainfarn	tanaceto
tea	thé	Thee	te
templin (fir cone)	strobiles de sapin blanc	Edeltannen Zapfen	piña de pino nóble
thyme	thym	Thymian	tomíllo
treemoss	mousse d'arbre	Baummoos	musgo de arbol
turpentine	térébinthine	Terpentinoel	trementína
valerian	valériane	Baldrian	
violet	violette	Veilchen	violetas
wallflower	giroflée	Goldlack (Levkoje)	alelí doble
walnut leaf	feuilles de noyer	Walnuss Blätter	nuez, hojas
woodruff	aspérule	Waldmeister	aspérula
wormseed	chénopode	Wurmsamen	chenopodium
wormwood	absinthe	Wermuth	absintio
zedoaria (rhizome)	zédoaire (rhizomes)	Zitwerwurzel	zedoario (raiz)

International and Latin botanical names have been omitted from this list, and so have names which show obvious similarity in the four languages.

INDEX
to Photographs

CPSIA information can be obtained
at www.ICGtesting.com
Printed in the USA
BVHW091500290620
582558BV00007B/308